P9-CBM-476

Environmental management

Environmental Management: science and politics

MORTON GORDEN

MARSHA GORDEN

Development Sciences, Inc.

Chapter Illustrations by Winnie Fitch

CARNEGIE LIBRARY
LIVINGSTONE COLLEGE
SALISBURY, N. C. 28144

Boston: Allyn and Bacon, Inc.

To Nicole and Lisa

This book is printed on 100 percent recycled paper.

© Copyright 1972 by Allyn and Bacon, Inc., 470 Atlantic Avenue, Boston. All rights reserved. Printed in the United States of America. No part of the material protected by this copyright notice may be reproduced or utilized in any form or by any means, electronic or mechanical, including photocopying, recording, or by any informational storage and retrieval system, without written permission from the copyright owner.

Library of Congress catalog card number: 70-188224

301.3/08
G661

Contents

85741

Chapter 4. Generation of wastes: unclosed materials cycles   153

Chapter 5. Values: the best ecosystem   199

Chapter 6. Research for environmental management: needed knowledge   265

Chapter 7. Environmental management: needed skills   377

Chapter 8. Implementation: from science to application   453

Chapter 9. Conclusions: can we manage the environment?

Epilogue

Preface

This book seeks to identify the kinds of information scientists can produce to best integrate their professional concerns into the political processes of environmental management. It is a "second generation" book. Unlike the first wave of environmental books designed to *pose* the problems of environmental damage and to motivate us to action, the concerns facing us now evolve out of trying to *solve* the problems of the environment. We must now mix political considerations with the technical aspects, because effectively dealing with environmental issues involves society's collective judgment and a great deal of its resources. Therefore, this book is presented in the hope that the overspecialization which is partially responsible for our present plight can be overcome.

While the articles collected here lean most heavily in the technical direction, they are posed in the context of problems which politically oriented people must address. The technical side is also emphasized, for politically minded people will have to stretch their scientific competence to solve the problems of the environment. The issues involved are too serious to allow either technical incompetence by politicians or political insensitivity by scientists and engineers.

We do not expect the material to represent more than a departure into environmental education. How we can deal with the uncertainties of environmental phenomena and how we will make the value choices involved will take some time to answer in the present political process. The search for solutions poses a burden for scientist and politician alike.

The issue for the scientist is not merely his public relations, but his public relevance. For the politician, it is not merely his control of technocrats, but the control nature imposes on him. If ever there was a set of issues requiring communication among the academic disciplines, it is management of the environment.

The sciences will have to go farther than they usually do toward specifying assumptions, levels of confidence, new information required, and levels of criticality. Because the political demands will require prediction as well as description, dynamic models must be greatly expanded in areas where they have been heretofore missing.

Policy groups must learn to read the signs scientists make and to set priorities on some difficult decisions. Most environmental decisions are limiting rather than expansive. We need to know not only how to make our economies grow, but how to grow now without paying undue costs later. The environmental implications of growth require much more technical information than we have now, for nature's feedback has not been well incorporated into economic projections.

This book makes a start toward showing scientists and politicians the issues which bring them together. "Third generation" books will no doubt deal with new issues and old ones formulated in new ways. Now, in the early 1970s, we must re-think basic relations of science and government so as not to embark on simple solutions which will catch up with us in later costs not now foreseen.

For this reason, the phrase "environmental management" was chosen as a central theme. Management means manipulating and guiding forces. Successful management will require more information than we now have. The book points to some of the implications of that need. Also, we have to define the boundaries of environment-related activity and we must decide for whom we are managing it.

Thus, we have to range far and wide. In Chapter 1, Stanley M. Greenfield and Russell Train introduce the issues. Chapters 2 and 3 introduce concerns about science's ability to inform us. Chapter 4 develops some points of entry into the essential problem — man's interference with materials cycles through the interaction of incomplete technology with nature. We proceed to Chapter 5 to recognize that the choices needed for environmental decision making quickly enter the realm of social values. Given these dimensions, Chapters 6 and 7 identify information and skills required to deal with the issues. Chapter 8 calls attention to the fact that understanding must eventually be applied to be useful. In Chapter 9 and the brief epilogue, the editors offer their own estimation of where we are and where we must go to manage the environment successfully — through the skills of both scientist and politician.

Acknowledgments

As the reader will shortly recognize, this book is the product of many. We gratefully acknowledge the contributions of our commentators who were kind enough to give the time and effort to apply their working experience to the issues addressed. Mr. Russell Train and Dr. Stanley Greenfield gave commentaries of a breadth and depth that few men can draw upon.

The staff of Development Sciences, Inc., especially Mr. Charles Flinkstrom and Mrs. Marjorie Ellis, made comments, provided logistics, and picked up the burdens we dropped while working on the manuscript.

The chapter illustrations, which sensitively portray the meaning of this book through line rather than word, were accomplished by Winnie Fitch. We appreciated the enjoyable hours of conversation leading to them.

The library staff of the Marine Biological Laboratory at Woods Hole is to be thanked for their direct and indirect support, as their excellent facilities were made available to us.

We deeply appreciate the permission to reprint given by the authors and publishers whose cooperation contributed to this volume.

Our patient children, who pitched in with help suitable to their ages, have to be acknowledged. Mrs. Bess Warner kept us going by managing our household during many extra hours we spent at the office.

Thanks to them all.

East Sandwich, Massachusetts

Chapter 1

Introduction

The era of ecological awareness has dawned, and concerns which have been expressed range from fear of the planet's destruction to disgust over beer cans cast by the roadside. All manner of problems between the two extremes have been placed on the public docket, as concerned citizens, professionals, and officials have taken up the challenge to action.

The call to do something has ranged from laissez-faire, so that nature can take its course, to extreme forms of environmental alteration to protect us from ourselves. Here, too, is a wide array of proposals that would affect all of us — from our status as biological entities to our status as economic beings.

It is difficult for laymen and professionals alike to orient themselves to this wealth of information, some of which does not even qualify as information; for ecology has become an ideology to some, and sensitizing through fear and emotion has replaced enlightenment through facts. Nonetheless, we can probably all agree that modern man must re-learn to come to terms with nature — this time not through magic and ritual, but through science. This realization poses a substantial concern for scientists, for we need not only a better understanding of man's effects on nature, but we also need to change the behavior of man as he affects nature. In this sense, we need a comprehensive view of how men can manage themselves to better manage the environment in keeping with the dictates of nature. Management implies operations on nature and feedback from nature that prohibit or encourage men to take action. Environmental management is the science of regulating nature and man's relation to nature. This dual definition suggests that man never acts *on* nature, but *with* the forces of nature.

ISSUES OF MANAGEMENT:

Information, values, application, and geographic scope

Management today is a technically oriented information science. It entails not only the organization of men, but the assembly of pertinent data to bear on allocation decisions. Environmental management can be viewed in that context, for while there is no corporate director or senior vice president in charge of the globe, some such function need be performed, for the acts of individuals increasingly have global effects that are unforeseen, but real in their consequences.

As the environment becomes saturated with waste, each new act has more repercussions. In some locales, the repercussions can be irreversible and deleterious. We thus far have been rather unconcerned, or when concerned, relatively uninformed about the environmental impact of actions we take. While our capacity to gather and understand information is growing rapidly, we still have much less information than impact. To talk about our capacity to manage the environment, we are going to have to talk about a prerequisite for good management: knowledge about consequences of actions. A good manager tries not to deal with unimportant matters; when he deals with critical phenomena, he tries to have solid information about the results of his actions.

Chapters 2 and 3 deal with the kinds of information available to aid us in the task of environmental management and some complications involved in the job. The articles were selected with an eye to probing the difficulties facing us so that we can determine what needs to be done before taking on the mantle of manager. Many would argue that nature's complexity makes it impossible for man to manage the environment; his qualifications are too few and his views too parochial. Such critics even suggest the very attempt belies our folly and is responsible for the grief now upon us.

Ultimately, events will prove the "hands off" critics tragically right or alarmistly wrong. Whatever conclusion the reader would like to draw at this point is essentially irrelevant, because man cannot cease to manipulate natural phenomena. There are already too many humans on the globe for a return to a state where we all fish and hunt, clothed in leaves and skins. We will then only fall to hunting each other as the competition for scarce resources reaches survival proportions.

Whether we are managing or mismanaging resources today, we cannot call for a return to innocence. Most assuredly we cannot call for a return to ignorance. We need more information before we can act on our ultimate objective: a quality environment.

The editors asked Dr. Stanley M. Greenfield, Assistant Administrator for Research and Monitoring, U.S. Environmental Protection Agency, to comment on the information needed. This interview, conducted on April 8, 1971, is printed below.

Interview with Stanley M. Greenfield:

GORDEN: The focus of our interview is on research rather than on solving the problem directly. The slot you have in government allows us to talk mostly about research. I would like to ask you about different classes of research: research on monitoring, on effects, on environmental dynamics, and so on.

GREENFIELD: I'm not sure I want to talk just about research on monitoring; I'd rather talk about research on monitoring technology, research on monitoring instrumentation, and separate that from the idea of research on monitoring strategy. These are really two different things. I think you have to break out effects in terms of ecological, health, social, economic effects — all of which must be considered, and all of which are probably different. I'd rather talk about research on abatement technology, control technology.

We should also talk about research on the dynamics of the environment, research on implementing solutions within the fabric of society — how you get people to do certain things or to accept certain things, agree to pay the costs of a given pollution solution. What are the alternative means available to you: regulations, incentives, public education? You realize, we know very little about the dynamics of society, and how to — not control — but interact dynamically with society. We can research the impact of man's activities on the environment.

Here we're talking about dealing with the secondary and tertiary effects of man's activities on the environment, as well as the primary effects. And, as soon as you get into the secondary and tertiary effects, you're into the question of how man's activities act as forcing functions in the development of land use, economic systems, and the full range of man's other activities.

GORDEN: There is a long agenda of research: effects, abatement technology, dynamics, research on society itself, and the impact of man's activities. We are also likely to find out that there are different levels for managing that correspond to the problems we're talking about. Let's go further into the agenda you propose for research.

GREENFIELD: Certainly. Although we will address these issues, especially at the management levels, we're into a bind immediately because we don't have clear-cut boundaries between various managerial components — global, national, regional, etc. You're constantly fighting the battle of how to operate across these boundaries. How do you cause them to interact in the proper way to manage the environment?

GORDEN: That decision presumably comes out of the research results.

GREENFIELD: Well, not necessarily. You're still dealing with political entities and political realities, and you've got to recognize they're national and local and state and extra-national as well.

GORDEN: Let us get into some priorities in effects research. Monitoring technology is where we began. I think it might be useful to indicate, as of now, the perspective on research priorities, maybe the top two or three issues in each area to which students should turn their attention. The first can be monitoring technology, although these issues are not clearly in order of importance. Maybe you want to rank order the importance first.

GREENFIELD: I have difficulty rank ordering. I say to myself, "What do I need to do my job?" Mostly, the issues are of equal importance. The only difficulty is that I could view the environmental management problem as really a two-phased problem, not really sequential, but considered simultaneously. The first phase is the obvious one: How do you clean up the mess we have now? And, the second phase is how do you prevent the mess from occurring to an even greater extent in the future? Both of these have equal rank in my mind; although the body politic, and the body popular, are interested in what they see today — pollution in the streets, in the skies, in the water. So, there may be a difference in my priority system and the priorities determined by the amounts of money provided.

GORDEN: Why don't you give your own opinions.

GREENFIELD: Okay. I would not rank-order the items on this list. They don't represent a ranked list of things I would do if I had various amounts of money. The different tasks represent the sum of what we must do if we are to manage the environment. And I don't allow any one group to be eliminated from consideration. If you accept that, then we can begin to start talking about things like monitoring. I'm not saying it's the first thing to do, but it can be the first thing to talk about.

Monitoring, to me, has a very broad connotation. I've got to talk about it in a broad context first, because only then can I discuss the technology problem and the strategy problem. Monitoring means the whole class of things from gathering data for research up to and including gathering information to enable one to go into court and sue somebody because he is not obeying the law. It includes, within this very broad spectrum, the questions: How do you provide a network that can warn you when you're reaching certain thresholds of danger? How do you provide a sieve with a large degree of serendipity that can catch the next potential "mercury" when you cannot identify it today? How do you provide a national network that gives you a sense of "how goes it," that enables you to say, "Here's where we were yesterday, here's where we are today, and here's the trend" in the quality of the environment? The latter question is very important, because it's the one you present to the people; it's the one that justifies your being and the funds this society is spending on the environment. It's also the one that maybe allows you to operationally address the environment in a broad sense. By this, I mean to include in my concept of a monitoring capability a capability to present timely information to decision makers, and to the public. It's almost, in a sense, an ability to construct an imaginary environmental war room where you can call up today's information and compare it graphically to where you were yesterday. That ability may ultimately allow you to examine what happens if perturbations are provided to the environment. Then you can utilize the models you have built; you can see what happens if we change the ice content of the Arctic Ocean or build a new powerplant or transportation system. Monitoring, in form, is the construction of the proper data bases, which allow you to properly measure departures. So, the strategy is a multifaceted strategy that deals with national networks, global networks, and the questions: How many materials do you have to sample to acquire some sense of the environmental quality? Do tracer materials give a broader sense of what's going on? (If we are forced to monitor everything over the globe, I'm in a very desperate situation, because I don't have enough money ever to do that.) How do you deal with the concept of environmental quality? What are the quantitative indicators that allow one to assess environmental quality? How do you deal with the concept of a serendipitous network?

I think, for example, that, in the latter case, a serendipitous network is not one set up in a rigid way; it's one that draws upon the capabilities that currently exist, of people analyzing and examining tissues, all over the country, as they are now. This serendipitous network should be one that provides the incentive for laboratories to send information or tissue samples to some central collecting place and provides a capability at the center for collating and extracting from this information some knowledge of trends, some sense of what materials are beginning to appear in larger concentrations in tissues. This information permits you to select the materials that should receive a more intensive examination.

From the standpoint of technology, you always run the danger of setting your sights so high in terms of air quality or water quality that you no longer are able to measure in a reproducible, accurate manner that which you are trying to establish.

GORDEN: I don't understand a high standard's being hard to identify.

GREENFIELD: Well, for example, suppose there's a possibility of setting a standard in the atmosphere for oxidant levels which are met by naturally occurring oxidant levels in the environment. I can go out and measure this; I find that in many cases I reach an oxidant level that exceeds my standard. Is that being produced by natural pollutants or by man-made pollutants? I get to the point where I produce so much natural noise that I cannot extract the information that I want.

The other danger is that I'm exceeding my sensing technology, that the necessity of measuring concentrations of so many parts per million of a substance exceeds the ability of the current instrumentation. In essence, I can't get reproducible results, and the manufacturer or industrialist who tries to meet the standards can never be really sure that tests he runs on his product provide correct results.

The other danger is the question of standardization — the danger of proliferating instrumentation to sense one parameter may make for such a variety of types that it is impossible to compare results. These are the types of things you have to guard against when developing a sampling technology. Technology, you wish, you hope, would be pushed toward automatic as opposed to manual — we need to get away from requiring a man to constantly sit over the instrument itself. That is very costly and prohibits you from proliferating your monitoring network. We need technology that might permit remote sampling of pollution content in an accurate manner. These are the directions I think we must push the technology.

GORDEN: Let's go on to effects research, of which there are a great number. You wanted to break it down into ecological, social, economic effects, and so on. Let's tap some of the things on the top of your list of things to do.

GREENFIELD: In the health effects area, what is the effect on man of various materials appearing in the environment? Right now, we just don't know. We have the problem of what happens to man under stress of low-dose, long-term exposures to many substances, and they vary from a host of hazardous materials, radiation effects, air pollutants — all the things man produces that may hurt him and that may indeed be identified as harmful when taken in drastic doses. You would like to address the question of what happens when man is exposed to low doses of these materials over long periods of time. This is a very difficult type of effect to sort out because normally such effects require a host of statistics extending over long periods of time — probably many lifetimes, maybe generations of animal experiments.

GORDEN: There are variations — within SO_2, for example, we have some reasonably good data on effects on different ages.

GREENFIELD: We know little bits and pieces. We have information of the harmful effects of SO_2 on cardiac patients, on people with chronic respiratory illnesses. We have some very interesting information recently published by Cornell Medical Lab that indicated that it's not what happens as a direct result of SO_2 on a healthy patient, but rather, given incidences of increased SO_2, unhealthy patients tend to be pushed over the line. In essence, a sick patient is turned into a mortality. This very interesting data, taken in New York City, seems to indicate when you eliminate all other apparent causes and go after the statistics on days highly polluted with SO_2, that you wind up with a residual of a thousand deaths a year apparently due to pushing cardiac and respiratory patients over the line. That's a pretty interesting statistic. But — and here's the problem — in almost every area you can think of, we don't really have enough information today to set specific standards with the proper margin of safety. You know, I can say to you that mercury's a "bad actor." And, you nod your head and say, "Yeh, mercury's a bad actor." But, what is the effect of metallic mercury on a person? Downwind of a chloral alkalide plant — say two miles — I can breathe in on the order of 40 micrograms of one form of metallic mercury per day. I know that methel mercury is a deadly poison, and that the Public Health Department has established levels of no more than 30 micrograms per day. Now, how do I equate these two? What is the meaning of this amount of metallic mercury? I just don't know at the present time.

GORDEN: So that is clearly high on the agenda for research to be done.

GREENFIELD: It goes to the thread that you will find winding its way through all effects research: namely, what are the routes, fates, and effects of all the pollutants we put into the environment? If I apply a pesticide on the soil, what are its pathways to the point where it either metabolizes into a harmless material or disappears from the environment entirely? Until I know that, I cannot completely answer the question of what the effect of that material is, because it may show up many times in the environment. It may show up as a direct hazard, as a metabolized hazard, as a catalytic hazard. There are a large number of places at weak points in the environment where it might show up. I don't know.

GORDEN: This poses a question we'll get to later when we talk about communications to Congress, but let me ask just one more question on health effects. It has often been suggested that, essentially, what you want to know is unknowable. That is, multivariate analysis, no matter how good, is not able to separate out all those inputs to man in a highly saturated environment; we may never really be able to separate these things out, no matter how much money we spend. Radiation hazards, for example — we've spent enormous amounts of money without really answering the question. Is there an order of subjects such that no matter how much money we spend, we're still going to be in ignorance?

GREENFIELD: Well, you can argue against the environmental imperative, that we will never have enough information to set standards, regulate, and stop polluting, and so on. I get very worried about whether we're really addressing the synergistic problem in the environment. For example, in EPA we are setting up what we call mega-mouse facilities. Now a mega-mouse facility is one in which we provide huge numbers of carefully controlled mice in controlled environments. Now, you say, I'm going to look at the effect of a hazardous material on this mouse population to get some feel of what happens with small doses over long times. Well, as soon as you say that, if you're anything of a scientist, you say, "Now wait a minute; I can't stop with this one stressor; the test population is now isolated from the world. What about all the other stresses? What about the synergistic effects?" As soon as you ask that question, you're in a quandry. What happens to people under multiple stresses? Noise stress interacts with radiation stress, with drugs, with any number of things. You are never going to be able to answer that in a completely satisfactory manner.

GORDEN: Your first answer was about listening to the environmental imperative. What did you mean by that? It sounds like a point of faith on which you interpret research. Can you elaborate?

GREENFIELD: Well, the environmental imperative to me is the idea of the absolute necessity of maintaining a certain quality in the environment that allows man as a being on this earth to go on existing. That allows him to maintain a quality of life. Now, this is a highly subjective criterion because my quality of life may not be the same as yours; for example, I don't want to spend the rest of my life immersed in a carefully controlled bubble where my environment's filtered in and out and I'm carefully protected from all the hazards around me. I want to partake of the world around me. So, to me my environmental imperative is to keep the quality of the environment such that I can go on existing within the total ecological structure of this time. That's my environmental imperative; you may have a different one, but that's mine.

GORDEN: I wanted that digression because it seems to have been a touchstone, and we may have to come back to it. Okay. So much for health effects. How about ecological effects?

GREENFIELD: Ecological effects are a host of things that are not health effects, not economic effects, not social. Yet they represent an impact on the ecological structure of the time. For example, the Ponderosa pines up near Lake Arrowhead are being killed by the smog from Los Angeles. The redwoods are being damaged by air pollution; in fact, they're also being damaged by the fact that we carefully control them and keep forest fires from occurring. These examples represent man's activities interfering with the ecological balance, so there's an environmental impact of man on ecology. This may be the removal of certain species from our environment, the impact on wild vegetation, the changes in land use, acclerated erosion and what have you. It's the entire mix of things that evidence the presence of man "in spite" of his environment.

GORDEN: How do you research the impact of man reducing species?

GREENFIELD: Well, there's a whole body of ecological research that has dealt with this. You know, for generations we've had ecologists who dealt with small plots of land in isolation — small tidal pools and what have you. And out of this type of research, we have gained a great deal of knowledge on the development of an ecological system, the development from low order to high order of occupants. There's an interdependence, one on the other: the proportionately larger amount of lower order species needed to support the higher order, and so on. What happens if you disturb that system? The ecologist is very careful to point out that given an ecological system in which a hierarchy of living things is built up from the beginning of time in the system, it is a very careful and tender balance. Now I come in and "hit it" and, say, I destroy the system. This, by the way, may not have to be a very hard hit; it just has to be something that unbalances the system and it is destroyed. It turns out, in an ecological system, that if you perturb an ecological system hard, the higher order of living items disappears first, and the effect cascades down. What happens then — and this they know fairly well — is that the system doesn't recover. Instead, what you wind up with, to use the ecological vernacular, is a system consisting primarily of roadside weeds. We don't recover the higher orders of the system.

GORDEN: There's a very excellent article in this book by Woodwell which demonstrates that.

GREENFIELD: Woodwell is my source.

GORDEN: One of the problems in that position is — pardon the analogy — the problem of applying Newtonian physics when you get into high energy levels. The laws of smaller systems don't really apply to higher energy levels. I don't know if there's enough research yet to buy the point that a large system is going to respond the way the small systems have.

GREENFIELD: I agree. One of the items I'm very interested in is the concept of a global ecological system. For example, I think we have enough information now to conceive of a global ecological model — very crude, very gross, but there are just enough data, enough models around to allow you to at least put together this first hazy outline of a grand, global ecological model. And if you kept in mind the qualifications on how crude it was, it would still allow you to pull out gross quantitative information on what happens globally when you produce such perturbations as increasing the ice in the arctic, changing the CO_2 content of the entire globe, and so on.

The reason I say this is useful is for two purposes, and this goes to the question of the kind of research you can do in this area. First, it starts to provide quantitative information on a lot of environmental fears that have just been handwaving arguments up to now — the postulated consequences of removing the polar ice are handwaving arguments; Barry Commoner's and Paul Ehrlich's arguments are primarily handwaving arguments. I'm in total sympathy with them, but they are almost indefensible; we should give quantitative basis to these arguments, or abandon them. The second purpose, and maybe the most interesting, is that in fact the model becomes a planning mechanism. It tells you where research has to be done to make the model more sophisticated. As in human research, you add data into this first model; gradually it becomes more and more reliable. That is what I mean by ecological research.

GORDEN: Let's go to the social and economic effects, and the things we need to research there.

GREENFIELD: This is the ghastly question of what is the impact of environmental protection or nonprotection on the economic and social structure of our society. It involves all the cost-benefit analysis you want to do; it involves all the sociological impressions you want to deal with. For example, what effect does polluted air in cities have on the degradation or brutalization of people in the cities? What effect does it have on their interaction? I take Los Angeles, I take a hot summer, I provide the ingredients of a great deal of smog; is that the sufficient final element for a Watts riot? Or is it sufficient cause to keep a Watts riot going? Or is it sufficient cause to sensitize people so that only a little spark is needed to get a Watts riot going? Nobody knows.

There is a question of one nation affecting another in an environmental way. Sweden's agriculture, hence its whole economy, is affected by acid rains due to possible air pollution produced in the Ruhr or England or what have you. The fact is that air knows no political boundaries; what I do in my small area can affect you economically and, through the health standpoint, socially. We know a little bit about health effects; we are beginning to know a little bit about the physical environment; we know almost nothing about the economic and social environment and how it interacts with the physical environment.

GORDEN: Let's go on to abatement technology and the research there. Presumably it falls out of effects research, but maybe not.

GREENFIELD: Not necessarily. I think there's a different way to look at it. In this two-phase system, you've got to "clean up" what you've already done in the first phase; in this case the development of abatement technology is probably the most important element of your research activity during that phase. How do you go about cleaning up your backyard? How do you build a vacuum cleaner if you have to clean up your house?

There's another part of this, as far as I'm personally concerned in this agency: The requirement to make sure that development of abatement technology goes hand in glove with standards we set. You're not playing a fair or intelligent game if you keep demanding that certain standards be met without having an ability to meet the standards. Now, I can argue on both sides. One side says I've got to set the standards high, even though I

don't have the technology to accomplish it, because that will provide incentive to develop the technology. But I can throw the baby out with the bathwater, so to say, because I can set my standards so high that rather than provide incentive for development of technology, I can just kill that segment of the economic structure. So, I've got to watch that aspect very carefully. I've got to make sure that I'm within striking distance of the necessary technology, to go hand in glove with the required standards.
GORDEN: You've got to have a time frame there to help you make that decision. Power, for instance, is one of the industries in that bind right now. Do we hold back production of power until we get better SO_2 scrubbers, or shall we let them go in place without them? It's possible — you won't kill electricity, but you will greatly attenuate its growth. Now, how will you set up the research to solve that problem? How much can we lead the power industry?
GREENFIELD: You have to approach that sort of problem from two directions. One is the question of providing incentive, and maybe even subsidizing the industry to develop the technology. Maybe the government can actually go out and help develop the technology. And as you do this, you also push industry as hard as you can in terms of standards; you don't let them get away with having different standards than the Air Quality Standards demand in the area where they are building. In other words, you don't make them a special case: you provide them with as much incentive as possible, and you also require them to meet the standards.

At the same time, you had better start doing some research on the whole question of energy use in our society. Do we really have to use that much energy in our society? I look at the population expansion in this country doubling in every 65 years, but the electric power industry is doubling every ten years. Increased population is not the main source of the demand for electrical power; demands for goods and services and affluence are. So it's a matter of changing the way we look at our need for goods and services. The other side of the coin is something of a self-fulfilling prophecy in the projected requirement for increased electrical power capacity: you predict ten-year doubling time; there is a ten-year lead time to acquire the equipment; and sure enough ten years later you've doubled the capacity, and you have to go out and sell it. So, all I'm saying is that the example you chose is a particularly interesting one, because it contains the elements of how you continue to pressure industry to meet standards. But it also contains elements that say, "Hey, wait a minute, let's go back and look at the first principle again. Do we really need all the energy that power companies say we need?"
GORDEN: That's a big assignment for a research person to determine how much energy a society needs, because the need structure, in our culture at least, has been defined by the consumer. Now, doesn't your effects research have to be good before you convince the consumer?
GREENFIELD: I cannot see in my agency this research program really getting into that facet of the problem. I'd be worried, however, if nobody were. But at this time, the National Science Foundation has a strong

program looking at exactly that side of it, a necessary complementary program to what we have here.

GORDEN: The abatement technology is primarily addressed to the clean-up point of view. Could we talk now about the preventive point of view also? Presumably, abatement technology in the prevention sense is somewhat different.

GREENFIELD: Oh yes. You always ask how to handle the near-term problems of the environment. And there are always two answers to that. One is to clean up what you spill, and the other is to prevent spills in the first place. So there is a whole category of abatement technology that goes into cleaning up things or preventing emissions at the source.

GORDEN: But when you get into those technologies, the fear is often expressed that you end up creating another technology to clean up the technology, and that you're into an endless and vicious circle, using a lot of energy to save energy, and so on. I wonder if in the notion of abatement technology — the Apollo syndrome is what I'm referring to — there isn't the notion that we can cure all technological ills with more technology. Is there in abatement technology a way of evaluating whether or not you want to do that as opposed to, say, not produce an item at all?

GREENFIELD: That, once again, gets into the whole area of the economics-social question. If you talk about costs and benefits, then you should extend the cost-benefit analysis to where it should really be extended. You should not be afraid to ask the ultimate trade-off question. Do you really try to control that marginal plant, or do you shut it down? And what are the costs of shutting it down? There are social costs and economic costs. That is a question that should be addressed. Nobody's really addressing the total economic questions: Where are we driving our society and what is happening to our sense of values?

GORDEN: Well, I presume that will happen in time. We can then oppose paying for environmental protection because we say it's not worth it. However, as soon as we say it's not worth it, the burden of proof fosters the research for trade-offs.

GREENFIELD: But look at that other part of the second phase I talked about, which asks: How do you prevent the degradation of the environment over the long term? It indeed goes to the fact that it's not just source emissions you worry about. It goes to how you use land — what are the determining factors that allow you to build a new power plant or put in a new transportation system? You've got to wait a moment, and consider: If I do that it provides a forcing function for something else, and I don't want that to happen, so I'd better not do this, or I'd better reexamine carefully whether I really want to do this.

GORDEN: The next item of research is environmental dynamics. I consider this especially important because, as you mention before, small hits can have very large effects. What kind of priorities do you establish in looking at dynamics?

GREENFIELD: I'm very much with modeling, with discretion. I say it that way because I've worked too long with models — the physical type — not to know every modeler faces a professional danger sometime in his

life when he's convinced himself that he has captured the real world on his
computer. At that time, if he is not careful, he closes all doors to the
outside world and enters a fool's paradise. You've got to guard against that.
But models can be very useful for exploring trends, exploring how things
possibly interact, how they respond to boundary changes. It's an
insightful type of research. Modeling research itself adds to our dynamic
knowledge of the environment, but it also requires great understanding of
the dynamics of the systems themselves. And I don't stop at physical
systems; it also has to do with economic systems, social systems, the whole
business. So dynamics research starts with attempting to understand
systems we deal with — how they interact across disciplinary boundaries,
if you will — and drawing from them some sense of the dynamics of
interactions to the extent that you begin to look at them almost as a
microcosm of the world you wish to explore. In this sense, and with
suitable qualifications, you may explore your system in the large — what
happens if I do this and what happens if I do that — how effects perturb
and perturbate through the system.

GORDEN: What's your long-term prospect? Is your prognosis good for
many of the things we need to know?

GREENFIELD: Oh yes. I think the largest amount of current research
is into understanding physical systems. I think we're beginning to see
the beginnings of attempts to understand economic and social systems.
I think there is a long way to go, but I think we'll get there eventually.
Physical systems are a long way down the pike; we're really beginning to
understand both the systems and their limitations. We're beginning to
understand what we can and cannot do with them, and, maybe more
important, we're beginning to get the physical tools, the computing
machinery, that will allow us to really do it.

GORDEN: Some men, perhaps Van Allen, might not agree we have good
enough models in atmospheric information. We have to make an awful
lot of assumptions.

GREENFIELD: Ah, but wait. There are different uses for the model. If
you attempt to use the model in the truly predictive sense, I agree with you.
I start off with an initial set of conditions, change the boundary
conditions a bit, representing this perturbation; and I'm going to predict
what happens a hundred years from now. I don't have enough information;
I can't go five days before the prediction deserts reality and I don't know
where the hell I am. Instead of doing that, I can see that the model is
physically consistent internally; it's not losing or gaining energy. It does
represent, within certain limitations, most of the feedback mechanisms
I have to deal with. I have a fairly accurate filtered data base to start
with. Now I start, and zap, I run it for real time of a hundred years, ten
years, five years. At that point I stop, and I set everything back to zero
again and make my small boundary change, and I run it again. Now
I'm not at all interested in the moment-to-moment detail given to me by
the model. What I *am* interested in is the ultimate difference between
the two models' runs, in some sort of raw, average, conglomerate way.
Where are we trending? The climate of the earth: Does this perturbation

produce noticeable change in the way this climate evolves? In this case it forces me, for example, to run my models sufficiently to build up a model climatology, to run the model for five years' real time, and determine what the statistical fluctuations are in this model; so as to have the ability to ask questions like: Is this difference statistically significant? Then I'm beginning to ask the right questions. I'm not trying to ask in detail what will happen, whether a new ice age will occur. I'm asking whether this anomaly I've created can produce a noticeable change. If it can, that sounds an alarm in my head: Don't let that happen, because that will have a noticeable effect, and you'd better know what that noticeable effect is before you act.

GORDEN: When you don't know where the model is going, how can you set a level of criticality and uncertainty? And what's your behavioral response to high uncertainty or high criticality?

GREENFIELD: To a certain extent this is still subjective, but let me set two criteria. One is that almost all massive climate change — let me use that as an example — may be beneficial, detrimental, or both. Change that can be brought about by man's activities demands knowledge of what this change is before you initiate the action. That's a simple criterion: I dare not meddle around with somebody else's environment, climatology, life, without both sides' being perfectly aware of what I'm about to do.

GORDEN: In the concrete, that's very difficult. For example, if an underdeveloped country wants to cut down rain forests, you've got to be reasonably certain to create enough authority to be able to stop them from doing it if you believe it has an impact on climate. So the real case doesn't often meet that criterion you established.

GREENFIELD: That's right. All we're trying to do right now is to establish a need for that sort of authority, that sort of a body of knowledge and analytical expertise, if you will. This need is gradually being recognized at the international level; there are groups in the International Committee for Scientific Unions now who are beginning to recognize the need for an international body to provide that capability to provide the warning cry that we may be initiating something irreversible or at least deleterious, and that we better know what we are doing before we do it. It's also involved in obtaining a greater amount of information that allows us, with time, to improve our ability to predict the probable change involved.

GORDEN: The next research area is how to get society to accept or do the kinds of things that are necessary.

GREENFIELD: Well, that's easy to say and hard to accomplish. It has to do with the fact that implementing solutions in our society is not an easy task. It involves recognizing the fact that the solutions may produce an economic and social impact that you must get people to accept; the question is how best to approach this. One approach, obviously, is the regulatory approach: you just say that's the regulation you've got to follow, and here is the penalty schedule involved. A second way is possibly to provide tax incentives for companies or individuals not to pollute.

GORDEN: Are you, then, interested in the research end of the possibility of carrying out the program?

GREENFIELD: Well, answering that question poses the same problem I'm faced with when I talk to the rest of my agency. It is *not* the job of research to set regulations or decide on tax incentives. I do, however, want to provide the techniques that allow us to assess the efficacy of various available alternatives. And you haven't really addressed the implementation problem unless you've examined questions such as these. Right now, we don't quite have the analytical capability. A typical example of an area where we don't have the regional analytical capability is that involving the broad discipline of sociology. How do you change people's minds about things? How do you get them to accept concepts such as quality of life, or changing life style? How do you educate them to the necessity of paying the costs?

GORDEN: One thing you mentioned was the impact of man's activities, secondary and tertiary particularly — the "forcing function."

GREENFIELD: Let me give one example of what I mean by a "forcing function." If you wish to establish a new transportation system in a region, it is relatively easy to determine the "primary" polluting effects due to the system (i.e., the pollution due to the system itself). It is very difficult to determine the secondary, tertiary, and higher order effects that probably produce a much greater environmental impact. These effects include the fact that the presence of this transportation system changes the land use for a considerable distance around it, changes the population distribution, changes the industrial complex, etc. In essence, this single activity of man acts as a forcing function in the development of an entire area, which produces significant feedback on the environment. We are not, as yet, capable of analytically handling such events.

I should point out that this also infers another concept that deserves highlighting. The environment can never be thought of in terms of a single category or medium (e.g., air, water, pesticides, etc.). The environment is a totality. To protect it we must continuously consider the impact of our actions on the integrated whole.

GORDEN: Amen. But many people don't understand that yet. The last item we can quickly address, from the point of view of science communications, is what difference it makes to you, as a research director, that the public and politicians are consumers of what you do? How does this affect the research in some way?

GREENFIELD: It affects me very directly, because unless I can get my message across as to what is happening, then their environmental imperative is not invoked, and it is important that we invoke the environmental imperative of the entire country, the entire world. Because it's obvious that whether we're going to turn the thing around is in the final analysis going to depend on the acquiescence of most people, plus a knowledge of what the effects and costs are, a knowledge of where we're going and what the possible outcomes might be of our actions and technology, etc. All these things must be brought clearly to the people and the politicians, because they're constantly being bombarded with the desirability of striving for the "good life" — spend, expand, develop, utilize. And that's been the driving force up to this point in time. You're not going to counter that unless you can effectively communicate your side of the argument.

GORDEN: What does the communication do?

GREENFIELD: In a crass way it provides human support for what the research is trying to do. If you can't communicate the results, if you can't communicate your concern with the outcome you seek, then you cannot communicate the need to do the research.

GORDEN: The problem of trying to make science relevant to people is what we're after, and I'd just like to try to find some examples so the student would recognize the difference between what you'd do as a scientist ten years ago when we didn't worry about relevance and what you have to do now.

GREENFIELD: It is no longer possible to sell science for the sake of science. The question of relevance is very much to the fore. Let me give you an example. When I was at RAND Corporation as head of Environmental Sciences, I was extremely interested in developing a program on man's impact on climate. To do this, it was necessary to start a program that covered almost the entire spectrum from the interaction of cloud particles up to global circulation. Now we brought together a host of people, ostensibly all atmospheric scientists. And I said to myself, all I have to do is sit them down in the same room and some magic will occur. Magic does occur, but it occurs for a different reason than you originally imagine. Each of these people was an expert; each was very capable in his own field. I had, for example, a scientist who had been fascinated for a number of years with the interaction and growth of small water droplets — he had developed the appropriate equations and was actively engaged in determining the effects of electrical charge and electronic field on these interactions — in a sense examining all the multitude of elusive things that one does as he tries to tear a subject apart and understand it down to the finest point, the complete understanding of the way water droplets grow. If I left this man alone, he could possibly spend the remainder of his life dealing with what happens to particles interacting. And what would come out would be a beautiful piece of research, and you and I as scientists looking at it would say, in admiration, "He really has delved into and understood and revealed the whole subject." Now, that's fine in an era when you have patrons and the luxury of doing that type of research. In that case, time has no relevance, and you have a chance to deal with the beauty of the subject.

But if you have a goal that demands a direction really much larger than that subject you're dealing with, then something else happens. Suddenly this scientist who is interested in two droplets interacting is put cheek-to-jowl with somebody interested in the next scale up — a distribution of droplets, the cloud — who is put cheek-to-jowl with somebody concerned with the next scale up — a field of clouds — and from a field of clouds, an entire atmosphere. Suddenly the next scale up begins to ask very relevant questions of the guy with the two droplets, because what he's trying to do is parameterize the knowledge at this smaller scale into the larger scale, so that he can develop his beautiful model, and each man asks questions from above and, in turn, is asked questions from below. I'm saying that this vector, provided by a specified goal, provides a gradient which permits information to flow across these little disciplinary boxes we allow ourselves to be put into when we are doing research.

GORDEN: Thank you, Dr. Greenfield.

II

As indicated by the foregoing interview, what we need to know as scientists and professionals includes a technical body of knowledge essential for successful management. However, scientific data alone leads us into the trap of elitism and technocracy, where the technical information is held by a very few but affects the lives of very many. Because environmental management touches the lives of so many people and takes place at levels of authority as localized as the town planning board, a program of mass information sharing is a necessary component of the information requirement.

For in a democracy, we expect people to participate in decisions affecting how to use land and what resources to protect and what efforts to make for future generations. While these questions have components which rely on technical information for their answers, they also require the understanding of large numbers of people who elect officials who then put scientists' advice into practice. We will also call attention to the nontechnical or value choices which environmental management must incorporate from public participation, but value choices take place outside the context of environmental sciences. The information requirement of the choices includes a technical portion: we must know what values are at stake and what the consequences of those values will be when acted upon. This entails a program of mass education to act sensitively and sensibly in the face of ecological consequences. We will have to convert men who have made successful careers in consumer advertising into men who at least think about ecologically sane consumption patterns.

It is necessary to know not only how to manage the environment, but also for whom and for what ends, which again is a question of values. Should we encourage hardwoods over soft, carp over trout, songbirds over quieter species? Should we allow goods to be produced which result in nondegradable wastes? Dare we even ask these questions for fear our disturbance of nature's course, as outlined in Chapter 3, will set unforeseen consequences in motion? To take the risk or not is itself a value-laden question, for the loss–gain calculation is clouded with uncertainty. Chapters 4 and 5 raise issues that require value trade-offs and delineate some risks of over- and under-utilization of natural resources.

The value questions are not easily solved, yet they directly relate to management decisions. While natural resource exploitation was still in the pioneering stage — using land until it was worn out, then leaving it for new land — there was little thought to future generations. Now, if we value the future, we must start thinking of a resource policy that uses only the "interest" and leaves the "capital" to spawn more interest.

Nor can we avoid value decisions when we undercut economic productivity and jobs in order to clean up a stream where pollution offends public health and taste. If the cost of doing business cleanly rises, capital is taken away from potential production. While such a choice may be easy for an affluent society, not all classes nor all societies are affluent. In some countries, pollution is a result of industrialization to fend off the horrors of an agrarian economy which has not produced enough for human subsistence. Advanced agriculture and industrialization go together in many instances, and if the poor are ever to leave the vicious cycle of poverty, some pollution may be necessary. In this world, international specialization of labor constrains what economies can afford. However, there is a scientifically determinable line between aesthetically offensive pollution which is temporarily tolerable, and biologically irreversible damage which is not.

Nor can we avoid value judgments when we attack power plants as the villains producing sulfur gases injurious to public health when the public's individual home heating systems account for more sulfur in the air than the power plant produces.

Environmental management involves value decisions not only in terms of what natural resources to encourage or exploit, but also in terms of potential gains or losses to some segments of the world's population. There are public choices in terms of national policy and personal choices in terms of child-bearing decisions. We cannot escape value choice.

The editors requested Russell E. Train, Chairman of the President's Council on Environmental Quality, to identify the choices and procedures involved in seeking a quality environment. The resulting interview, conducted on April 1, 1971, is printed below.

Interview with Russell Train:

GORDEN: We are in this decade going to have to re-pose environmental issues. They have been posed with some difficulty, and they suggest a set of value questions that need to be answered. The sort of issues involved in values are numerous; value is a very large word. One way into value questions is a description of what you do in the Council of Environmental Quality. Because you're involved with quality, clearly your agenda is America's agenda on quality.

TRAIN: Well, let's start with what the Council does. The Council on Environmental Quality, as you know, was established by the National Environmental Policy Act on January 1, 1970, and is situated in the Executive Office of the President. We are a three-man advisory group to the President, with a staff of about 54 people in 1971, with a budget of a million and a half dollars. Hopefully, both our staff and our budget will grow in 1972. Our primary function to the President is in the area of policy development, and in this sense we tend to be different, say, than the Environmental Protection Agency, whose primary function is administrative, regulatory — dealing with enforcement problems. EPA is a line agency; CEQ is not. As I said, we are policy oriented and advisory. We do have, in addition to the policy function in the broad sense, the day-to-day responsibility of overseeing all federal programs to monitor their impact on the environment. These are our two broad areas of responsibility. We have some specific functions such as the preparation of an annual report on the State of the Environment. Our first report was transmitted to Congress by the President in August 1970. This is a very time-consuming responsibility.

Now in terms of specifics, going back to the two functions of policy formation and program oversight, our policy function is best exemplified by the message on environment the President transmitted to Congress on February 8. Last summer [1970], we were asked by the White House to take the lead in developing the President's 1971 environmental legislative program and such administrative initiatives as he might want to take in this area. Starting as soon as we finished our annual report in mid-summer, we identified major likely areas for legislative and administrative initiative and put together an interagency steering group to advise us as the program developed. And, as we determined to get into various areas such as noise pollution, we set up small working groups drawn from appropriate agencies that had some program interest in the effort. We developed the decision papers and policy proposals, did the actual drafting in most cases, wrote the President's message — did the whole thing, right through the interagency clearance. I suppose that is the most specific example of actual policy work. As you know, from that effort evolved a very comprehensive program covering a wide range of pollution and land use proposals.

Another example of policy development we are engaged in is exemplified by the study we undertook late last spring and the report we submitted to the President in October 1970, which he transmitted to Congress at that time, calling for a new national policy with respect to ocean dumping. That of course, again, was implemented by the President with detailed legislative proposals this February. So during the course of the year, we do undertake special studies in specific areas, sometimes at our own initiative, sometimes at the initiative of the President.

In the area of supervision, which requires a great deal of our time, we work with substantially all federal agencies, because there is practically no federal program that does not in fact have impacts on the environment to some extent; and, some of these, I think, are not the ones one normally thinks of. For example, tax policy, through the Treasury, creates very significant impacts on the environment — an area in which I'm particularly interested, perhaps because of my own background as a tax lawyer.

Every federal agency is required by the National Environmental Policy Act to do a careful analysis of the environmental implications of every one of its actions, at least to the extent that significant environmental impacts are involved. This requires a report to our Council of these environmental impacts under Section 102 of the Act. This again provides us with a tool for review of legislative proposals by agencies and gives us an opportunity to identify adverse environmental impacts in advance of decision making, and an opportunity to follow this up with discussions with the agency itself at various levels — staff level; or between myself and the agency head or Cabinet officer, as the case may be; or in the final analysis, if it's important enough, a report by me to the President on the particular program requesting his intervention. That in general is how these two broad areas work.

Now, the legislative program was characterized by several key considerations. Initially, of course, it dealt with a number of familiar areas, such as water pollution. At the same time, we were moving into areas in which the federal government had by and large in the past taken either no role at all or a limited role, such as in noise pollution. Another characteristic was that many of our pollution and environmental programs have tended to be reactive in nature — dealing with problems after they've become problems. I suppose this is not unexpected in view of the fact that the environment is relatively new as a major policy concern. But, we've tried, in the current legislative program, to identify emerging problems and to deal with them, to present proposals for getting on top of them before they reach crisis proportions. Ocean dumping, I think, is a good example. The President's proposal with respect to toxic substances is another example. Here we're dealing with a large number of chemical substances, new plastics and things of that sort, that are introduced into the environment every year with little or no testing of environmental effects and little or no public control.

Another earmark of the legislative program is the provision for the first time of economic levers. As economists have been telling us for some time, one reason for our environmental pollution problem, at least in terms of industrial pollution, is that the external costs or social costs of pollution, while very real, are not usually borne by the discharger himself. They are borne by the community around him, or by society as a whole, or perhaps even by future generations. So economists have urged that if we could internalize these costs in some fashion, the normal competitive forces of our economic system would work to drive these costs down and thereby reduce or eliminate the pollution effects. So in this area, for example, the President has proposed a Clean Air Charge, essentially a tax on sulfur oxide emissions, to provide industry with an increasingly strong economic incentive to eliminate sulfur oxide emissions and to develop the technology to do the job. This approach represents a significant new policy direction.

Finally, in respect to the legislative program, there's a recognition for the first time that wise land use and effective management of land resources is a critical determinant of environmental quality. This recognition gave rise to the Presidential proposal for a national land use policy — federal regulation of the environmental effects of surface and subsurface mining, and also regulation of power plant siting, among other land use initiatives.

Of course, I've only taken any of this so far to the point of submission of legislation. We're now at the point of holding hearings. I've been testifying both in the House and Senate before various committees because environmental legislation doesn't go before just one committee. It involves half a dozen committees on both sides of Capitol Hill. So we're going to have a very busy schedule of hearings.

In developing environmental policy, there are obviously a number of factors that have to be taken into account. I hasten to say, at this point, that our understanding in this whole area is very limited. Hopefully, we're going to have far more wisdom in a few years, but our processes at this time are admittedly imperfect.

High on our list of environmental values is human health. I think this is the issue to which the public responds most quickly, and certainly any environmental impact that gives rise to disease, injury, even death, is one that we put at a very high level of priority for action. Thus, health is an important value consideration. This leads us, for example, to deal as a matter of urgency with problems such as sulfur oxide emissions, giving rise to the President's proposal of a Clean Air Charge. We estimate that health bills to the American people annually from sulfur oxide emissions alone are running at about the rate of $3.3 billion. But we don't quantify the health concern entirely this way. As long as sulfur oxide emissions can be identified as closely related to bronchial disease, lung cancer, and so forth, we know that dealing with this is a matter of urgency. So that's one aspect.

Environmental damage, as contrasted to direct and rather immediate human health damage, is increasingly a value with which we deal. This is borne out in the language of our legislative proposals; pesticides, for example, are not dealt with simply as health hazards but also as environmental hazards. On a somewhat different scale, the legislation dealing with noise ties the federal policy not only to the control of noise in order to protect the public health, but also to protect the public welfare. That term "welfare," ill-defined as it necessarily is, comprises that somewhat amorphous but very real area of community environmental values, and it is essential to the effectiveness of this legislation. The industries affected would rather we limit noise controls to determinable health impacts. Yet I think most of us recognize that while the kind of noise we're hearing right now from the street may be a nuisance and may be creating very real stresses, it is pretty hard to measure any direct health impact.

The quality of the urban environment is very much tied to our ability to control that kind of indirect impact. So we increasingly are looking not only to direct health effects, but to broader environmental effects. This has been a steady trend, one of the identifiable trends in this whole business of environmental management. Thus, the water pollution control program started off as a public health program administered by the Department of Health, Education and Welfare. It was only after it had been in effect for some time that it was recognized that the emphasis on public health was building in a limiting factor. It was discovered that if you approach the problem primarily as a health matter, unless you could really prove you've reached a threshold of effect on human health, you can't do anything about the pollution problem. Yet stinking streams would exist, sport fishing would disappear, pleasure boating would disappear, swimming in the vicinity of urban communities would disappear — all this wide range of very real environmental values would not be taken into account. So that program changed; the public welfare concept was built into it; it was transferred to the Department of the Interior, and, of course, it has been brought now under the Environmental Protection Agency. So, I think this is one of the real trends working steadily in this entire field.

GORDEN: Can we pursue that trend a little bit? When you moved from health to welfare, you began to open up certain issues which are more difficult to define. Let's take some concrete cases. For example, you mentioned land use before; while some of the land use problem is an impact problem and degradation-due-to-impact problem, much of it primarily involves opportunity costs for future generations, or future opportunities for the present generation. These last are more difficult to measure. They include issues such as using the Atlantic flyway for homesites or for birdlife, or siting a power plant on the coastal zone when the same site could have been used for other welfare activity. How does one make policy in areas where, essentially, the electorate has not made its judgments or values known?

TRAIN: Well, first, let me repeat what I said at the beginning: We don't know all those answers. We have just started down this road of decision making. We're all feeling our way. There's a strong sense abroad in the land and in government that there are ranges of values important to decision making of which we were not aware a few years ago. We may have known they existed, but we didn't think of them as important to decision making. We looked at the economic values, or the engineering values, or perhaps the public health values. So we're dealing with a new animal, really. I frequently say we're dealing with a revolution in the way our society looks at problems and in the way we make decisions — not just in government, but in our business relationships and in our family and home relationships, as well.

   Let me pick something easier, first, than land use examples. To go back to the pesticide case, one of the main concerns in dealing with pesticides is their introduction into food chains and the appearance — particularly of persistent pesticides such as the chlorinated hydrocarbons — in tissues of shellfish, birds, and other living things. We are satisfied that they involve, in many cases, very real adverse effects on those forms of life. In most of these cases, with respect to this particular range of pesticides, the adverse direct effects on human health are still conjectural. Of course, some of the pesticides are acutely toxic — the organo-phosphate group in particular. But among the chlorinated hydrocarbons such as DDT, the adverse human health effects are, as I said, really still speculative.

But there are very real effects within the ecosystem surrounding man, so this we consider to be a major adverse environmental impact. The destruction and disruption of the naturally functioning ecosystem is an environmental cost that is taken into account in decision making. So here is a kind of biological effect, if you will, not necessarily directly related to human health, which we are increasingly building into our value system for public decision making.

That is — as difficult as it is — a fairly easy example to deal with. The kinds of things you referred to are becoming far more difficult, for example, the value of the continued existence of a wild river, as opposed to its being dammed and turned into a lake.

We sometimes tend to be discouraged about the range of problems and the imperfect state of our ability to deal with them. I'm not personally discouraged, because I think the really promising thing is that we have finally identified these values as real and as needing some kind of quantification and some kind of regular building into our decision process — something we had no clue of five, ten years ago. So, we have come a long way, I think, in reaching that point in human wisdom of knowing that the preservation of a river or a species or of landscape diversity is important and that these things have intrinsic values.

In some cases, I despair that we will ever be able to quantify these. You have to make a policy judgment, maybe a political judgment in the broadest sense. For example, how do you quantify the survival of the blackfooted ferret as a species? There are too few of them left to consider them as an effective control over the prairie dog population, so the economic value of the blackfooted ferret today is really minimal. But it is a distinct species, evolved over millions of years, and so on. I think our range of values today is reaching the point where we as a matter of judgment will insist that a species of that sort must not be destroyed if we can help it, irrespective of our ability to quantify its survival in some economic terms.

GORDEN: Well, even if we can't quantify that decision, we still have to say that this species is of more value than some other species. It isn't necessary that we quantify, but we must at least rank order if we have a choice. For instance, take the case of, say, pesticides and the damage they do certain species, as opposed to the aid they have to other species, namely, man.

TRAIN: All right, we have to make this kind of judgment all the time, and we don't have any very ready yardsticks. It's pretty much a seat-of-the-pants kind of thing. A recent example involves the use of a pesticide called Mirex by the Department of Agriculture for either the control or the eradication of fire ants in certain areas of the South. Mirex is a persistent pesticide, and it is considered to be at least a potential cancer-causing agent. But evidence of this is completely uncertain at the present time. We know it does have some adverse effects, or at least it is believed to have some adverse effects, on shellfish and other elements of the ecosystem. The fire ant is not a particularly serious agricultural pest. Its mounds in fields cause some inconvenience in the use of equipment, but it does not attack crops to any significant extent. Its adverse effects come from its extremely painful bite, so it is a nuisance. There are some cases of illness, and I think even one or two deaths reported from the bite of a fire ant, but this is akin to the allergy reactions of some people to bee stings. It's an unusual occurrence. So we have here a complex problem of weighing costs and benefits. We really don't have a very clear picture on either side of the equation. All things being equal, we'd probably just as soon get rid of the fire ant, if this were possible in some convenient way. It's an exotic species and doesn't belong here in the first place. Its bite is acutely uncomfortable and a damn nuisance. On the other hand, we have these possible adverse effects in the environment and to human health from Mirex. Granted, these effects are not entirely clear at the present time. Our conclusion here at the Council is that, given this state of facts, the possible adverse effects — the costs, if you will, of using Mirex — outweigh the benefits. And it's been our recommendation that the program stop.

That's like so many of these cases. They are not very clear. They are not black and white. And in a case such as that of Mirex, you have to add a political ingredient to the equation. People in the South in many areas are fed up with the fire ant, and want to get rid of them.

GORDEN: There's an article in this book, by the way, about the fire ant, and the conclusion the scientists come to is essentially the same one you came to. This poses, though, a very tricky question about whether or not management can ever be a seat-of-the-pants, informal judgment. Many decisions we have to make are based on class or cultural values that don't have a biological back-up. For example, the amount of open space an American needs, or whether or not he should be able to eat shellfish are culturally determined rather than biologically determined, and making policy about these things, which have in fact differential impact on economic classes and so on, gets very difficult.

TRAIN: Of course, in many cases if you wait until you have all the evidence, you never do anything. That's the constant problem in dealing with pollution issues. The cry always is "you need more evidence it's being harmful," or something of that sort.

GORDEN: Then it's a question of risk assessment, which is traditionally the role of politicians in a society; it's not the role of scientists. I think we must somehow assign risk. There are ways of assigning risk in other endeavors; and as a management task, even though we're talking about risks of decline of quality or welfare or health, there has to be some way to articulate them and to "calculate" them.

TRAIN: Don't you have to weigh it against something? I'm just thinking out loud. I wonder whether risk in the abstract is terribly meaningful. Now, if it's an acute risk of some sort — if you do something that's going to cause a thousand deaths or something very obvious — you have something to act on. But generally speaking, the risks aren't that obvious, and you have to weigh a shade of concern against the real economics of the situation. We haven't talked about this yet. For example, let's say we get 90 percent of a certain harmful emission out of the effluent of a particular plant, which will cost "X" dollars, while the remaining 10 percent might well cost a hundred times that because the marginal cost of removal becomes so great. This is typically the case. Even though we might concede that the particular effluent does pose adverse health effects, these may not be sufficiently significant to indicate that we should go beyond that 90 percent, given the fantastic costs involved — not because we wouldn't like to get rid of that extra 10 percent, but because probably we could use those additional funds to greater advantage somewhere else. Every problem requires that kind of weighing of priorities.

GORDEN: Isn't it rare in the political system that the right priorities come up to be traded off against each other at the right time?

TRAIN: Why, sure. It's very difficult. It's nice to talk about these things as if they were all part of a systems approach, and we recognize, of course, that budgets surface from some forty different agencies in the federal government, none of which are related to one another in the process, and the Office of Management and Budget tries to put these together and does to an extent try to prevent overlap and competitive programs — Lord knows not with complete success — and, hopefully, to arrive at some form of national priorities in this process. Then this imperfect instrument is sent to Congress, where the budget is broken down once more in terms of a whole group of different appropriations subcommittees, each with its own constituencies and interests. So I guess the answer to the question is no, we don't have a real system to deal with it.

GORDEN: Democracy includes a process of accommodating plural values among people who don't agree about the risk assessment or whether the fire ant is that much of a nuisance. In the system we have, there is a process of compromise by which all these various values finally get settled. However, this is a difficult process for environmental issues because you can incrementally destroy the environment. Without some holistic sense, it becomes very difficult to assess the value of a single incremental change. You might well pass on an incremental change in one of your impact statements and it's all right, but seventeen changes would be very harmful to a local ecosystem.

TRAIN: I remember dealing with this in the Department of the Interior in the case of dredge and fill permits coming from the Army Corps of Engineers to the Department for comment. The particular one I was concerned with at the time was a stretch of mangrove shoreline in Florida. In itself, that particular stretch — a mile or whatever — was of no great significance to the fish and wildlife population of the Gulf of Mexico. But if all the rest of the coast went the same way that one apparently was heading — it was about to be filled and bulkheaded and the natural systems completely disrupted — it would have great significance. So, I looked at it just as you've suggested now, as the beginning of an incremental process. We should look at the whole package in arriving at a judgment of what to do on one element. I lost that particular fight, but that was the way we were trying to look at it, and you are quite right this is an important element in the problem. The guidelines which our Council has published to govern compliance by federal agencies with the National

Environmental Policy Act require that this approach be taken.
GORDEN: Now this would mean, if you extend it to our logical end, if
we had our 'druthers — and I won't answer who "we" is right now because
it's very important whose 'druthers are being had — that would mean a
land use policy which would tend to describe quality as a sense of
proportion. Quality in music, in fact, is a sense of proportion, and quality
in land use might well be defined the same way: so much for the power
plants, so much for the marinas, so much for the fish at sea, and so on. And
one cut at it might be trying to assign these priorities in the sense of
meeting all the various pluralistic values for the demands in the coastal
zone. Is there a chance that one could come to formulate a land use policy
like that, leaving aside all the cultural problems of private property
ownership and so on — or maybe we can't leave that aside. But the
question: is there a way to proportion? Is proportion the clue to this thing?
TRAIN: I don't know whether it is or isn't. I would say this: we're
working in that direction, certainly. It's a little hard for me to really come
to grips with this particular area because, as you recognize, most of
the authority over land use traditionally has been exercised by state and
local jurisdictions, and the federal government has had very little to do
with this. But there is no reason why your question can't be applied to the
state situation. One of the problems in the state situation has been that
there has been no single point where the various land use interests and
decisions involved could be brought together and sorted out.

   This is one of the things, maybe the major thing, that we are trying
to accomplish with our power plant siting legislation. We're requiring
each state to set up one single certifying agency to consider the plans of all
its electrical generating public utilities — this will include environmental
aspects as well as the energy demand part of the equation — to provide
methods for public notice, public hearings concerning this whole complex
of information. Of course, you can immediately say power plants are
just one aspect of the whole problem. And of course that's quite right. We
have so far to go, I don't really think you can go the whole way at once.
Power plants are a highly critical part of land use problems, and if we
can get a much better handle to that part, at least, it will be a significant
improvement.

   At the same time a little over a year ago, the Administration
submitted its proposals on coastal zone management legislation to
Congress. This, again, accepted the fact that the basic authority lies with
the states. But with a combination of sticks and carrots, the traditional
federal approach to these things, we were trying to induce each state to
set up a single coastal zone management agency and develop a single
coastal land use plan which would take into account the environmental
needs, economic needs, development needs, and so forth. Recently, the
President proposed a national land use policy which has, as a key element,
encouraging each state to develop a statewide land use control program.
It's a limited objective, of course, because we're asking them essentially
to deal with what we call areas of critical environmental concern; we're
not trying to tell them to develop statewide land use controls covering

everything, city planning and so forth, because we're afraid the whole thing would fall on its face. We're trying to pick a few critical areas. We've identified the institutional inadequacies as being really crucial.

What I'm saying in response to your question is that we have a long way to go. We are, I think, making some starts. And we do recognize the need for more centralized systems for dealing with these problems. GORDEN: We talked about always responding to demand, that many environmental crunches we're in now are essentially to provide power, to provide homesites, to provide, to provide — essentially on the feeling that there is an obligation to supply demand. We haven't talked yet about controlling demand in some way. Most of the arguments for siting power plants are based on projections of future electricity requirements. Is there any sense in which one can affect the demand side? TRAIN: I have several things to say on this. I think we're becoming skeptical of the kind of demand projection on which most planning has typically proceeded. This is true in the energy field; energy demand has doubled every ten years — every five years in Florida — so we proceed to make our plans for new capacity on the assumption that the projection will continue indefinitely. Any sane man knows it cannot continue indefinitely in that fashion. The traffic field is another example: we keep projecting traffic demand and, therefore, have to build new highways and expressways around cities to accommodate that projection, thereby attracting more traffic so it is more congested — in a sense, creating self-fulfilling prophecies. As I say, I think we're getting more and more skeptical of this approach. I made a speech recently in Florida to a group of power executives. I said that we are going to have to approach the demand as well as the supply side of the energy equation in the future. And I suggested perhaps limiting demand in some fashion. Now, there are several ways of getting at this. The economists would say that if the price of products included all the real costs, including the social costs of production, or the external costs as they are sometimes called, this in itself would tend to limit or shift demand; and this is another reason why it's important to internalize such costs to the extent we can. If industry is emitting 13 million tons of sulfur into the air per year and this is a substantial health hazard — a substantial damaging factor as far as plant equipment is concerned, as well as a damage to vegetation — and 55 percent of that sulfur comes from electric energy, shouldn't the people who use electricity bear those costs directly? We think there's no question about it: They should. This may be something of a doctrinaire economic approach, but I have no doubt it is valid. To the extent prices do not reflect true costs, there can easily be a misallocation of resources.

Another approach is a direct frontal assault through the tax system. We've done this over the years, but not for environmental reasons. Thus, years ago oleomargarine had a direct tax on it to make it noncompetitive with butter. We have considered taxes on a variety of things. I have mentioned sulfur dioxide. A tax was proposed last year on lead additives in gasoline. There are suggestions from time to time of a tax on throw-away beverage containers, a tax on phosphates in detergents, tax disincentives or tax incentives — depending on which way you put them — to discourage the use of virgin raw materials and to encourage the use of reused, recycled, or scrap materials. There are a lot of ways the tax system could be used for environmental intervention.

There is the regulatory approach, for example, requiring automobile manufacturers to install certain safety devices whether the consumer wants to buy them or not. This is a direct example of what government can do by using the commerce power to change consumer products in some fashion. Labeling is another way of influencing consumer choice.

The noise legislation the President has sent to Congress includes not only authority for the administrator of EPA to establish noise standards with respect to certain equipment manufactured and shipped in interstate commerce — primarily transportation equipment, construction equipment such as pneumatic drills and air compressors — but also to require labeling of the noise characteristics of certain consumer products. For example, air conditioners could be labeled so that a consumer could go into a store and make a choice based, in part at least, on the noise characteristics of different products. We think this, again, is a very important development. We're not making a value judgment in the sense we were talking about earlier. We're not saying this noise level is bad for you, or this air conditioner is better or worse. We are saying this one is going to be noisier, leaving it to the individual to make the decision.
GORDEN: Isn't that a problem with a lot of programs you mention, that we leave the decision to the individual, and once again we're back to whether he should be offered that choice, in the sense that the incremental impact would be great if each person bought an air conditioner. You might walk down the street on a summer day when everybody has his air conditioner on, and each one may have made an intelligent purchase but the street is noisy. This is the problem of incremental toleration and destruction of the whole again. You're talking about a form of limiting demand based on the economic theory that people will either refuse to pay for that thing, and therefore the manufacturer will quiet it or make it safer, or, if the price of electric power goes up, fewer people will use it. There are certain elasticities here that assume the marketplace will operate. And the theory of the marketplace in this may be less good as a guiding hand than, if you will, science.
TRAIN: I will hasten to say that we don't rely on the marketplace; in fact, we don't rely on any particular tool. Until we know a lot more than we do now, we will have to rely on a little bit of everything. And, of course, an important factor in all this is the institutional aspect. In the noise field, for example, we certainly don't feel that it would be appropriate for the federal government to set community noise standards. By that I refer to what should be the noise level on the street outside this office. That is a matter for local regulation, and as you know, most communities haven't regulated this at all. I suspect they probably will be moving in that direction. But it is far too early, in my view, to suggest that the federal government allow only fifty air conditioners of a certain decibel level operating on a given block in an urban community. First of all, we don't know enough to make that kind of judgment. On the other hand, we do think it is proper now for the federal government either to regulate

or, through the use of labeling, to enforce noise levels on given products, and we do feel that, imperfect as it is, a sufficiently competitive market exists to create effective pressure in reducing noise levels. At the same time, community noise is institutionally a problem for local government, so we don't get into that.

GORDEN: It's a little bit reminiscent of the era when the Interstate Commerce Commission began, and started trying to define the authority of the federal government. Ecosystems and nature don't really correspond to this constitutional heritage of ours. I wonder what the prospects are for matching authority levels with control programs that biology or meteorology or whatever require. We now have Air Quality Control Regions, or water quality standards, and when they cross state lines they create enormous difficulties of jurisdiction. I wonder if there is another way to design the relationship. The interstate commerce clause is a very interesting one, because it does get specific and through interaction with the Supreme Court over the years, it has found rather good solutions to some of those problems. Can you foresee a future down the road somewhere when we begin to say that some microclimate problems are not the role of the state because microclimate changes create problems farther down the coast or in other people's weather systems? Can you foresee some way to structure that?

TRAIN: I'd be the last one to look down any road and say it is unlikely that something will happen, because things have a tendency to move so rapidly nowadays, and in such unexpected ways, it would be foolish to speak of the future with any great confidence. The political boundaries of the states, I suspect, are going to be with us for a very long time, and I don't see these being done away with in any fashion and some new organizational structure created. At the same time, we understand today, far better than we ever have before, that many seemingly local actions have impacts on neighboring states or neighboring communities. In terms of our land use proposal, the main problem is that most land use decisions are made on the local level, yet many of these locally made decisions have significant environmental impacts that go far beyond the border of the community.

An example I frequently use, while certainly atypical, is the Everglades jetport, which everybody knew had an adverse impact on a national asset, Everglades National Park. But beyond that, it had a disruptive effect on the water regime, the ecology if you will, of all southern Florida. Probably it would have had a major adverse effect on the water supply of western Florida communities. It was designed to deal with the transportation needs of all southeastern United States; it was to be the major international air terminus for flights from South America and Africa, yet the decision as to where this extraordinary complex was to be located was made by something called the Dade County Port Authority, which had little or no communication with the state, let alone the federal government. This is the kind of problem with which we are trying to deal. In both the air and the water pollution field, we are recognizing increasingly the inadequacies of standards locally arrived at, and we're moving more and more in the direction of national emissions standards of various kinds. I think this, again, is a way of recognizing the point you're making. Likewise, when standard setting is entirely a local responsibility, serious competitive inequalities tend to arise.

Take ocean dumping legislation. It's often very difficult to establish that a certain amount of waste discharged off the coast of a state is really going to have an adverse effect on the marine environment as a whole — maybe yes for a square mile in a given place, but in the marine environment as a whole, no. Yet we have made a policy determination that the healthy functioning of the natural systems of the seas is critically important to our well-being and our survival, and that really every degradation, even if only incremental in nature, should be avoided. Having established such a policy, we still cannot take an all-or-nothing approach and say it must stop immediately. Because if it must stop, where does the waste go? The alternatives have to be weighed. Goals have to be achieved over time.

I think we are looking at these larger impacts more and more in making policy determinations. I think we're going more and more to the river basin as a basis of planning, calling for at least statewide land use plans. We're requiring in our proposal that federal programs and activities must conform and not be inconsistent with state plans once they're approved. So here is a way of trying to mesh national policies with local programs.

GORDEN: You were escalating up a scale, and I was wondering if you were going to get to international relations within the biosphere, because so far we've confined ourselves to the U. S. problem. There is a pluralism of values in the world on this issue clearly, and not all people would agree with what you're apparently describing as a leadership role that has to be taken.

TRAIN: Let me talk about the international side for a minute because we're very much involved here in the Council. It happens to be an area in which I've always been interested. In fact, I sort of backed into the environment through the international door, and it's a fascinating arena.

It goes without saying that the environment is global and the relationships in which we are involved are global in nature. We're all caught up in one biosphere. Certain kinds of problems can only really be dealt with on an international basis. This isn't a matter of ecological theory. The fact is, if you want to prevent oil spills on the high seas, there is no way that an individual nation can really effect this. So, in certain key areas such as marine pollution, we must have international cooperation if we're really going to do the job. At the same time, we also need national initiatives such as we are trying to take with our own ocean dumping legislation. In another kind of area, the field of environmental monitoring — particularly in the atmospheric field and again in the marine field — the only way we can have an effective system of data and baseline indices for monitoring the environment is through an international system.

There is an increasing awareness of environmental values, certainly

all through the more developed countries, technologically and economically.
This is true both among western countries and among eastern nations,
including Soviet Russia. I even understand there is considerable interest
developing in mainland China. Among the less developed countries is
certainly far less concern about pollution, and in many cases a very real
concern that the burgeoning excitement among developed countries
about pollution may have an adverse effect on their own development
plans. I talked to a young man from the Congo about this yesterday.
This is something we have to accept as a real problem. It is probably silly
to say that you must have the same automobile emissions standards in
Nairobi as you do in Los Angeles, or the same sulfur oxide emissions in
Dar Es Salaam as in Pittsburgh. There is such a thing as too much of a
good thing. At the same time, I think it important that undeveloped nations
understand the implications of environmental problems and, to the
extent possible, avoid some of the mistakes we have made. One reason
the costs we are now encountering are so terribly high is that we've put off
doing anything about these things so long. And underdeveloped countries
are going to face the same problem not so many years down the road
if they don't make a start now. Environmental problems exist in all
countries; it's obvious we all belong within the same global environment.
The problems tend to differ among nations and regions, both in nature
and in degree. In the United States, we tend to be concerned particularly
with air pollution problems such as sulfur oxide emissions and automobile
emissions. These would be less important in some less developed
countries. I say that with a good deal of qualification, because Mexico
City, Seoul, Ankara, Sao Paulo, to name a few, have about as bad air
situations as exist in the world. Most developing countries typically
have severe problems of erosion, water resource management, timber
management, resource management generally, agricultural development,
environmental health, and human waste treatment in cities. Many less
developed countries have the most acute problems of over-rapid,
unplanned urbanization in the world. Places like Djakarta have fantastic
waste problems. These pose major human health threats, and I'm sure
they contribute heavily to disease levels which hold down productivity and
so forth. I am trying to say that developing countries have very real
environmental problems. They tend to be somewhat different than ours,
but they should recognize them. There is a great deal that we can do
to contribute to their rational solution.

There is much international activity in the environmental field at the
present time. First, let me point out that a number of nations are
unilaterally gearing up to deal with these problems effectively. England
has just designated a Secretary of State for the Environment, Peter
Walker. He has a combined ministry made up of the Ministry of Housing,
Ministry of Transport, Ministry of Public Works and Local Government,
I think. Here is an example of a government trying to centralize
environmental management in effective fashion. Canada has recently
designated one minister, Jack Davis, as Minister of Environment and
Natural Resources, to be the focal point for environmental policy making

in the Canadian government. Likewise with Germany, Minister of the
Interior Gentscher is the focal point. They have a federal system in
Germany and are going through some of the throes we have gone through.
Many of their water and air programs are administered by their states,
primarily, and they're trying to bring this back into the federal government.
France has a new Minister Delegate for the Environment, M. Poujade.
I understand the new Norwegian government may establish a ministry
of the environment, within a matter of days.

The President asked me to visit the Prime Minister of Japan following
the coincidence of major air inversions that both countries had last
August — the East Coast here and Tokyo. Last October I went to Japan
and visited with Prime Minister Sato and several other ministers in the
government, talking about mutual problems and possibilities of mutual
cooperation. The Japanese are establishing an Environmental Agency
as of the first of July. So this kind of thing is going on unilaterally around
the world.

There are a great many bilateral relationships developing as a
result — the United States and Canada, for example, on the Great Lakes.
We have a ministerial level task force on the Great Lakes which I chair
for the U.S. The Japanese are coming over here in June. About three
weeks ago, I visited London, Bonn, and Brussels to touch the various bases
I have been describing. In Brussels, there is a NATO Committee on the
Challenges of a Modern Society (CCMS) — a sort of new environmental
dimension of NATO, and I am the United States' representative to that
Committee. This, I think to many people's surprise, is turning out to
be a very effective operation which is coming up with some rather useful
things, such as stopping all international oil discharges on the high seas
by 1975 if possible, or no later than 1980. This is quite a dramatic
accomplishment. Now the Intergovernmental Maritime Consultative
Organization, known as IMCO, in London, has agreed in its committee on
maritime safety to this same principle, and with the cooperation of
Soviet Russia has extended it to "other noxious substances." This indicates
how the work of NATO and CCMS has been effective and how some of
the products of CCMS activities are being utilized in other international
agencies. The results of CCMS activities are fully available to non-NATO
governments, including the Eastern European countries.

There is also the Organization for Economic Cooperation and
Development in Europe (OECD), headquartered in Paris. OECD has an
environmental committee on which Dr. Gordon MacDonald of our Council
is the principal U. S. spokesman. Its particular area is the field of
economic analysis, trade effects, things of this sort, which are highly
significant areas of environmental concern. Japan is also a member of the
OECD. There is the Economic Commission for Europe (ECE), in Geneva,
which is having a major conference on environment in Prague in May.
I'm chairman of the U. S. delegation to that one. ECE provides a major
linkage between eastern and western countries; the Soviets, Eastern
Europe, the U. S., and the Western European countries belong. We hope
it will become a useful forum for communications in the field of

environment between East and West. There are various other regional activities in Africa, South America, and Asia, but these are not as strong as they should be. Most important, there is a United Nations conference scheduled for Stockholm in 1972 on problems of the human environment. This is going to be a somewhat unwieldy but at the same time very hopeful enterprise. It represents the first time that governments as such on a worldwide basis will meet to discuss the environment. Here we are finding a possible split of interest between less developed and developed countries. And one of the very important efforts we are making here in this Council in our work with the State Department is to build into the conference items that are of real significance to the developing countries. As I said earlier, they have a tremendous stake in all this. I think the conference must have positive benefits for them.

Those are some of the things going on internationally. The trade implications are very important. Certainly, if one country imposes environmental controls on its manufacturers, it's increasing the cost of its products, and if competing countries don't impose similar costs, a trade gap is created. Of course, this is simply one element of a very complex picture. Labor, transportation, and raw material costs are far more significant. Environmental costs tend to get overemphasized frequently by those who would just as soon not see them proposed. But at the same time, I don't mean to brush them off; they're real. It's to the advantage of the United States to work with other nations for development of improved environmental standards. Not only is it protecting the global environment on which we all depend, but it also has important connotations as far as trade is concerned. It works both ways. Our environmental controls are also thought to create nontariff trade barriers with respect to some foreign products, as foreign automobiles. We certainly have to impose the same standards on imports as on our own products, but we have to be sensitive to these problems and understanding about them.

There is far less public excitement about the environment in most countries than here. There is a great deal of interest in Japan. The average Japanese newspaper has as much or perhaps more environmental coverage than the *New York Times*, and that's saying quite a bit.
GORDEN: And they've been sensitized by a number of bad experiences.
TRAIN: They've had certain harsh, dramatic health effects from mercury poisoning, cadmium poisoning, which are tremendously influential on public opinion.
GORDEN: They also have an interesting philosophy vis-à-vis nature which makes them more sensitive. Lord knows how they created that mess, but now they've created it, they're terribly sensitive to it.
TRAIN: Traveling around the Japanese countryside and seeing the extent to which they are insensitive to litter, made me question this premise we have assumed. You go into a Japanese national park and stop at one of the really fantastic scenic overlooks, replete with the picturesque pine trees and distorted rocks that make a Japanese landscape so fascinating. And you stand knee-deep in throw-away bottles and cans.

GORDEN: But that is really a question of scale. Americans think of the outdoors the way the Japanese think of a garden. And in a Japanese garden you get none of the litter business.

TRAIN: But he would throw it over his wall.

GORDEN: There's a lot of what the Japanese call "my home-ism" — what you do in your home is very different from what you do outside.

TRAIN: I didn't see this, but somebody described to me a Japanese family picnicking in a large public park. Each family tends to form a little circle with their backs to their surroundings; they put the box of food down in the middle of the circle and, as they eat, throw the wrappings, bones, box, etc., over their shoulders. At the end of the day, when everybody's gone, you see round circles of cleanliness scattered through this incredible litter. I talked to some Japanese about this, and it is interesting to see the difference of perspective.

Well, I was talking about the extent of public interest in this; there is more interest on the part of the press than there was a short while ago.

GORDEN: I've been impressed with the sense of public interest and action closing in on each other. Also, the Japanese governmental structure is very different and their capacity to deal with the problem is probably a lot better than our own. They've begun some very clever technologies — to design a city, for example.

TRAIN: Oh, in some of the new towns abroad, in dealing with solid waste and so forth, they're way ahead of us. It's interesting, talking with people abroad; they tend to deprecate their state of development on certain problems and say "you in the U. S. know all the answers," "you have a lot of money," and indicate that any exchange on these problems is basically a one-way street. I always try to emphasize that they are ahead of us on some things — land use, for example, town planning. The Japanese have got some very good monitoring technology, and they've done quite a bit of research on human health impacts of air pollutants. So, there is a basis for a real exchange among developed countries on these problems. One of the difficulties is that the personnel in European governments is typically very limited insofar as ability to deal with these problems. They need more trained people.

GORDEN: That's true in a lot of cases, personnel problems, almost everywhere that you go.

TRAIN: I think the training need is one thing that could be addressed internationally.

Another issue I find abroad is the question of costs and who should bear them. In Japan, for example, there tends to be a suggestion, by industry at least, that these really are public benefits, and therefore the government should pay by way of subsidy. I've made a very strong point about this in discussions, that I think this is clearly the wrong way to go. I'm not trying to suggest how they should organize or institutionalize their handling of these problems because different cultures with different traditions suggest different approaches; but we, at least, have adopted the principle that the polluter should pay to clean up his own pollution.

GORDEN: It doesn't really work that way in a lot of cases. Over 50 percent of the cost is in fact absorbed through tax benefits or one way or another.

TRAIN: That is true of all costs, not just pollution costs. Deduction of operating costs or depreciation of capital investment results in tax deductions which have, as you say, been passed on to the public generally. This is typical in all countries; tax systems operate roughly the same way. But I feel in principle, at least, that the cost of cleaning up pollution is as much a cost of doing business as paying wages or protecting the health and safety of your workers. Also, if a company has to pay its own costs of clean-up, it's probably going to do it with the least cost, the greatest efficiency, and these efficiencies should be passed on so the public will be getting the most value for the dollar it will be paying. Government subsidy generally doesn't have this kind of efficiency built in. This is making some assumptions that all countries might not accept, but it is certainly good free enterprise theory, and I found the Japanese very responsive to this.

GORDEN: You mentioned, a moment ago, training people to deal with this problem. As I go back over things we've talked about, we have to have a Solomon's great judgment; we have to have an economist who's gone beyond contemporary theory; we have to have scientists who know more than they know now, and so on. The human talent needed to make this thing go is tremendous, and I don't know if there's any way we can generate that; I guess it is forged out of experience. But we are addressing a group of people who may think about being environmental managers. Some readers of this book are thinking about being scientists or politicians involved in some way with this problem. One usually puts this question: "Is there a word of advice for the neophytes?" Is there something you see that's a key?

TRAIN: This is really a tough one! I think that, as you gathered, I have a few things to say on almost everything! I've given a little thought to this. Throughout our educational system, speaking not in terms of professional training in the environmental sense but rather of the general educational system, there is a need for conveying from the earliest level a sense of understanding of man's relation to his environment, starting from the simplest concepts in preschool and carrying this on to increasingly complex understandings. I think this is quite crucial to the ability of our citizens to understand problems, to deal with information on environmental matters, and to make intelligent choices. Having said that, I think there is, on the part of both scientist and nonscientist policy maker — politician if you will — a need to increase knowledge about the other fellow and his side of the thing. We tend to feel scientists are often not very helpful in the field of policy development. Usually they think they do know all the answers as far as policy is concerned. My experience is that it is a hard job to transfer scientific information into usable policy determinations. On the other side of the coin, I think there is a real need for politicians and policy makers to know more about science than they do. So I don't see the fault as being entirely on the side of the scientist. Most policy makers don't have a clue about science; in fact, they're often scientifically illiterate. It's not the scientist's fault that we can't translate scientific evidence into meaningful lay terms. None of us seem to know enough about the other fellow's language. Hopefully, improved environmental education generally will help this situation, because everybody would have basic environmental literacy.

Additionally, I think that there is an extraordinary need for environmental managers who do have some strong environmental disciplinary background. It's important to have a strong background in wildlife ecology, sanitary engineering, resources economics, or whatever. But with that, and this is the toughest thing of all, also to have a real interdisciplinary sensitivity and not be blind to the larger picture is perhaps the biggest need we have. We need specialists, because the world has gotten so complex; but the specialists must be able to understand the interrelationships and be able to communicate with other disciplines. Most of these problems can only be dealt with by interdisciplinary efforts. They are systems problems, and the last thing we need is some of the mission-oriented specialists who are blind to the bigger picture — that's what's got us in the trouble we're in. This means our educational institutions are going to have to make some pretty substantial changes in curriculum. They're also going to have to do something about the system of higher education — the departmental structures, the way their faculties relate to one another. We really need some basic reforms in our schools, and this is about the hardest kind of reform to come by that I know. It's easier to change the bureaucracy in government than it is to change a university faculty. But there is hope. Students are helping to force some of this change. The lack of interrelationship among courses and departments has been a major complaint on the part of young people in recent years. Students are insisting faculty take this need into account.

As you will have gathered from all my answers, we need lots of basic changes; they can't be accomplished overnight. But we are moving ahead. We are making important starts. We need to do a lot more. And we need a lot more knowledge of what to do and how to do it.

GORDEN: Thank you, Mr. Train.

With the knowledge our commentators seek and with the values we choose as guidelines, allocation decisions will have to be made. The process of making these decisions must be able to handle uncertainty in information and pluralism in values, which are part of the regular diet of decision making in a democracy.

Executives and legislators deal with problems of this kind as their stock in trade. What is different about environmental choices is that they may have more chance of physical irreversibility, and the assessment of risk and the different value conflicts may be more subtle than many other public decisions. In this sense, environmental decisions resemble those of high national security. Whether or not we approve of the allocation process for military affairs and security, we must give some thought as to how the process of decision making can handle these special characteristics of uncertainty and value differences. In Chapters 7 and 8, we give some thought to these elements of environmental management.

Even if we overcome these barriers, there comes the moment of truth when decisions will have to be implemented and enforcement must begin. The passing of legislation points the way to solutions of problems, but solving problems in their place needs field work and bureaucratic operations, such as the issuance of permits. If issuing permits degrades the environment, then the policies articulated in the legislature, no matter how refined, are worth little but psychological comfort.

To move from policy making to enforcement is a critical and difficult step. It is analogous to moving from a controlled experiment in the laboratory where only selected variation is permitted to a factory production process where real uncontrolled psychological and economic factors affect the outcome. New variables enter the picture and contingencies of time and place cause plans to go awry. In Chapter 8, we explore some of these vicissitudes as they apply to environmental management.

Environmental management deals with phenomena which respect no political boundaries. If Great Britain solves its sulfur disposal problems by using tall stacks to disperse obnoxious gases, that solves the problem of meeting sulfur dioxide standards in Britain. However, it makes life difficult for the Scandinavians, for rain clouds carry the emissions from Britain and dump them hundreds of miles away. Our environment neither originates nor ends with the political units which "control" it.

The problem of coordinating political units is always difficult and coordinating policy in environmental matters, having global impact, is even more difficult. Ecological awareness varies tremendously throughout the globe. Furthermore, pluralism of values is multiplied throughout the world, and asking developing countries to pay for a clean environment, when they already have so many bills to pay, is a difficult matter. To complicate this still further, the pollution of affluence, which the developed countries are only beginning to understand, is different in kind from the pollution of poverty which plagues poor nations. Erosion and soil depletion from centuries of poor agricultural practices are just as much an environmental problem for poor countries as over-fertilized soils and waters are for wealthy countries. The difference is that all environmental problems are more difficult to solve when there are few resources to go around.

Thus there is a wealth of problems and not enough wealth to solve them. We need to know more. We need to clarify our values and process the demands we make on our environment in a scientific and humane way. We need to enforce our decisions and see that the control mechanisms have sufficient geographic scope to deal with the interconnectedness of our environment. The winds and waters of the globe circulate and make us all neighbors. The energy we consume, stored in the earth for millions of years, has a finite capacity under existing technology — due both to insufficiency of source and limiting effects of pollution.

Difficult decisions will have to be made about priorities for resource use. Environmental management places demands on science and on political processes. We must recognize these demands while the choices are still open. The longer we wait, the fewer will our options be and the louder will be the lament that we let nature, in its destructive mode, solve our problems for us.

Chapter 2

Uncertainty: new demands
on the sciences

Environmental management requires information that is exceedingly difficult to obtain within the constraints of the present state of the art. There
are important uncertainties in our information storehouse which must be
resolved to provide the basis for intelligent environmental decisions. These
deficiencies cannot be made up swiftly by a massive injection of research
dollars or by scanning known information in a new way. There are major
obstacles to immediate solution, and an exploration of these difficulties
must be our first step in determining where to make new departures and
where to assign priorities and improve our management capacity.

There are three major areas of concern that lead to uncertainties in
our information. Scientists will have to respond to these demands. The
first question is one of scale — encompassing the range of environmental
dynamics moving from large weather systems to biological mechanisms
of a particular marsh. The second uncertainty is the capacity of organisms
to adapt to changes in the environment. The third question is in the area of
measuring the effects of change on human organisms and other forms of
life.

The question of scale is addressed in the first four selections of this
chapter. Using the question of atmospheric oxygen–carbon dioxide balance
as a case, it becomes clear that neither panic nor complacency can follow
from presently available information. Francis S. Johnson, in "The Balance
of Atmospheric Oxygen and Carbon Dioxide," expresses a need to have
further empirical materials backing the assumptions necessary to understand the basic dynamics of such a large-scale system as the atmosphere.
Dr. Johnson outlines the difficulties of quantification and expresses particular concern about our inability to understand the trigger mechanisms
through which small changes can lead to larger reactions.

While the optimism of both Wallace S. Broecker's "Man's Oxygen
Reserves" and S. Fred Singer's editorial may survive the questioning of
unsettled and unsettling issues, their optimism is really based on an assessment of the absolute amounts of change that we find in our oxygen supply.
However, while absolute change may be small, the consequences of small
changes can be very large indeed. The uncertainties of the issues raised in

these articles point to real difficulties in dealing with large-scale phenomena and in assessing the conclusions made on fundamentally different assumptions about absolute amounts versus trigger mechanisms with multiplier effects.

From the point of view of demands on the physical sciences, some of the uncertainties indicate that predictive science will need a fuller understanding of the dynamics of change before predictions can be acted upon by environmental managers — who need to know the limits and consequences of their actions. The trigger mechanisms, which result in more change than would be expected from assessing absolute change, create the problem of linking local effects to global phenomena as well. Mathematics and chemistry already have a well designed methodology for dealing with the general problem. In the chemists' labs, studies of rates of change and the impact of catalysts to speed up or slow down this rate of change are well known and carried out under controlled conditions. However, the scale of global interactions and general data availability leave many uncertainties to the environmental planner.

These uncertainties are not only a problem for the physical scientist; the social scientist also is faced with a difficulty if he cannot know the link between local and global interaction. The politician's role is to provide control mechanisms for undesirable change, and if he cannot assess the impact of small, local changes on a larger geographic scale, then he cannot design appropriate geographic units to handle control requirements. We have legal precedents for one geographic unit to control the behavior of a neighbor, but we must know who our neighbor is. The United States Congress is allowed to regulate interstate commerce for the national good. What is taking place in global commerce, and who should have authority over it? Such uncertainties raise problems for everyone involved in environmental management.

The uncertainties of large-scale phenomena with trigger mechanisms are not the only issues that place demands on us. Closely related is the problem of organism adaptation to small changes. While a substantial number of articles could have been chosen to illustrate adaptive capacity, only one is necessary to indicate the problems remaining to be solved. "Carbon Dioxide Exchange Patterns of Cacti from Different Environments," by D. T. Patten and B. E. Dinger, illustrates how small changes force organisms to adapt to a new environment, and it shows this can sometimes be done "successfully."

The first problem is whether we can predict the form adaptations will take. Darwin was able to predict accurately what an organism would look like if he knew its environment. He successfully hypothesized the length of a bird's beak, for instance, by knowing its food source. Can we expand the prediction to define the limits of the environment that will sustain life on earth? Can we predict what life would be like with a changed environment?

For physical scientists, prediction in a system composed of an enormous number of variables is a most difficult task. For social scientists, predicting whether or not the adaptation will be "successful" is an ethical judgment involving a complex of value decisions. The "easy" solution —

accepting survival of the fittest — has been rejected since the Social Darwinism movement was rejected early in this century. Furthermore, environmental managers now have the power to pick the terms of survival. Survival is no longer simply nature's choice, but involves choice by men, using technology.

Related to questions of scale and adaptability is the question of measurement. Two articles on radiation illustrate the complexities and uncertainties of measuring radiation effects. Very quickly the measurement issue raises the same concerns identified earlier in this chapter and repeats the demands on the sciences. One major new element, however, is who shall be responsible for assessing risk? The scientific inputs help us define the levels of risk, but who is to say what is an acceptable level? The last selection in Chapter 2, taken from congressional discussions with scientists, shows the problem in a slightly different context. Extrapolation of health hazards from lower animals to humans is fraught with uncertainty, and it is useful to see politicians deal with this burden on their capacity to assess risk.

This chapter illustrates some of the new demands on the sciences so that managers of environmental resources will know the basic features of their challenge. There are uncertainties which need to be resolved; and once these are settled, there will probably be still new tasks as we reach new levels of demands on the environment. The theme is constant vigil and more research. Monitoring the environment is Step One in getting the historical data we need. As this chapter illustrates, the monitoring will have to be continuous, and the critical levels for trigger mechanisms will have to be better understood. The challenge for future scientists is demanding and profound in its implications.

FRANCIS S. JOHNSON
The Balance of Atmospheric Oxygen and Carbon Dioxide

SOURCE OF THE ATMOSPHERE

There is substantial evidence that the earth's atmosphere was not formed at the same time as the earth, but rather that it gradually evolved through release from the earth's interior, followed by important modifications brought about by chemical and vital processes. The most impressive evidence for this is pro-

Dr. Francis S. Johnson, "The Balance of Atmospheric Oxygen and Carbon Dioxide," *Biological Conservation*, vol. 2, no. 2 (January 1970), pp. 83–89. Reprinted by permission.
The author is Director, Space Sciences Center, Southern Methodist University; Acting President, Southwest Center for Advanced Studies, Dallas. This research was supported by the National Aeronautics and Space Administration under grant NGL 44-004-001.

vided by the relative scarcity of noble gases on earth, as compared to their abundance in the universe. This fact was noted by Aston (1924), who suggested that it indicated that the earth was formed by processes which systematically excluded the noble gases. Such a process is the agglomeration or accumulation of small particles or planetesimals to form the earth; as the noble gases can not in general form chemical compounds, they would not be constituents of the planetesimals, and hence they would have been systematically excluded from an earth formed in this manner.

This viewpoint is buttressed by a comparison of the abundances of all the various elements making up the earth with their abundances in the universe. Not only are the noble gases relatively very rare on earth, but other elements that tend to form gaseous compounds are also depressed in their relative abundances. Hydrogen is a notable example; in terms of numbers of atoms, it makes up 92 percent of the universe but only 0.8 percent of the earth. Carbon and nitrogen are also depressed in their relative abundances, but not so markedly as hydrogen. The noble gases, on the other hand, are less abundant on earth than in the universe by many orders of magnitude; the one exception to this is argon 40, which is relatively abundant on earth because it has been released by the radioactive decay of potassium 40.

The total release of gas from the earth's interior has greatly exceeded the amount now present in the atmosphere. First of all, all the water in the oceans might be included, because the water was also released from the earth's interior, and it may have been released in the form of vapour. The total quantity of water on earth is about $1 \cdot 5 \times 10^{24}$ gm. As such large quantities are difficult to visualize with proper perspective, it may be more meaningful to state the amount of water available per square centimetre of the earth's surface; a total mass of water on earth of $1 \cdot 5 \times 10^{24}$ gm is equivalent to an average of 3×10^5 gm for each square centimetre of the earth's surface, or 3×10^5 gm/cm^2 — corresponding to an average depth of water over the whole earth of 3×10^5 cm or 3 km.

This massive release of water vapour should be regarded as the biggest contribution that has been made to the earth's atmosphere, even though most of it has condensed to form the oceans. The phase in which water is found on earth might be regarded as an accident of the earth's average temperature; were the earth as cool as Mars, nearly all of the water would have gone into ice deposits, and were the earth as warm as Venus, nearly all of the water would exist in gaseous form in the atmosphere.

Perhaps surprisingly, the next most plentiful gas supplied to the atmosphere has been carbon dioxide. The evidence for this is the vast deposits of sedimentary carbonate rocks. These have resulted from the weathering of volcanic rocks, which has released calcium and magnesium ions among others; the calcium and magnesium ions have combined with carbonate ions formed by the dissolving of carbon dioxide in water to form the sedimentary carbonate deposits. Sometimes this deposition has resulted from a chemical reaction, and sometimes it has been accomplished by means of vital processes (for example, shells from lime-secreting organisms), but the end result has been the same: carbon dioxide has been removed from the atmosphere to form the sedimentary carbonate rocks. The best estimate of the quantity of carbon dioxide that has been consumed in this way is about 5×10^4 gm/cm^2 (Poldervaart, 1955), where the amount is again expressed in terms of the average mass per unit area over the whole earth. This amount of carbon dioxide can be compared with the amount now present in the atmosphere, which is 0·45 gm/cm^2. The amount dissolved in the oceans exceeds that in the atmosphere by a factor of about 60, so the amount in the ocean, expressed in terms of an average over the entire earth, is 27 gm/cm^2.

The most plentiful gas now in the atmosphere, nitrogen, owes its predominance there to its chemical inactivity. Approximately 90 percent of all the nitrogen that has been released from the earth's interior remains in the atmosphere. As the amount in the atmosphere is about 800 gm/cm^2, the total release has been near 10^3 gm/cm^2. A fraction of the atmospheric nitrogen, amounting to 1 part in 10^8, is fixed each year (Donald, 1960), but most of it does not remain fixed for very long; it is taken up by growing plants and returned to the atmosphere when the plants decay.

ATMOSPHERIC OXYGEN

Oxygen is in many respects the most important constituent of the atmosphere, and it is not a constituent that is to be expected among the gases that are released from the earth's interior. The earth's interior is underoxidized, and the gases released from the interior (mainly through volcanic activity) are at least weakly reducing. The degree of reduction is in much doubt, as measurements of volcanic gases free from contamination by atmospheric gases are difficult to make.

In the earliest geological times, gases emanating from the earth's interior may have been highly reduced, and hydrogen, ammonia, and methane, may have been present. However, when the earth's core formed, and metallic components gathered at the earth's centre, the average degree of oxidation of the material outside the core — the mantle — increased, and the gases released from the mantle after that event must have been much less reduced. This event occurred relatively early in geological times, at least $3·5 \times 10^9$ years ago. There is probably no reason to suppose that the degree of reduction of gases issuing from the earth's interior has changed much since the formation of the core, and they are only weakly reducing. Oxygen must have been provided by some endothermic process: two such processes have been recognized which might accomplish this — the photodissociation of water vapour and photosynthesis.

Oxygen from dissociation of water vapour

Water vapour can be dissociated by extreme ultraviolet solar radiation. The hydrogen that is released is sufficiently light to escape into space fairly readily from the top of the atmosphere, because an appreciable fraction of the hydrogen atoms have more than escape energy as a result of their thermal motions. If the hydrogen atoms did not escape, their ultimate fate would be recombination with oxygen atoms that were produced in dissociation events, and there could be no net accumulation of oxygen resulting from the dissociation events. In fact, the rate at which hydrogen escapes from the upper atmosphere provides a measure of the net rate at which oxygen is released into the atmosphere by photodissociation of water vapour. At the present time, this rate is less than 10^8 atoms per square centimetre per second (Donahue, 1966). If this rate were to prevail over geological time, approximately $1\cdot5 \times 10^{17}$ sec, the total hydrogen escape would be $1\cdot5 \times 10^{25}$ atoms/cm² or 25 gm/cm². This would involve the photodissociation of 225 gm/cm² of water, releasing about 200 gm/cm² of oxygen. This is about equal to the amount of oxygen actually present in the atmosphere at the present time, but this is an accidental coincidence, because, as will be discussed later, a much greater quantity of oxygen has been removed from the atmosphere by the oxidation of surface materials of the earth and by oxidation of partially reduced gases that have been emitted from the earth's interior.

The rate at which oxygen has been supplied by photodissociation in the past is not necessarily the same as the present rate. The photodissociation process as a source of atmospheric oxygen has been described as a self-limiting process (Urey, 1959; Berkner & Marshall, 1966) because the accumulation of oxygen in the atmosphere slows the process down by absorbing the ultraviolet radiation before it can be absorbed by water vapour. Berkner & Marshall suggest that this self-limitation effect limits the oxygen concentration that can be produced in this way to 1 part in 10^3 of the present atmospheric abundance. This limitation has been questioned by Brinkmann (1968), who indicates that the limitation is really not effective; that this is so is obvious from the present escape rate of hydrogen, which indicates that today there is a significant rate of addition of oxygen to the atmosphere by photodissociation, even with the present high level of atmospheric oxygen. However, the problem is really one of the supply relative to the demands (oxidation of newly weathered materials at the earth's surface and of partially reduced gases being emitted from the earth's interior), and this cannot be evaluated satisfactorily at the present time. What is clear is that oxygen in the atmosphere reduces the rate of photodissociation of water vapour, because the oxygen absorbs much of the ultra-violet sunlight and reduces the amount available for absorption by water vapour.

Oxygen from photosynthesis in excess of decay

The second source of atmospheric oxygen is photosynthesis by green plants *in excess of decay*. During the process of photosynthesis, carbon dioxide and water are combined to form a carbohydrate, releasing oxygen in the process. A highly simplified summary of the reaction is the familiar

$$CO_2 + H_2O + h\upsilon \;\rightarrow\; \{CH_2O\} + O_2$$

where $\{CH_2O\}$ represents the carbohydrate, the simplest form of which is $C_6H_{12}O_6$, and $h\upsilon$ represents the energy input from absorbed sunlight. The normal fate of the carbohydrate is oxidation, during which as much oxygen is consumed as was produced during its formation, releasing carbon dioxide and water vapour; this oxidation may be through the process of respiration, through combustion, or through slow decay. For there to be any lasting input of oxygen into the atmosphere from photosynthesis, there must be a corresponding accumulation of non-oxidized, or less-than-fully oxidized, organic material. One means of estimating the total contribution of photosynthesis to the oxygen content of the atmosphere is to evaluate the total earth inventory of non-oxidized organic material. The coal and oil reserves represent one obvious component of this reservoir.

The first life on earth apparently originated over 3×10^9 years ago. Cloud (1968) associated this early life with the banded iron formations because the earliest expected life-forms could not survive in the presence of free oxygen and would require some external receptor to remove the oxygen. Cloud identifies ferrous ions as the external oxygen receptor, with ferric iron the end product, which was then deposited in the banded iron formations. Appreciable quantities of free oxygen could not have been expected in the atmosphere in this era. Berkner & Marshall (1964) estimate the upper limit of atmospheric oxygen then as one-thousandth of the present atmospheric concentration. At some later time, peroxide-mediating enzymes arose that permitted the life-forms to exist in the presence of oxygen, and so an oxygen receptor was no longer needed. The last of the banded iron formations was formed about 2×10^9 years ago. From this time on, photosynthesis was capable of adding oxygen to the atmosphere, and the rise in oxygen content of the atmosphere commenced.

Berkner & Marshall (1964) identify the beginning of the Cambrian period, 6×10^8 years ago, as the time when the atmospheric oxygen content reached one percent of its present value. This would have two important effects. The first is that, at this level of oxygen concentration, the so-called Pasteur point, respiration becomes more efficient than fermentation as an energy-releasing mechanism, and organisms can be expected to evolve in the direction of respiration. The other is that, in addition to oxygen in the atmosphere, ozone will also be present, and the amount of it will be such that the atmosphere plus only a thin layer of water is sufficient to filter out the ultra-violet sunlight in the germicidal wave-length range. Prior to the attainment of this level of oxygen concentration, a layer of water several meters thick was required to filter out the radiation. Thus, the attainment of the one percent level for oxygen, relative to the present atmospheric concentration, opened an evolutionary opportunity for a massive expansion of life in the oceans. It is this expansion of life that Berkner & Marshall associate with the beginning of the Cambrian period. Others feel that this level of atmospheric oxygen was probably reached at a somewhat earlier time. Schopf & Barghoorn (1969) believe that organisms exhibiting oxidative respiration existed 10^9 years ago, which would place the one percent level for oxygen at least that far back in time.

Atmospheric oxygen probably reached 10 percent of its present abundance near the beginning of the Silurian period, $4 \cdot 2 \times 10^8$ years ago (Berkner & Marshall, 1964). The basis for this statement is that such a level of atmospheric oxygen is sufficient to support an ozone level in the atmosphere high enough to shield land areas from germicidal radiation, thus permitting life to exist on land. The fossil record shows that it was indeed early in the Silurian period that life spread rapidly from the oceans over the land areas.

TOTAL OXYGEN REMOVED FROM THE ATMOSPHERE

The total amount of oxygen that has been released into the atmosphere far exceeds the totality of what is there now, as great amounts have been consumed in the oxidation of surface rocks and gases that have been emitted from the earth's interior in at least partially reduced forms. The total amount consumed can be estimated only crudely. One large sink for oxygen is the oxidation of ferrous iron to ferric iron. Igneous rocks contain on the average about $3 \cdot 8$ percent of ferrous oxide. A total volume of 4×10^8 km^3, or 10^{24} gm, of sedimentary rocks exists on earth, and these have been formed ultimately by the weathering of igneous rocks. The sedimentary rocks contain on the average only 0.9 percent of ferrous oxide. Assuming that all of the missing ferrous iron in the sedimentary rocks, compared with that which could have been expected to be present in the igneous rocks that were weathered to form the sedimentary rocks, has been oxidized to ferric iron, 3×10^{20} gm of oxygen has been consumed. In addition, 22×10^{20} gm of sulphur, 300×10^{20} gm of chlorine, and 42×10^{20} gm of nitrogen, exist in the atmosphere, in the oceans, or in sedimentary deposits (Rubey, 1951), and these have been emitted from the earth's interior — in some cases, at least, in a less oxidized degree than they now are. The sulphur was presumably emitted as H_2S or SO_2, and it has been oxidized to SO_3; this required 11 to 44×10^{20} gm of oxygen, depending upon whether it was emitted as SO_2 or H_2S. If the nitrogen were released as NH_3, 84×10^{20} gm of oxygen would have been required to free the nitrogen; however, it is probable that the nitrogen was released as N_2. The chlorine was probably released as HCl, which would not require the consumption of oxygen.

Finally, carbon dioxide must also be considered, as it may have been released as carbon monoxide; the amount of carbon dioxide has already been mentioned as 5×10^4 gm/cm^2, which corresponds to a worldwide total of $2,500 \times 10^{20}$ gm, and if it were released as carbon monoxide, 900×10^{20} gm of oxygen would have been consumed. Thus, the total oxygen requirement for oxidation of the earth's surface and gases appears to lie near 100×10^{20} gm if carbon dioxide were the form in which carbon was released from the earth's interior, or $1,000 \times 10^{20}$ gm if carbon monoxide were the predominant form of the carbon release. By comparison, the present oxygen content of the atmosphere is about 10×10^{20} gm.

Another means of estimating the total oxygen release on earth is to look at the unoxidized organic carbon. The National Academy of Sciences (1962) has estimated the coal, oil, and other hydrocarbon reserves to amount to 0.03×10^{20} gm. The carbon in living matter and undecayed organic matter amounts to 0.015×10^{20} gm (Rubey, 1951). Sedimentary rocks contain, on the average, about 0.5 percent of organic carbon; this is largely concentrated in shale deposits, where the percentages run much higher. As the total mass of sedimentary rock is about 10^{24} gm, the total organic carbon is about 50×10^{20} gm.

The net amount of oxygen that would have been released when associated with the formation of this amount of organic carbon is about 130×10^{20} gm. To this should be added the oxygen produced by photodissociation; if the present rate is assumed as appropriate for all of geological time, this would add 10×10^{20} gm, giving a total of 140×10^{20} gm. Comparing this with the figures given above suggests either that carbon has been released from the earth's interior mainly in the form of the dioxide, or else that the supply of oxygen from photodissociation of water vapour was much greater in earlier times than now — in order to produce an adequate source of oxygen to oxidize the carbon monoxide to dioxide.

It is speculative to attempt to say how uniform the rate of oxygen production over geological time has been. On one hand, life probably evolved rather slowly, at first occupying only shallow basins of suitable depth, and later spreading over more extensive areas — suggesting an increasing rate of oxygen production with time. On the other hand, the efficiency of net oxygen production must decrease rapidly with increasing oxygen content of the atmosphere and ocean, because, with a high oxygen content, a greater portion of the newly-grown organic material will become oxidized rather than become fossilized without undergoing oxidation. Lacking guidance on this point, we may assume a uniform rate of oxygen production over a period of 3×10^9 years. Though arbitrary, this gives some useful perspective on the oxygen problem. If the oxygen production has been 140×10^{20} gm over a period of 3×10^9 years, the average rate of production has been 5×10^{12} grams per year.

OXYGEN FROM PHOTOSYNTHESIS AND ACCUMULATION OF ORGANIC CARBON

The rate of photosynthesis nowadays has been evaluated as releasing 8×10^{16} gm of oxygen per year (Leith, 1963). Comparison of this figure with the mean rate of 5×10^{12} gm per year cited above, indicates that the degree of oxidation of the products of photosynthesis is very nearly complete. About one part in 10^4 of the products of photosynthesis needs to become fossilized, while escaping decay, in order to provide an oxygen supply equal to the average rate of supply that has been required over geological time. If we take into account the fact that the degree to which oxidation of organic materials occurs increases with the oxygen content of the atmosphere, then the fraction of new organic materials escaping oxidation today must be correspondingly less than one part in 10^4.

The carbon dioxide annually consumed in photosynthesis is 11×10^{16} gm. However, most of this is returned to the atmosphere by the decay and oxidation of the plant materials; as indicated above, the fraction that escapes decay is less than one part in 10^4, or less than 10^{13} gm per year, and this represents the rate of fossilization of organic carbon. This presumably occurs mainly in a few special areas — ocean basins with anoxic bottom conditions, peat-bogs, etc. In the case of the basins with anoxic bottom conditions, life exists in the oxygen-rich surface water, but some of the life products fall to the bottom before becoming oxidized; in the anoxic area near the bottom of the basin, oxidation cannot occur, so organic carbon accumulates, and the oxygen that was released during its formation accumulates in the atmosphere and is available for oxidation of newly exposed geologic materials.

Some unoxidized organic material accumulates in sediments in open ocean areas, but the rate of accumulation in these relatively oxygen-rich areas must be much less than in the anoxic areas, and most of the accumulation probably occurs in the anoxic areas. In peat-bogs, also, organic material accumulates without undergoing oxidation, so the oxygen associated with the production of the plant materials there becomes available for other purposes.

FOSSIL FUELS AS A SOURCE OF CARBON DIOXIDE

The natural cycle of carbon dioxide has been severely disturbed by the rapid rate of burning of fossil fuels, which now releases $1 \cdot 5 \times 10^{16}$ gm per year of CO_2. This is more than a factor of 10^3 greater than the rate of deposition of carbon into the fossil reservoir, and it is a significant fraction — $\frac{1}{7}$ — of the rate at which carbon dioxide is taken up by photosynthesis and returned to the atmosphere by decay. This has caused a perceptible increase in the carbon dioxide content of the atmosphere. The present concentrations are about 6 percent* greater than values that existed near the turn of the century; but an exact figure is not available because of uncertainties associated with the old measurements. However, very careful recent measurements by Pales & Keeling (1965) show a rate of increase of $0 \cdot 7$ ppm per year from 1958 to 1963. This corresponds to an increase of $0 \cdot 5 \times 10^{16}$ gm per year in the atmospheric carbon dioxide. This can be compared with the release rate of $1 \cdot 5 \times 10^{16}$ gm per year**; the fact that the figures for release rate and rate of increase in atmospheric carbon dioxide do not agree can be explained on the basis that some of the carbon dioxide released by combustion becomes dissolved in the oceans. The apparent discrepancy disappears if the average time required for carbon dioxide to move from the atmosphere to the ocean is accepted as 5 years.

As the total estimated reservoir of fossil fuel is 3×10^{18} gm, we can estimate the effect on the atmospheric oxygen of burning the entire reserve. This would involve the consumption of 6×10^{18} gm of O_2. The total atmospheric oxygen is 10^{21} gm, so only about $0 \cdot 5$ percent of the atmospheric reservoir would be depleted by the total consumption of the fossil fuel reservoir. However, this would involve the release of 8×10^{18} gm of CO_2 — almost four times the amount currently in the atmospheric reservoir. Actually, a much smaller increase than this is to be expected, because of the degree to which carbon dioxide would enter the oceans.

The burning of fossil fuels is contributing to world-wide pollution in the sense that the concentration of carbon dioxide in the atmosphere is being increased. At the present rate of increase, $0 \cdot 7$ ppm per year, it would take about 40 years to produce a further 10 percent increase. However, the rate of usage of fossil fuels is increasing so rapidly that a 10 percent increase above

* According to Dr. Johnson (*in litt.*), the widely-quoted figure of 10 percent is based on questionable data. — Ed.
** In answer to my query, Dr. Johnson writes (*in litt.*) 'The clearing of land has not likely produced a perceptible effect on CO_2 removal from the atmosphere. The tropical rain forests and the oceans are the principal areas of photosynthesis. Contamination of the oceans may in time present a problem here.' — Ed.

present levels will more likely be reached in 20 years or less; the total increase up to the present can only be estimated because good measurements were not made before the extensive burning of fossil fuels commenced, but it is probably about 6 percent (*see* above). An increase of 10 percent should cause only a negligible temperature increase on earth unless some instability is thereby triggered; further, the warming effect of increased carbon dioxide concentration† is opposed by another pollution effect of rapidly increasing importance — increased dust and aerosols introduced in the atmosphere by man's activity on earth.‡ The increased carbon dioxide content may, however, produce a significant effect on the rate of photosynthesis on earth.

ATMOSPHERIC TIME-CONSTANTS

Some time-constants are shown in Table I. These are obtained by dividing the atmospheric content of several gases by the rates at which they enter or leave the atmosphere. Thus, for carbon dioxide, the rate of photosynthesis, 11×10^{16} gm per year, would use up all the atmospheric carbon dioxide, $2 \cdot 25 \times 10^{18}$ gm, in 20 years, if it were not being replenished by decay of plant material etc. Combustion is adding $1 \cdot 5 \times 10^{16}$ gm per year of CO_2 to the atmosphere, which would double the atmospheric concentration in 150 years; the observed

Table I. Time-constants

CO_2	Rate	(Atmospheric Content)/Rate
Photosynthesis	$1 \cdot 1 \times 10^{17}$ gm per year	20 years
Combustion	$1 \cdot 5 \times 10^{16}$	150*
Fossilization	$<10^{13}$	$> 2 \times 10^5$
O_2		
Photosynthesis with no decay	8×10^{16} gm per year	10^4 years
Net Organic Production	$<5 \times 10^{12}$	$> 10^8$
Photodissociation and hydrogen escape	2×10^{11}	5×10^9
N_2		
Bacterial action	4×10^{13} gm per year	10^8 years

* Present observed rate of increase of atmospheric CO_2 is $0 \cdot 7$ ppm per year, for which the time-constant is 450 years. The difference is explained by a portion of the carbon dioxide becoming dissolved in the oceans.

rate of increase corresponds to a time of 450 years to double the concentration, and the difference between these two figures is due to the rate of transfer of CO_2 from the atmosphere to the oceans. The rate of fossilization of carbon, consuming $<10^{13}$ gm per year of CO_2, would deplete the atmospheric reservoir in $>2 \times 10^5$ years if it were not for replenishment from other sources

† Due to its 'greenhouse effect' in reducing re-radiation of solar energy from the earth's surface.
‡ *See also* the paper by Wendland & Bryson on pp. 125–8. — Ed.

CARNEGIE LIBRARY
LIVINGSTONE COLLEGE
SALISBURY, N. C. 28144

(normally, gases released from the earth's interior — a process that is now overwhelmed by the burning of fossil fuel).

The rate of release of oxygen by photosynthesis, assuming no oxidation of the products of photosynthesis other than respiration, is 8×10^{16} gm per year; this would provide an amount of oxygen equal to that now in the atmosphere in 10^4 years, as indicated in Table I. However, most of the products of photosynthesis become oxidized in a relatively short time. If the fraction escaping oxidation were one part in 10^4, indicated earlier as an upper limit, then the time required for photosynthesis in excess of decay, to provide an amount of oxygen equal to the amount now in the atmosphere, would be 10^8 years. This interval is much shorter than the period over which this oxygen source has been active, because most of the oxygen produced by this source has been used to oxidize geological materials. The rate at which oxygen is produced by photodissociation of water vapour, followed by hydrogen escape to space, is sufficient to produce the oxygen content of the atmosphere in 5×10^9 years, as indicated in Table I.

The nitrogen cycle is relatively slow. Nitrogen fixation proceeds at a rate sufficient to remove all the atmospheric nitrogen in 10^8 years. However, the fixed nitrogen is utilized in plant growth, and the nitrogen is returned to the atmosphere during the decomposition processes that ultimately destroy the plant matter.

ATMOSPHERIC INSTABILITIES

Questions arise as to the problems created by the massive release of carbon dioxide by burning fossil fuels. The increase in carbon dioxide in the atmosphere must increase the hothouse effect on earth. However, Manabe & Strickler (1964) calculated that an increase or decrease by a factor of two in the atmospheric carbon dioxide would produce an average $2 \cdot 4°C$ temperature increase or decrease, respectively. It is unlikely that such a large temperature change will actually be produced, if only because such a large change in atmospheric carbon dioxide will probably not occur; however, a temperature change of this magnitude might be tolerable on earth.

More concern needs to be felt about instabilities that have not been investigated. Can a small increase in temperature drive enough carbon dioxide from the oceans into the atmosphere to amplify the increase to the point of instability? Is it possible that natural oscillations of this sort have been a factor in the production of ice-ages, and, if so, is it possible that a serious change in climate is being triggered by the burning of fossil fuels? Would it be possible to stop such an instability once it was triggered?

Another question that arises is the possibility of influencing the carbon dioxide–oxygen balance by other environmental changes. Pesticides have become spread around the earth and are found even in mid-ocean areas. Great changes are occurring in the rates at which plant nutrients are being carried to the seas, owing to use of fertilizers and to increased animal life on earth. Both of these factors influence the phytoplankton in the oceans, which are responsible for about half the conversion of carbon dioxide on earth. There is the possibility of inhibiting this photosynthesis by the spread of pesticides, or stimulating it by increased flow of nutrients to the seas. The possibilities of creating serious imbalances ought to be considered extremely carefully.

References

Aston, F. W. (1924). The rarity of the inert gases on the earth. *Nature (London)*, 114, 786.

Berkner, L. V. & Marshall, L. C. (1964). The history of oxygenic concentration in the earth's atmosphere. *Discussions of the Faraday Society*, No. 37, 122–41.

Berkner, L. V. & Marshall, L. C. (1966). Limitation on oxygen concentration in a primitive planetary atmosphere. *J. Atmos. Sci.*, 23, 133–43.

Brinkmann, R. T. (1968). The dissociation of water vapor and evolution of oxygen in the terrestrial and cytherean atmospheres. *Trans. Am. Geophys. Union*, 49, 706.

Cloud, P. E., Jr. (1968). Atmospheric and hydrospheric evolution on the primitive earth. *Science*, 160, 729–36.

Donahue, T. M. (1966). The problem of atomic hydrogen. *Am. Geophys.* 22, 175–88.

Donald, C. M. (1960). The impact of cheap nitrogen. *J. Aust. Inst. Agric. Sci.*, 26, 319–38.

Leith, H. (1963). The role of vegetation in the carbon dioxide content of the atmosphere. *J. Geophys. Res.*, 68, 3887–98.

Manabe, S. & Strickler, R. F. (1964). Thermal equilibrium of the atmosphere with a convective adjustment. *J. Atmos. Sci.*, 21, 361–85.

National Academy of Sciences (1962). Energy Resources Report 1000-D.

Pales, J. C. & Keeling, C. D. (1965). The concentration of atmospheric carbon dioxide in Hawaii. *J. Geophys. Res.*, 70, 6053-76.

Poldervaart, A. (1955). Chemistry of the earth's crust. Crust of the Earth. *GSA Special Paper No. 62*, 119–44.

Rubey, W. W. (1951). Geologic history of sea water. *Bull. Geol. Soc. Am.*, 62, 1111–48.

Schopf, J. W. & Barghoorn, E. S. (1969). Microorganisms from the Late Precambrian of South Australia. *J. Paleontology*, 43, 111–18.

Urey, H. C. (1959). The atmospheres of the planets. Pp. 363–418 in *Astrophysics III: The Solar System. Handbuch der Physik*, Vol. LII, Ed. S. Flugge. Springer-Verlag, Berlin, 601 pp.

WALLACE S. BROECKER
Man's Oxygen Reserves

In almost all grocery lists of man's environmental problems is found an item regarding oxygen supply. Fortunately for mankind, the supply is not vanishing as some have predicted. There are hundreds of other ways that we will hazard the future of our descendants before we make a small dent in our oxygen supply. A few basic facts will make clear why this is the case.

First of all, each square meter of earth surface is covered by 60,000 moles of oxygen gas (1). Plants living in both the ocean and on land produce annually about 8 moles of oxygen per square meter of earth surface (2). Animals and bacteria destroy virtually all of the products of this photosynthetic

Wallace S. Broecker, "Man's Oxygen Reserves," *Science*, vol. 168 (June 26, 1970), pp. 1537–1538. Copyright 1970 by the American Association for the Advancement of Science. Reprinted by permission.

The author is professor of earth science at Columbia University and is in charge of the geochemistry laboratory at the Lamont-Doherty Geological Observatory, Palisades, New York.

activity; hence they devour an amount of oxygen nearly identical to that generated by plants. If we use the rate at which organic carbon enters the sediments of the ocean as a measure of the amount of photosynthetic product preserved each year we find that it is about 3×10^{-3} mole of carbon per square meter per year (3). Thus animals and bacteria are destroying all but 4 parts in 10,000 of the oxygen generated each year. The net annual oxygen production corresponds to about 1 part in 15 million of the oxygen present in the atmosphere. In all likelihood even this small amount of oxygen is being destroyed through the oxidation of the reduced carbon, iron, and sulfur being exposed each year to weathering processes. Thus, in its natural state the oxygen content of our atmosphere is exceedingly well buffered and virtually immune to change on a short time scale (that is, 100 to 1000 years).

Man has recovered altogether about 10^{16} moles of fossil carbon from the earth's sedimentary rocks (4). The fuels bearing this carbon have been combusted as a source of energy. The carbon dioxide produced as a by-product of this enterprise is equal in amount to 18 percent of the carbon dioxide contained in our atmosphere (5). Roughly 2 moles of atmospheric oxygen was required to liberate each mole of this carbon dioxide from its fossil fuel source. By so doing we have used up only 7 out of every 10,000 oxygen molecules available to us (6). If we continue to burn chemical fuels at our currently accelerating rate (5 percent per year), then by the year 2000 we shall have consumed only about 0.2 percent of the available oxygen (20 molecules in every 10,000) (7). If we were to burn all known fossil fuel reserves we would use less than 3 percent of the available oxygen. Clearly a general depletion of the atmospheric oxygen supply via the consumption of fossil fuels is not possible in the foreseeable future.

Even in a large urban center oxygen depletion is a second-order problem. For examples, auto exhausts contain about one molecule of carbon monoxide for each ten molecules of carbon dioxide (8). Continuous exposure to carbon monoxide contents of 100 parts per million creates serious physiological problems (9). If automobiles account for 50 percent of the total oxygen demand in an urban area, carbon monoxide would reach the critical level before the oxygen content of the air had dropped by 2 percent (10).

There has been considerable reference to man's alteration of photosynthetic rates and the resulting change in the oxygen content of the atmosphere. From the above it should be clear that the oxygen supply is immune to such changes. The extreme case makes this point. What would happen if all photosynthetic activity were to cease and animals and bacteria were to destroy the organic debris in existing living tissue and in the humus stored in soils and the sea? There is roughly 200 moles of carbon per square meter of earth surface available in this form (11). Complete oxidation would require only a fraction of 1 percent of atmospheric oxygen. Although changes in the rate of primary photosynthesis are certainly critical to man's food resources, they have no bearing on his oxygen supply.

The situation with regard to our natural waters is quite different. There is no doubt that the high oxygen demand of organic and inorganic material added to our lakes and streams has, in many cases, reduced the standing level of oxygen in these waters below that required by fish and other aerobic organisms. Although the oxygen content of the atmosphere is immutable, the finite invasion rates of this gas into natural waters often cannot meet the high demands generated by man's pollutants. A disproportionate amount of the photosynthetic product is being dumped into these very limited reservoirs.

Were man to dump all his sewage into the deep sea would he endanger the oxygen supply of this vast reservoir? If spread over the entire earth, this reservoir would have a mean depth of about 2500 meters. The oxygen content of this water averages about 2.5 cm³ at standard temperature and pressure per liter (0.1 mole/m³) (12). Hence, for each square meter of earth surface, we have available in the deep sea about 250 moles of oxygen gas. Since the oxygen content of the waters in the deep sea is renewed with a time constant of about 1000 years on a time scale of decades, this reservoir can be considered static (13). To gain a feeling for the magnitude of this oxygen reservoir, let us first consider how long the reservoir would last if the entire terrestrial photosynthetic product were dumped each year into the deep sea. The annual oxygen demand of this material would be about 5 mole/m² of earth surface (2). Thus our supply of deep-sea oxygen would last 50 years. If we limit the input to the waste products of 1 billion people, each contributing 100 kilograms of dry organic waste per year, this consumption would use only 0.01 mole of oxygen per square meter of earth surface (14). At this rate of usage, the oxygen supply in the deep sea would last 25,000 years.

In conclusion it can be stated with some confidence that the molecular oxygen supply in the atmosphere and in the broad expanse of open ocean are not threatened by man's activities in the foreseeable future. Molecular oxygen is one resource that is virtually unlimited. If man's existence is to be threatened by pollution of the environment he will succumb to some other fate long before his oxygen supply is seriously depleted. We are faced with so many real environmental crises that there is no need to increase the public concern by bringing out bogeymen. Hopefully the popular press will bury the bogeyman it created.

References and notes

1. The weight of the gas above each square meter of earth surface is about 10^7 g. Of this, 20 percent is O_2. As the molecular weight of O_2 is 32, this corresponds to 6×10^4 moles of O_2 above each square meter.

2. Rates of plant productivity for the ocean have been estimated by studies on ^{14}C uptake. The ocean-wide average is about 6 mole/m² [see J. D. H. Strickland, in *Chemical Oceanography*, J. P. Riley and G. Skirrow, Eds. (Academic Press, New York, 1965), pp. 478–595]. That for the land is less accurately known but is thought to be about 12 mole/m² per year [G. E. Hutchinson, in *The Earth as a Planet*, G. P. Kuiper, Ed. (University of Chicago Press, Chicago, 1954), pp. 371–433].

3. Since the final resting place for all detritus formed on the earth's surface is the ocean floor, any organic material which survives oxidation must reach this sink. The average rate of sediment accumulation in the sea is about 1 cm per thousand years [T.-L. Ku, W. S. Broecker, N. Opdyke, *Earth Planet. Sci. Lett.* 4, 1 (1968)]. Since the dry density of such material averages 0.8 g/cm³, this corresponds to an accumulation of detritus of 8 g/m² per year. The mean for the organic carbon content of this detritus is about 0.5 percent [G. Arrhenius, in *Report of the Swedish Deep-Sea Expedition* No. 5, Goteburg (1952)]. Since the molecular weight of carbon is 12, 3×10^{-3} mole of organic carbon accumulate on each square meter of sea floor each year. About 1.2 moles of oxygen is left behind in the atmosphere for each mole of organic carbon stored in the sediment. Thus the net production of oxygen must be about 3×10^{-3} mole per square meter of earth surface each year.

4. R. Revelle and R. Fairbridge, *Geol. Soc. Amer. Mem.* 67, 239 (1957).

5. Prior to man's use of fossil fuels, the air contained 3×10^{-4} mole of carbon dioxide per mole of air. Since the area of the earth is 5×10^{14} m^2 and since the amount of total gas above each square meter is 3×10^5 mole, the natural carbon dioxide burden of the atmosphere was 5×10^{16} moles.

6. Man-made carbon dioxide amounts to about 20 moles per square meter of earth surface. About 2 moles of oxygen is required to produce each mole of carbon dioxide. Thus of the available 60,000 moles of oxygen above each square meter, only 40 have been consumed.

7. The assumption is made that 4 percent of our total fossil fuel reserves have been consumed.

8. Committee on Chemistry and Public Affairs, American Chemical Society, "Cleaning our environment — the chemical basis for action" (a report by the subcommittee on environmental improvement, 1969), pp. 23–92.

9. H. E. Stokinger and D. L. Coffin, in *Air Pollution,* A. C. Stern, Ed. (Academic Press, New York, 1968), vol. 1, chap. 13.

10. For each 20 moles of carbon dioxide produced in the city about 40 moles of oxygen would disappear and 1 mole of carbon monoxide would appear. The carbon monoxide content of clean air is less than 1 ppm, and the oxygen content is 200,000 ppm. Thus when the carbon monoxide content reaches 100 ppm the oxygen content will have dropped only 4000 ppm (that is, 3 percent).

11. The amount of humus in the sea is about 3×10^{-4} g of organic carbon per liter. Since for each square meter of sea surface there are 4×10^6 liters of sea water, this corresponds to 100 moles of organic carbon per square meter of sea surface. The average terrestrial soil is about 10 cm thick and contains 5 percent of organic carbon (dry weight). Taking the dry density to be 1 g/cm³ this yields 5000 g (400 moles) of organic carbon per square meter of land surface.

12. H. U. Sverdrup, M. W. Johnson, R. H. Fleming, *The Oceans, Their Physics, Chemistry and General Biology* (Prentice-Hall, Englewood Cliffs, N. J., 1942).

13. W. S. Broecker, in *The Sea.* M. N. Hill, Ed. (Interscience, New York, 1963), vol. 2, pp. 88–108.

14. The carbon content of 100 kg of dry organic matter is about 4000 moles. If the amount of oxygen required to oxidize this material is 1.2 moles per mole of organic carbon, then 5000 moles of oxygen would be required per year by each person. Since the area of the earth is 5×10^{14} m², each of the billion people has 5×10^5 m². Hence, per square meter, the oxygen demand would be only 1×10^{-2} mole per year.

15. Lamont-Doherty Geological Observatory Contribution No. 1539.

S. FRED SINGER

The Energy Revolution: Population Growth and Environmental Change

The following editorial by S. Fred Singer, Deputy Assistant Secretary for Scientific Programs, U. S. Department of the Interior, shows the kind of reasoning that leads to an assessment of the effect of greater populations on the world's environment. He uses Professor Broecker's assumptions on the oxygen level and others' opinions on the climate to put his own reasoning into perspective. But he avoids the concept

S. Fred Singer, "The Energy Revolution: Population Growth and Environmental Change," *Bioscience,* vol. 21, no. 4 (February 15, 1971), p. 163. Copyright 1971 American Institute of Biological Sciences. Reprinted by permission.

of a trigger mechanism that might upset this balance of regulating forces, even though, as he says, "the Earth as a planet has a history of violent upheavals, triggered by a variety of poorly understood causes." It takes much data carefully gathered over time in order to determine both the rate of the reaction and the mechanism by which the reaction proceeds. An expanded assessment could include the mechanisms of change as explained by Leigh Van Valen in "The History and Stability of Atmospheric Oxygen" in the February 5, 1971, issue of Science. *He shows the regulation of oxygen concentration by the mechanisms for increase and decrease over a period of time and concludes that the cause of the initial rise in concentration is still unknown. Also see the article by John Cairns in Chapter 4 of this book for an interesting discussion of environmental stresses which exhibit thresholds of tolerance, beyond which a particular ecosystem may collapse.*

Man has roamed the planet Earth for perhaps a million years — leading a precarious existence for most of this time. In the last few thousand years he has achieved modest control of his immediate environment and some degree of security. But only within the last few decades has he learned to use energy in concentrated form. Now within an incredibly brief span of human history, less than three or four centuries, he will have used up most of the fossil fuels that were stored over the last several hundred million years. This "energy revolution" has had an impact not only upon man himself but also upon the environment. It has produced spectacular advances and spectacular problems. It has created for a large part of the world's population an undreamed-of standard of living, permitted the accumulation of wealth, provided leisure — and enough time and money for science and technology.

As a consequence, advances in medicine and agriculture have produced unprecedented population growth, as well as increased levels of consumption of resources — and of pollution both locally and on a worldwide basis. Man's activities are now making a measurable impact on the global environment — an impact which will increase as world population grows and reaches even higher levels of consumption. We know, of course, that vast environmental changes have taken place in the past *without* human intervention: ice ages, cataclysmic floods, huge volcanic eruptions and earthquakes, episodes of mountain building, the drift and break-up of continents, indeed even profound chemical changes of the whole atmosphere. The Earth as a planet has a history of violent upheavals, triggered by a variety of poorly understood causes. Are we in danger of entering a region of instability from which we may not recover? Can mankind survive a major environmental change?

I must confess that I am more optimistic about the environmental problems than I am about the social problems and upheavals which are likely to be caused by continued population growth. I believe that local environmental problems — pollution — can be handled, but at a cost which will rise steeply as population density increases. Global environmental effects are not of immediate concern, but they must be monitored — constantly and carefully. It is clear that the oxygen level will not be lowered by more than a fraction of a percent, even if all fossil fuels are burned (Broecker, 1970). The effects of

DDT on oceanic phytoplankton and on oxygen have been overstated (Ryther, 1970). Carbon monoxide, although produced in huge quantities by the burning of gasoline, has not built up in the Earth's atmosphere (Jaffe, 1970). While the concentration of CO_2 has increased measurably and will continue to increase as more oil and coal are burned, the effects on the Earth's climate are not clear-cut, and may, in the final analysis, be overbalanced by other effects — some natural, some man-made (Mitchell, 1970). Heat released in energy production turns out to be a tiny fraction of the solar energy which is actually absorbed by the Earth, although the high concentration of waste heat in the neighborhood of cities can and will cause local climatic variations (Singer, 1970).

But the threat of social upheaval and international warfare becomes greater as the supply of natural resources, which is essentially finite, is made to satisfy an ever-increasing world population. The warning signs are there for all to see. It will take the most urgent efforts of our technologists to avoid an energy crisis by the timely development of nuclear fusion power which is essentially inexhaustible, and it will take the best efforts of social scientists and politicians to avoid a world crisis which could bring to a close a man's sojourn on this planet.

References

Broecker, W. S. 1970. *Science*, 168: 1537.
Jaffe, L. S. 1970. *In: Global Effects of Environmental Pollution,* Springer-Verlag New York, Inc., p. 34–39.
Mitchell, J. M., Jr. 1970. *In: Global Effects of Environmental Pollution,* Springer-Verlag New York, Inc., p. 139–155.
Ryther, J. H. 1970. *Nature*, 227: 374.
Singer, S. F. *Sci. Amer.*, 223 (3): 174. See also: *Man's Impact on the Global Environment,* 1970. MIT Press, Cambridge, Mass.

D. T. PATTEN & B. E. DINGER

Carbon Dioxide Exchange Patterns of Cacti from Different Environments

This paper shows how two species of plant have adapted to different locations on a mountainside. Since the two varieties of cacti live at different altitudes and experience different nighttime temperatures, they have adjusted their nighttime intake of CO_2 to these different temperatures.

D. T. Patten and B. E. Dinger, "Carbon Dioxide Exchange Patterns of Cacti from Different Environments," *Ecology*, vol. 50, no. 4 (Summer 1969), pp. 686–688. Reprinted by permission.
The authors are members of the Department of Botany, Arizona State University. This study was supported in part by a grant from the University Grants Committee, Arizona State University.

INTRODUCTION

Metabolism of cacti is interesting in two ways. First, the succulent nature of the plant allows metabolic processes to continue in times of drought through stored water in mucilaginous cells, and secondly, cacti exhibit a form of acid metabolism or non-autotrophic carbon dioxide fixation (Ting and Dugger 1968) that allows storage of CO_2 as organic acids. In general, acid metabolism includes two processes, acidification and deacidification. Acidification occurs most predominantly at night when CO_2 from respiration and atmospheric uptake is internally converted to organic acids (mostly malic acid) which appear to be stored in the vacuoles (Ransom and Thomas 1960). Deacidification can occur at night or in the daylight but is much more active in the latter. As the acids are broken down CO_2 is released internally and is available for photosynthesis. The unused CO_2 is released externally. The advantage of acid metabolism to desert succulents is one of CO_2 fixation at night and internal deacidification and photosynthesis during the day with the stomata closed thus preventing excessive water loss.

METHODS

Carbon dioxide exchange was determined as the difference between ambient CO_2 and plant chamber CO_2 with a Beckman infrared gas analyzer and a light source of 6,500 ft-c at plant level. Experimental temperature regimes including controlled abnormal photoperiod and temperature cycles are explained with the results. All rates of CO_2 exchange are compared to cactus internal stem temperature because non-autotrophic CO_2 fixation in succulents is more closely correlated with this temperature than with ambient air temperature.

Most work utilizing the infrared gas analyzer to measure metabolic processes in plants has employed a chamber in which a portion of a large plant or the whole aerial part of a small plant is sealed. Cacti, because of the spines, are difficult to seal into a chamber; therefore, most studies have been manometric determinations of gas exchange using cactus slices. We have found that if we use the whole plant (if it is a small plant) with the roots excised and the base sealed, the plant responds the same as intact plants. All experiments have been carried out on plants that have been maintained in well-watered soil for a period of time, thus avoiding the problem of rapid increase in all metabolic processes which occurs shortly after watering cacti that have been under drought conditions (Kausch 1965). The acid metabolism cycle, often appearing as an endogenous rhythm in succulents (Wilkins 1960), prevents short-term measurements of cactus metabolism; therefore, all studies lasted at least 24 hr.

All measurements were taken on plants that had been growing in a growth chamber with a 12-hr photoperiod and a 30°C–12°C day-night temperature regime. Data presented represent the response of individual cactus plants, but they are typical of the CO_2 exchange patterns found for two or more individuals of a species from the same collection. Collections were taken at 335 m near Phoenix, Arizona, and at 1,950 m and 2,835 m in the Pinaleno Mountains (Mt. Graham), Arizona.

RESULTS AND DISCUSSION

Carbon dioxide exchange rates of cacti are not uniform for a given internal plant temperature. Fluctuations in CO_2 exchange occur both in the light at a constant temperature (external temperature also being constant) and in the dark at constant temperatures, although a CO_2 cycle is established (Fig. 1). This cycle of net CO_2 release (production) during the day and uptake at night is similar to those found in *Kalanchoe* by Gregory, Spear, and Thimann (1954). If tests of a few hours are made, the time of day of the experiment should be considered in the results. For example, CO_2 release from *Opuntia acanthocarpa* Engelm. and Bigel. at an internal temperature of 34°C in the light was equal to 5.0 mg CO_2/100 g fresh weight per hour at 1300 hr and 4.3 mg CO_2/100 g fresh weight per hour at 1700 hr. Even greater fluctuations developed in the dark (Fig. 1).

Plant surface-to-volume (or fresh weight) ratios also appear to influence CO_2 exchange rates. Although we did not measure surface-to-volume ratios, the data presented in Fig. 1 represent CO_2 exchange from a small barrel cactus (*Ferocactus acanthodes* (Lemaire) Britt. and Rose) which had a single barrel-shaped stem weighing 468 g fresh weight, and from three stem segments of staghorn cholla (*Opuntia acanthocarpa*) weighing a total of 166 g. The CO_2 exchange per 100 g fresh weight from the barrel cactus is much less than that

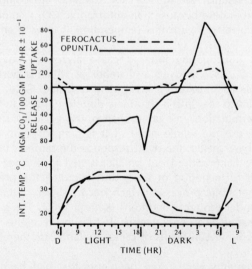

Figure 1. Carbon dioxide exchange patterns of barrel (Ferocactus acanthodes) and staghorn (Opuntia acanthocarpa) cacti from 335 m elevation during a typical 24-hr day-night temperature regime. Although internal temperatures remain constant during much of the day and night, CO_2 exchange rates fluctuate and vary depending on the time of day.

from the staghorn apparently because of less surface area per total fresh weight (representative of volume).

To study the relative roles of light and temperature on gas exchange of cacti the environment of plants that had been under a normal photoperiod-temperature regime as in Fig. 1 was altered to one of continual darkness at temperatures equal to the low of the normal regime (ca. 20°C). Release of CO_2 occurred during the "daylight" hours including a peak release after 1800 hr (Fig. 2), but the normal nighttime uptake did not occur although there was a decrease in CO_2 release, especially in *Opuntia*. This breakdown of the normal cycle was also shown by Wilkins (1959) in *Bryophyllum* but at a constant 26°C in the dark in a CO_2-free atmosphere. These fluctuations in CO_2 exchange point out the problems of experimenting with a cactus plant in the dark at low temperatures during the normal daytime cycle. The plants were then kept in the dark and the internal temperature was increased to that of a normal light period (ca. 35°C). This caused a great increase in CO_2 release (Fig. 2), more than in the light because of the lack of photosynthesis to utilize the gas. A cooling at the end of the "day" produced a drop in CO_2 release similar to a normal pattern. However, there was no uptake of CO_2 as normally found when the night temperatures drop. Apparently there is a period of light, as suggested by Gregory et al. (1954), or some other temperature fluctuation required to create a net CO_2 uptake that could not be recreated at these temperatures in the dark.

The unusual cycling of the acid metabolism of cacti and our results indicating irregular environmental influence on CO_2 exchange of cacti lead to the conclusion that one way to use CO_2 exchange as a measurement of physiological variations between cacti is to create a normal photoperiodic cycle and

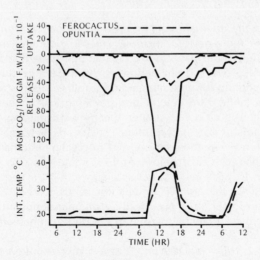

Figure 2. Carbon dioxide exchange patterns of barrel and staghorn cacti in continual darkness. Temperatures were maintained near 20°C for a 24-hr period preceding temperature fluctuations simulating a "typical" 24-hr period of 35°C "daytime" and 20°C "nighttime" temperatures.

fluctuate the internal temperatures to determine optimum temperatures for maximum net CO_2 uptake. Cacti from two different high elevation collections were used to show the determination of temperature requirements for optimum net CO_2 uptake. When plants from a population of hedgehog cacti (*Echinocereus ledingii* Peebles) from 1,950 m were treated for a few days to a nighttime temperature of 20°C, a temperature which allowed CO_2 uptake in low elevation species (Fig. 1), there was no apparent CO_2 uptake (Fig. 3).

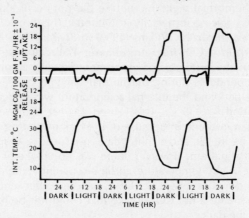

Figure 3. Carbon dioxide exchange rates of Echinocereus ledingii weighing 232 g fresh weight from 1,950 m elevation. The first two 24-hr cycles with nighttime plant internal temperatures near 20°C show net CO_2 losses of 4.90 and 6.18 mg CO_2/100 g fresh weight/24 hr; however, a net CO_2 uptake of 12.44 mg CO_2/100 g fresh weight/24 hr occurs at internal temperatures of 10°C (third 24-hr cycle) and 15.54 mg CO_2/100 g fresh weight/ 24 hr at 5°C (last 24-hr cycle).

However, when the internal temperature was dropped at night to 10°C there was CO_2 uptake and a net CO_2 increase. Further cooling of the nighttime internal temperature of the plants to 5°C created only a slight additional increase in net CO_2 uptake over a 24-hr period. Nighttime temperatures around 5°C appear to be optimum for maximum net CO_2 uptake in this cactus population.

The same method for determining optimum low temperatures for CO_2 uptake at night was used on another species of hedgehog cactus (*Echinocereus triglochidiatus* var. *polyacanthus* (Englm.) L. Benson) from 2,835 m. Night temperatures were lowered every 24 hr creating internal plant temperatures that reached 10°C and below. At 15°C there was CO_2 uptake but not a net uptake; at 10°C there was a net uptake over a 24-hr period, but at lower temperatures (5°C) the amount of net uptake decreased. Thus an internal plant temperature near 10°C may be the optimum temperature for net CO_2 uptake and therefore potential maximum net photosynthesis in this particular population of cacti.

Although *E. triglochidiatus* grows at a higher elevation than *E. ledingii*, its requirement for a warmer optimum internal nighttime temperature suggests that it grows in a warmer nighttime environment. The habitat of the high-elevation population is exposed southwest-facing rock outcrops, whereas the lower elevation species is located in dry valleys and on dry slopes. Retention of heat due to the clumped, decumbent growth of *E. triglochidiatus* as well as heat released from rocks help maintain warmer plant temperatures than those of *E. ledingii* found in lower valleys where cold air drainage at night and rapid reradiation from erect, isolated stems cause a greater cooling of the tissue.

Daytime internal plant temperatures do not appear to have as much influence on 24-hr CO_2 exchange as nighttime temperatures. Excessive heating of the cactus stem during the day, or in the dark, causes a great release of CO_2, but under normal conditions the CO_2 released during the day can be compensated for by night CO_2 uptake, if the nighttime internal plant temperatures are low enough for the particular population. This attainment of critical low night temperatures probably is a major factor in controlling net CO_2 uptake and species distribution in cacti.

Literature cited

Gregory, F. G., I. Spear, and K. V. Thimann. 1954. The interrelation between CO_2 metabolism and photo-periodism in *Kalanchoe*. Plant Physiol. 29: 220–229.

Kausch, Walter. 1965. Beziehungen zwischen Wurzelwachstum, Transpiration, und CO_2 —Gaswechsel bei einigen Kakteen. Planta 66: 229–238.

Ransom, S. L., and M. Thomas. 1960. Crassulacean acid metabolism. Ann. Rev. Plant Physiol. 11: 81–110.

Ting, Irwin P., and W. M. Dugger, Jr. 1968. Non-autotrophic carbon dioxide metabolism in cacti. Bot. Gaz. 129: 9–15.

Wilkins, M. B. 1959. An endogenous rhythm in the rate of CO_2 output in *Bryophyllum*. I. Some preliminary experiments. J. Exp. Bot. 10: 377–390.

———. 1960. An endogenous rhythm in the rate of CO_2 output in *Bryophyllum*. II. The effect of light and darkness on the phase and period of the rhythm. J. Exp. Bot. 11: 269–288.

R. SCOTT RUSSELL

Contamination of the Biosphere with Radioactivity

INTRODUCTION

It is now a quarter of a century since it first became necessary to consider the effects of radioactive products of nuclear fission which have been released into the environment. Probably no other aspect of the protection of Man's environment was, at first, so difficult to judge objectively. The effects of ionizing radiation had been little considered by the majority of scientists, and were virtually unknown to the public until nuclear weapons were developed,

R. Scott Russell, "Contamination of the Biosphere with Radioactivity," *Biological Conservation,* vol. 2, no. 1 (October 1969), pp. 2–9. Copyright 1969 Elsevier Publishing Company Ltd. Reprinted by permission.
The author is Director, The Letcombe Laboratory (formerly The Radiobiological Laboratory), Agricultural Research Council, Wantage, Berkshire, England.

so that, from the outset, the presence of radioactive substances in our environment was closely associated in people's minds with the most destructive of all weapons — a view which received further encouragement in the late 1950s when radioactivity from weapon-testing could be detected in the food supplies and bodies of the human population of the entire world.

In addition, there was clear evidence of the great harm which high doses of radiation can cause. Many years before the first nuclear reactor was constructed, the biological effect of high dose-rates had been apparent from sufferings of the early workers with radium and X-rays. No other noxious agent seems so insidious; for exposure was undetectable by the human senses, the effects could be long delayed, and by the time the effects became apparent they were incurable. The intensive research and discussion — both at scientific meetings and in national and international committees — which these gloomy forebodings encouraged, now make it possible to assess more objectively the effects which may result from the release of radioactive substances, intentionally or accidentally, and also to consider the need for their control and how this can be achieved.

The main sources of information used in the preparation of this review are cited in such publications as United Nations (1962, 1964, 1966), International Commission on Radiological Protection (1966, 1966a, 1966b), Glasstone (1962), Hungate (1966), Russell (1966), and Aberg & Hungate (1967). The International Commission on Radiological Protection (ICRP) and the United Nations Scientific Committee on the Effects of Atomic Radiation (UNSCEAR) are the two most important international organizations concerned with this subject. ICRP is the accepted source of guidance on standards for radiation protection throughout the world. UNSCEAR studies the significance and extent of radiation in the environment. It consists of scientists nominated by fifteen nations: Argentina, Australia, Belgium, Brazil, Canada, Czechoslovakia, France, India, Japan, Mexico, Sweden, USSR, United Arab Republic, the United Kingdom, and the United States of America. There could scarcely be a better guarantee that its conclusions should be free from bias!

The opening parts of the present survey are concerned with the requirements for an adequate assessment of environmental radioactivity and with the significance of the exposures which have hitherto been experienced from world-wide fallout. Subsequently the types of situation which it may be prudent to envisage under peace-time conditions in the future, and possible control measures, are examined. Civil defence problems in areas devastated by nuclear weapons are not considered. The situations which would then arise differ so fundamentally from those due to fallout, or to peace-time discharges, that their conjoint consideration would encourage misunderstanding. Moreover, several surveys on the effects of nuclear warfare are available (e.g. Glasstone 1962; Brunner & Prêtre, 1968).

THE ASSESSMENT OF ENVIRONMENTAL RADIOACTIVITY

The biological effects of radiation are due to the absorption into living tissues of energy from ionizations to which radiation gives rise. Injury depends on the absorbed dose* of radiation, irrespective of its origin. At the moderate or low doses to which contamination of the biosphere could normally give rise, injury caused by radiation becomes apparent only after a latent period which may exceed a decade in length, and it is the total dose absorbed, not the rate at which it is delivered, that is the relevant measure of risk.† Thus, if the significance of a particular source of radioactive contamination in the biosphere is to be correctly assessed, the resultant *increase* in the total radiation dose received by organisms from internal and external sources of radiation must be known. Measurements of the concentration of radioactive nuclides do not themselves provide this information and, unbacked by other data, can be misleading. For example, the statement that the concentration of a radioactive fission product has lately doubled in an organism may by itself seem alarming; but if the dose from this source is still only a minute fraction of that due to other sources, including natural background, its consequences will be undetectable. Again, even if a radioactive nuclide is shown to become highly concentrated in small organisms, for example Algae or insects, it cannot be concluded that they are subject to a corresponding radiation dose. The range of energetic beta or gamma radiation is such that only a fraction of it — sometimes a very small one — will be absorbed by such organisms, the rest being dissipated in the surrounding medium, thus making no contribution to the radiation dose.

The first requirement in surveys of environmental radioactivity is therefore obvious — measurements must be interpretable in terms of the integrated radiation doses received by living tissues. A second requirement follows from the fact that the dose delivered by unit quantity of different nuclides within the body varies widely, depending on both physiological and physical factors; individual nuclides must be measured separately if the radiation dose is to be determined. Despite the fact that mixed fission products contain a large number of nuclides, this requirement can be satisfied relatively easily in a well-equipped laboratory, because usually a very few nuclides are the dominant source of radiation dose, the contribution of others being trivial by comparison. Attention can thus be confined to these *'critical' nuclides*. Similarly, it is usually adequate to consider the exposure to radiation of only *critical groups* of organisms which are subject to the greatest radiation risk, and their internal radiation dose is often due to the passage of radioactivity through certain *critical food-chains*; when these are known, surveys of limited scope can reveal the significance of environmental situations.

This approach is not a mere theoretical idea — its applicability has been widely demonstrated in the assessment of the exposure of Man (International Commission on Radiological Protection, 1966), and there are abundant reasons

---

* The absorbed dose is measured in *rads* (1 rad = 100 erg/g). The dose equivalent (measured in *rem*) is the dose in rads multiplied by a quality factor to take account of differences in the magnitude of effect caused by the same absorbed dose from different types of radiation. However, as the quality factor is 1 for beta and gamma radiation, and these are of dominant concern in the present discussion, all doses are here expressed as rads.
† In contrast, the effects of very high doses of radiation become manifest rapidly, and in such cases the dose rate can have an important effect on the extent of injury.

for regarding Man as the critical organism whenever radioactive materials are widely dispersed in the environment. The main delayed effects of radiation — namely, increased incidences of cancer in the exposed individuals and of genetic injury in future generations — are for obvious reasons of vastly greater significance in Man than in other organisms. Thus, for example, it has been estimated that the levels of ingested strontium-90 which will cause economically significant injury in cattle are more than 50 times greater than those which make their milk unacceptable by present standards as a food for infants (Garner, 1963).

Apart from the special consideration Man gives to his own species, he is among the most sensitive of organisms to radiation. A detailed comparison of the relative sensitivity of different types of organisms is complicated by many factors, but some indication is provided by estimates of the LD50 (*i.e.* the dose that is lethal to 50 percent of the population) in acute exposure to external radiation. For mammals the values range from 200–1,000 R,* that for Man being at the lower end (United Nations, 1962); for insects and micro-organisms, LD50s appear to range up to about 10^5 and over 10^6 R, respectively. In continuing exposure to low dose-rates, the sensitivity of Man may well be considerably greater, relative to many other animals, than the above figures suggest, as his longer life-span gives greater opportunity for the delayed effects of radiation to become manifest. In the plant kingdom sensitivity to radiation varies largely, though not entirely, with the interphase chromosome volume; gymnosperms, which have relatively large chromosome volumes, show LD50s in acute exposure that are comparable to those for mammals, but with angiosperms the values range up to over 17,000 R (Sparrow *et al.*, 1968).

Taking all aspects into account, risks to Man are the most appropriate general basis for assessing the significance of the contamination of the biosphere with radioactive substances — except in special cases when the doses received by Man are very much lower than those to which other organisms are exposed. Thus the final step in the assessment of the significance of such contamination of the biosphere is usually the assessment of the risks to Man resulting from the estimated radiation dose he has received.

With other potentially noxious substances, risks are usually assessed from direct observation of dose/response relationships, and levels of exposure which have led to no detectable effect in careful studies are regarded as safe. An entirely different and more scientific basis has been adopted for the risks of radiation: here it is assumed that some effect, however slight or infrequent, may occur down to the lowest levels of exposure, no dose thus being 'safe' in the strict meaning of that word. This does not, however, imply that all radiation doses — however small — are 'dangerous' in the sense in which that term is normally used. This is evident from a report on risks from low doses of radiation, issued by the International Commission on Radiological Protection (1966a), which explains that a major obstacle to estimating the effects of low doses of radiation is the fact that some types of injury, both genetic and somatic, which radiation can cause, also arise frequently from

---

* The Rontgen (R) is now used to describe exposure to radiation measured in terms of the ionization produced in air.

other, unidentified causes — in common parlance, from 'natural causes.' The only practicable way to estimate the effects of low doses of radiation is to assume that the response per unit dose at very low doses is the same as that observed in exposures which are sufficiently high to allow reasonably quantitative observation of their effects. It is explained in the report that this procedure is likely in the majority of cases to indicate an upper limit of risk; but such calculations as are now possible none the less show that the risk of genetic injury and of all malignant diseases, from doses of radiation recommended as the maximum permissible in occupational work, are very small in comparison with the normal incidence of such effects.

An alternative way of considering the significance of environmental contamination is to compare the doses from this source with the average dose from natural background radiation; as the effects of radiation depend on the dose absorbed by tissues, irrespective of its origin, the *comparative risk* from the two sources is validly shown. This procedure has been used by UNSCEAR to assess world-wide fallout. The estimated average dose from natural background to the world's human population is shown in Table I. Considerable variation occurs: doses from cosmic rays increase with altitude above sea level, and in some limited regions high levels of terrestrial radiation from the underlying rocks causes the background dose to approach ten times the average; variations by 10 to 20 percent are relatively common.

Investigations in areas of high radiation background have provided no evidence of an enhanced incidence of abnormalities, so that doses in the range of the normal natural background cannot be expected to engender detectable ecological change. Nonetheless it is highly desirable that each potential new source of radiation to which modern technology may give rise should be carefully examined, especially if it is likely to affect large populations over an extended period. Otherwise the cumulative total of numerous

Table I. Radiation dose-rate due to natural sources in normal areas (United Nations, 1966)

	Dose rates (mrad/year)		
Source of irradiation	*Gonads*	*Bone*	*Bone marrow*
External irradiation			
Cosmic rays			
Ionizing component	28	28	28
Neutrons*	0.7	0.7	0.7
Terrestrial radiation (including air)	50	50	50
Internal irradiation			
Potassium-40	20	15	15
Rubidium-87	0.3	<0.3	<0.3
Carbon-14	0.7	1.6	1.6
Radium and decay products*	0.6	3.7	0.6
TOTAL	100	99	96

* If the doses were expressed in *rem* (*see* first footnote), these components of background would be increased because of the higher biological effectiveness of alpha radiation and neutrons (*see* United Nations, 1962).

small changes might become unacceptable. The manner in which these matters should be judged has been referred to by the International Commission on Radiological Protection (1966*b*).

RADIATION DOSES RECEIVED HITHERTO
FROM ENVIRONMENTAL CONTAMINATION

Judged on the global scale, world-wide fallout is the predominant source of radiation, additional to natural background, to which the biosphere has been exposed. The results of extensive surveys in many countries have been assembled by UNSCEAR, which has computed the 'dose commitment' to the world's population from this cause: the dose commitment can be approximately defined as the integrated average dose to different types of living tissue which have been or will be received in consequence of the release of fission products.

UNSCEAR's latest estimate of the effects of all weapons-testing before 1965 is shown in Table II. An assessment for the United Kingdom is comparable (Medical Research Council, 1966), and it is known that the more recent weapons-tests caused only a very small addition to the dose commitment. For reasons which will be explained later, one significant component of world-wide fallout, iodine-131, is excluded from Table II. In contrast with strontium-90 and cesium-137, which are formed by nuclear fission, carbon-14 is an 'induced activity' created by the capture of neutrons by nitrogen. Moreover, unlike the other nuclides shown in Table II, carbon-14 has always been present in the environment — it arises from the interaction of cosmic rays with nitrogen in the atmosphere and thus contributes to the normal background radiation dose (*see* Table I).

The dose commitment to the gonads, on which genetic effects depend, is equivalent to about 8 months' background; that to the bone marrow, which is of particular interest in relation to the induction of leukaemia, represents about 18 months' background, while the corresponding period for bone itself

Table II. Dose commitments* to the world population from nuclear explosions up to 1965 (United Nations, 1966)

Source of radiation	Gonads	Bone mrads	Bone marrow
External: short-lived	23	23	23
Cesium-137	25	25	25
Internal: Strontium-90	—	156	78
Cesium-137	15	15	15
Carbon-14	13	20	13
Strontium-89	—	0.3	0.15
TOTAL	76	240	150
Period in which equivalent dose is delivered by natural background	*Months*		
	8	30	18

* Dose commitments are calculated from the commencement of weapons-testing until the year 2000. After that date carbon-14 will continue to deliver some dose because of its very long half-life (5,760 years), but at a much-reduced rate.

is about two-and-a-half years. When is it borne in mind that the dose commitment is the total exposure from fallout during half-a-century, it is evident that, on the world average, the components of fallout listed in Table II have made but a very small increase in the total radiation dose.

This conclusion is unchanged when account is taken of iodine-131. Because of its short half-life (8 days), this nuclide is deposited for only short periods after weapons have been detonated, and for reasons which are considered later, considerably higher doses are received by infants in the first year of life than by other members of the human community. It is estimated that in 1961 and 1962, when the rate of deposition of iodine-131 was highest, infants in many parts of the northern hemisphere may have received about 170 millirads per year if they were fed on fresh milk — the foodstuff from which iodine-131 mainly enters the body (United Nations, 1964; International Commission on Radiological Protection, 1966a). These doses were not recurrent, those received by the older age-groups being considerably smaller.

Considerable local variations in doses from worldwide fallout have been identified. Of these perhaps the most interesting are the much-enhanced doses from cesium-137 which occur in the far north of Europe and North America (Aberg & Hungate, 1967). The highest body-burdens of this nuclide, representing 10–100 times that in temperate latitudes, are received by persons who consume relatively large quantities of the flesh of reindeer and caribou; this is due to the very efficient entrapment of the deposit in the slowly-growing cryptogamic and other vegetation on which these animals graze. In some of these northern areas, levels in freshwater fish have also been considerably higher than elsewhere, largely on account of the low mineral content of the water (United Nations, 1966). In more temperate regions, the entrapment of strontium-90 and cesium-137 in the surface mat which develops under slowly-growing pastures in cool, moist areas, often on hills, has sometimes caused dietary contamination to approach 10 times the normal average.

On a few occasions, unexpected weather conditions have caused small populations near weapon-testing grounds to receive, from local fallout, radiation doses considerably above the world-wide average, and so remedial action has been taken (Cohn *et al.*, 1960; Bostrom, 1962). None the less, the fears once widely voiced that world-wide fallout has created a serious new risk on a global scale appears unfounded. Indeed, the average extra radiation due to this source was less than the change in background radiation which is not infrequently experienced when people move their homes from one locality to another. The most lasting value of the investigations of past worldwide fallout, as opposed to surveillance near weapon-proving grounds, is perhaps the information they have provided for the more efficient and economical investigation of situations that may arise in the future.

POSSIBLE FUTURE SOURCES OF CONTAMINATION IN PEACETIME

The careful control which has always been exercised over the operation of nuclear installations ensures satisfactory conditions in their normal operation. The main causes of environmental contamination which it is necessary to envisage for the future, other than fallout from nuclear detonations, are industrial accidents. Any release of fission products would almost always occur predominantly into the atmosphere, so that they would be deposited both on the land surface and on water. The deposit on dry land could be directly entrapped on plants and animals, whereas material entering water would be subject to dilution with stable elements before entering food-chains. Thus considerably higher radiation doses would usually be experienced by terrestrial organisms. This is illustrated by results of surveys of worldwide fallout; even in those countries where marine foods are most extensively consumed, they have contributed but small fractions of the total radioactivity ingested by the population, and the highest levels of radioactivity in fish have been considerably below those found in the flesh of terrestrial animals (United Nations, 1966).

Discharges into the atmosphere

The contrasting half-lives of different fission products cause their relative abundance to vary greatly with time, but irrespective of the circumstances in which mixed fission products enter the atmosphere, or the interval of time since they were produced, isotopes of iodine, strontium, and cesium, will always deserve the greatest consideration as sources of internal radiation (Russell, 1966; Food and Agricultural Organization, in press); for they are the critical nuclides.* No other fission products of appreciable half-life enter so freely into biological systems — iodine is accumulated in the thyroid glands of animals, strontium like calcium is deposited in bone, and cesium like potassium circulates throughout the body. Moreover, these three elements are transferred rapidly from the diet of cattle to their milk. This fact, combined with the efficient retention of finely-divided airborne debris on the herbage of pastures, and the wide areas on which cattle graze, is likely to cause milk to be the most contaminated food-source after fission products have been deposited.

Iodine-131 would be of particular concern if children were fed on fresh milk. This nuclide is considerably more abundant in fresh fission products than are the isotopes of strontium or cesium, and despite the small size of the thyroid glands of an infant (2 g or less at six months), one quarter or more of the dietary intake may be deposited in it; no comparable concentration occurs with other nuclides. Adults are likely to receive much lower doses from iodine-131 than infants who are fed on fresh milk — both because milk is less important in the adult diet and because although the thyroid glands of adults are about ten times the size of those of infants, they absorb only about the same fraction of the ingested iodine, so that the radiation dose from the same intake of iodine-131 is correspondingly smaller. After accidents to nuclear reactors, the significance of iodine-131 relative to other fission products can be further enhanced because its volatility is likely to cause it to be preferentially released (Farmer, 1967); under these circumstances the ingestion

---

* Induced activities, for example of carbon-14, could accompany the fission products but are unlikely to be of major concern.

of all other nuclides is by comparison insignificant. Similarly, if fallout descends rapidly near sites where nuclear detonations have taken place, iodine-131 is again of dominant concern from the viewpoint of ingestion, being indeed the only nuclide that is likely to deliver internal radiation doses which are appreciable relative to the external dose from short-lived nuclides (Russell, 1968).

The short half-life of iodine-131 causes its effects to abate rapidly in contrast with those of the longer-lived isotopes of strontium and cesium. Soon after fission has occurred, strontium-89 (half-life 51 days), which is then much more abundant than strontium-90 (half-life 28 years), can deliver higher doses; but after five or six months the longer-lived nuclide becomes dominant. The half-life of strontium-90 is a little shorter than that of cesium-137 (30 years), but its effects are likely to be more prolonged, as it is not only retained for longer periods in the body but it usually enters plants, and hence animals, more freely from the cumulative deposit in the soil.

Detailed discussions of the food-chains which these nuclides traverse are available (e.g. United Nations, 1962; Russell, 1966). Recent research has shown that the continuing risk from strontium-90 was formerly overestimated. Because considerably higher concentrations of strontium-90 are found in the bones of infants than of adults soon after fallout has been deposited, it was at one time imagined that they were undergoing correspondingly greater risk than were adults; this is now disproved by evidence that strontium is eliminated much more rapidly from the bones of the young (Fletcher *et al.*, 1966). Moreover, strontium-90 enters plants from the soil to a smaller extent than it was prudent to suspect when information was scarce (Russell & Bruce, in press). Taking account not only of these facts but also of the composition and physical form of the fission products which may be released under different circumstances, it seems most unlikely that strontium-90 will be the major source of internal radiation after any release of mixed fission products which causes widespread problems; the same is true of cesium-137.

For obvious reasons it is impossible to predict the possible scale on which contamination with mixed fission products may occur in the future. Massive detonation of nuclear weapons could cause alarming depositions of iodine-131 over a wide area, as well as world-wide fallout on a vastly greater scale than has hitherto been observed. However, the worst and most improbable accidents arising from the peacetime uses of nuclear energy (Farmer, 1967) would create only local problems — not more than a small fraction of the country's milk supply would be affected.

Attention has sometimes been given to the possible effects of the release of fissile materials such as plutonium. Mishaps to aircraft carrying unarmed nuclear weapons could give rise to such situations. The available reports (Brunner & Prêtre, 1968), however, encourage the view that their biological effects would be small — if indeed detectable — even if no remedial action were taken. Accidents are conceivable at installations where fission products are being processed or when isotopes are being used in industry, medicine, or scientific research; however, in the worst such circumstances it is difficult to imagine effects comparable to those which could follow reactor accidents.

Discharges directly into water

With the exception of accidents to nuclear-powered vessels, discharges of radioactivity directly into water are likely to arise solely from the planned discharge of dilute radioactive effluence from nuclear installations. At first sight the intentional releases of such material into water, whether fresh or marine, may seem a negation of the prudent principle that all doses from radiation should be kept as low as is practicable. That, however, is an unrealistic attitude. All natural water contains radioactive substances in amounts which are readily measurable by modern procedures. The average concentrations of a number of naturally-occurring nuclides in the oceans are given in Table III. Fresh water usually has a lower burden of radioactivity — except for thermal springs in some areas. The rational approach is clear; if the discharge of radioactivity into water is proved not to cause an unacceptable increase in the doses received by organisms, it is an acceptable practice. Procedures whereby wastes can be safely discharged have been examined in considerable detail (International Atomic Energy Agency, 1966).

Table III. Naturally occurring radioactivity in the oceans, based on data assembled by Chipman (1966)

Primordial isotope	*Picocuries per litre*
Uranium-238	1·0
Uranium-235	0·045
Thorium-232	<0·002
Thorium-230	<0·05
Radium-226	0·1
Rubidium-87	2.6
Potassium-40	280
Produced by cosmic rays	
Carbon-14	0·10–0·14
Tritium	0·70–5

Both the nature of the nuclides which may be released in dilute effluent and the critical food-chains that they traverse, may vary widely — depending on the type of nuclear installation. Thus in the Columbia River, USA, the discharge of phosphorus-32 is given special consideration — especially as the water may be used downstream for the spray-irrigation of crops (Kornberg & Davis, 1966). In contrast at Windscale, where discharges are made into the Irish Sea, the adsorption of ruthenium-106 into a seaweed which is eaten by a limited population-group, constitutes the critical food-chain (Preston & Jefferies, 1967).

Although under careful supervision it is reasonable to dispose of appreciable quantities of dilute radioactivity into water, it must be recognized that, despite their large content of natural radioactivity, the oceans are not 'sumps' of infinite capacity into which radioactive debris could indefinitely be poured or deposited in solid form.

REMEDIAL MEASURES

The necessity of remedial measures against environmental radioactivity could arise in nuclear war, locally after major accidents to nuclear reactors, or some-times close to weapons-proving grounds, through unpredicted patterns of fallout.

When radioactive substances have escaped into the environment, the mitigation of the radiation doses to which they may give rise can be achieved only by action which interferes to a greater or lesser extent with the normal habits of the population. All such action — whether it be the change of one source of diet for another, evacuation from an area of high external exposure, or the ingestion of substances which reduce the radiation dose — may directly or indirectly create some new risks to the population. The logical basis for deciding whether counter-measures are advisable is thus to compare the risk from radiation which can be avoided with the possible risk of the proposed counter-measures (International Commission on Radiological Protection, 1966b); attention is directed to this obvious principle because when problems of environmental radioactivity were less familiar than they are today, it was not always borne in mind.

For reasons already explained, the presence of iodine-131 in fresh milk consumed by children would be the most probable situation which would call for remedial action; this need could arise in nuclear war, locally after major accidents to nuclear reactors, or sometimes close to weapons-proving grounds after unpredicted patterns of fallout. Provided that alternative sources of milk for infants, for example dried milk, are available, protection could be readily arranged. The relatively short half-life of iodine-131 causes it to decay by a factor of over 100 in six weeks. Thus milk which was unacceptable in the initial period could be safely used for manufactured products which are stored for some months before use — for example dried milk, butter, cheese, or chocolate. The alternative procedure of feeding cattle on stored food might sometimes be appropriate, and it may be noted that during the winter in the cool-temperate regions, when cattle are normally fed in this manner, the contamination of milk would create no problem. The deposition of iodine-131 in the thyroid can also be much reduced by the administration of tablets containing stable iodide. However, a large measure of protection is provided only if this is done within a few hours of exposure (Pochin & Barnaby, 1962); this type of action might therefore be more appropriate for dealing with the inhalation of iodine-131 (which might be confined to a few hours) than against dietary contamination which would proceed, although at a decreasing rate, for some weeks.

The reduction by a large factor of doses due to strontium-90 would present considerably greater problems, and it is therefore fortunate that this nuclide is unlikely ever to be the major source of radiation on a wide scale. The removal of strontium-90 from milk by ion exchange has been discussed, but it could provide only a small degree of protection even to children, as they would ingest appreciable quantities of strontium-90 in other foods. The application of lime to land, and other agricultural measures, would also be of little effect in the majority of circumstances (Russell, 1966). Moreover, as in all conceivable environmental situations strontium-90 would be but one, and frequently not the major, source of radiation dose, its complete removal from diet, even if it were possible, would mitigate the total radiation dose by only a relatively small factor.

CONCLUSION

The aim of this survey has been to encourage perspective in the discussion of risks which may occur through the contamination of the biosphere with radioactive substances. Three circumstances have assisted greatly in the study of this difficult subject. Firstly, the great sensitivity with which radioactive substances can be detected has made it possible for their behaviour in the environment to be examined with much greater facility than is possible with many other toxic agents. Secondly, natural background radiation provides a valid basis against which the possible effects of low doses of radiation can be assessed. Thirdly, public interest has stimulated the detailed study of this subject whereas many other potential environmental pollutants have been ignored until their ill-effects have become widely manifest.

The future cannot be foretold but it is evident that, provided the holocaust of nuclear warfare is avoided, risks due to the entry of radioactive substances into the biosphere are considerably smaller than it was prudent to suspect when the subject first attracted wide attention.

References

Aberg, B. & Hungate, F. P., Eds. (1967). *Radioecological Concentration Processes*. Proc. International Symposium held in Stockholm, Pergamon Press, London, xiv + 1040 pp.

Bostrom, R. G. (1962). Iodine-131 in milk and vegetables associated with July 1962 fallout in Utah. *Radiological Health Data*, 3, 501–11.

Brunner, H. & Prêtre, S., Eds. (1968). Proc. Symposium. *Radiological Protection of the Public in a Nuclear Mass Disaster*, Fachverband für Strahlenschutz, Bern, 688 pp.

Chipman, W. A. (1966). Food chains in the sea. Pp. 419–53 in *Radioactivity and Human Diet*, Ed. R. Scott Russell, Pergamon Press, Oxford.

Cohn, S. H. Robertson, J. S. & Conard, R. A. (1960). Radioisotopes and environmental circumstances: the internal radioactive contamination of a Pacific island community exposed to local fallout. Pp. 306–30 in *Radioisotopes in the Biosphere*, Eds. R. S. Caldecott & L. A. Snyder, University of Minnesota Press, Minneapolis.

Farmer, F. R. (1967). Siting criteria — a new approach. Pp. 303–29 in *Containment and Siting of Nuclear Power Plants*, International Atomic Energy Agency, Vienna.

Fletcher, W. Loutit, J. F. & Papworth, D. G. (1966). Interpretation of levels of strontium-90 in human bone. *British Medical Journal*, 2, 1225–30.

Food and Agriculture Organization of the United Nations, International Atomic Energy Agency and World Health Organisation (in press). Seminar on *Agricultural and Public Health Aspects of Environmental Contamination by Radioactive Materials*, International Atomic Energy Agency, Vienna.

Garner, R. J. (1963). Environmental contamination and grazing animals. *Health Physics*, 9, 597–605.

Glasstone, Samuel, Ed. (1962). *The Effects of Nuclear Weapons*. Department of the Army Pamphlet, No. 39-3, United States Atomic Energy Commission, xvi + 730 pp.

Hungate, F. P., Ed. (1966). *Radiation and Terrestrial Ecosystems*. Proc. Hanford Symposium held in Washington, Pergamon Press, London, ii + 420 pp. (Also *Health Physics*, 11, 1255–675, 1965.)

International Atomic Energy Agency (1966). *Disposal of Wastes in Seas, Oceans and Surface Waters.* International Atomic Energy Agency, Vienna, 898 pp.

International Commission on Radiological Protection (1966). *Principles of Environmental Monitoring related to the Handling of Radioactive Materials,* ICRP Publication 7, Pergamon Press, London, iv + 11 pp.

International Commission on Radiological Protection (1966a). *The Evaluation of Risks from Radiation.* ICRP Publication 8, Pergamon Press, London, v + 60 pp.

International Commission on Radiological Protection (1966b). *Recommendations.* ICRP Publication 9, Pergamon Press, London, v + 27 pp.

Kornberg, H. A. & Davis, J. J. (1966). Food-chains in fresh water. Pp. 383–418 in *Radioactivity and Human Diet,* Ed. R. Scott Russell, Pergamon Press, Oxford.

Medical Research Council, (1966). *The Assessment of the Possible Radiation Risks to the Population from Environmental Contamination.* HMSO, London, ii + 16 pp.

Pochin, E. E. & Barnaby, C. F. (1962). The effect of pharmacological doses of non-radioactive iodide on the course of radioiodine uptake by the thyroid. *Health Physics,* 7, 125–6.

Preston, A. & Jefferies, D. F. (1967). The assessment of the principal public radiation exposure from, and the resulting control of, discharges of aqueous radioactive waste from the United Kingdom Atomic Energy Authority factory at Windscale, Cumberland. *Health Physics,* 13, 477–85.

Russell, R. Scott, Ed. (1966). *Radioactivity and Human Diet.* Pergamon Press, Oxford, xi + 552 pp.

Russell, R. Scott (1968). Dietary contamination — its significance in an emergency. Proc. Symposium on *Radiological Protection of the Public in a Nuclear Mass Disaster,* Eds H. Brunner & S. Prêtre, Fachverband für Strahlenschutz, Bern, pp. 279–306.

Russell, R. Scott & Bruce, R. S. (in press). Environmental contamination with fallout from nuclear weapons — a review. In *Agricultural and Public Health Aspects of Environmental Contamination by Radioactive Materials.* International Atomic Energy Agency, Vienna.

Sparrow, A. H., Rogers, Anne F. & Schwemmer, Susan S. (1968). Radiosensitivity studies with woody plants — I. Acute gamma irradiation survival data for 28 species and predictions for 190 species. *Radiation Botany,* 8, 149–86.

United Nations (1962). *Report of Scientific Committee on the Effects of Atomic Radiation.* Seventeenth Session, Suppl. No. 16 (A/5216), New York, iv + 442 pp.

United Nations (1964). *Report of Scientific Committee on the Effects of Atomic Radiation.* Nineteenth Session, Suppl. No. 14 (A/5814), New York, iv + 120 pp.

United Nations (1966). *Report of Scientific Committee on the Effects of Atomic Radiation.* Twenty-first Session, Suppl. No. 14 (A/6314), New York, iii + 153 pp.

PHILIP M. BOFFEY

Radiation Standards: Are the Right People Making Decisions?

Last month the National Council on Radiation Protection and Measurements (NCRP) issued a reassuring report which concluded that existing radiation standards are adequate, with minor exceptions, to protect the public and radiation workers from harmful exposure. Lauriston S. Taylor, president of the

Philip M. Boffey, "Radiation Standards: Are the Right People Making Decisions?" *Science,* vol. 171 (February 26, 1971), pp. 780–783. Copyright 1971 by the American Association for the Advancement of Science. Reprinted by permission.

NCRP, commented that a 10-year study by his organization had found "no basis for any drastic reductions in the recommended exposure levels despite the current urgings of a few critics." Taylor also charged that two of the most outspoken of these critics — namely, John Gofman and Arthur Tamplin of the Lawrence Radiation Laboratory — have been guilty of making "highly irresponsible" statements when they suggest that the existing standards could ultimately result in some 32,000 extra cancer and leukemia deaths and some 150,000 to 1.5 million extra genetic deaths in the United States each year.

The NCRP had barely issued its report, however, before Gofman was counterattacking the organization for its alleged pronuclear bias. "The NCRP represents the radiology profession, the Atomic Energy Commission, the Defense Department, Westinghouse, and General Electric," Gofman told *Science*. "It's very difficult to conceive of an organization with a greater vested interest in the preservation of high levels of radiation. I know of no reason why the organization exists unless you want to label it a public relations firm."

Thus the sharp national debate over radiation safety seems likely to continue despite the NCRP's efforts to lay the matter to rest. But the exchange between Gofman and the NCRP has served to focus attention on the important question of how radiation protection standards are set. Previous articles in this magazine have discussed the scientific basis of the dispute over existing standards (*Science*, 6 February 1970) and a subsidiary controversy involving charges by Gofman and Tamplin that they have been harassed by the Atomic Energy Commission (*Science*, 28 August 1970). This current article will discuss such matters as who sets the standards, how they go about their business, and how adequate the whole mechanism appears to be.

The three most important bodies affecting standards in this country have been the NCRP, the International Commission on Radiological Protection (ICRP), and the Federal Radiation Council (FRC). The first two are private groups whose recommendations are, in theory at least, purely advisory. The ICRP was formed in 1928 by medical experts whose chief goal was initially to devise some means of protecting doctors from the hazards of handling x-rays and other radiation tools. The NCRP was set up a year later in an effort to give the United States a unified voice at meetings of this international group. Such unity was sought because, at the first international meeting in 1928, competing delegations from two American radiological societies had each claimed to be the authoritative body representing this country, with the result that no agreed upon American position was possible and recommendations prepared by a British protection committee were adopted by default.

Over the next two or three decades, these two organizations — the NCRP and the ICRP — held almost undisputed sway over the setting of radiation standards used to protect workers and, ultimately, the general public in this country. Their recommendations were by and large accepted by the medical profession, by industry, and by various government agencies. The NCRP's recommendations were issued in handbooks bearing the name of the National Bureau of Standards and they were widely regarded as government policy, but the government took no official responsibility for the standards and considered itself merely the "publisher" of NCRP's reports. It was not until 1959, after the advent of the atomic age had aroused public fears over fallout

from nuclear weapons, that the government suddenly realized that it was rely-
ing primarily on private organizations to determine acceptable radiation protection standards. As a result, a new governmental organization, the Federal
Radiation Council, was established to promulgate more "official" guidelines.
The FRC — which came to consist of the heads of seven major agencies,
namely, Atomic Energy, Defense, Commerce, Labor, Health, Interior, and
Agriculture — was empowered to recommend standards which, after promulgation by the President, would then become official guidance for all federal
agencies dealing with radiation. Such a subordinate agency as the AEC, for
example, would have to make its rules governing nuclear reactors compatible
with the overall guides developed by the FRC. The FRC was recently abolished and its functions were transferred to the new Environmental Protection
Agency (EPA), but the government will continue, through the new agency, to
promulgate standards of its own.

The work of these standards setting groups has been greatly assisted by
various studies of the biological effects of radiation carried out by the U.S.
National Academy of Sciences, the British Medical Research Council, and the
United Nations Scientific Committee on the Effects of Atomic Radiation,
among others. Thus it must be acknowledged that the existing standards carry
an impressive imprimatur from some rather prestigious national and international organizations. When asked by a Congressional committee for his
opinion of the NCRP and ICRP Lee A. DuBridge, President Nixon's first science
adviser, replied: "There certainly is no group that has any greater expertise
than they or greater access to technical information."

The standards promulgated by these various groups are remarkable in
their unanimity. The standards are expressed in a variety of ways — allowable
whole body exposure, dose limits for critical organs, allowable body burdens
for particular isotopes, maximum permissible concentrations of these isotopes
in air, water, and food that may be ingested, and so forth — and different dose
limits are recommended for radiation workers, for the general public, for pregnant women, and for other categories of the population. But, according to
almost every expert who has testified before Congress in recent years, this
bewildering array of numbers issued by the various standards-setting groups is
by and large consistent.

The significance of this unanimity can be looked at in two ways. Officials
of the standards-setting organizations argue that the unanimity underscores
the validity of existing standards, for different bodies of the world's leading
radiation experts have all looked at the relevant scientific literature and
reached essentially the same conclusions as to allowable exposure levels.
However, critics of the standards charge that the various groups are so similar
in outlook and have such overlapping memberships that they are merely
different parts of the "nuclear energy lobby" wearing different hats and rubber-
stamping each other's decisions. Perhaps the leading hat wearer of them
all is Lauriston Taylor, who was key radiation protection official at the National
Bureau of Standards for several decades, has been head of the NCRP ever
since it was established, served on the ICRP from its formation until 1969 (he's
still a member emeritus), was heavily involved in the FRC until the mid-1960's,
and served on a radiation committee of the Public Health Service.

Taylor readily acknowledges that there is considerable swapping of experts and expertise among the various groups, but he believes this has simply enabled each group to avail itself of the latest knowledge without in any sense turning the groups into mere "rubber stamps" of each other. As an example, he cites a situation which developed in 1956–57 at the time of the last major revision in recommended standards. He recalls that a National Academy of Sciences committee recommended a tightening of standards based on genetic considerations, a British Medical Research Council group came to essentially the same conclusion, and the ICRP and the NCRP, which were both aware of these developments, made similar recommendations. "A lot of things happened simultaneously because there was so much cross membership, so it's pretty hard to say who did what first," Taylor says. "But I regard all four actions as independent. No one or two or three persons could swing a position on any of these groups."

Figuring out which, if any, of these organizations is the most important force in developing standards is difficult, but several experts believe it is probably the NCRP. Paul C. Tompkins, former executive director of the FRC and now acting head of the division of criteria and standards in EPA's radiation program, told *Science* that "NCRP is the most important organization without doubt." Similarly, Lauriston Taylor told *Science* that, although the ICRP generally set the pace from 1928 until World War II, the NCRP took the lead in the postwar period and was dominant until about 1956 when, as mentioned above, a number of organizations more or less simultaneously brought about the last major revision in standards. Thus it seems appropriate to take a closer look at the NCRP to see just what kind of a body it is that has been dominating the standards-setting business.

When the NCRP was first established in 1929 it tended to represent medical-radiological interests and industry. Taylor, who was at the National Bureau of Standards, was the first chairman of the organization, which then had the title "Advisory Committee on X-Ray and Radium Protection." The rest of the committee consisted of representatives appointed by two radiological societies, the American Medical Association, and the x-ray equipment manufacturers. According to Taylor, the three societies and the electrical manufacturers continued to appoint the members until after World War II, when the NCRP's operations grew to such a point that new procedures had to be worked out. Finally, in 1964, the NCRP was granted a federal charter and the members then serving became a self-perpetuating body, responsible for electing their own new members. Thus the medical and industrial interests that originally dominated the organization lost their direct voice in its affairs, but they have continued to exercise a powerful indirect influence. The NCRP operated last year on a budget of about $140,000, most of which came from government contracts, and contributions given by more than 20 medical and industrial groups. According to Taylor, each of the various collaborating groups has one of its members on the NCRP — though that member is not considered a representative of his organization and is not necessarily even nominated by his organization. And while the collaborating groups have no veto power over the wording of NCRP reports, they are frequently consulted and are kept posted on the progress of reports and studies.

Currently, the NCRP has some 65 members plus an additional 150 or more participants who serve on the Council's 36 scientific committees but are not full-fledged members. Taylor estimates that about two-thirds of the committee chairmen are NCRP members, with the remaining third being outsiders of unusual competence in particular areas. Taylor believes the group is reasonably broad-gauged. He told *Science* that one recent breakdown indicated the NCRP itself consisted of 15 health physicists (mainly industry oriented), 11 radiological physicists (mainly medically oriented), 8 physicists (mainly specialists in measurement rather than protection), 10 medical doctors, 17 radiobiologists, 4 general biologists and pathologists, 4 public health specialists, and 3 geneticists. (The total adds up to more than 65 because some members qualify in more than one specialty.) Breaking the Council down another way, Taylor said that 33 members — a majority — are from the universities, 4 are from government agencies, 12 are from government contract laboratories such as Argonne or Brookhaven, and the remaining 16 are split up among various sources, including industry.

HOW NCRP OPERATES

In assembling a report, the NCRP goes through an elaborate study and review process aimed at producing a consensus on the matters under consideration. Topics for study are usually generated within the NCRP itself, though occasionally a specific study may be undertaken in response to an outside request. Once the Council has identified an area needing investigation, the problem is referred to one of the scientific committees for a review of the relevant literature. The committee drafts a report and recommendations which are then reviewed by a handful of NCRP members who are particularly knowledgeable in the field. Approval by these "critical reviewers" is required before the report can go any further. Once past this hurdle, the report is sent out to all 65 NCRP members. According to Taylor, a "great majority of the members, which is usually taken to mean at least three-fourths, must approve the report, but if someone with prime understanding of the problem does not approve, the report is not issued no matter how many others endorse it. Critical comments are also frequently sought from outsiders. The latest report from the NCRP — the one which asserts that existing standards are by and large valid — was ultimately approved by about 60 of the NCRP members, according to Taylor. The remaining members did not object to the report, Taylor said, but simply failed to return their comments. Thus the existing standards can be said to have the essentially unanimous backing of the NCRP. The report was even approved by NCRP member Karl Z. Morgan, a health physicist at Oak Ridge, who has been critical of some aspects of the standards-setting process.

How good is the system used to determine acceptable radiation standards in this country? Are the right people making the right decisions in the right way?

The nuclear critics say the system is biased in the direction of allowing excessively high exposures to radiation. They contend that the NCRP and ICRP are dominated by "vested interests" whose careers are dependent on the use of radiation or of atomic energy, and that such people will hardly be eager to restrict the development of their fields by imposing stringent safety standards.

MENTAL OR MONETARY BIAS?

Egan O'Connor, a staff aide to Senator Mike Gravel (D–Alaska) who has played a key role in Gravel's attacks on the nuclear establishment, recently asserted that at least 25 of the NCRP's 64 members (one seat is vacant) are supported financially by the AEC, while another six receive grants from the Defense Department or work directly for Westinghouse or General Electric, two major manufacturers of nuclear reactors. She also deplored the fact that there are so few geneticists and public health experts on the NCRP, and asked: "Does it make sense to ask experts who have devoted their lives to promoting medical, military, and peaceful uses of nuclear energy for an objective analysis of its safety? My answer is: NO. It is human nature for such experts to have either a psychological or monetary bias — or both."

In rebuttal, however, Taylor argues that the experts on the NCRP are "inherently honest" and would certainly not endanger the public merely because they are funded by the AEC or have other nuclear interests. Moreover, Taylor asserts that "if you are going to work in the radiation field and call on the experts, you probably can't put together anything but a very small committee if you are going to avoid people who supposedly have a vested interest."

Nevertheless, an arguable case can be made that both the NCRP and ICRP are dominated by people who are "pronuclear" (though whether this necessarily makes them antisafety is another question). The situation is much less clear, however, when one examines the memberships of some of the other standards-setting bodies. The now-defunct Federal Radiation Council, for example, had representatives from agencies, such as Health and Labor, that would seemingly be more concerned about the safety of people than about the promotion of nuclear energy. Indeed, the FRC was occasionally sharply split on safety issues, with the health-labor forces opposing the atomic energy-military-commerce forces. One member of the White House Office of Science and Technology who kept tabs on FRC affairs told *Science*: "The FRC was pretty broad-gauged. It had the health nuts as well as the technological development nuts." Whether the FRC actually exerted much influence over most standards, however, is a matter of dispute. The FRC essentially adopted the standards previously recommended by NCRP and ICRP. Taylor, who was a member of the FRC group, claims the FRC went over the NCRP/ICRP recommendations with "a fine tooth comb" and concluded it could not improve upon them. But nuclear critics have accused the FRC of "rubber stamping." And even members of other standards-setting bodies acknowledge that the FRC was often disappointingly passive.

The standard that is most controversial today is one which stipulates that the radiation dose received by the general population should not exceed a yearly average of 170 millirems per person (exclusive of medical exposures and natural background radiation). This is the standard which has been specifically attacked by Gofman and Templin and which has been used in their calculations of the number of deaths that would allegedly result if the general public actually received this permissible dose. Significantly, both Taylor and Tompkins assert that this standard did not really originate with either the NCRP or ICRP but was essentially derived from a number originally proposed by a group of geneticists assembled by the National Academy of Sciences. The Academy's recommendation was put forth in a report issued in 1956 by the so-called BEAR committee, which studied the Biological Effects of Atomic Radiation under a special grant from the Rockefeller Foundation. The study was prompted by concern over fallout and was meant to provide an independent evaluation of the hazards of radiation. The key genetics committee was headed by Warren Weaver, of the Rockefeller Foundation, and included Nobelists George W. Beadle and the late H. J. Muller, as well as geneticists at AEC-supported laboratories. Defenders of the standard suggest that it is unfair to accuse this eminent group of a "pronuclear" bias.

Some critics carry the argument a step farther and claim that even if the scientists on the standards-setting groups have no nuclear biases at all, they are still not the appropriate people to make decisions on allowable exposure levels. Harold P. Green, a Washington attorney who specializes in nuclear matters, describes the standards setters as "a very narrow group" who are probably competent to estimate the risks involved in radiation but are hardly fit to decide what risks are "acceptable" to society. "The scientists don't have very much knowledge or experience with human values generally," he says. "Nor do they have any real degree of accountability to the public." Green suggests that the responsible groups should be more broadly representative, perhaps including economists, political scientists, sociologists, lawyers, theologians, psychiatrists, and others. But even that would probably not be enough, he suspects. "What is really needed is the kind of thing Gofman and Tamplin are doing — the stimulation of public debate," Green says. "Risk-benefit decisions are not scientific problems. They're political concerns and should be debated in the rough-and-tumble of the political process. What benefits does the public want and what risks is it willing to assume? The NCRP, in effect, has been saying to the public: 'You are going to have to assume these risks in order to have the benefits we say you want.'"

Neither the NCRP nor most other standards groups, it should be noted, deliberately sought this role. The literature of virtually all standards groups is laced with warnings that the standards involve value judgments and that the final decisions should be made by society, but thus far society has not really come to grips with the complex problem and the scientists have been left in charge by default.

As far as can be determined by the public record, the scientists have not really tried to perform a quantitative risk-benefit analysis in developing the standards. The various standards groups have refused to get involved in "the numbers game" of estimating how many deaths might result if the public received the radiation allowed by the standard. Nor have they tried to quantify the presumed benefits of atomic energy. Thus the public is left with little more than an assurance that the risk is "acceptable."

The standards are currently undergoing an intensive governmental review — the first in more than a decade. The new Environmental Protection Agency — which has assumed various radiation responsibilities from the old FRC, the Public Health Service, and the AEC — is coordinating the effort, and there will be input from the Academy and from the NCRP, among others. But there have already been charges that the Academy committee is biased, and there are continued grumblings about the closed-to-the-public nature of the process. Thus the review, whatever its findings, may not succeed in dissipating the reservoir of distrust in the public mind. A number of nuclear critics have suggested that there should be a searching public "trial" of the standards, with proponents and critics presenting their evidence before a neutral, qualified jury of some kind. That proposal has not gained much support. But it would seem highly desirable that some way be found to assure the public that its fate does not lie solely in the hands of a small group of scientists meeting behind closed doors.

HAROLD N. MacFARLAND
Congressional Testimony
on Environmental Quality

In the congressional hearing reprinted below, the problems associated with measuring human health hazards are examined by scientists and politicians. The discourse reveals skepticism that can only be removed by increasing proof of the fundamental assumptions involved in assessing risks to health. Dr. Harold N. MacFarland's statement is an attempt to provide the needed information.

Mr. Daddario. I would then like to go to Dr. MacFarland's statement.
Dr. MacFarland. Mr. Chairman and gentlemen, I thank you for the opportunity to present testimony to this committee.

My primary purpose today is to describe to you two large experimental investigations having to do with the biological effects of air pollutants which are presently being conducted at Hazleton Laboratories, Inc. Hazleton Laboratories is an independent life sciences research firm which performs contract research for Government and industry. Its laboratories are located just a few miles from here, near Falls Church in northern Virginia.

Reprinted from *Environmental Quality: Hearings* before the Subcommittee on Science, Research, and Development of the Committee on Science and Astronauts, U. S. House of Representatives, on HR 7796, HR 13211, HR 14605, HR 14627, 90th Congress, 2nd Session, 1968 (Washington, D.C.: Government Printing Office, 1968), pp. 136–146.
The author is Director, Inhalation Division, Hazleton Laboratories, Inc.; and Vice President and Director, Resources Research, Inc., in which position he provides toxicological interpretation of air pollution findings, among other duties.

In the last 2 days the need for additional knowledge in order to determine meaningful criteria and to set objective standards for air pollutants has been emphasized more than once. Specialists in this field have been aware for many years of the deficiencies that exist in our knowledge, but it has been only comparatively recently that adequate funding has become available to undertake the rather extensive investigations that are required.

What are the deficiencies and what needs to be done? Examination of existing experimental studies on the biological effects of air pollutants reveals a pattern which is readily understandable. The first investigators — toxicologists, physiologists, and scientists from cognate specialties — examined some of the simple gaseous pollutants, such as sulfur dioxide, in short-term or acute studies. In order to increase the chances of seeing biological responses, they worked with very high concentrations of these agents. And since one tends to do the simple and inexpensive thing first, these early trials were performed with small laboratory rodents as the test species. The measures of response in these animals were also simple and obvious — gross pathological damage and death. Although it was appreciated that human populations are scarcely ever exposed to just a single pollutant, investigators nonetheless usually only looked at single pollutants and almost no work was done with mixtures of pollutants.

But what is the real problem that confronts us? We want to know the effects of pollutants, particularly mixtures of them, on human subjects undergoing very long-term exposures to quite low concentrations. So, it would seem that the work that had been done was just the opposite of what was needed. And, to add the coup de grace, enough was known about the effects of air pollutants on human populations to realize that certain predisposed individuals — the respiratory cripples, asthmatics, chronic bronchitics and cardiopulmonary cases — were especially liable to adverse effects. But there were no analogous experimental studies on such special types of population; that is, animals in which a functional impairment had been established before exposing them to pollutants.

We approached representatives of the coal-burning electric power utilities a few years ago with the suggestion that biological studies be undertaken in which many of the defects seen in earlier work would be overcome by means of adequate experimental design. In due course, the Edison Electric Institute and the National Coal Association, with minor contributions from two or three other sponsors, authorized a five-and-a-half-year series of investigations at a cost of $2.2 million. A recent analysis indicates that the program will actually require 7 years to complete and the total cost will be $3.3 million. The work on this program commenced in June 1966, a year and a half prior to the adoption of the Air Quality Act of 1967.

Mr. Daddario. Has that 7-year and $3.3 million proposal been approved? Do you have the funds for it? Are you going ahead with it?

Dr. MacFarland. We haven't the funds for it yet.

Mr. Daddario. You have the funds for the 5-year study at $2.2 million, but do you expect the same people would support the additional expenses?

Dr. MacFarland. We have hopes of getting an additional sponsor now to provide the remaining $1.1 million that we need. In the months preceding the authorization of this contract in June 1966, we had approached the U.S. Public Health Service to see if they would contribute to the financial support of this project. They refused. More recently, particularly with the enactment of the Air Quality Act, we believe there is a possibility now that they may be prepared to reconsider their earlier decision. So we have started to approach them with a view to seeing if they might provide the additional $1.1 million that will be needed to complete the program.

Mr. Daddario. Was the Public Health Service refusal based on financial reasons or was it based on their disagreement with the way in which the studies would take place?

Dr. MacFarland. I think for financial reasons. The history of the development of this project, and the design of the experiments is a rather long and involved one, and the opinion of experts in the field was solicited many times before the project took its final form. Among the experts whose opinions were sought were some from the Public Health Service, so that when the final proposal was prepared it carried the imprimatur of the Public Health Service. They had no objections from a technical point of view. I assume, then, it was a financial limitation that resulted in their refusing to help at that time.

Let me give some of the details of the design of this study. The pollutants selected for examination are sulfur dioxide, a gas; sulfuric acid mist, a droplet aerosol; and fly ash, a particulate aerosol. These are the three most conspicuous pollutants emitted from the stacks of coal-burning powerplants. Graded levels of these substances, spanning the range of concentrations that have actually been measured in polluted urban atmospheres, are being employed. Exposures are being conducted in large chambers operated on an around-the-clock basis so that the daily exposure exceeds 22 out of the 24 hours, 7 days a week, for uninterrupted periods of a year or a year and a half. Two species of animals are under test, guinea pigs, which get the 1-year exposure, and monkeys, which get the year and a half. The greater emphasis in the work attaches to the primates, and it is rather easier to extrapolate from the monkey to man than to make the jump from a mouse to man. Guinea pigs were included in order to provide a connecting link with some of the earlier published studies. In the various trials which make up the complete program, the animals are being exposed not only to the single agents, but also to some of the binary and ternary mixtures of them. It is not feasible to examine all of the theoretically possible combinations, but an adequate and representative number of them have been selected.

Let us turn now to a most important consideration — the measures of response in the animals. In a biological study of this magnitude and duration, it is customary to perform certain conventional or routine tests. Thus, basic hematological and clinical parameters, X-rays, electrocardiograms, and growth data will be collected throughout the study. However, we do not anticipate that any striking changes will be seen in these variables, although we may be surprised.

Our interest is focused intensively on the results being obtained from a battery of very advanced and highly sensitive pulmonary function tests. These include measures of the mechanical, ventilatory, and diffusional characteristics of respiratory function. With the aid of an online computer facility, about 3 dozen primary and derived parameters are obtained. The tests are performed on all animals on a scheduled basis prior to, during, and at termination of the exposures. It is possible to apply these tests on this repetitive basis because they are what we call nondestructive, that is to say, the animal under examination requires no anesthetic, operative procedures or other techniques which would interfere with the test or preclude its repeated performance. It is only at the termination of the year or year and a half of exposure that we add one or two final tests that will render it necessary to sacrifice the animal after conducting them. At this point, a thorough gross and microscopic examination of all major tissues and organs of the animal completes the experimental phase of the investigation.

Although this program was authorized a year and a half ago, it is too early yet to speak of the results which are beginning to accumulate. When the results are available from each series of exposure trials, the final phase of the investigation may be entered into. This will be an evaluation and interpretation of the findings as they relate to the standards for the specific pollutants and their mixtures. The objectives of the study, then, are of a quite practical significance.

Mr. Daddario. Mr. MacFarland, what are the difficulties in extrapolating this information obtained through your animal studies to man? What do we learn? How far can we go? What do we then need to do? Where do your studies bring us?

Dr. MacFarland. This is a long and difficult question.

The experimentalist is always asked, How do you get from your animals to man? It must be admitted that all or nearly all work with experimental animals has as its ultimate objective something that applies to man.

Experience has shown that if you work with an organism or species which is far removed from man on the phylogenetic scale, if you work with a mouse rather than, say, with a dog, the danger of extrapolation that you will ultimately make is increased. It is, therefore, as a general rule, considered a little safer to jump from, let us say, a subhuman primate to man. What kind of results are we talking about and what is this jump? One of the things that may be of interest to you is the qualitative nature of the responses you are seeing. If you do examine the effect of something on a series of animals moving up the phylogenetic tree and you see much the same kind of effect occurring in each one of them, you will feel fairly confident that if man were exposed to the same thing he would exhibit the same signs and symptoms. You can appreciate that if you had only done the work with mice and then jumped to man that there is a possibility that there might be a striking species difference which would vitiate your extrapolation.

So there are these questions of the qualitative similarities that may or may not be present when you do this kind of work. There is also a question of the quantitative nature of the responses and the same sort of considerations apply.

Now, as to the next part of your question, suppose we had results in various species, including the primate, and we want to jump over to man, can we do this, or what other work is indicated? One of the things, of course, that one would like to think of as a theoretical possibility, perhaps, is: Could we do experiments on men? This question is not at all ridiculous and, in fact, we do do experiments on men.

One of the factors that will govern this is the nature of the kind of things we are working with and the nature of the effects they produce.

It is fortunate, in this sense, that the sort of pollutants that I have been talking about are not noted for their high toxicity. They are irritating materials and they do fall into a class where considering the possibility of doing human experiments is quite on the books. As a matter of fact, we have proposed to our sponsors in a tentative form a possible continuation of some of the work that we are doing in human subjects. However, there are difficulties. I mentioned at the beginning what we really want to know is the effect of very low concentrations of these pollutants over protracted periods of time. Well, you can put an animal in a chamber and conduct experiments on him for a quite high fraction of his total lifespan or, in fact, for his total lifespan, but you cannot do this with human subjects. So it is a little difficult at the moment to see how we can perform the necessary experiments on human beings. Short-term ones we can do, but short-term ones are not what we are really interested in.

I seem to have talked around this question, Mr. Chairman. I do not know whether I have answered your question.

Mr. Daddario. Well, we can get into it more deeply later. I do think this is important to us, however, so that we might know what time scale we are talking about and how, in fact, we can have confidence in criteria to be established through such laboratory techniques, recognizing they are extremely important. I do not assume that this is not an important piece of work to be doing because it is; it is just that we ought to have it generally recognized what the limitations are, both to know what it can accomplish and what it cannot.

Dr. MacFarland. Yes. In my opening sentence I referred to two large air pollution studies in progress at Hazleton Laboratories and I would like now to give a description of the second program. You will be pleased to learn that this can be done rather briefly and without quite so much detail.

By way of background on the second study I will remind you that there have been a few air pollutant visitations sufficiently severe to be labeled "disasters." The London smog of 1952 is the most well known of these disasters and some 4,000 excess deaths were attributed to it. Monitoring stations were in operation during that "killer smog" and levels of sulfur dioxide and suspended particulate were measured. The maximum sulfur dioxide concentration, recorded briefly at one station, was 1.34 parts per million; the peak level of suspended particulate matter was 4.46 milligrams per cubic meter. To the air pollution control officer, the increase in the concentration of both these pollutants over background levels was the salient observation; but, to the toxicologist, the absolute value of the concentrations, vis-a-vis the mortality incidence, appeared anomalous. It is true that those who succumbed were, for the most part, not healthy adult men but, rather a group suffering from preexisting cardiopulmonary insufficiency, or else were very young or very old. But, even allowing for these facts, it is still difficult to see how such toxicologically low levels of sulfur dioxide and suspended particulate matter could elicit such a drastic response as death in 4,000 victims.

Some theories have been advanced which, if true, might explain the observations just cited. One of the more promising ones has to do with what is called a synergistic effect. This is an enhanced response to a mixture of pollutants greater than would be expected from the sum of the responses to each component when acting singly. You can probably anticipate what a review of the literature on synergistic effects among mixtures of common air pollutants is going to reveal. Very few studies have been performed. Those that have are of a short-term, acute nature, employing unrealistically high concentrations of pollutants, and they have been conducted exclusively in small rodents.

In 1966 we suggested to members of the American Petroleum Institute that a study of synergistic effects, in which the deficiencies noted above had been corrected, was worthy of support. In January 1967 the American Petroleum Institute authorized our proposal for a $3^{1}/_{2}$-year program, costing $1.6 million. The details of the design and the battery of test procedures are quite similar to those in use in the power utilities program. Again, the main test species is the primate, although a limited amount of work in rats is also being performed. The main points of difference should be mentioned. The pollutants under examination are the gases sulfur dioxide, carbon monoxide, and nitrogen dioxide, and two particulates, lead chlorobromide and calcium sulfate. Lead chlorobromide is the main lead compound found in the exhaust of automobiles using leaded gasoline as fuel.

Calcium sulfate typifies the ubiquitous "particulate sulfate" found in urban atmospheres. The effects of these five materials acting singly are being determined in several trials, but the bulk of the work will be performed on a selection of the various gas-gas and gas-particulate combinations. At the end of the study the computer will help us perform the rather complex statistical analyses of the data that will reveal whether or not synergistic actions have occurred and, if so, their magnitude. When we consider that human populations are almost invariably exposed to mixed pollutants, the potential value of the results that will be forthcoming from the American Petroleum Institute study is evident.

Mr. Daddario. Dr. MacFarland, getting back to the preceding page, the last sentence of your statement on page 5: "Even allowing for these facts, it is difficult to see how such toxicologically low levels of sulfur dioxide and suspended particulate matter could elicit such a drastic response as death in 4,000 victims." You are talking about those who have a predisposition to such a situation. Can we assume that a higher concentration of such pollutants could affect great numbers of people who do not have such predispositions, since the death of so many allows you to come to this conclusion?

Dr. MacFarland. Yes; it is undoubtedly true that a normal subject would be adversely affected if the concentrations were high enough. The question that remains, then, is: How high is high enough? And some of the types of experiments we are doing, hopefully, will give some indications in this direction.

Mr. Daddario. Would you assume because people have died from such concentrations whom would you not expect to, even though they have a predisposition, that you could take the next logical step and say that healthy people subjected to high concentrations would also die? If that is so, then we are talking about a very dangerous situation because you are talking about the possibility of death of an untold number of people who somewhere in this scale will be affected as these 4,000 were?

Dr. MacFarland. I think this may be possible. The difficulty here is that we are talking about something where we simply do not know the answer at this point. We have not enough knowledge. Many people cannot even smell a concentration of sulfur dioxide of one and one-third parts per million. This particular visitation lasted about 5 days. Now, it is inconceivable on toxicological evidence that a person could not stand one and a third parts per million of sulfur dioxide for 5 days. Let me bring in something that may illuminate this a bit.

I sit on a committee which is concerned with the establishment of threshold limit values. These are numbers to be used in industries which produce airborne hazards and they purport to be a sort of maximum allowable concentration that a normal working man can be exposed to for 8 hours a day, 5 days a week, for a working lifetime of 40 to 50 years without adverse effect.

Now, what is the threshold limit value, this industrial standard, for sulfur dioxide? The value currently used is five parts per million. This standard has been in existence for many years and there simply is no evidence to indicate that it is too high. We do not anticipate that this number will be revised downward on the basis of any evidence presently available. So then if this number is a valid one, and it must be admitted that the reliability of these numbers in the threshold limit value list varies from number to number, depending on the evidence that lies behind them, but if we accept the five parts per million then this standard purports to say that a man can be exposed 8 hours a day to five parts per million for 5 days a week, for 40 to 45 years. Now, maybe this will help you to get an impression of the kind of thing that makes me say that one and a third parts per million of sulfur dioxide is toxicologically a pretty low concentration, particularly when the one and a third was only a peak value seen very briefly at one station, while the average concentration was below this and the whole duration of this episode was about 5 days.

So, there is some kind of a quantitative anomaly between what are really, toxicologically speaking, low levels of these things as compared with the very drastic outcome, 4,000 people dying, which is a pretty severe response.

Mr. Daddario. Dr. MacFarland, I think this has some bearing on it. The New York Times this morning has an article on emphysema and the effect of air pollution. I would like to pass these to all of you just so that you can take a look at them, in case you have not seen the article. The article says:

Emphysema, the lung disease that often suffocates its victims, strikes earlier and pushes them faster toward death in air-polluted industrial cities than in nonindustrial, unpolluted communities, experts said here this week.

It goes through to prove these points and concludes them by saying:

There was more emphysema in St. Louis than Winnipeg, it was evident at an earlier age and appeared to progress more rapidly.

It goes on:

The importance of environmental pollution is suggested by the fact that the incidence of severe emphysema in smokers is four times as high in St. Louis as it is in
Winnipeg.

Taking what you have said and extrapolating this into the overall situation, it indicates that there are varying degrees of severity, that people with a
predisposition, with a disease such as emphysema, can be more affected in
an industrial area. I would think that people who do not have the predisposition are also in a more dangerous situation as a result of finding themselves in
a highly industrialized area where high pollution percentages exist.

Dr. MacFarland. Yes, but this needs to be analyzed a little further. The people
who succumb, or the bulk of the people who succumb in this kind of disaster,
are the respiratory cripples. These people have one foot through the door any-
how.

Mr. Daddario. So do we all.

Dr. MacFarland. It takes a very little to push them over. If you were to place
a normal individual, a person with adequate pulmonary function, we will say,
into this kind of an atmosphere, this is not going to bother him at all. Suppose
that a normal person lives in this kind of atmosphere over a long period of
time — suppose he grows up in this industrial area and he begins to develop
the early changes, which if they go on to completion, will lead to emphysema
and other respiratory disease. He is not a normal, healthy individual, he has
already suffered the beginnings of a process that will result in overt disease
ultimately. If you put this man in a heavily polluted atmosphere such as may
occur in one of these incidents, you would anticipate that he would tend to
be adversely affected more severely and sooner than a stranger who just
happened to be visiting this city at the time and who was completely normal.

Mr. Brown. Mr. Chairman.

Mr. Daddario. Mr. Brown.

Mr. Brown. May I just interject a thought here. I think what you said is absolutely correct, Doctor, but don't we also need information as to the extent or
degree to which these so-called pulmonary cripples have been created by
these same conditions at a lower level prior to the episode? Obviously we do
not have this information? But if there is any basis for this assumption that the
pulmonary cripples are more susceptible to an episodic situation — and this
is created by the same kind of conditions — then the episode merely adds
the final touch to something that has been created by the lower conditions
over a period of many years. Therefore, what I am asking is: Don't we need
considerable information about the degree to which the cripples themselves
may have been created by the lower concentrations of some of these contaminants over a long period of time?

Dr. MacFarland. Yes, indeed we do need this information, and much has
been done to try and garner this information. It is done in part by epidemiological techniques of looking over the history of what has happened, looking
at the medical records and trying to correlate these with occurrences of elevated pollutant levels.

Again, from an experimental point of view, it is rather difficult to envisage how could you try to simulate this kind of situation in human subjects. It can be done with experimental animals. The trouble is that this is going to be a costly and long term program.

Mr. Brown. The whole point of this New York Times article seems to be an environment in which the pollution exists compared with an environment in which the pollution does not exist. It will exist at these very low levels — was not St. Louis one of the cities mentioned?

Mr. Daddario. Yes.

Mr. Brown. St. Louis has never had an incidence of severe pollution comparable to the London incidence. The evidence seems to be quite clear that the incidence and severity of emphysema is substantially greater there than in any area such as Winnipeg where the pollution does not exist. Isn't this the kind of pollution you are talking about?

Dr. MacFarland. Yes, this kind of evidence is usual. It provides directives for us, and I do not see that there is any argument about the validity of this kind of thinking.

Mr. Daddario. I bring it up only because it seems to logically follow from your testimony. How do you view it? Because there is such a base of information and so many points of reference that you have to take into consideration, recognizing how difficult it is, it is information such as this which does have a tremendous effect on the public generally. They read into it almost what they want to. It is therefore more important that we, as we analyze this information, develop a mechanism through which confidence can be built.

Dr. Eckardt, do you have a point here?

Dr. Eckardt. I simply want to comment about the disease emphysema a bit.

The medical profession today really does not understand what causes emphysema but they do know there are several factors that contribute to it. We do know, for instance, that the asthmatic who suffers from pollenosis over many, many years may develop emphysema. It is conceivable, although I am not saying this is the case, that the pollen count in St. Louis is quite different from that in Winnipeg. Another factor that we know is of importance in emphysema production is genetics. The best example I know of is this isolated island in the middle of the South Atlantic called Tristan Da Cunha, where there was a population isolated since the time of Napoleon which reached a peak population of about 250 people in about 1960 or 1961. At that time this island threatened to erupt volcanically and these people were removed and brought back to England ultimately and examined. Over 50 percent of these people suffered from chronic bronchitis or emphysema. This is a highly inbred population, again suggesting that there is a genetic factor in the production of emphysema.

Finally, in a recent epidemiology meeting that I attended in New York in December of 1967, Dr. Patrick Lawther from England indicated that there is something in the particulate pollutant from a city which stimulates the growth of an organism called Hemophilus influenzae. This same organism is found clinically by the physician. It will be found probably in small numbers in anybody's throat culture, but it is found in large numbers in people who are suffering from acute bronchitis. We in the medical profession feel that this organism may be in some way related to bouts of acute bronchitis which also, we feel, are related to the production of chronic bronchitis and, ultimately, emphysema.

Now, this growth-stimulating factor present in the particulate matter from urban communities — and I presume that this was London though he did not elaborate on it — is also present in cigarette smoke and certain phenols have the same effect. It does not stimulate certain other organisms that do not seem to be related to bronchitis. The organism that he specifically mentioned was staphylococcus. The point I am trying to make here is that the factors we are trying to control in air pollution, even if they are related to chronic bronchitis and emphysema may not be known. We might well clear up the industrial pollution in these cities as suggested — the New York Times article is suggestive that this is related to industrialization — we might clean these up but we might not influence the incidence of emphysema one bit because of the other factors that might be involved, such as the pollenosis, perhaps materials in the air not related to or ordinarily considered pollutants and because of genetic differences between the population. I am sure there are genetic differences between the people who live in St. Louis and those who live in Winnipeg.

Mr. Daddario. Dr. MacFarland, I think we should proceed.

Dr. MacFarland. Yes. Gentlemen, I believe that programs such as the two which formed the subject of my testimony will help to fill some of the gaps in our knowledge of the nature of the action of pollutants and the concentrations at which they occur, and thus contribute to the solution of the problems that concern us all — the development of meaningful criteria from which scientifically objective standards of air quality may be derived.

Mr. Chairman, you have intimated to several of the witnesses that you may invite them to pay a return visit to this committee. May I, on my part, extend to you and the members of the committee, taken singly or in mixture, an invitation to visit at your convenience the Inhalation Division of Hazleton Laboratories to see the programs I have described in progress.

Mr. Daddario. Considering the fact that you are looking for human subjects, that might be an ominous invitation.

Mr. Brown, do you have some questions of Dr. MacFarland?

Mr. Brown. No.

Mr. Daddario. Dr. Eckardt, your last statement indicates to me that there is some question about the quality of air we should be striving to achieve. When you relate diseases to the effect that air quality may have in the initiation of these diseases, or the effect that they could have on the diseases already existing, I wonder if you have any view or theory about this? How do you, in fact, separate it? Or should it in fact be separated, recognizing that emphysema most likely does arise in a multitude of ways and recognizing, too, as I understand the New York Times article, it does not indicate that industrialization's pollutants cause emphysema but that it has a greater effect on those already having it? Then that gets us to the development of a capability to get air quality to the highest possible level we can, regardless of our lack of ability, lack of knowledge about the causes, effects and initiation.

Dr. Eckardt. I am not sure just what the implication of this study is, not having read the original one, but I personally feel that air pollution is going to be controlled; it should be controlled, but it probably will not be controlled on the basis of health. I often like to make the example of the use of the sanitary toilet and sanitary sewers. This primarily arose because people got sick and tired of the stench of human excrement in the streets and they wanted to do something else with it, put it some place else. I personally think air pollution has a stench at times, it looks bad, and I think we are going to control it on this basis. I like to go back to when I was a boy traveling between Long Island and New York City past what now is the old New York World's Fair site and La Guardia Airport. Both of these areas were huge burning garbage dumps. As we used to go through Flushing at that time, we invariably as children used to go through holding our nose because it stenched so bad. This has been cleared up and not because it was a health effect, but because people apparently got sick and tired of this stench. I think basically we are going to clean up our cities, unrelated to health effects, and even before we find out whether or not there are health effects, other than the acute episodic health effects. I think we are going to clear them up, every city, to a certain degree, but I am concerned that this is going to have no effect on the health of the people of the United States even though we do clear them up, because I am not convinced, other than the episodic area, that health effects have clearly been demonstrated for low level, long-term air pollution levels.

This does not mean to say you do not clear it up for other reasons. I think you can clear up air pollution as a public nuisance. I think, for instance, in my town they have decided that they do not want people to burn leaves.

Now, I get nostalgic when I smell burning leaves, again because of my boyhood, I suppose, but some people do not like it. I do not think this has been demonstrated to be a health effect, but they do clean it up. They find other methods of disposing of leaves and I think we will do the same thing; as our technology improves, we will improve our air pollution control and clean up our cities, unrelated to health effects.

Mr. Daddario. Will you theorize a little bit on this, Dr. MacFarland?

Dr. MacFarland. I agree with Dr. Eckardt that this is probably how it will go. I agree, too, that the direct cause-and-effect relationship between low levels of pollutant and health effects has certainly not been convincingly demonstrated at the present. I believe, however, that in time, as the evidence comes in from studies such as the ones I have described, and others, that the evidence will become clear that there is a relationship and it will, hopefully, define just what sort of a concentration we are talking about. Is it true that if a man is exposed all his life to a tenth of a part per million of sulfur dioxide that he runs such-and-such a percentage increased risk of emphysema? Or should the figure be at 0.5, or at 1, or at 1.5? I think this kind of information will gradually accumulate and I think it will be found that there are, indeed, some levels at which health effects ultimately will be manifest.

Dr. Eckardt. Let me say I do not disagree with this statement. I am only disagreeing, at present levels of air pollution in our major cities, I do not think there are chronic health effects.

Mr. Brown. May I comment?

Mr. Daddario. Mr. Brown.

Mr. Brown. I want to make a remark which I do not want to be construed as in any way bearing on the present witnesses. But several years ago I conducted a hearing on the effects of lead additives in gasoline and possible health effects upon populations as this concentration increased. We had some very able scientific witnesses there who, at the end of the time, left me almost convinced that the more lead we got in the atmosphere the healthier it would be.

Mr. Daddario. You did not believe that?

Mr. Brown. No. It runs against the grain of what you might call just normal human logic. But science does run against the grain of conventional, normal human logic. I think that there is a very sound point which has been made here. I offer the possibility and ask for comment on the history of certain types of human disease resulting from biologic agents in which the process of human adaptability has seemed to be able to develop immunities and even strength as a result of this. I am not saying that the increased intake of pollutants is going to make people live longer, but in the nature of science and the human being, I suppose there is always this possibility that could occur. We seem to have, for example, in Vietnam evidence that the natives over there have learned to develop immunities to certain types of malaria, which immunities we do not have over here. What you are saying about low-level pollutants in the atmosphere of cities, is conceivable that we could develop immunities to these things and that we would not have a long-term health effect. Basically, we would seek to eliminate them ultimately for other reasons such as they are not esthetic or they represent a waste in the production process. Is this the sort of thing that you are trying to point to here? Do you find any sympathy with what I am saying?

Dr. Eckardt. I am not sure that there is an immunity developed to air pollutants in the sense that we know of immunity to bacterial agents. This is a different process to me. I am not convinced that you could develop an immunity to air pollutants. I do know one small piece of information that was told to me by a man who has been working with lead, who was doing tissue culture. This happens to be Dr. Leonard Goldwater, now on leave of absence from Columbia Medical School. He said he had a tissue culture individual working for him. That person used extremely pure ingredients in the culture medium and they would not grow until they added miniscule quantities of lead to the culture material. Then the tissue cultures grew. This type of thing suggests that there may be some — and I am certainly not advocating this — but there may be some level of pollutant that is not necessarily bad for us. I would not want to try to put my finger on this level right now, certainly.

Mr. Brown. The thing that strikes me from what you have said and for many other reasons, a much broader research concept than we probably have is envisioned so far for this whole problem. I think we need extensive monitoring systems and extensive reporting systems on the incidence of disease throughout this country and in areas where there are no pollutants, for example, merely to set standards by.

Dr. Eckardt. I agree with this.

Mr. Daddario. Of course, Dr. Eckardt, we have been defining this as against man. We must add plant and animal life to our determination as criteria are established, because this is an important aspect of this whole thing. If in fact we can, one way or the other, establish that there are certain causes and effects in these areas and can prove it in a way so that confidence can be developed, our programs would be better supported. There is concern that there is danger to health. There is question as to whether there is or is not. Because we are in this ambivalent position, we are not really able to get these kinds of programs going as soon as we should. Those dumps you were talking about could have been cleared up a long time earlier if in some way action could have been focused, and probably should have been. We ought not to wait until you finally reach the point where it gets overwhelming. We in this committee feel a great responsibility in the legislative process of seeing if we can anticipate these problems, taking into consideration the very great danger that can come, and see if we can then be of help in solving them sooner rather than later.

Dr. Eckardt. I agree. I think we will clean up our cities. I do not think there is any doubt of this.

Mr. Daddario. The hour has gone by again. This is a subject which could keep us going through the balance of the day, but we will be in touch. We will see if we can take you up on your invitation some time, Dr. MacFarland.

Dr. MacFarland. It was meant seriously.

Mr. Daddario. I understand that. Thank you.

This committee will adjourn until Wednesday, January 31, at 10 o'clock, in this place.

Chapter 3

Complexities of interactions:
foreseeing consequences

Chapter 2 explored some of the problems of uncertainty on key issues in environmental management. In this chapter, we explore some reasons why the uncertainties arise. Our environment is a web of interactions among different forms of life and their support systems. The systems become so complex that it is difficult to foresee the consequences of change. Following are articles selected to illustrate some of the biological, chemical, and societal interactions that make foresight more difficult than it might appear.

Berton Roueché's article, "Annals of Medicine: Insufficient Evidence," portrays interaction only understood by chance. If a scientist's secretary had not cleaned out her files and thereby called attention to a possible interconnection between a mysterious illness and its source, identification of the interaction patterns would have been either overlooked or delayed. Interactions among biological phenomena are indeed complex, and the interpretations need to be well tied to evidence.

The discussion of mercury illustrates how moving from an ore to a finished product proliferates ways in which harmful materials can be released to the environment. It is a large task to trace the path of every material from mined ore to final disposition. Heavy metals have been accumulating in our environment for some time, and mercury is an example of one known to have harmful effects. Over time, these accumulations of materials can interact with other materials, natural and manmade, with consequences few people had foreseen.

The short article on DDT further evidences that unsuspected consequences of DDT use were not readily predictable at the time of first use. Several years passed before the cause and effects could be identified.

G. M. Woodwell's article points to profound effects of pollution which are pervasive and ultimately highly deleterious to ecosystems. If human intervention through pollution and its control ends up in destabilizing ecosystems and creating a complex route to unforeseen and undesired outcomes, the job of environmental management may be nearly impossible. Technological tinkering to modify foreseen effects of pollution may not solve the long-term instability caused by man's attempt to dominate the natural environment. This article may have to be read twice by the nontechnical person, but the argument is worth following, for the implications are essential to grasp.

Three additional articles illustrate that interaction phenomena are complex not only in biological and chemical forms, but interactions among humans and between humans and lower forms of life are also difficult to master.

"The Ant War" by Donald W. Coon and Robert R. Fleet deals with the relations between man and ant. Cultural differences among men — values, political forces, advertising, ignorance — all play a role in the war between ant and man. While Coon and Fleet may assert some relationships not yet fully proven, they are willing to take a stand before all the damage is done and the post-mortem says we should have given the benefit of the doubt to man's ability to tolerate the ant. The authors raise issues which affect our capacity to manage lower forms of life in our alleged self-interest.

The brief piece on starfish infestation must remain speculative until more research is done. However, activities of man precede research and go on at a faster rate than we can acquire knowledge. That problem calls for a decision by the environmental manager to suspend operations or run the risk of further damage. While the evidence is insufficient at this time, that insufficiency is often the case in a complex interacting environment. Unfortunately, the old adage, "the proof of the pudding is in the eating," doesn't apply, for the result isn't often anything as pleasant as pudding. Proof is in the destruction — and then it is too late.

"Green Mountains, Green Money" by Richard M. Klein points to a similar problem in controlling of human interactions with nature. Human social systems have to be dealt with before some control over destruction can be achieved. The law, until recently, required that damage be done before land development could be arrested. Scientific forecasts were insufficient in the eyes of old laws. The land-use planners, ecologists, and engineers must be able to preview consequences with reasonable assurance when they compete with land developers for the community's judgment and authority.

This chapter makes it clear that the interactions are not always clear and that foreseeing consequences will require an advancement of the art and some judgments must be made about what can be done while the information is still incomplete.

BERTON ROUECHÉ
Annals of Medicine: Insufficient Evidence

The telephone rang, and Dr. Likosky — William H. Likosky, an Epidemic Intelligence Service officer attached to the Neurotropic Viral Diseases Activity of the Center for Disease Control, in Atlanta — reached across his desk and

Berton Roueché, "Annals of Medicine: Insufficient Evidence." Reprinted by permission: Copyright © 1970 The New Yorker Magazine, Inc.

answered it, and heard the voice of a friend and fellow-E.I.S. officer named Paul Edward Pierce. Dr. Pierce was attached to the New Mexico Department of Health and Social Services, and he was calling from his office in Santa Fe. His call was a call for help. Three cases of unusual illness had just been reported to him by a district health officer. The victims were two girls and a boy, members of a family of nine, and they lived in Alamogordo, a town of around twenty thousand, just north of El Paso, Texas. The report noted that the family raised hogs, and that several months earlier some of the hogs had become sick and died. The children were seriously ill. Their symptoms included decreased vision, difficulty in walking, bizarre behavior, apathy, and coma. This complex of central-nervous-system aberrations had immediately suggested a viral encephalitis, but that, on reflection, seemed hardly possible. The encephalitides that he had in mind were spread by ticks or mosquitoes, and the season was wrong for insects. This was winter. It was, in fact, midwinter. It was January — January 7, 1970.

"I'm afraid I wasn't much help," Dr. Likosky says. "I could only listen and agree. It was just as Ed Pierce said. The clinical picture was characteristic of the kind of brain inflammation that distinguishes the viral encephalitides. More or less. But there were certainly some confusing elements. It wasn't only that the time of year was odd for arthropod-borne disease. The attack rate was odd, too. There were too many cases. A cluster like that is unusual in an arbovirus disease. Also, the report to Ed had made no mention of fever. That was odd in a serious virus infection. It was odd, but not necessarily conclusive. The report was just a preliminary report. It was very possibly incomplete. At any rate, Ed was driving down to Alamogordo the following day and he would see for himself. Things might look different on the scene. Meanwhile, about all I could suggest was the obvious. Verify the facts. Check into the possibility of a wintering mosquito population. Check up on the hogs. This might be a zoonosis — an animal disease. It might be a disease of hogs that the three children had somehow contracted. Review the signs and symptoms. Not only for fever but also for stiff neck. Stiff neck is particularly characteristic of encephalitis.

"That was a Wednesday. Ed called me from Alamogordo on Friday. He and one of his colleagues — Jon Thompson, supervisor of the Food Protection Unit of the Consumer Protection Section of the state health department — had been out of the house, and he had some more information. The victims were children of a couple named Huckleby. They were Ernestine, eight years old; Amos Charles, thirteen; and Dorothy, eighteen. Ernestine was in the hospital — Providence Memorial Hospital, in El Paso. She had been there since just after Christmas. Amos Charles and Dorothy were sick at home. None of the other children — two girls and two boys — were sick, and neither were the parents. Huckleby worked as a janitor at a junior high school in Alamogordo. He only raised hogs on the side. All that was by way of background. The interesting information was about the Huckleby hogs. There were several items. The hog sickness happened back in October. Huckleby had a herd of seventeen hogs at the time, and all of a sudden one day fourteen of them were stricken with a sort of blind staggers — a stumbling gait and blindness. Twelve of the sick hogs died, and the two others went blind. That was interesting enough, but it was really only the beginning. In the course of their talk with Huckleby, Ed and Jon Thompson learned that the feed he gave his hogs included surplus seed grain. Well, seed grain isn't feed. Seed grain is chemically treated to resist all manner of diseases, and when it is past its season and loses its germination value, it is considered waste and is supposed to be destroyed. Huckleby said that the grain — it was a mixture of several grains, apparently — was the floor sweepings of a seed company upstate. He said a friend had given it to him, and he knew it contained treated grain. Or, rather, he knew it included treated grain. It was also partly chaff and culls. But he took care of that by cooking it with water and garbage in a metal trough before he fed it to his hogs. He said he had been given about two tons of the grain, and he still had some left. He also said that he had slaughtered one of his hogs back in September for home use. They had been eating it right along, but there was still some left in his freezer. Ed told him to leave it right where it was. There might be nothing wrong with it, but there was no use taking chances.

"Poison was a tempting possibility. The symptoms had the look of poison, but it wasn't a look that any of us were familiar with. That was the trouble. Nothing seemed to fit. Huckleby was even a little vague about whether the slaughtered hog had been fed the seed-grain feed. Moreover, he wasn't the only Alamogordan to feed that grain to his hogs. He said that five of his friends had got the same grain from the seed company, and none of their hogs had become ill. Apparently, that was true. Ed and Jon had talked with the other hog raisers. They weren't quite sure about the grain they had used, but they were positive that none of their hogs had sickened or died. The local records confirmed what they said. The local records also confirmed that the human outbreak was confined to the Huckleby family. There were no comparable illnesses anywhere in the Alamogordo area. Ed and Jon had visited the butcher shop where the Huckleby hog had been processed. The butcher testified that the meat had appeared to be in prime condition. An examination of the shop was negative — there was nothing to suggest that the meat might have become contaminated during processing. And, finally, there was the fact that others in the family had eaten quantities of the pork, and only those three were sick. Nevertheless, Ed was taking the usual steps. He had samples of grain from Huckleby's storehouse, samples of pork from the family freezer, and samples of urine from all members of the family then at home — that is to say, all but Ernestine. He had arranged for the State Laboratory to examine those for viral or bacterial contamination, and he was sending specimens to William Barthel, chief of the Toxicology Branch Laboratory of the Food and Drug Administration, in Atlanta, for toxicological analysis. But even that wasn't all. Ed had still another piece of information. The clinical picture was pretty much as originally reported. Except in one respect. Ernestine's symptoms *did* include fever. High fever. A local doctor reported that her temperature at one point got up to 104 degrees. And — oh, yes, there were no mosquitoes in Alamogordo in January.

"I talked to Ed again on Saturday. He was back in Santa Fe, and that was the reason for his call. He called to invite me to participate in the field investigation. Ed had a big rubella-immunization program coming up at a Navajo reservation the next week that he couldn't put off, and there was nobody to run it but him. It was up to him to at least get it started. He had talked to his chief in New Mexico, Dr. Bruce Storrs, director of the Medical Services Division of the state health department, and he had talked to my boss at C.D.C., Dr. Michael Gregg, chief of the Viral Diseases Branch. They both approved the proposal. So did I. I was very eager."

Dr. Likosky left Atlanta by plane the following morning. That was Sunday, January 11th. He flew to Albuquerque, where, by prearrangement, he met Dr. Pierce in the early evening. They talked and ate dinner and talked until nearly eleven. Dr. Likosky then rented a car and drove down through the mountains and the desert to Alamogordo. He spent the night (on Dr. Pierce's recommendation) at the Rocket Motel there, and on Monday morning (following Dr. Pierce's directions) he drove out to the Huckleby house.

"I wasn't checking up on Ed or Jon Thompson or the district health officer, or anything like that," Dr. Likosky says. "I simply wanted to see for myself. I wanted to start at the beginning. I got to the Huckleby house at about eight-thirty. Huckleby was at work, at the school, but Mrs. Huckleby was at home, and she received me very nicely. The first thing I learned was that Amos Charles and Dorothy were now also in Providence Memorial Hospital. They were too far gone in coma to be treated at home anymore. They had been taken down to El Paso only the day before. I liked Mrs. Huckleby at once. You could tell she was a good mother. Easygoing, but kind and loving. And she was going to be a mother once again. She was very obviously pregnant. The baby was due, she said, sometime in March. She was a religious woman, too, and that gave her a certain serenity. She believed that everything was in the hands of God. She was also an excellent historian. She remembered every detail of each child's illness. We began with Ernestine. She came home sick from school a little before noon on December 4th. She said she had fallen off the monkey bars at recess, and she had a pain in her left lower back. Mrs. Huckley said she felt hot to the touch. A few days went by, and Ernestine continued to complain of pain and just not feeling right. On December 8th, Mrs. Huckleby took her to a neighborhood doctor. It was he who found that she had a temperature of 104, but he found nothing else of any significance. He prescribed aspirin and rest in bed. There was still no improvement, and on December 11th Mrs. Huckleby took her back to the doctor. It was a different doctor this time — the first doctor was off that day — and he did find something. He noticed that Ernestine wasn't walking right — that she was staggering — and he arranged to have her admitted to Providence Memorial the next day for observation. I got the details later from the doctor. Ernestine's walk and the history of her fall had frightened him a little. It raised the possibility in his mind of a subdural hematoma. A subdural hematoma is a gathering of blood between certain membranes that cover the brain. It is usually caused by a blow or a fall, and it can be extremely dangerous. I saw his point. It was a perfectly reasonable suspicion. But, of course, he was mistaken. It wasn't that. The hospital made the various tests, and ruled it out.

"Mrs. Huckleby told me that the hospital sent Ernestine home for Christmas. She was discharged on December 19th. She got steadily worse during her stay at home, and she was readmitted on December 27th. It was a pretty dreary Christmas for the Hucklebys. Amos Charles took sick while Ernestine was home — on Christmas Eve. He went to bed with an earache, and when he woke up on Christmas morning, he said he couldn't see very well. The next day, Dorothy took sick. It began as a generalized malaise. Then she began to feel 'woobly.' Then she couldn't walk at all, and her speech began to slur. Meanwhile, much the same thing was happening to Amos Charles — trouble walking, trouble talking, trouble seeing. Then he went into what Mrs. Huckleby called a 'rage.' It was a good descriptive word. He was wild, uncoördinated, thrashing around on the bed. He and Dorothy both got steadily worse. They sank into coma. And, finally, on Sunday, they had to go into the hospital. I spent the rest of Monday talking to the Alamogordo doctors, and then to Huckleby. He wasn't easy to talk to. He was shy, and he didn't say much. He raised his hogs in a couple of pens he rented at a hog farm on the outskirts of town. He collected garbage from his neighbors, and he fed his hogs a mixture of that and grain and water. He cooked it because the law required that garbage be treated that way for feed. He stored his grain in a shed at home, and he kept the shed locked. I saw the grain — what was left of it. It was a mixture of grain and chaff. Anyone would have wondered about it. Most of the grain was coated with a pink warning dye. Huckleby said he had stopped feeding the grain as soon as he heard it was dangerous. I said I certainly hoped so. I questioned him particularly about the sickness that had afflicted his hogs in October. He told me this. When he saw his hogs one morning, they were well. When he saw them next, around four o'clock that afternoon, they were blind and staggering, sick and dying. That was strange. I hadn't ruled out encephalitis in the children, but this was different. There almost had to be a connection between the sick hogs and that chemically treated grain. And I couldn't connect a sudden illness and sudden death with any chronic poisoning.

"Everybody was still thinking in terms of encephalitis. That was the admitting diagnosis on Amos Charles and Dorothy at Providence Memorial Hospital. I spent Tuesday and Wednesday in El Paso. I read the records and I talked to the doctors involved. The relevant test results were either normal or not very helpful. The children's kind of blindness was identified as tunnel, or gunbarrel, vision — a constriction of the visual fields. Urinalysis was positive for protein in all three patients, and the presence of protein in the urine always indicates some impairment of function, which is unusual in most encephalitides. And I saw the patients. It was terrible. I'll never forget them. It was shattering. Amos Charles was a big, husky, good-looking boy, and he lay there just a vegetable. His brain was gone. Ernestine was much the same. Dorothy was a little more alive. Her arms kept waving back and forth. Pendular ataxia, it's called. The charts on the children spelled everything out.

"I talked to Ed on Tuesday afternoon, and he drove down to El Paso that night. He had his rubella campaign well started, and he was eager to get back into the Huckleby investigation. He brought some confusing news along. One of Jon Thompson's people had run down the source of Huckleby's grain and identified at least one formulation of the material it was treated with. It was a fungicide called Panogen. Panogen is cyano methyl mercury guanidine. And mercury is a classic poison. It's one of the most dangerous of the heavy metals. Well, that should have clarified things a bit, but it didn't. It only added to the confusion. Because the clinical picture the Huckleby children presented looked nothing like classic mercury poisoning. The textbook symptoms of acute mercury poisoning are essentially gastrointestinal — nausea, vomiting, abdominal pain, bloody stools. That and severe kidney damage. Chronic mercury poisoning is entirely different. The kidneys are not seriously involved. Apparently, they can safely handle small amounts of mercury. The features in chronic mercurialism are an inflammation of the mouth, muscular tremors — the famous hatter's shakes — and a characteristic personality change. Shyness, embarrassment, irritability. Like the Mad Hatter in 'Alice in Wonderland.' We didn't know what to think.

"We couldn't dismiss the possibility of mercury. But we couldn't quite accept it, either. The only thing we were finally certain about was that we weren't up against an acute viral encephalitis. The clinical picture — particularly the gradual development of symptoms — and the epidemiology made it quite unlikely. It made it incredible. We decided that we were left with two general possibilities. One was a more insidious kind of encephalitis — a slow-moving viral infection of the brain. The other was an encephalopathy. Encephalitis is a disease of the gray matter — or gray nervous tissue — of the brain. Encephalopathy involves the white matter — the conducting nerve fibres. A toxic encephalopathy was the kind we chiefly had in mind. The cause could be one of a variety of substances. The heavy metals, of course. Arsenic. Or numerous drugs on the order of sedatives and tranquilizers. The slow-moving-viral possibilities were more exotic. Rabies is in that class. And kuru, a fatal neurological infection in New Guinea that is perpetuated by cannibalism. And scrapie, a disease of sheep, but a human possibility. And others. The trouble was that Ed and I weren't neurologists. But I had a friend who was — Dr. James Schwartz, at Emory University, in Atlanta. So, just on a chance, I called him up and gave him the clinical picture and asked him what *he* thought it sounded like. He gave us quite a shock. He said it sounded a lot like one of the multiple scleroses — a rapidly progressive demyelinating process called Schilder's disease. Except, he said, three cases would constitute an epidemic, and an epidemic of Schilder's disease had never been reported before. He was inclined to doubt that one ever would be. Another, and more reasonable, possibility, he said, was heavy-metal poisoning. Except that our picture wasn't quite right for lead. Or mercury. Or anything else that readily came to mind. I thanked him just the same. Ed and I decided we had better go back to Alamogordo.

"We went back on Thursday. Jon Thompson joined us there, and we spent most of the day at the Huckleby house, taking it apart. It would have been very exciting to turn up the first epidemic of Schilder's disease in history, but we decided that my talk with Dr. Schwartz had just about narrowed the possibilities down to a toxic encephalopathy, and we were looking for a possible source of poisoning. Ed and Jon had already searched the house, of course, but this time we really left no stone unturned. We went through every room and everything in every room. We went through the medicine cabinet. We checked the cooking utensils. Some pottery clay, for example, is mixed with lead, and there is sometimes lead in old pots and pans. We looked for spoiled food. We examined everything in the family freezer, including what

was left of the hog they slaughtered back in September. We didn't find anything new or suspicious, though. We had another useless talk with Huckleby,
and ate dinner and went back to the motel, and we were sitting there around
eleven o'clock trying to think of what to do next — when the telephone rang.
It was a call for me from Dr. Alan Hinman, in Atlanta. Alan was one of my
bosses. He's the assistant chief to Mike Gregg in the Viral Diseases Branch at
C.D.C., and he was calling from his office — at one o'clock in the morning!
It was fantastic. And then it got more fantastic.

"Here's what Alan had to tell me. That afternoon, he said, just before
quitting time, Mike Gregg had gone in to see Alexander Langmuir — Dr. Langmuir was then director of the Epidemiology Program at C.D.C. — about something, and as he was leaving, he mentioned the Huckleby outbreak. Mike said
there was this damn disease out in New Mexico with gun-barrel vision and
ataxia and coma, and we didn't know what to make of it. Dr. Langmuir said
oh? Then he stopped and blinked, and said it sounded to him as if it might
be Minamata disease. Mike looked blank. Dr. Langmuir laughed, and picked
up a reprint on his desk. He said his secretary had dumped a pile of accumulated reprints on his desk to either discard or keep on file, and this was one
he had just finished looking at. It was a paper from *World Neurology* for
November, 1960, and it was entitled 'Minamata Disease: The Outbreak of a
Neurologic Disorder in Minamata, Japan, and Its Relationship to the Ingestion
of Seafood Contaminated by Mercuric Compounds.' Well, Mike took it home
and read it, and it struck him just as hard. So he called up Alan, and Alan came
over and got the reprint and read it, and he reacted in the same way, only
more so. He drove down to the office and got into the library and checked
the references, and there wasn't any question in his mind. Our problem was
Minamata disease. He read me the original paper. It began like this: 'In 1958,
a severe neurologic disorder was first recognized among persons living in the
vicinity of Minamata Bay, Japan. Now 83 cases have been recorded, most end-
ing fatally or with permanent severe disability. Epidemiologic investigations
. . . helped to establish the relationship of this illness to the consumption of
seafood from Minamata Bay. The effluent from a large chemical-manufacturing
plant which emptied into the bay had been suspected as the source of a toxic
material contaminating fish and shellfish. Subsequent work has provided evidence that the responsible toxin is associated with the discharge of organic-
mercury-containing effluent from the chemical factory.' The clinical features
had a familiar sound. Ataxic gait. Clumsiness of the hands. Dysarthria, or
slurred speech. Dysphagia, or difficulty in swallowing. Constriction of the
visual fields. Deafness. Spasticity. Agitation. Stupor and coma. And this: 'Intellectual impairment occurs in severely affected patients; children seem
particularly liable to serious residual defects.' And, finally, there was this:
'When the first cases were recognized, Japanese B encephalitis was considered
as a diagnostic possibility; however, evidence against encephalitis (aside from
the cardinal clinical features) includes the following: the onset of symptoms
was usually subacute and not accompanied by fever, cases were limited geographically, and they occurred throughout the year.' The Minamata paper
would have been enough for me, but Alan had found another that was even
more convincing. It had the title 'Epidemiological Study of an Illness in the

Guatemala Highlands Believed to Be Encephalitis,' and it had been published in the *Boletín de la Oficina Sanitaria Panamericana* in 1966. The passage that really clinched it was this: 'Possible toxic elements in food, such as edible mushrooms, were investigated. In the course of this investigation it was noted that during the period of the year in which the illness occurred, many families, and especially the poorest, ate part of the wheat given them for seed, which had been treated with a fungicide known commercially as Panogen — an organic-mercury compound.'

"That was the key — that word 'organic.' It instantly clarified everything. Panogen is cyano methyl mercury guanidine, and cyano methyl mercury guanidine is an *organic* mercury compound. Ed and I were perfectly well aware of that, but the significance just hadn't penetrated. When we thought of mercury, we naturally thought of *inorganic* mercury. That's the usual source of mercurialism. But the pathology of the two afflictions is very different. *Organic*-mercury poisoning has always been something of a rarity. Until recently, anyway. At the time of the Minamata report, the total number of cases of organic mercurialism on record was only thirty-nine. And only five of them were American. Well, I finally finished talking to Alan and gave the news to Ed and Jon, and we all immediately agreed. It was a fantastic kind of coincidence — Dr. Langmuir, Minamata, Guatemala. But it fitted to the letter. Or practically. Talking it over, we did see one objection. The behavior of the Huckleby hogs. Chronic poisoning doesn't produce a sudden, fatal illness. It doesn't, and — the way it turned out — it didn't. On Monday, January 19th, I went out and had another talk with Huckleby, and I don't know why, but this time we got along much better than we had before, and he finally said that he could have been mistaken — that it probably wasn't all that sudden, that his hogs probably did get sicker and sicker over a period of several weeks.

"The only thing we needed now was proof. It arrived that night — Monday night — in another call from Alan. He had had a call from Mr. Barthel at the Toxicology Laboratory. Mr. Barthel had analyzed Ed's samples of grain and pork and urine, and he had found mercury in everything but two of the urine samples. The two negative samples were those of the two youngest Huckleby children. One of them was two years old and the other was just ten months, and neither of them had eaten any of the pork. The highest mercury levels were found in the patients' urine. That, of course, was as expected. One of the lowest was Mrs. Huckleby's. Which was fortunate. After all, she was pregnant. But the fact that she and the other asymptomatic members of the family showed any mercury at all was unexpected. It raised a question, and it was a question that would have bothered us if we hadn't been doing a little reading in the literature on our own. The question was: Why didn't *all* the pork-eating Hucklebys get sick? They all consumed about the same amount of meat. We found an acceptable answer in a 1940 paper in the British *Quarterly Journal of Medicine*. The paper was entitled 'Poisoning by Methyl Mercury Compounds,' and the relevant passage read, 'The fact that eight men, exposed in a similar way to the four patients, excreted mercury in the urine, yet showed no symptoms or signs of disease, suggests that most of the workers absorbed mercury compounds, but that only four . . . were susceptible to them.' That was the best explanation — Ernestine and Amos Charles and Dorothy were simply more susceptible to mercury than the others. It satisfied me, anyway. And the next day I flew home to Atlanta."

The chain of laboratory evidence that linked the Huckleby children's affliction to the diet of the Huckleby hogs brought the epidemiological investigation of the outbreak to an end. As it happened, however, that was not the end of the case. On Monday, January 19th — the day on which Dr. Likosky and Dr. Pierce and Mr. Thompson wound up their joint investigation — the case took a new and ominous turn.

The turn occurred in Clovis, New Mexico, a livestock center some two hundred miles northeast of Alamogordo, and it was set in motion by a state sanitarian on duty there named Cade Lancaster. Mr. Lancaster was the investigator who had identified Panogen as a chemical contaminant in the Huckleby grain. His second contribution to the case stemmed from a monitoring impulse that prompted him to leaf through the recent records of a Clovis hog broker. He didn't have far to look — only back to Friday, January 16th. On that day, he was interested to read, the broker had bought a consignment of twenty-four hogs from a grower in Alamogordo. What particularly interested Mr. Lancaster was the grower's name. He knew it: the man was one of the Huckleby group who had included treated grain in their hog feed. He also knew that all the growers in that group had been instructed to withhold their hogs from market until otherwise notified. The feeding of treated grain had been stopped by horrified common consent at the very start of the investigation, but that was not enough to render the hogs safe for immediate use. Organic mercury is eliminated slowly from living tissue. It has a half-life there of two or three months. Mr. Lancaster sought out the broker. The broker stood appalled. He hadn't known. He had no way of knowing. What was worse, he added, he had already disposed of the hogs. They were part of a shipment of two hundred and forty-eight hogs that had gone out on Friday afternoon to a packing plant in Roswell. Mr. Lancaster turned to the telephone.

The recipient of Mr. Lancaster's call was Carl Henderson, chief of the Consumer Protection Section of the New Mexico Health and Social Services Department, and he received it in his office at Santa Fe. He thanked Mr. Lancaster for his enterprise, and sat in thought for a moment. Then he himself put in a call — to the packing plant in Roswell. The manager there heard the news with a groan. Yes, he said, he had the Alamogordo hogs, but that was the most he could say. He didn't know which they were. They were no longer hogs. The big Clovis shipment had been slaughtered on Saturday, and it was simply so many carcasses now. In that case, Mr. Henderson said, he had no choice but to immobilize the lot. The plant was therewith informed that all those two hundred and forty-eight carcasses were under state embargo. Mr. Henderson hung up and moved to reinforce his pronouncement. His move was at once effective. The following day, January 20th, the United States Department of Agriculture, through the Slaughter Inspection Division of its Consumer and Marketing Service, placed the state-embargoed carcasses under the further and stronger restraint of a federal embargo, and arranged for a sample of each carcass to be tested for mercury at the Agricultural Research Center, in Beltsville, Maryland. That same day, the state extended its embargo to the grain-fed hogs still in the possession of Huckleby and his five companion growers in Alamogordo. The next day, the hogs were tallied and found to total two hundred and fifteen head. One hog was selected from each grower's herd and killed and autopsied, and specimens were sent to the Toxicology Laboratory of the Food and Drug Administration, in Atlanta, for definitive examination.

Two days later, still shaken by Mr. Lancaster's discovery, the New Mexico Health and Social Services Department took another protective step. A cautionary letter, signed by Dr. Bruce D. Storrs, director of the Medical Services Division, was distributed to every physician and veterinarian in the state. The letter read:

A recent outbreak of central-nervous-system disease among three children of an Alamogordo family has been traced to the ingestion of pork contaminated with a methyl-mercury compound. The animal involved had been fed over a period of several weeks with grain treated with this material. At the time it was butchered, the hog appeared to be in good health, and visual inspection of the carcass during processing failed to reveal any significant abnormalities. Laboratory analysis of the meat eaten by the family, however, revealed a high concentration of methyl mercury.

The grain had been obtained by the children's father, free of charge, in the form of castoff "sweepings" from a seed company located in eastern New Mexico. This was mixed with garbage and fed to the hogs despite the knowledge that it had been treated with the fungicide. Several weeks after slaughter of the boar, 14 of the family's remaining 17 hogs became ill with symptoms of blindness and staggering gait. Over a three-week period, 12 died and the remaining two were permanently blind.

Because of the potential danger to humans of ingesting meat contaminated with methyl mercury (all three children are comatose and in critical condition), as well as the likelihood that the practice of feeding treated grain may be widespread among indigents raising livestock in the state, this matter is being brought to your attention. The possibility of methyl-mercury poisoning should be considered in any outbreak of . . . unusual central-nervous-system illness. Please notify the Preventive Medicine Section (Phone 505-827-2475) of any such occurrence, and we in turn will be happy to provide technical advice and assistance.

The letters were mailed out on Thursday, January 22nd. The Preventive Medicine Section spent Friday and the week-end waiting for the ring of the telephone and the urgent voice of a doctor. But nothing happened. Nothing happened the following week. February loomed, and began. Still nothing. The Preventive Medicine Section sat back and relaxed. They let themselves assume — correctly, as it turned out — that the outbreak was confined to the Huckleby family.

Nevertheless — as it also turned out — the danger of an epidemic had been real. Early in February, the results of the hog examinations were announced. The first report was on the embargoed packing-plant carcasses. It seemed to justify Mr. Lancaster's investigatory zeal, but its meaning was otherwise not entirely clear. Of the two hundred and forty-eight carcasses examined by the Department of Agriculture, one — just one — was found to contain a high concentration of mercury. The others, curiously, were uncontaminated. The contaminated carcass was ordered destroyed, and the others were released to the market. The Toxicology Laboratory's report on the hogs taken from the Alamogordo pens was very different. Six hogs were examined, and

all six were found to be dangerously contaminated with mercury. The unequivocal finding condemned the remaining hogs in the pens, and the state issued
an order for their destruction.

Dr. Likosky returned to Atlanta with the Huckleby outbreak still very
much on his mind. What particularly disturbed him was its implications. This
led him back to the library, and he undertook a comprehensive exploration
of the literature on organic mercury compounds and organic mercurialism. It
was not a reassuring experience. Mercury fungicides, he learned, were developed in Germany around 1914 and came into almost universal use shortly
after the First World War. He learned that the Minamata episode was not the
only outbreak of organic-mercury poisoning caused by contaminated fish. It
was merely the first. In 1965, despite the morbid Minamata example, a similar
outbreak occurred on the Japanese island of Honshu. A total of a hundred
and twenty people were stricken there, and five of them died. He learned
that the Guatemalan episode was not the only instance on record of poisoning
caused by eating treated grain. A similar outbreak occurred in Iraq in 1961,
and another in Pakistan in 1963. A total of almost five hundred people were
struck down in the three outbreaks, and the mortality rate was high. He
learned that the Huckleby hogs were not the first American hogs to be stricken
with chronic mercury poisoning. They were merely the first involved in human
mercurialism. He learned that Sweden had, on February 1, 1966, revoked the
license for the use of certain highly toxic mercury compounds (including
methyl mercury) in agriculture. He learned that the 1969 pheasant-hunting
season in the Canadian province of Alberta had been cancelled after a survey
of the pheasant population showed an average mercury level of one part per
million — a hazardous concentration. And, closer to home, he learned that a
similar survey in Montana that same year revealed a level of mercury contamination that prompted the State Game Commission to advise hunters against
eating the birds they shot. In both instances, the pheasants had been exposed
in the field to treated seed.

Dr. Likosky arose from his reading with a sense of apprehension. He
sought out two of his colleagues, Dr. Hinman and Mr. Barthel, chief of the
Toxicology Branch, and found that they shared his concern about the proliferating casual use of a substance as toxic as methyl mercury. They also felt
that a broader discussion of the matter was desirable, and Mr. Barthel arranged
for a meeting in Washington with interested representatives of the Department of Agriculture and of the Food and Drug Administration. At the meeting,
which was held on February 12th, Dr. Likosky, Dr. Hinman, and Mr. Barthel
reviewed the Huckleby case and its varied antecedents, and suggested that
they constituted a looming public-health problem. Their arguments were well
received, and on February 19th the Department of Agriculture issued a statement on the subject. It read:

The U. S. Department of Agriculture has notified pesticide manufacturers that Federal registrations are suspended for products containing cyano methyl mercury guanidine that are labeled for use as seed treatments.
U.S.D.A.'s Agricultural Research Service suspended cyano methyl mercury guanidine
fungicide because its continued use on seeds would constitute an imminent hazard to
the public health. Directions for proper use and caution statements on labels of the

product have failed to prevent its misuse as a livestock feed. The U.S.D.A.-registered label specifically warns against use of mercury-treated seed for food or feed purposes. The pesticide may cause irreversible damage to both animals and man.

The action was taken following the hospitalization of three New Mexico children after they ate meat from a hog which had been fed seed grain treated with the now-suspended mercury compound. Subsequently, 12 of the remaining 14 hogs also fed the seed died.

"Other movements of this treated seed that found its way into livestock feed posed a potential for similar incidents," Dr. Harry W. Hays, director of the Pesticides Regulation Division, U.S.D.A.-A.R.S., said in announcing the suspension action. "In each case, U.S.D.A. and state public-health officials have taken prompt action to protect the public health." Dr. Hays also announced that the A.R.S. had asked the Advisory Center on Toxicology of the National Research Council to review the uses of other organic-mercury compounds to determine whether similar hazards to human health existed in connection with the use of these compounds.

March came on. Ernestine and Amos Charles Huckleby were discharged from Providence Memorial Hospital, in El Paso, and transferred to the chronic-care facility of a hospital in Alamogordo. They were still comatose. (Ernestine will probably be permanently comatose. She is almost certainly blind. Amos can communicate on a primitive level. He, too, is blind.) At the same time, Dorothy Huckleby was removed to a rehabilitation hospital in Roswell. (It is expected that she may in time recover enough to care for herself under general supervision.) Meanwhile, Mrs. Huckleby's term approached. Because of the delicate nature of her pregnancy, state health officials had recommended that her confinement take place in the scientifically sophisticated environment of the University of New Mexico Medical Center, in Albuquerque, and she was admitted to a maternity ward there. Her condition was satisfactory and her course was uneventful. On Monday, March 9th, she was delivered of a seven-pound boy. At birth, the baby appeared to be physically normal, but a few hours later he experienced a violent convulsion. He survived the seizure, and recovered. The prognosis, however, was uncertain. It is very possible, in view of his long fetal exposure to mercury, that some physical or mental abnormalities will eventually manifest themselves.

April arrived. Manufacturers affected by the federal suspension order on seed dressings containing cyano methyl mercury guanidine stirred, and suddenly struck. On April 10th, Morton International, Inc., and its subsidiary Nor-Am Agricultural Products, Inc., the makers of Panogen, applied in United States District Court in Chicago for an injunction relieving the company of compliance with the suspension order, and the application was granted by Judge Alexander J. Napoli. The grounds for granting the injunction were that the Department of Agriculture had acted without holding a hearing to establish the hazardous nature of the fungicide.

The government appealed, and on July 15th a three-judge panel of the Court of Appeals turned the government down, again citing insufficient evidence. The government has petitioned for a review by all six judges of the Court of Appeals, but the Court has not acted on the request. There the case rests.

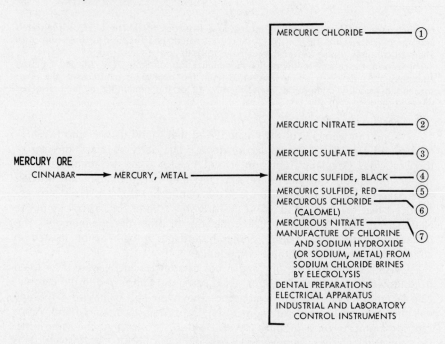

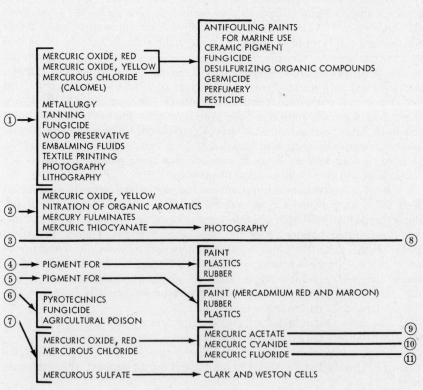

MORTON & MARSHA GORDEN
Tracking Mercury

Mercury is a silvery-white metal generally found as the ore cinnebar, as the chart shows. Its best known use, since it freezes at a low temperature and expands uniformly with temperature rise, is as an indicator for thermometers. But this is actually only the beginning. As a metal, it is also used in electrical and other control devices, most importantly as the cathode in the electrolytic production of chlorine and caustic soda.

In compounds, it takes two forms: *mercuric,* as in mercuric chloride ($HgCl_2$ or corrosive sublimate — a violent poison), and *Mercurous,* as in mercurous chloride (Hg_2Cl_2 or calomel — a common fungicide). The most common compounds are the chlorides and the oxides, but there are many others. Mercury is also able to bond with nitrogen and carbon; thus it forms organic compounds such as ethyl mercuric chloride, commonly known as Ceresan, used as a fungicide for treating seeds and as an antimildew agent for paint.

The flow chart, which shows the most important uses of mercury, also explains why it is so often difficult to identify the source of mercury in a stream or lake where there is no obvious industrial use. Is it the paint on a sailboat, the fungicide used on a neighboring golf course, or is it some discarded electrical device?

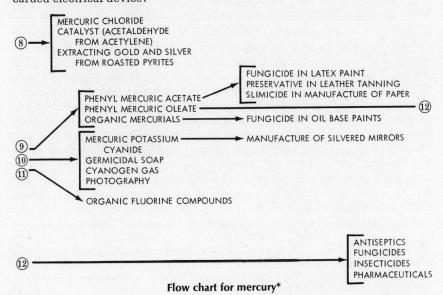

Flow chart for mercury*

* "Flow Chart for Mercury Ore," *Chemical Origins and Markets,* 4th ed. (Menlo Park, California: Stanford Research Institute, 1967), pp. 46–47. Reprinted by permission.

JOEL BITMAN, HELENE C. CECIL & GEORGE F. FRIES

DDT-Induced Inhibition of Avian Shell Gland Carbonic Anhydrase: A Mechanism for Thin Eggshells

The following research program was designed to study the mechanism that produces thin eggshells in the Japanese quail and the part that DDT or one of its products might play in this mechanism. It shows the effect of these pesticides on the eggshell-forming glands in these birds and suggests one mechanism for this reaction.

The pesticide DDT (1) produces a decrease in eggshell thickness in Japanese quail (2), sparrow hawks (3), and mallards (4). The content of calcium in the eggshell declined (2) and reproduction was impaired (3, 4) by the direct addition of DDT or DDE (1) to the diet, thus confirming correlative evidence (5, 6) that DDT and related organochlorine compounds decrease eggshell thickness. We investigated carbonic anhydrase (CA) (E.C.-4.2.1.1) in the shell-forming gland of Japanese quail fed DDT or DDE to determine whether decreased activity could account for the defect in eggshell formation.

The Japanese quail were housed in individual cages on a schedule of 14 hours of light and 10 hours of dark. They were fed diets containing 100 ppm of p,p'-DDT or 100 ppm of p,p'-DDE for 3 months. Diets of both adequate (2.5 percent) and low (0.6 percent) calcium content were used. Activity of CA was assayed electrometrically by the Wilbur and Anderson procedure (7) as modified by Woodford et al. (8), in which substrate is supplied in the form of gaseous carbon dioxide. The saturated KCl solution of the combination electrode of the Corning model 12 pH meter was replaced with $4M$ KCl to prevent freezing out of KCl in the asbestos fiber salt bridge and in the body of the electrode. All pH standardizations and reactions were conducted at 0°C. The CA standard was a purified preparation from beef blood (Worthington Biochemical Corp.).

Birds were killed by decapitation 6 to 8 hours before estimated oviposition, at which time a calcifying egg was present in the shell gland. Whole blood was collected in oxalated tubes. The samples of blood (0.5 to 1.0 ml) and weighed samples of whole shell gland (300 to 400 mg) were homogenized

Joel Bitman, Helene C. Cecil, and George F. Fries, "DDT-Induced Inhibition of Avian Shell Gland Carbonic Anhydrase: A Mechanism for Thin Eggshells," *Science,* vol. 168 (May 1970), pp. 594–596. Copyright 1970 by the American Association for the Advancement of Science. Reprinted by permission.
The authors are with the Animal Husbandry Research Division, U. S. Department of Agriculture, Beltsville, Maryland.

in ice-cold water for 3 minutes. The homogenates were centrifuged at 2500g for 15 minutes at 0°C. The supernatant solutions were then centrifuged again at 9500g for 20 minutes at 0°C. The opalescent supernatants (or a dilution) were then assayed immediately for CA activity. Calcium was determined by atomic absorption spectrophotometric analysis of solutions obtained by wet-ashing eggshell in concentrated HCl. Pesticide residues were determined in body fat and eggs by gas-liquid chromatography with an electron capture detector (9).

Carbonic anhydrase activity was lower in both the shell gland and blood of the treated Japanese quail (Table 1). Decreases of 16 to 19 percent occurred

Table 1. Carbonic anhydrase activity in the shell gland and blood of control quail and quail treated with DDT or DDE. Results are expressed as the number ± standard error.

Group	N	Shell gland weight (g)	Shell gland Unit/g	Shell gland Total units	Blood (unit/ml)
Control	20	1.59 ± .09	186 ± 7	298 ± 22	1184 ± 96
p,p'-DDT	18	1.54 ± .08	156 ± 12*	242 ± 18†	924 ± 82†
p,p'-DDE	11	1.57 ± .07	150 ± 10*	235 ± 18†	663 ± 56‡

*$P < .01$.   †$P < .05$.   ‡$P < .001$.

in CA from the shell gland of Japanese quail fed p,p'-DDT or p,p'-DDE. There were no differences in the weights of the shell glands among the groups. It was not possible to determine whether DDT and DDE caused a decrease in the total amount of enzyme or whether they partially inhibited the enzymatic activity in these extracts. The activity of CA in the blood of the quail treated with DDT or DDE exhibited larger declines — 22 and 44 percent, respectively (Table 1).

The concentrations of pesticides in the lipid and eggs and the percent of calcium in the eggshells were determined (Table 2). Pesticide concentration in the eggs was approximately one-eighth of the body lipid concentration. Eggshell calcium was significantly lower in eggs from the quail treated with DDT or DDE.

Table 2. Eggshell calcium and pesticide concentration in lipid and eggs of quail treated with DDE or DDT. Eggshell calcium is expressed as a percentage of egg weight.

Group	Eggshell calcium (%)	Eggs DDE (µg/g)	Eggs DDT (µg/g)	Lipid DDE (µg/g)	Lipid DDT (µg/g)
Control	2.58 ± .06	0.20	0.40	1.47	3.70
p,p'-DDT	2.37 ± .03*	48	196	483	1373
p,p'-DDE	2.38 ± .07†	196		1610	

*$P < .005$.   †$P < .05$.

Carbonic anhydrase is inhibited by DDT in human blood (*10*) and a sensitive method for DDT detection has been based on inhibition of bovine erythrocyte CA by DDT (*11*). In contrast, Anderson and March (*12*) were unable to demonstrate an effect of DDT on insect CA either in vivo or in vitro.

In the formation of the avian eggshell, CA is believed to be necessary to supply the carbonate ions required for calcium carbonate deposition. Several investigations have supported an active role for CA in eggshell formation (*13*), showing that CA was lower in shell glands producing soft-shelled eggs or no eggs than in glands producing normal eggs. Bernstein *et al.* (*14*) have provided additional evidence for an obligatory role for CA in eggshell formation.

Mueller (*15*) has questioned this role for CA because he did not find significant differences in CA activity in the shell gland at different stages of egg formation, suggesting that active shell formation was not accompanied by increased CA activity. Heald *et al.* (*16*) also did not find a significant correlation between CA activity and shell strength.

Treatment with DDT results in decreased CA activity in the avian shell gland. This demonstration in vitro does not preclude normal functioning of the CA enzymatic machinery in the intact tissue in vivo. Under the conditions of our experiments, however, the percentage declines in shell gland CA activity were 16 to 19 percent, amounts which could account for observed decreases in eggshell thickness of 10 to 15 percent in birds treated with DDT or DDE (*2–4*). The limitation by carbonic anhydrase of carbonate ions needed for the deposition of the calcium carbonate of the shell could provide the mechanism by which chlorinated hydrocarbons affect eggshell thickness.

References and notes

1. Abbreviations: *p,p'*-DDT, 1,1,1-trichloro-2,2-bis(*p*-chlorophenyl)ethane; *p,p'*-DDE, 1,1-dichloro-2,2-bis(*p*-chlorophenyl)ethylene.
2. J. Bitman, H. C. Cecil, S. J. Harris, G. F. Fries, *Nature* 224, 44 (1969).
3. R. D. Porter and S. N. Wiemeyer, *Science* 165, 199 (1969).
4. R. G. Heath, J. W. Spann, J. F. Kreitzer, *Nature* 224, 47 (1969).
5. D. A. Ratcliffe, *ibid.* 215, 208 (1967).
6. J. J. Hickey and D. W. Anderson, *Science* 162, 271 (1968).
7. K. M. Wilbur and N. G. Anderson, *J. Biol. Chem.* 176, 147 (1948).
8. V. R. Woodford, N. Leegwater, S. M. Drance, *Can. J. Biochem. Physiol.* 39, 287 (1961).
9. H. C. Barry, J. G. Hundley, L. Y. Johnson, Eds., *Pesticide Analytical Manual* (U.S. Dept. of Health, Education and Welfare, Food and Drug Administration, 1963; revised 1964 and 1965), vol. 1.
10. C. Torda and H. Wolff, *J. Pharmacol. Exp. Ther.* 95, 444 (1949).
11. H. Keller, *Naturwissenschaften* 39, 109 (1952).
12. A. D. Anderson and R. March, *Can. J. Zool.* 34, 68 (1956).
13. R. H. Common, *J. Agr. Sci.* 31, 412 (1941); M. S. Gutowska and C. A. Mitchell, *Poultry Sci.* 6, 196 (1945).
14. R. S. Bernstein, T. Nevalainen, R. Schraer, H. Schraer, *Biochim. Biophys. Acta* 159, 367 (1968).
15. W. J. Mueller, *Poultry Sci.* 41, 1792 (1962).
16. P. J. Heald, D. Pohlman, E. G. Martin, *ibid.* 47, 858 (1968).

G. M. WOODWELL

Effects of Pollution on the Structure and Physiology of Ecosystems

The accumulation of various toxic substances in the biosphere is leading to complex changes in the structure and function of natural ecosystems. Although the changes are complex, they follow in aggregate patterns that are similar in many different ecosystems and are therefore broadly predictable. The patterns involve many changes but include especially simplification of the structure of both plant and animal communities, shifts in the ratio of gross production to total respiration, and loss of part or all of the inventory of nutrients. Despite the frequency with which various pollutants are causing such changes and the significance of the changes for all living systems (1), only a few studies show details of the pattern of change clearly. These are studies of the effects of ionizing radiation, of persistent pesticides, and of eutrophication. The effects of radiation will be used here to show the pattern of changes in terrestrial plant communities and to show similarities with the effects of fire, oxides of sulfur, and herbicides. Effects of such pollutants as pesticides on the animal community are less conspicuous but quite parallel, which shows that the ecological effects of pollution correspond very closely to the general "strategy of ecosystem development" outlined by Odum (1) and that they can be anticipated in considerable detail.

The problems caused by pollution are of interest from two viewpoints. Practical people — toxicologists, engineers, health physicists, public health officials, intensive users of the environment — consider pollution primarily as a direct hazard to man. Others, no less concerned for human welfare but with less pressing public responsibilities, recognize that toxicity to humans is but one aspect of the pollution problem, the other being a threat to the maintenance of a biosphere suitable for life as we know it. The first viewpoint leads to emphasis on human food chains; the second leads to emphasis on human welfare insofar as it depends on the integrity of the diverse ecosystems of the earth, the living systems that appear to have built and now maintain the biosphere.

The food-chain problem is by far the simpler; it is amenable at least in part to the pragmatic, narrowly compartmentalized solutions that industrialized societies are good at. The best example of the toxicological approach is in control of mutagens, particularly the radionuclides. These present a specific, direct hazard to man. They are much more important to man than to other

G. M. Woodwell, "Effects of Pollution on the Structure and Physiology of Ecosystems," *Science*, vol. 168 (April 24, 1970), pp. 429–433. Copyright 1970 by the American Association for the Advancement of Science. Reprinted by permission.
The author is a member of the Biology Department, Brookhaven National Laboratory, Upton, New York.

organisms. A slightly enhanced rate of mutation is a serious danger to man, who has developed through medical science elaborate ways of preserving a high fraction of the genetic defects in the population; it is trivial to the rest of the biota, in which genetic defects may be eliminated through selection. This is an important fact about pollution hazards — toxic substances that are principally mutagenic are usually of far greater direct hazard to man than to the rest of the earth's biota and must be considered first from the standpoint of their movement to man through food webs or other mechanisms and to a much lesser extent from that of their effects on the ecosystem through which they move. We have erred, as shown below, in assuming that all toxic substances should be treated this way.

Pollutants that affect other components of the earth's biota as well as man present a far greater problem. Their effects are chronic and may be cumulative in contrast to the effects of short-lived disturbances that are repaired by succession. We ask what effects such pollutants have on the structure of natural ecosystems and on biological diversity and what these changes mean to physiology, especially to mineral cycling and the long-term potential for sustaining life.

Although experience with pollution of various types is extensive and growing rapidly, only a limited number of detailed case history studies provide convincing control data that deal with the structure of ecosystems. One of the clearest and most detailed series of experiments in recent years has been focused on the ecological effects of radiation. These studies are especially useful because they allow cause and effect to be related quantitatively at the ecosystem level, which is difficult to do in nature. The question arises, however, whether the results from studies of ionizing radiation, a factor that is not usually considered to have played an important role in recent evolution, have any general application. The answer, somewhat surprisingly to many biologists, seems to be that they do. The ecological effects of radiation follow patterns that are known from other types of disturbances. The studies of radiation, because of their specificity, provide useful clues for examination of effects of other types of pollution for which evidence is much more fragmentary.

The effects of chronic irradiation of a late successional oak-pine forest have been studied at Brookhaven National Laboratory in New York. After 6 months' exposure to chronic irradiation from a ^{137}Cs source, five well-defined zones of modification of vegetation had been established. They have become more pronounced through 7 years of chronic irradiation (Fig. 1). The zones were:

1) A central devastated zone, where exposures were > 200 R/day and no higher plants survived, although certain mosses and lichens survived up to exposures > 1000 R/day.
2) A sedge zone, where *Carex pensylvanica* (2) survived and ultimately formed a continuous cover (> 150 R/day).
3) A shrub zone in which two species of *Vaccinium* and one of *Gaylussacia* survived, with *Quercus ilicifolia* toward the outer limit of the circle where exposures were lowest (> 40 R/day).

Figure 1.   The effects of chronic gamma radiation from a 9500-curie ^{137}Cs source on a Long Island oak-pine forest nearly 8 years after start of chronic irradiation. The pattern of change in the structure of the forest is similar to that observed along many other gradients, including gradients of moisture availability and of exposure to wind, salt spray, and pollutants such as sulfur dioxide. The five zones are explained in the text. The few successional species that have invaded the zones closest to the source appear most conspicuously as a ring at the inner edge of zone 2. These are species character-istic of distributed areas such as the fire weed, Erechtites hieracifolia, and the sweet fern, Comptonia peregrina, among several others. [The successional changes over 7 years are shown by comparison with a similar photograph that appeared as a cover of Science (16)].

4) An oak zone, the pine having been eliminated (> 16 R/day).

5) Oak-pine forest, where exposures were < 2 R/day, and there was no ob-vious change in the number of species, although small changes in rates of growth were measurable at exposures as low as 1 R/day.

The effect was a systematic dissection of the forest, strata being removed layer by layer. Trees were eliminated at low exposures, then the taller shrubs (*Gaylussacia baccata*), then the lower shrubs (*Vaccinium* species), then the herbs, and finally the lichens and mosses. Within these groups it was evident that under irradiation an upright form of growth was a disadvantage. The trees did vary — the pines (*Pinus rigida*) for instance were far more sensitive than the oaks without having a conspicuous tendency toward more upright growth, but all the trees were substantially more sensitive than the shrubs (3). Within the shrub zone, tall forms were more sensitive; even with the lichen popula-tions, foliose and fruticose lichens proved more sensitive than crustose lichens (4).

The changes caused by chronic irradiation of herb communities in old fields show the same pattern — upright species are at a disadvantage. In one old field at Brookhaven, the frequency of low-growing plants increased along the gradient of increasing radiation intensity to 100 percent at > 1000 R/day (5). Comparison of the sensitivity of the herb field with that of the forest, by whatever criterion, clearly shows the field to be more resistant than the forest. The exposure reducing diversity to 50 percent in the first year was ~ 1000 R/day for the field and 160 R/day for the forest, a greater than fivefold difference in sensitivity (3).

The changes in these ecosystems under chronic irradiation are best summarized as changes in structure, although diversity, primary production, total respiration, and nutrient inventory are also involved. The changes are similar to the familiar ones along natural gradients of increasingly severe conditions, such as exposure on mountains, salt spray, and water availability. Along all these gradients the conspicuous change is a reduction of structure from forest toward communities dominated by certain shrubs, then, under more severe conditions, by certain herbs, and finally by low-growing plants, frequently mosses and lichens. Succession, insofar as it has played any role at all in the irradiated ecosystems, has simply reinforced this pattern, adding a very few hardy species and allowing expansion of the populations of more resistant indigenous species. The reasons for radiation's causing this pattern are still not clear (3, 6), but the pattern is a common one, not peculiar to ionizing radiation, despite the novelty of radiation exposures as high as these.

Its commonness is illustrated by the response to fire, one of the oldest and most important disruptions of nature. The oak-pine forests such as those on Long Island have, throughout their extensive range in eastern North America, been subject in recent times to repeated burning. The changes in physiognomy of the vegetation follow the above pattern very closely — the forest is replaced by communities of shrubs, especially bear oak (*Quercus ilicifolia*), *Gaylussacia,* and *Vaccinium* species. This change is equivalent to that caused by chronic exposure to 40 R/day or more. Buell and Cantlon (7), working on similar vegetation in New Jersey, showed that a further increase in the frequency of fires resulted in a differential reduction in taller shrubs first, and a substantial increase in the abundance of *Carex pensylvanica,* the same sedge now dominating the sedge zone of the irradiated forest. The parallel is detailed; radiation and repeated fires both reduce the structure of the forest in similar ways, favoring low-growing hardy species.

The similarity of response appears to extend to other vegetations as well. G. L. Miller, working with F. McCormick at the Savannah River Laboratory, has shown recently that the most radiation-resistant and fire-resistant species of 20-year-old fields are annuals and perennials characteristic of disturbed places (8). An interesting sidelight of his study was the observation that the grass stage of long leaf pine (*Pinus palustris*), long considered a specific adaptation to the fires that maintain the southeastern savannahs, appears more resistant to radiation damage than the mature trees. At a total acute exposure of 2.1 kR (3 R/day), 85 percent of the grass-stage populations survived but only 55 percent of larger trees survived. Seasonal variation in sensitivity to radiation damage has been abundantly demonstrated (9), and it would not be surprising to find that this variation is related to the ecology of the species. Again it appears that the response to radiation is not unique.

The species surviving high radiation-exposure rates in the Brookhaven experiments are the ones commonly found in disturbed places, such as road-sides, gravel banks, and areas with nutrient-deficient or unstable soil. In the forest they include *Comptonia peregrina* (the sweet fern), a decumbent spiny *Rubus,* and the lichens, especially *Cladonia cristatella.* In the old field one of the most conspicuously resistant species was *Digitaria sanguinalis* (crab-grass) among several other weedy species. Clearly these species are generalists in the sense that they survive a wide range of conditions, including exposure to high intensities of ionizing radiation — hardly a common experience in nature but apparently one that elicits a common response.

With this background one might predict that a similar pattern of devastation would result from such pollutants as oxides of sulfur released from smelting. The evidence is fragmentary, but Gorham and Gordon (*10*) found around the smelters in Sudbury, Ontario, a striking reduction in the number of species of higher plants along a gradient of 62 kilometers (39 miles). In different samples the number of species ranged from 19 to 31 at the more distant sites and dropped abruptly at 6.4 kilometers. At 1.6 kilometers, one of two randomly placed plots (20 by 2 meters) included only one species. They classified the damage in five categories, from "Not obvious" through "Moderate" to "Very severe." The tree canopy had been reduced or eliminated within 4.8 to 6.4 kilometers of the smelter, with only occasional sprouts of trees, seedlings, and successional herbs and shrubs remaining; this damage is equivalent to that produced by exposure to 40 R/day. The most resistant trees were, almost predictably to a botanist, red maple (*Acer rubrum*) and red oak (*Quercus rubra*). Other species surviving in the zones of "Severe" and "Very severe" damage included *Sambucus pubens, Polygonum cilinode, Comptonia peregrina,* and *Epilobium angustifolium* (fire weed). The most sensitive plants appeared to be *Pinus strobus* and *Vaccinium myrtilloides.* The pine was reported no closer than 25.6 kilometers (16 miles), where it was chlorotic.

This example confirms the pattern of the change — first a reduction of diversity of the forest by elimination of sensitive species; then elimination of the tree canopy and survival of resistant shrubs and herbs widely recognized as "seral" or successional species or "generalists."

The effects of herbicides, despite their hoped for specificity, fall into the same pattern, and it is no surprise that the extremely diverse forest canopies of Viet Nam when sprayed repeatedly with herbicides are replaced over large areas by dense stands of species of bamboo (*11*).

The mechanisms involved in producing this series of patterns in terrestrial ecosystems are not entirely clear. One mechanism that is almost certainly important is simply the ratio of gross production to respiration in different strata of the community. The size of trees has been shown to approach a limit set by the amount of surface area of stems and branches in proportion to the amount of leaf area (*12*). The apparent reason is that, as a tree expands in size, the fraction of its total surface devoted to bark, which makes a major contribution to the respiration, expands more rapidly than does the photosynthetic area. Any chronic disturbance has a high probability of damaging the capacity for photosynthesis without reducing appreciably the total amount of respiration; therefore, large plants are more vulnerable than species requiring less total respiration. Thus chronic disturbances of widely different types favor plants that are small in stature, and any disturbance that tends to increase the amount of respiration in proportion to photosynthesis will aggravate this shift.

The shift in the structure of terrestrial plant communities toward shrubs, herbs, or mosses and lichens, involves changes in addition to those of structure and diversity. Simplification of the plant community involves also a reduction of the total standing crop of organic matter and a corresponding reduction in the total inventory of nutrient elements held within the system, a change that may have important long-term implications for the potential of the site to support life. The extent of such losses has been demonstrated recently by Bormann and his colleagues in the Hubbard Brook Forest in New Hampshire* (*13*), where all of the trees in a watershed were cut, the cut material was left to decay, and the losses of nutrients were monitored in the runoff. Total nitrogen losses in the first year were equivalent to twice the amount cycled in the system during a normal year. With the rise of nitrate ion in the runoff, concentrations of calcium, magnesium, sodium, and potassium ions rose severalfold, which caused eutrophication and even pollution of the streams fed by this watershed. The soil had little capacity to retain the nutrients that were locked in the biota once the higher plants had been killed. The total losses are not yet known, but early evidence indicates that they will be a high fraction of the nutrient inventory, which will cause a large reduction in the potential of the site for supporting living systems as complex as that destroyed — until nutrients accumulate again. Sources are limited: the principal source is erosion of primary minerals.

When the extent of the loss of nutrients that accompanies a reduction in the structure of a plant community is recognized, it is not surprising to find depauperate vegetation in places subject to chronic disturbances. Extensive sections of central Long Island, for example, support a depauperate oak-pine forest in which the bear oak, *Quercus ilicifolia,* is the principal woody species. The cation content of an extremely dense stand of this common community, which has a biomass equivalent to that of the more diverse late successional forest that was burned much less recently and less intensively, would be about 60 percent that of the richer stand, despite the equivalence of standing crop. This means that the species, especially the bear oak, contain, and presumably require, lower concentrations of cations. This is an especially good example because the bear oak community is a long-lasting one in the fire succession and marks the transition from a high shrub community to forest. It has analogies elsewhere, such as the heath balds of the Great Smoky Mountains and certain bamboo thickets in Southeast Asia.

The potential of a site for supporting life depends heavily on the pool of nutrients available through breakdown of primary minerals and through recycling in the living portion of the ecosystem. Reduction of the structure of the system drains these pools in whole or in part; it puts leaks in the system. Any chronic pollution that affects the structure of ecosystems, especially the plant community, starts leaks and reduces the potential of the site for re-

---

* See chapter 6 of this text for more details of this and other research at Hubbard Brook — Eds.

covery. Reduction of the structure of forests in Southeast Asia by herbicides has dumped the nutrient pools of these large statured and extremely diverse forests. The nutrients are carried to the streams, which turn green with the algae that the nutrients support. Tschirley (11), reporting his study of the effects of herbicides in Viet Nam, recorded "surprise" and "pleasure" that fishing had improved in treated areas. If the herbicides are not toxic to fish, there should be little surprise at improved catches of certain kinds of fish in heavily enriched waters adjacent to herbicide-treated forests. The bamboo thickets that replace the forests also reflect the drastically lowered potential of these sites to support living systems. The time it takes to reestablish a forest with the original diversity depends on the availability of nutrients, and is probably very long in most lateritic soils.

In generalizing about pollution, I have concentrated on some of the grossest changes in the plant communities of terrestrial ecosystems. The emphasis on plants is appropriate because plants dominate terrestrial ecosystems. But not all pollutants affect plants directly; some have their principal effects on heterotrophs. What changes in the structure of animal communities are caused by such broadly toxic materials as most pesticides?

The general pattern of loss of structure is quite similar, although the structure of the animal communities is more difficult to chart. The transfer of energy appears to be one good criterion of structure. Various studies suggest that 10 to 20 percent of the energy entering the plant community is transferred directly to the animal community through herbivores (14). Much of that energy, perhaps 50 percent or more, is used in respiration to support the herbivore population; some is transferred to the detritus food chain directly, and some, probably not more than 20 percent, is transferred to predators of the herbivores. In an evolutionarily and successionally mature community, this transfer of 10 to 20 percent per trophic level may occur two or three times to support carnivores, some highly specialized, such as certain eagles, hawks, and herons, others less specialized, such as gulls, ravens, rats, and people.

Changes in the plant community, such as its size, rate of energy fixation, and species, will affect the structure of the animal community as well. Introduction of a toxin specific for animals, such as a pesticide that is a generalized nerve toxin, will also topple the pyramid. Although the persistent pesticides are fat soluble and tend to accumulate in carnivores and reduce populations at the tops of food chains, they affect every trophic level, reducing reproductive capacity, almost certainly altering behavioral patterns, and disrupting the competitive relationships between species. Under these circumstances the highly specialized species, the obligate carnivores high in the trophic structure, are at a disadvantage because the food chain concentrates the toxin and, what is even more important, because the entire structure beneath them becomes unstable. Again the generalists or broad-niched species are favored, the gulls, rats, ravens, pigeons and, in a very narrow short-term sense, man. Thus, the pesticides favor the herbivores, the very organisms they were invented to control.

Biological evolution has divided the resources of any site among a large variety of users — species — which, taken together, confer on that site the properties of a closely integrated system capable of conserving a diversity of life. The system has structure; its populations exist with certain definable, quantitative relationships to one another; it fixes energy and releases it at a measurable rate; and it contains an inventory of nutrients that is accumulated and recirculated, not lost. The system is far from static; it is subject, on a time scale very long compared with a human lifespan, to a continuing aug-mentive change through evolution; on a shorter time scale, it is subject to a succession toward a more stable state after any disturbance. The successional patterns are themselves a product of the evolution of life, providing for sys-tematic recovery from any acute disturbance. Without a detailed discussion of the theory of ecology, one can say that biological evolution, following a pattern approximating that outlined above, has built the earth's ecosystems, and that these systems have been the dominant influence on the earth through-out the span of human existence. The structure of these systems is now being changed all over the world. We know enough about the structure and function of these systems to predict the broad outline of the effects of pollution on both land and water. We know that as far as our interests in the next decades are concerned, pollution operates on the time scale of succession, not of evolution, and we cannot look to evolution to cure this set of problems. The loss of structure involves a shift away from complex arrangements of special-ized species toward the generalists; away from forest, toward hardy shrubs and herbs; away from those phytoplankton of the open ocean that Wurster (15) proved so very sensitive to DDT, toward those algae of the sewage plants that are unaffected by almost everything including DDT and most fish; away from diversity in birds, plants, and fish toward monotony; away from tight nutrient cycles toward very loose ones with terrestrial systems becoming depleted, and with aquatic systems becoming overloaded; away from stability toward instability especially with regard to sizes of populations of small, rap-idly reproducing organisms such as insects and rodents that compete with man; away from a world that runs itself through a self-augmentive, slowly moving evolution, to one that requires constant tinkering to patch it up, a tinkering that is malignant in that each act of repair generates a need for further repairs to avert problems generated at compound interest.

This is the pattern, predictable in broad outline, aggravated by almost any pollutant. Once we recognize the pattern, we can begin to see the mean-ing of some of the changes occurring now in the earth's biota. We can see the demise of carnivorous birds and predict the demise of important fisheries. We can tell why, around industrial cities, hills that were once forested now are not; why each single species is important; and how the increase in the temperature of natural water bodies used to cool new reactors will, by aug-menting respiration over photosynthesis, ultimately degrade the system and contribute to degradation of other interconnected ecosystems nearby. We can begin to speculate on where continued, exponential progress in this direction will lead: probably not to extinction — man will be around for a long time yet — but to a general degradation of the quality of life.

The solution? Fewer people, unpopular but increasing restrictions on technology (making it more and more expensive), and a concerted effort to tighten up human ecosystems to reduce their interactions with the rest of the earth on whose stability we all depend. This does not require foregoing nuclear energy; it requires that if we must dump heat, it should be dumped into civilization to enhance a respiration rate in a sewage plant or an agricultural ecosystem, not dumped outside of civilization to affect that fraction of the earth's biota that sustains the earth as we know it. The question of what fraction that might be remains as one of the great issues, still scarcely considered by the scientific community.

References and notes

1. E. P. Odum, *Science* 164, 262 (1969).
2. Plant nomenclature follows that of M. L. Fernald in *Gray's Manual of Botany* (American Book, New York, ed. 8, 1950).
3. G. M. Woodwell, *Science* 156, 461 (1967); ——— and A. L. Rebuck, *Ecol. Monogr.* 37, 53 (1967).
4. G. M. Woodwell and T. P. Gannutz, *Amer. J. Bot.* 54, 1210 (1967).
5. ——— and J. K. Oosting, *Radiat. Bot.* 5, 205 (1965).
6. ——— and R. H. Whittaker, *Quart. Rev. Biol.* 43, 42 (1968).
7. M. F. Buell and J. E. Cantlon, *Ecology* 34, 520 (1953).
8. G. L. Miller, thesis, Univ. of North Carolina (1968).
9. A. H. Sparrow, L. A. Schairer, R. C. Sparrow, W. F. Campbell, *Radiat. Bot.* 3, 169 (1963); F. G. Taylor, Jr., *ibid.* 6 307 (1965).
10. E. Gorham and A. G. Gordon, *Can. J. Bot.* 38, 307 (1960); *ibid.*, p. 477; *ibid.*, 41, 371 (1963).
11. F. H. Tschirley, *Science* 163, 779 (1969).
12. R. H. Whittaker and G. M. Woodwell, *Amer. J. Bot.* 54, 931 (1967).
13. F. H. Bormann, G. E. Likens, D. W. Fisher, R. S. Pierce, *Science* 159, 882 (1968).
14. These relationships have been summarized in detail by J. Phillipson [*Ecological Energetics* (St. Martin's Press, New York, 1966)]. See also L. B. Slobodkin, *Growth and Regulation of Animal Populations* (Holt, Rinehart and Winston, New York, 1961) and J. H. Ryther, *Science* 166, 72 (1969).
15. C. F. Wurster, *Science* 159, 1474 (1968).
16. G. M. Woodwell, *ibid.* 138, 572 (1962).
17. Research carried out at Brookhaven National Laboratory under the auspices of the U.S. Atomic Energy Commission. Paper delivered at 11th International Botanical Congress, Seattle, Wash., on 26 August 1969 in the symposium "Ecological and Evolutionary Implications of Environmental Pollution."

DONALD W. COON & ROBERT R. FLEET
The Ant War

Mirex (Dodecachlorooctahydro-1,3,4-metheno-2H-cyclobuta [cd] pen-talene) is a chlorinated hydrocarbon insecticide which until recently was considered harmless to wildlife and the aquatic environment.*

Mirex

Further studies, however, have shown it to be carcinogenic (cancer-producing) in laboratory mice. It also has the ability to become concentrated in species near the end of the food chain, thus to be consumed by animals and humans. In an attempt to delay the spraying, the President's Council on Environmental Quality unsuccessfully questioned the environmental impact statement on this insecticide submitted by the U. S. Department of Agriculture.

BACKGROUND

An article appearing on April 30, 1970 in the Bryan-College Station (Texas) local newspaper, The Daily Eagle, was the first indication that the imported fire ant had been found in Brazos County, Texas. The article discussed the "large, cement-like mounds on agriculture land . . . the extremely painful bite which . . . frequently causes the death of young livestock and wildlife," and "treatment with Mirex granules which . . . does not affect common red ants, wildlife or humans."

A second article in the Daily Eagle of May 3, 1970 indicated that 5,200 acres, including parts of the city of Bryan, would receive an initial treatment

Donald W. Coon and Robert R. Fleet, "The Ant War," reprinted by permission from the December issue of the magazine *Environment,* a publication of the Committee for Environmental Information. Copyright 1970 by the Committee for Environmental Information. For further information, write *Environment,* 438 North Skinker Blvd., St. Louis, Mo. 63130.

The authors are graduate research assistants in the Department of Wildlife Science at Texas A&M University. The views expressed in this article are those of the authors and are not intended to represent those of Texas A&M.

* *Cleaning Our Environment: The Chemical Basis for Action* (Washington, D. C.: American Chemical Society, 1969), p. 222.

against the imported fire ant beginning Monday, May 4, 1970. The area was to be treated with Mirex bait granules distributed by low-flying aircraft at the rate of one and one-fourth pounds per acre. The remainder of the article discussed Mirex bait and its supposedly low toxicity to other animal life.

The lack of documented information concerning both the imported fire ant and Mirex, along with incorrect information apparently provided to the newspaper, suggested to us that the proposed treatment should be temporarily halted until further studies could be made of its long-term environmental effects. Such studies may be requested by private citizens under Section 102 of the National Environmental Policy Act of 1969.

Thus, on the morning of May 5, 1970 we and Sidney E. Forsyth, all residents of College Station, Texas and students at Texas A&M University, attempted to obtain an interview with persons in charge of the imported fire ant control program in Brazos County. It was determined that the personnel connected with the project were employed by the U.S. Department of Agriculture (USDA). None of these people could be contacted prior to the spraying activities.

When the USDA district supervisor for the Plant Protection Division heard of our request for an interview, the single aircraft being used in this particular instance was recalled while we presented our case. We were informed by Mr. John Landrum, the USDA district supervisor, that in his opinion the imported fire ant was a menace, Mirex was safe, and aerial distribution of Mirex was the most economical method of treatment. He further stated that the only person able to stop the Mirex application was the director of the Plant Protection Division of the USDA in Hyattsville, Maryland. The aerial distribution program was subsequently resumed and the initial treatment was completed by the evening of May 5, 1970.

This report is an attempt to assess both the role of the imported fire ant as an economic pest and the use of Mirex as a control measure.

An insect called the imported fire ant has a bad name in the Southeast. Whether the reputation is valid is open to serious question. The question is important, since considerable money and large volumes of pesticides have been earmarked for a massive eradication campaign which some experts believe will do more environmental harm than good.

The imported fire ant (IFA) was introduced to the U.S. accidentally from South America early this century, but has become widespread only in the past two decades. As it spread, state and federal agricultural officials issued alarming warnings about the ant's capacity to injure crops, wildlife, and people. Local eradication programs began in 1937 and intensified with more recent widespread use of long-lasting insecticides. Such activities culminated in an organizational meeting on September 8, 1969 in Montgomery, Alabama. Members of IFA eradication committees and other interested persons from thirteen southern states unanimously approved a twelve-year eradication program developed jointly by the Southern Plant Board and the U.S. Department of Agriculture (USDA). The program calls for the Agricultural Research Service of the USDA and cooperating state agencies to treat 120 million acres in nine southeastern states three times with 1.25 pounds of Mirex (a chlorinated hydrocarbon insecticide) per acre per treatment.[1] The new program would cost about $200 million.

The exact date, manner, and source of the importation of the fire ant, which has the scientific name *Solenopsis saevissima richteri,* is not known. The first official recognition of the fire ant was made by H. P. Loding in an observation dated July 15, 1919 in *USDA Insect Pest Survey Bulletin 9.*[2] Loding indicated that this species had appeared in Mobile, Alabama in 1918. Mr. Loding reported his findings to Dr. William S. Creighton of Harvard University, who included the species in a work on the genus in 1930. This delay in recognition of the IFA was probably due to its similarity to native fire ants. (The IFA is blackish with a dull orange band at the base of its abdomen.)

It seems reasonable to assume that the IFA was inadvertently introduced to the U.S. via ship from South America, where it is native to Argentina and Uruguay. For about ten years it lived within or near the city limits of Mobile.[3] Then, about 1930, another form of the same species, smaller and pale red in color, appeared in the Mobile area. This variety is common in Brazil and Paraguay, and the evidence indicated a new importation rather than a mutant form. (The new, pale phase has mostly replaced the dark form,[4] which has had a very slow rate of spread, generally an outward expansion of one mile per year or less.)

In 1932, the pale variety's rate of expansion increased from one to three miles per year and after 1950 tended to become exponential. By 1963 the imported fire ant occupied roughly 31 million acres in nine southeastern states. Its present range encompasses 120 million acres within an area from eastern Texas and Arkansas eastward into North Carolina with the exception of Tennessee, from which it apparently has been eliminated.[5]

The first significant effort at eradication-control of the IFA was carried out in Baldwin County, Alabama in 1937 by the Alabama Department of Agriculture and Industries and the U.S. Public Works Administration. The campaign was soon abandoned, and the effects were short-lived. In the spring of 1948 the Mississippi state legislature appropriated $15,000 for the control of the IFA in that state. This project, like its predecessor in Alabama, was soon abandoned. Quantities of chlordane insecticide were furnished free by Alabama in 1949, and at cost by Louisiana in 1952, to provide local control.[6]

Then, in 1957, the USDA launched a campaign against the IFA, utilizing press releases, newspaper articles, and motion pictures.[7] Later that year the USDA requested congressional funding for eradication of the IFA. Congress responded with a $2.4 million annual allocation approved with the stipulation that local matching funds be made available.[8]

Spraying with two pounds of dieldrin per acre began in November 1957. Heptachlor at 1.00 to 1.25 pounds per acre was substituted in 1958, and this dosage was later reduced to two applications of 0.25 pound spaced three or four months apart. Not until the spraying program was under way were wildlife and health authorities notified about the use of these powerful, chlorinated hydrocarbon insecticides.[9] Immediate and widespread objections to the program by biologists were largely ignored by the USDA. Massive die-offs of fish, wildlife, and domestic animals occurred.[10]

In 1959, the Food and Drug Administration set a zero level of tolerance for heptachlor and its epoxide derivative in food. This action, coupled with continuing outcries by such distinguished biologists as Rachel Carson and Dr. Clarence Cottam and the obvious fact that the IFA was not being controlled, let alone eradicated, moved the Alabama legislature to withdraw matching funds in 1959. The Florida legislature followed suit in 1960.[11]

In 1961, Mirex (also a chlorinated hydrocarbon, but supposedly without the decided disadvantages of earlier pesticides) was developed by the Allied Chemical Company for control of several ant species. The federal program from 1961 until 1969 used Mirex and was aimed at containment rather than eradication.

Evaluation as a Pest

A sampling of statements in agricultural and mass media publications reveals how the fire ant has acquired a bad name, particularly in the past fifteen years.

A formidable army of South American fire ants has invaded the United States. . . . Already the destructive insects have captured much of the South's best farmland and are eating their way northward and westward. Their onslaught, if unchecked, may not stop short of California and Canada.[12]

When their mound is disturbed, these ants attack by sinking powerful jaws into the skin, then repeatedly thrust their poisonous stingers into the flesh. Fire ants may attack and kill newborn pigs, calves, sheep, and other animals; newly hatched chicks; and the young of ground-nesting birds.[13]

Imported fire ants are destructive, costly and a nuisance. This ant can damage many kinds of young plants by gnawing holes in roots, tubers, stalks and buds.[14]

If you've never had a bout with stinging ants, consider yourself lucky. When the insect involved is the imported fire ant, the bout generally becomes a rout — and in short order! Imported fire ants are vicious stingers and attack without provocation.[15]

This ant damages vegetable crops by sucking juices from the stems of plants and by gnawing holes in roots, stalks, buds, ears, and pods. It injures pasture grasses, cereal and forage crops, nursery stock, and fruit trees.[16]

There is testimony aplenty that in areas where the imported fire ant has gained a stronghold, it inflicts losses on this game bird [bobwhite quail] so popular to Florida hunters. Although some reports on wildlife losses to the fire ant may have been exaggerated, extreme young of animals and birds certainly have been killed by this pest.[17]

Almost all of these statements are misleading in that they are half-truths.

It has been stated by many authors that the IFA is a menace to quail, particularly to the young birds as they emerge from the shell.[18] Statements such as "The ants enter the quail egg as soon as it is pipped and consume the entire chick before it can escape from the shell" and "quail chicks and their parents have been eaten while confined in brooder pens" are common in the literature.

A study conducted at Auburn University by the Alabama Cooperative

Wildlife Research Unit, however, produced different conclusions about the IFA and its damage to quail:

1. Imported fire ants rarely attack and kill normally hatching quail chicks. Most incidents of attack are confined to chicks that are not normal and healthy.
2. Death of chicks in many cases may be attributed to predation by ants when the actual cause of death was some other factor, the ants being attracted to the nests after the chicks had died.
3. Drought may prevent some chicks from escaping the shell after pipping. Ants may then be attracted to the nests, covering the living chicks trapped within the shells as well as those that have already died.
4. Adult birds can keep limited numbers of ants out of the nest. Deserted nests in which the chicks have survived to pip the shell, may become covered with ants, and the chicks may be killed in the shells.
5. The limited destruction of hatching chicks by IFA has no significant effect on overall quail populations.[19]

Several investigators[20] have stated that the IFA does not have any effect on the overall populations of birds and mammals in an infested area. "There are no published papers on imported fire ants as destroyers of birds and animals, but Travis . . . has discussed the destruction of quail by the less populous native fire ants."[21]

Fire ants native to the Southeast have behavioral patterns similar to those of IFA. They build small mounds, are insectivorous, and, when annoyed, sting with the same ferocity as the IFA. Bernard Travis[22] suggested that the IFA was responsible for the decline (reported by R. W. Williams in 1904[23]) in the number of ground doves in Leon County, Florida. However, this would have been impossible since the reduction of the dove population occurred 14 years prior to the ant's introduction into the U.S. and 46 years before its range encompassed Leon County, Florida. We were unable to find any documented reports of significant destruction of quail or other ground-nesting birds by the IFA.

Statements such as "These insatiable pests can kill newborn calves and pigs," and "They chase brooding hens from the nest and eat their chicks; they prey on the eggs and young of quail and other ground-nesting birds"[24] are without basis and serve as scare tactics to arouse public opinion.

Preference for insects

That the IFA feeds mostly on agricultural crops has been presented as a well-publicized fact. E. O. Wilson stated, "In Alabama and Mississippi sections of fields of newly sprouted corn, beans, and other principal crops have been cut down by the marauding worker ants; one picks up crumpled plants only to find their stems and roots riddled by feeding ants."[25] J. Wheeler said about the IFA: "Its appetite for seeds, plants, and trees makes it destructive to many agricultural crops."[26] A. Rankin stated,

The fire ant is one of the most conspicuous nuisances ever to threaten U.S. farmers and the citizenry at large. It damages practically all edible plants by sucking the juice from their roots, stems, seeds, and tender shoots. With the fiery sting that gives it its name, its legions rout field hands trying to gather row crops like potatoes, straw-berries, cotton.[27]

These and other reports of damage of varying degrees to major agricultural crops, young livestock, newborn wildlife, and to pasture grasses were based on hearsay, not on analytical studies.

Let us examine the research studies which have been completed on the biology of the IFA. In 1959 S. B. and K. L. Hays wrote:

Experiments were conducted in 1957 to determine food habits of the imported fire ant (*Solenopsis saevissima richteri*), by field observations and laboratory experiments. Ant mounds were dissected in the field to determine food storage, and ants were observed at work to determine the materials collected by the ant foraging parties.[28]

Stored food material included insects and other invertebrates such as termites, weevils, and beetles, cutworms, snails, and fire ants, indicating some degree of cannibalism. At all openings along the tunnels radiating from the mound, workers were observed bringing various insect parts to the mound entrances where the parts were devoured. Aphids, small spiders, various larvae, and some beetles were included. Fly larvae seemed to be a favorite food. Thus, the principal dietary items were insects, not plant material.

Laboratory studies by the same investigators[29] revealed that of seventeen kinds of dry seeds placed on the mounds, only peanuts were eaten. The ants neither damaged nor removed seeds of the other plants. Germinating seeds of the plants were also available to the ants, but only peanuts, okra, and corn were eaten. A thorough examination of roots and above-ground parts of eighteen species of seedling plants transplanted into mounds and allowed to grow for six weeks revealed no damage. Eighteen species of plants were pro-duced from seeds planted in the mound; there was no damage to the seeds, and, of the plants, only okra was eaten. Where food was not available, canni-balism occurred.

In a later study by H. B. Green,[30] visual examination of the ants returning from foraging trips to an eighteen-inch mound revealed that about 25 percent of them were carrying burdens in their mandibles; all of these burdens were parts of insects. The remains of pill bugs or other crustacea have often been found in the "kitchen middens" of the IFA. At some times of the year, small terrestrial snails seem to form part of the fire ant diet. The IFA has also been observed tending aphids, scale insects, and mealybugs, and feeding on the honeydew discharged by these insects.[31]

K. L. Hays in 1958 reported on an inspection trip he made to Argentina, the home of the IFA, with two USDA officials. He noted,

The food of the imported fire ant in Argentina is composed largely of insects. Argentine specialists have not noted injury to vegetation except in building of mounds. Occasionally, ants have been observed to feed on germinating seeds, particularly those of high oil content. Most specialists consider these ants beneficial because of this insectivorous habit. Many reported seeing ants stinging, killing, and carrying numerous harmful species of insects into their mounds. One specialist estimated he had seen more than 100 different species of insects stored in the mounds of these ants.[32]

Hays continued,

The specialists, agricultural workers, and farmers of Argentina do not consider the imported fire ant an economic pest. Since little or no hay is harvested and since farmers do not clip or mow their pastures, no damage to farm machinery was reported. A large proportion of the agricultural produce of Argentina is harvested by hand. Persons working in citrus and apple orchards and cotton fields reported being stung only when they stood on a mound. In frequently cultivated areas, very few mounds of the IFA were seen. It appears that the ants cannot tolerate cultivation or frequent disturbances of their mounds.[33]

These studies indicate that the IFA is primarily insectivorous and acts as a generalized predator on many species of insects, including some agricultural pests.

Allergic to sting

Some people are made ill by the sting of the IFA. The USDA reported: "The stings cause long-lasting sores that sometimes leave scars. People who are allergic to the stings may require medical care."[34] In 1958, Wheeler gave the following example of damage due to fire ant stings: a child in Jacksonville, Florida, in 1957, was found with a temperature of 106 degrees, and the attending physician reported that the illness was caused by fire ant stings. Fire ants are also thought to have been a contributing factor in the death of three people in Florida.[35] A USDA report described the fire ant sting as having a burning and itching sensation, followed by the formation of a white sore or pustule which may leave a permanent scar.[36]

Dr. Rodney Jung of the Tulane University School of Tropical Medicine found that the venom of the IFA is unlike that of other stinging ants, bees, and wasps. A person who is unusually sensitive to this venom may suffer chest pains, become nauseated, and even lapse into a coma from a single sting. Anyone who suffers severely from fire ant stings should be treated immediately for allergic reactions if stung.[37] G. H. Blake reported that IFA is a vicious stinger and attacks without provocation.[38] Rankin stated that "ordinarily the fire-ant sting brings only searing momentary pain followed by small, pimple-like pustules that last three to ten days. People oversensitive to their venom may feel sharp chest pains and nausea, gasp for breath, turn blue in the face, and lapse into coma."[39] Rankin then goes on to calm the fears of the reader by saying: "The sting is rarely fatal, however, and entomologists remind us that stings of bees and wasps can have the same violent effects on persons allergic to them."[40] Wilson wrote in 1959: "Actually, the sting of the worker ant is much less severe than that of a bee or wasp but this is more than made up for by the size and ferocity of the colonies; the slightest disturbance of a nest brings out hundreds or even thousands of workers which attack any moving object within reach."[41] The same can be said for native fire ants with respect to stinging ability, however.

Some people, when stung, have general (systemic) allergic reactions such as headache and nausea, in addition to a local reaction (which varies from one individual to another). Allergic responses have occurred in individuals receiving one or two or as many as fifty to one hundred stings. However, in all documented cases, a previous history of stings has been recorded. People suffering allergic reactions probably have become sensitized to the venom by previous stings of these or other species of ants.[42] According to three investigators, *all* species of ants accounted for only *four* of the 460 fatalities reported from venomous animals in the United States from 1950 through 1959.[43]

We have not tried to eradicate the wasp, the yellow jacket, the bumblebee (with a much worse sting), the hornet (even worse yet), or the common honeybee. All of these pack a large amount of venom and kill a number of people each year. Bees were the cause of 124 deaths from 1950 through 1959; wasps accounted for 69, yellow jackets 22, and hornets 10 in the same period.[44] People who are allergic to venom must take extra precautions to insure that they do not get stung. It would appear that the IFA fits into the same category as the other types of venomous insects. According to entomologists working with the IFA, the foraging workers do not attack when approached. Instead, they communicate, presumably via chemical substances, and retreat to the nearest entrance of their mound.

Anthills minor problem

Finally, mounds of the IFA are alleged to cause widespread damage to farm machinery with resultant economic loss to landowners. Several authors have suggested that blades of harvesting machinery may be damaged or broken when they strike the hard mounds.[45] It seems logical to assume that some working parts of harvesting machinery could become clogged with dirt from fire ant mounds and that rotary collection blades might be bent when striking the mounds. The idea that hard, steel cutting blades might be completely ruined seems highly doubtful. Information on the nature of the mounds of the IFA indicates that damage resulting from dirt clogging and bending would be limited to a few specific conditions. For example, mounds of the requisite height and hardness to cause damage are found only in clay soils, and the mounds are not maintained to their maximum height during dry months — when most harvesting would take place.

Control measures assessed

Before and after the initiation of the federal-state cooperative fire ant eradication program in 1957, many chemicals were used in the attempt to rid the country of this insect. S. W. Clark first reported on the use of calcium cyanide to control native species of fire ants in the Rio Grande Valley of Texas.[46] He also used poisoned baits that incorporated thallium sulphate as the active ingredient. Both of these treatments were successful in controlling the native fire ants under the conditions of his experiments. Apparently these methods were not suitable for the eradication programs planned by the USDA. New chemicals (super insecticides) were widely used instead. Among these were dieldrin, chlordane, and heptachlor — all chlorinated hydrocarbons, highly residual in nature, and requiring very small concentrations to be effective against non-target animals. Conservationists made their views known early in the campaign after several incidents of environmental damage were noted. Many reports appeared on the subject, all of them condemning large-scale use of "hard" pesticides.[47] Many instances of widespread damage to wildlife were reported. Maurice F. Baker said heptachlor or dieldrin applied by air at the rate of two pounds per acre resulted in a total kill of thirteen coveys of quail that ranged on the treated area. Two other coveys that ranged mostly off the treated land survived. A wide spectrum of other vertebrate animals was also killed.[48] Leslie L. Glasgow found a high rate of wildlife mortality following the application of two pounds of heptachlor per acre.[49] Redwing blackbirds and meadowlarks were reduced to zero in one study area, and earthworms, the chief food of the woodcock, contained heptachlor five months after treatment. In addition to the discovery that the control measures did more harm to wildlife than to the fire ant, incomplete control of the ant was noted in several of the studies. Reinfestation of treated areas was common, especially after one or two years.

The USDA, after consideration and study, discontinued large-scale use of these chemicals; however, chlordane is still used to treat specific areas.

More tests were conducted by the Plant Pest Control Division of the USDA on different compounds and baits (attractants and poisons) that would be more specific to the IFA and less dangerous to other animals.

Finally, as a result of these tests and other studies, a new chemical, the chlorinated relative of Kepone, Mirex, was studied extensively. It was determined that the main food item of the IFA is insects and that it feeds upon plant matter only as a last resort. It was further determined that the best baits for the IFA are those high in protein or fatty acids. Following up this lead, C. S. Lofgren, J. L. Thompson and USDA investigators[50] determined specifically that the best baits are cottonseed oil, soybean oil, peanut oil, fancy tallow, and lard. Soybean oil was chosen as the best single attractant and solvent for Mirex. A combination of Mirex at a concentration of between 0.075 and 0.45 percent dissolved in the soybean oil, then absorbed by ground corncob (grits) as a carrier, has proved to be the most effective insecticide for the IFA. Foraging workers bring food to the mound, where it is fed to the nest queen first. Next in line are the larvae. The slow-acting insecticidal action of Mirex insures the death of the colony; since there is only a single queen (the only female with reproductive capabilities) per nest, and no replacements for lost workers, the colony expires.

Entomologists and ecologists examined the effects of Mirex applications on the wildlife of treated areas. J. B. DeWitt and his colleagues found that Mirex was less toxic to quail than was an equal dose of Kepone.[51] Research in 1964 showed that Mirex was less toxic to pheasants and mallards than was Kepone.[52] Baker studied the possible effects of Mirex bait on bobwhite quail and other birds. Although there were no deaths of quail or other birds attributable to Mirex when used in field tests, there was a reduction in fertility and hatchability of quail eggs in pen studies (where the birds are caged in the field). However, Baker stated that the pen tests were inconclusive and recommended only that further investigation be conducted. He concluded that it would be safe to use Mirex under the operational conditions of the eradication program.[53]

Interference with reproduction

Baker[54] was the first scientist to check for and report on the long-term effects of Mirex on reproduction. Other researchers followed his lead. E. E. Good and his colleagues[55] demonstrated that Kepone, when fed at five parts per million (ppm) in the diet of the laboratory mouse, reduced litter frequency. Kepone apparently produced in the female test animals a hormonal imbalance which caused them to be in a continual state of sexual receptivity and prevented successful ovulation.[56]

Mirex, the more highly chlorinated relative of Kepone, has largely replaced Kepone for some uses, particularly IFA control in the South. It is much less toxic to quail,[57] pheasants, and mallards.[58] Little information is available regarding effects of Mirex on mammals. It has been reported that the amount required to kill 50 percent of a sample of male white rats was about three times that of Kepone.[59] However, preliminary tests with Mirex produced different results. George W. Ware and E. E. Good found that its toxicity was considerably greater than that of Kepone when fed continuously to one strain of laboratory mice. Dietary Mirex at 7 ppm produced greater mortality than 50 ppm of Kepone.[60]

In contrast to the findings with mice, Edward C. Naber and George W. Ware in 1965 found that much higher levels of Mirex than of Kepone (150 ppm Kepone as opposed to 660 ppm of Mirex) were required in the diets of laying hens to reduce hatchability of eggs.[61]

Another effect observed in experimental rats fed low dietary levels was the development of cataracts in the offspring. Litters from mothers that had not been fed Mirex were transferred at birth to foster mothers that had been fed Mirex at the rate of five ppm in their diets for 73 days. Not only was survival at weaning reduced (only 54 percent survived), but 37.5 percent of the infant rats from nine litters developed cataracts.[62]

Differences were found in the effects of Mirex, DDT, and Telodrin on two strains of laboratory mice. In one strain, the Mirex diet produced the smallest first litters, the smallest litters throughout the tests, and a significant increase in parent mortality. In the other strain, Mirex had no effect on parent mortality, but altered significantly the number of young per pair. In first litters, Mirex resulted in a significantly lower number of offspring produced per day than did DDT. "In all instances the Mirex diet resulted in reduced litter size and number of offspring produced per day."[63]

It is apparent, then, that Mirex is a poison that can, in certain concentrations, at least reduce reproductive success in certain mammals. Furthermore, a report on pesticides made to the Secretary of Health, Education, and Welfare by a special scientific commission lists Mirex as a carcinogen (cancer-producing agent) that induces tumors in mice.[64] The USDA believes, however, that in the small concentrations used in the eradication programs, the effects would be insignificant to species other than the several ant species for which Mirex is allegedly a specific toxicant.

The USDA policy differs with that of the Department of the Interior. The Secretary of the Interior recently announced a policy banning the use of 16 pesticides and sharply restricting the use of 32 others, including Mirex, on the 70 percent of all federal land holdings managed by the Interior Department.[65]

Concentrated in food chain

Generally ignored, however, is the question of food-chain buildup, that process by which environmentally persistent pesticides are concentrated within the ecosystem. Such buildups have occurred with other chlorinated hydrocarbons (such as DDT), which have turned up in high concentrations in the tissues of various vertebrates. Mirex, a chlorinated hydrocarbon, might also be expected to follow the route of biological concentration. Dr. L. D. Newsom, chairman, department of entomology, Louisiana State University at Baton Rouge, indicated in a personal communication to us on May 26, 1970 that this was indeed the case. The following is a statement by Dr. Newsom:

Data which have become available in the past few weeks have shown that Mirex has been accumulating in the wildlife of Louisiana. The potential importance of this new information is such that I am urging that the fire ant eradication program currently being undertaken by the USDA Plant Pest Control Division be halted immediately so that this program can be further studied.

In 1969 P. A. Butler studied pesticide residues in 5,000 samples of oysters and shellfish from estuaries on the Atlantic, Gulf, and Pacific coasts. He showed that over a three-year period Mirex was the fourth most frequently encountered pesticide residue. Mirex was exceeded only by DDT, endrin, and toxaphene.[66]

It has been noted that individual treatments of areas with Mirex have failed to control the IFA, much less eradicate it. L. D. Newsom stated that Mirex has been sprayed for several years in Louisiana and has failed to control the IFA for any extended period of time. This is true even after six applications of Mirex on some areas. F. Bellinger and his colleagues were even more blunt:

Based on data summarized in this report, the United States should free itself from any illusion that current airplane spray operations with Mirex [are] anything but a "control" operation, which will require reapplication more than once a year to the periphery of the infested area, even simply to prevent the spread of infestation.[67]

IN SUMMARY

Widespread danger to mankind from the IFA does not exist. Statements in the literature which indicate that the IFA kills livestock and wildlife, preys on the eggs of young quail, and is responsible for decreases in the numbers of ground-nesting birds have not been substantiated. Instead, such statements have been disputed with documented research.

The sting of the worker ant is less severe than that of a bee or wasp. Persons allergic to insect venom may suffer systemic reactions to the sting of the IFA, as they would to the stings of other venomous insects. *All* species of ants accounted for only *four* of the 460 fatalities reported from venomous animals in the United States from 1950 through 1959.

Under certain circumstances, working parts of harvesting machinery may become clogged with dirt from fire ant mounds, and rotary collection blades may be bent when striking the mounds, but there is little to indicate such damage has been an extensive agricultural problem.

Field observations and laboratory experiments indicate that the diet of the IFA is composed primarily of insects and insect products, not plant materials, as some proponents of eradication have claimed. In its Argentine homeland, the fire ant is considered beneficial to agriculture due to its diet of harmful insects.

Mirex, a chlorinated hydrocarbon, has been used since 1962 to control the imported fire ant. This chemical was believed to be safer to wildlife than heptachlor, chlordane, and other pesticides which have been used by the USDA in previous attempts to eradicate the IFA. Recently it has been shown that Mirex is accumulating in the tissues of several species of wildlife in Louisiana and Mississippi. Mirex is highly resistant to breakdown into nontoxic form and is responsible for a decrease in the reproductive ability of certain test animals. Mirex has failed to control its target species, the IFA, as is evidenced by the continued expansion in range of the insect to an estimated 120 million acres.

The IFA is not the danger that is alleged. The Mirex program to eradicate the IFA, on the other hand, is dangerous. It will kill myriads of nontarget organisms, and will not eradicate the fire ant.

Notes

1. Ferguson, D. E., "Fire Ant: Whose Pest?" *Science,* 169 (3946):630, 1970.
2. Cited in Green, H. B., "The Imported Fire Ant in Mississippi," *Bulletin of the Mississippi State University Agricultural Experiment Station,* 737:1–23, 1967.
3. Bellinger, F., R. E. Dyer, R. King and R. B. Platt, "A Review of the Problem of the Imported Fire Ant," *Bulletin of the Georgia Academy of Science,* 23(1):1–22, 1965.
4. Bellinger et al., *loc cit.* Green, *loc. cit.*
5. Bellinger et al., *loc. cit.* Agricultural Research Service, *Observations on the Biology of the Imported Fire Ant,* United States Department of Agriculture, ARS-33-49: 1–21, 1958.
6. Allen, Ralph H., "History of the Imported Fire Ant in the Southeast," *Proceedings of the 12th Annual Conference, Southeastern Association of Game and Fish Commissioners,* 1958, pp. 227–233. Bellinger et al., *loc. cit.*
7. Graham, F., Jr., *Since Silent Spring,* Houghton Mifflin Co., Boston, Massachusetts, 1970, 333 pp.
8. Allen, *loc. cit.* Carson, Rachel, *Silent Spring,* Houghton Mifflin Co., Boston, Massachusetts, 1962, 368 pp. Rudd, R. L., *Pesticides and the Living Landscape,* University of Wisconsin Press, Madison, Wisconsin, 1964, 320 pp.
9. Rudd, *ibid.*
10. Carson, *loc. cit.*
11. Rudd, *loc. cit.*
12. Rankin, A., "The Great Fire-Ant Invasion," *Reader's Digest,* 71(425):74–77, 1957.
13. Agricultural Research Service, *The Imported Fire Ant,* United States Department of Agriculture, PA-592, 1968, pp. 1–4.

14. Thomas, J. G., *Fact Sheet: How to Control the Imported Fire Ant,* Texas A&M University, Agricultural Extension Service, 1–384, 1967, 4 pp.

15. Blake, G. H., Jr., "Imported Fire Ant — On the March in Alabama," *Highlights of Agricultural Research,* Alabama Agricultural Experiment Station, 3(3):5, 1956.

16. Agricultural Research Service, *The Fight Against the Imported Fire Ant,* United States Department of Agriculture, PA-368:1–4, 1958.

17. Wheeler, Joe, "The Fire Ant," *Florida Wildlife,* March, 1958.

18. Stoddard, Herbert L., *The Bobwhite Quail, Its Habits, Preservation, and Increase,* Charles Scribner's Sons, New York, 1936, 559 pp. Travis, Bernard V., "The Fire Ant *(Solenopsis sp.)* as a Pest of Quail," *Journal of Economic Entomology,* 31(6):649–652, 1938. Travis, Bernard V., "Fire Ant Problem in the Southeast with Special Reference to Quail," *Transactions of the North American Wildlife Conference,* 3:705–708, 1938. Emlen, John T., Jr., "Fire Ants Attacking California Quail Chicks," *Condor,* 40(2):85–86, 1938. Rankin, *loc. cit.* Wheeler, *loc. cit.* Wilson, E. O., "Invader of the South," *Natural History,* 68(5):276–281, 1959.

19. Johnson, A. S., "Antagonistic Relationships Between Ants and Wildlife with Special Reference to Imported Fire Ants and Bobwhite Quail in the Southeast," *Proceedings of 15th Annual Conference of Southeastern Game and Fish Commissioners,* 1961, pp. 88–107.

20. Murray, Robert W., "A Synecological Study of the Effects of the Fire Ant Eradication Program in Florida," *Proceedings of the 16th Annual Conference of Southeastern Game and Fish Commissioners,* 1962, pp. 145–153. Rhoades, W. C. and R. W. Murray, "A Synecological Study of the Imported Fire Ant Eradication Program," *Bulletin of the University of Florida Agricultural Experiment Station,* 720:1–42, 1967. Arant, F. S., Kirby L. Hays and Dan W. Speake, "Facts about the Imported Fire Ant," *Highlights of Agricultural Research,* Agricultural Experiment Station, Alabama Polytechnic Institute, Vol. 5, No. 4, 1958.

21. Agricultural Research Service, *Observations . . . , loc. cit.*

22. Travis, "Fire Ant Problem . . . ," *loc. cit.*

23. Williams, R. W., Jr., "A Preliminary List of the Birds of Leon County, Florida," *Auk,* 21:449–462, 1904.

24. Rankin, *loc. cit.*

25. Wilson, *loc. cit.*

26. Wheeler, *loc. cit.*

27. Rankin, *loc. cit.*

28. Hays, S. B. and K. L. Hays, "Food Habits of *Solenopsis saevissima richteri* Forel," *Journal of Economic Entomology,* 52 (3):455–457, 1959.

29. *Ibid.*

30. Green, *loc. cit.*

31. *Ibid.* Agricultural Research Service, *Observations . . . , loc. cit.*

32. Hays, Kirby L., "The Present Status of the Imported Fire Ant in Argentina," *Journal of Economic Entomology,* 51(1):111–112, 1958.

33. *Ibid.*

34. Agricultural Research Service, *The Imported Fire Ant, loc. cit.*

35. Wheeler, *loc. cit.*

36. Agricultural Research Service, *The Imported Fire Ant Program and Progress,* United States Department of Agriculture, ARS-81-9-1, 1963, 10 pp.

37. *Ibid.*

38. Blake, *loc. cit.*

39. Rankin, *loc. cit.*

40. *Ibid.*

41. Wilson, *loc. cit.*

42. Bellinger et al., *loc. cit.*

43. Parrish, Henry M., "Analysis of 460 Fatalities from Venomous Animals in the United States," *American Journal of Medical Sciences,* 245(2):129–140, 1963. Pratt, Harry D. and John M. McDowell, "Current Status of Some of the Important Arthropod-borne Diseases in the United States," Report from Vector Control Services, Training Section, Training Branch, Department of Health, Education and Welfare, Atlanta, Georgia, 1963.

44. Pratt and McDowell, *ibid.*

45. Arant et al., *loc. cit.* Thomas, *loc. cit.* Agricultural Research Service, *The Imported Fire Ant . . . , loc. cit.*

46. Clark, S. W., "The Control of Fire Ants in the Lower Rio Grande Valley," *Bulletin of the Texas Agricultural Experiment Station*, 435:1–12, 1931.

47. Baker, Maurice F., "Observations of Effects of an Application of Heptachlor or Dieldrin on Wildlife," *Proceedings of the 12th Annual Conference, Southeastern Association of Game and Fish Commissioners*, 1958, pp. 244–247. Curl, L. F. "Aerial Application in Eradication Programs," *Agricultural Chemistry*, 13(4):42–44, 99, 1958. Cutler, M. Rupert, "Pesticides Versus Wildlife," *Virginia Wildlife*, 20:4–5, 1958. Glasgow, Leslie L., "Studies on the Effect of the Imported Fire Ant Control Program on Wildlife in Louisiana," *Proceedings of the 12th Annual Conference, Southeastern Association of Game and Fish Commissioners*, 1958, pp. 250–255. Kyle, George M., "These Died on 100 Acres of Fire Ant Treatment Area," Alabama State Department of Conservation, News Release, April 18, 1958, 4 pp. Lay, Daniel W., "Fire Ant Eradication and Wildlife," *Proceedings of the 12th Annual Conference, Southeastern Association of Game and Fish Commissioners*, 1958, pp. 248–250. Newsom, L. D., "A Preliminary Progress Report of Fire Ant Eradication Program," Concordia Parish, Louisiana, 1958. Rosene, Walter J., "Whistling-Cock Counts of Bobwhite Quail on Areas Treated with Insecticide and on Untreated Areas, Decatur County, Georgia," *Proceedings of the 12th Annual Conference, Southeastern Association of Game and Fish Commissioners*, 1958, pp. 240–244. Clawson, S. G. and M. F. Baker, "Immediate Effects of Dieldrin and Heptachlor on Bobwhites," *Journal of Wildlife Management*, 23(2):215–219, 1959. Gaines, J. F. and H. E. Lowry, "The Controversial Fire Ant," *Southeastern Veterinarian*, 12(1):122–124, 1960. Jenkins, J. H., "A Review of Five Years Research on the Effects of the Fire Ant Control Program on Selected Wildlife Populations," *Bulletin of the Georgia Academy of Science*, 21(1/2):3, 1963, Rusoff, L. L., R. S. Temple, R. G. Myers, L. D. Newsom, E. C. Burns, W. F. Barthel, Calvin Corley and Ava Allsman, "Residues in Fatty Tissues and Meat of Cattle Grazing on Pastures Treated with Granular Heptachlor," *Agriculture and Food Chemistry*, 11(4):289–291, 1963.

48. Baker, *loc. cit.*

49. Glasgow, *loc. cit.*

50. Agricultural Research Service, *The Imported Fire Ant Program . . . , loc. cit.* Lofgren, C. S., W. A. Banks and C. E. Stringer, *Toxicity of Various Insecticides to the Imported Fire Ant*, Agricultural Research Service, United States Department of Agriculture, 81-11:1–5, 1964. Thompson, J. L., "Baits and Natural Feeding Stimulants of the Imported Fire Ant," Unpublished Master's thesis. Department of Entomology, Mississippi State University, Starkville, Mississippi, 1967.

51. DeWitt, J. B., W. H. Stickel and P. F. Springer, *Pesticide-Wildlife Studies, 1961–1962*, U.S. Fish and Wildlife Service, Circular 167, 1963, pp. 87–88.

52. DeWitt, J. B., C. M. Menzie, J. W. Spann and C. Vance, *Pesticide-Wildlife Studies, 1963*, U.S. Fish and Wildlife Service, Circular 199, 1964, pp. 105–109.

53. Baker, Maurice F., "Studies on Possible Effects of Mirex Bait on the Bobwhite Quail and Other Birds," *Proceedings of the 18th Annual Conference, Southeastern Association of Game and Fish Commissioners*, 1964, pp. 153–160.

54. *Ibid.*

55. Good, E. E., G. W. Ware and D. F. Miller, "Effects of Insecticides on Reproduction in the Laboratory Mouse: I. Kepone," *Journal of Economic Entomology*, 58: 754–757, 1965.

56. Huber, J. J., "Some Physiological Effects of the Insecticide Kepone in the Laboratory Mouse," *Toxicology and Applied Pharmacology*, 7:516–524, 1965.

57. DeWitt, et al., *Pesticide-Wildlife Studies, 1961–1962, loc. cit.*

58. DeWitt et al., *Pesticide-Wildlife Studies, 1963, loc. cit.*

59. Martin, H., *Guide to the Chemicals Used in Crop Protection*, Publication 1093, Fourth Edition, Queen's Printer, Ottawa, Canada, 1961. Spencer, E. Y., "Supplement to the Fourth Edition," *Guide to the Chemicals Used in Crop Protection*, Publication 1093, Queen's Printer, Ottawa, Canada, 1964.

60. Ware, George W. and Ernest E. Good, "Effects of Insecticides on Reproduc-

tion in the Laboratory Mouse. II. Mirex, Telodrin, and DDT," *Toxicology and Applied Pharmacology*, 10:54–61, 1967.

61. Naber, Edward C. and George W. Ware, "Effect of Kepone and Mirex on Reproductive Performance in the Laying Hen," *Poultry Science*, 44:875–880, 1965.

62. Gaines, Thomas B. and Renate D. Kimbrough, "Oral Toxicity of Mirex in Adult and Suckling Rats," *Archives of Environmental Health*, 21:7–14, July 1970.

63. Ware and Good, *loc. cit.*

64. *Report of the Secretary's Commission on Pesticides and Their Relationship to Environmental Health*, U.S. Government Printing Office, Washington, D.C., 1969.

65. "Forty-Eight Pesticides Harnessed," *Sport Fishing Institute Bulletin*, 216:5, 1970.

66. Butler, P. A., "Monitoring Pesticide Pollution," *Bio-Science*, 19:889–891, 1969.

67. Bellinger et al., *loc. cit.*

RICHARD CHESHER

Research Shows Starfish Threat Is Extremely Serious

More dead coral on barrier reef — Another 50 sq mi of coral have been confirmed dead by a Queensland University research team returning from the Great Barrier Reef in December.

Dr. Robert Endean, reader in zoology, said this meant the known total area of coral killed by the Crown of Thorns starfish was 1,000 sq mi.

The newly confirmed area is off the Ingham-Innisfail coast and extends to the outer limit of the reef.

Suspicion that the U.S. Territory Islands in the South Pacific were being threatened by the coral-eating starfish, *Acanthaster planci*, has been confirmed by a study program directed by the Westinghouse Ocean Research Laboratory of San Diego, Calif.

The 16-island survey, by 10 teams of scientific divers, revealed degrees of infestation throughout the island chain that varied from mild reef damage at Palau to complete destruction of the protective reefs at Tinian.

Long-term effects of the loss of these living breakwaters can only be hypothesized, but the consensus among participating scientists is that loss of this important link in the marine ecosystem will reduce the supply of life sustaining protein food available to the island inhabitants. In the case of atolls, which are only one or two meters above mean sea level, loss of the reefs presents a serious threat of shoreline erosion.

A major problem facing the survey teams was the establishment of a reference baseline. The *A. planci* had been considered a relatively uncommon species, and little data was available about "normal" population densities.

Richard Chesher, "Research Shows Starfish Threat Is Extremely Serious," *Ocean Industry*, vol. 5, no. 2 (February 1970), pp. 52–54. Reprinted by permission.

A normal reef balance is, of course, one where the coral regrowth is equal to the predation pressure.

From observations made on healthy reefs, the average observable daytime starfish population was one to five specimens per kilometer of reef. Higher concentrations were observed in passes through barrier reefs where strong currents encourage lush coral growth. The lowest predator populations were found in the surf zone and on shallow reefs of windward buttresses. A "normal" population was arbitrarily established as no more than 20 specimens observed during a one nautical mile tow or swim along the reef.

The counts were made by divers towed behind a boat at a speed of 2 or 3 knots; where towing was not feasible, the divers swam the reef. Freshly killed coral was easily observed from the surface as a white patch in the characteristic reef color. Coral killed by the *A. planci* remains white for several days, then turns to gray-green as algae grows on the skeletal structure.

Although the starfish generally feed at night, the survey parties were able to determine many of the animals' feeding habits by study of several specimens found feeding during the day. Normally, the single animal attacked only part of a coral head, leaving the remainder alive. After feeding on a portion of the coral, the animal would proceed to another location, sometimes more than 30 meters away, before resuming feeding.

At any location where numerous or large patches of white coral were found, the scientists attempted to determine the specific cause of mortality. Other predators are known to cause similar destruction. In particular, the *Culcita,* or "pin cushion star," feeds on coral in the same manner as *A. planci,* but the resulting patches of dead coral are considerably smaller. Species-specific deaths have also been attributed to bacterial disease and other unknown agents.

Table 1 shows the over-all results of the survey. The conditions of the reefs were rated generally in six categories, ranging from Condition 1, which was a few observed starfish with generally healthy, undamaged reef structure, to Condition 5, where the island was heavily infested and surrounded by primarily dead reefs.

Table 1. Summary of starfish infestation

Category	Condition	Islands
Cond. I	Few A. planci; healthy reefs	Yap, Ifalik, Woleai, Lamotrek, Kwajalein
Cond. II	Many A. planci; slight reef damage	Palau, Majuro, Arno, Pingelap,* Kapingamarangi*
Cond. III	Many A. planci; extensive recent reef damage	Ponape
Cond. IV	Many A. planci; extensive damage, almost completely dead reefs	Saipan, Guam, Rota, Truk
Cond. V	Primarily dead reefs	Tinian, Ant, Kuop
Cond. VI	A. planci expansion did not pass Cond. II	Nukuoro, Pingelap,* Kapingamarangi*

* Requires confirmation after one year.

Determination of the causes for this proliferation of the starfish throughout the islands is not definite. Many non-participants have suggested that the population explosion is a natural phenomenon and that nature should be allowed "to take its course."

The participating scientists take a rather different attitude toward the problem. They feel that if it is a cyclic problem, to allow nature to take its course would be the same as allowing a forest fire to burn until it dies a natural death. Estimates for the length of time it would take for these reefs to recover from the damage already done by the *A. Planci* range from 200 to 1,000 years.

The preponderance of evidence collected by the observers does not support the "natural cycle" theory; instead, it points an accusing finger at man for once again intruding within the underwater ecological chain with little or no thought to the possible consequences.

Three specific causes have been suggested — all three supportable by discrete evidence, all three related to human activity — local destruction of reefs by construction and dynamiting, collection of triton shells by collectors and ordinary civilized pollution.

Killing of coral by construction and pollution allows a gradual buildup of large populations of starfish through the removal of larval-stage predation pressure. In natural balance, starfish larvae would be subject to feeding by the coral and zooplankton common to the reef environment. On dead coral, all balance is destroyed, and the larvae, which feed at this stage, are free to grow into a population capable of starting a major infestation. Pollution destroys coral in a less dramatic but no less effective manner than explosions, and results in an equally acceptable environment for larval growth.

For those *A. planci* that do reach adult size, predation pressure is not absent. Tritonian mollusks are known to feed upon fully grown starfish but, unfortunately, the triton has an unnatural predator that seeks him for profit. The triton shell is considered relatively "rare" among collectors, and commanding a good price, it is actively hunted. The only thing that has saved it from complete extinction near man's habitats is that, like the *A. planci,* it is normally a night feeder and cryptic during the day. The continuing collection of these shells over the past 25 years with the aid of new diving apparatus, has made the survival probability of the starfish considerably greater.

Regardless of the basic cause of these epidemic infestations, the research teams agreed that expeditious implementation of some form of control on the adult starfish is necessary. The most effective method of killing adult *A. planci* is by direct injection of formalin into the specimen. Although time consuming, it is the only method which does not require collection and disposal of the animals.

A three-phase program was recommended by the Westinghouse study:

1. Organize local populations and educate them in control procedures.
2. Organize groups of divers to kill existing major infestation and to protect valuable reefs.
3. Increase study in the biology and ecology of the *A. planci.*

Large quantities of the predators were destroyed during the study by the scientists, but a comprehensive continuing program of control is required if the threat to the reefs is to be minimized.

There is no current program authorized to effect the necessary controls, but a bill has been submitted to the U.S. Congress by the senators from Hawaii and Alaska to provide $4.5 million to the Department of Interior and the Smithsonian Institution for a 5-year control and study program. Favorable consideration of the bill is expected even under tight fiscal conditions and the program should be in operation by the spring of 1970.

RICHARD M. KLEIN
Green Mountains, Green Money

The state of Vermont and its people have a very favorable image throughout the United States. Visions of frosty mornings and horses pulling sledges of maple sap to a steamy sugar house, the Long Trail in the summer and ski trails in the winter, hillsides ablaze with autumnal colors, and residents with a reputation for honest taciturnity, frugality, and homespun hospitality make people beam when you say you are from Vermont. Surprisingly, all this is true: Vermont is a *Reader's Digest* ideal. Yet the state is caught in the grip of another part of the American ideal, the concept of rising material expectations, and is wrestling with the question of how to pay for it.

One solution attempted over the past few years has been to attract new industry whose activities will not destroy the land, the water, or the people. This has been reasonably successful; today, industry brings in more money than farming, and there are now more people in the state than cows — a reversal of the situation that prevailed not too long ago. To continue to attract clean, nonpolluting industry, electric power is required, and the current furor over the construction of atomic energy generating plants in Vermont is an ecological example of the academic "on the one hand, but then again, on the other. . . ." It is likely that there will be a second atomic energy plant built in the near future, but it is still an open question whether it will be rammed down our throats by Vermont Yankee Power and the Atomic Energy Commission or be designed so as to truly limit inherent environmental insults and provide additional benefits to the land and the people.

Utilization of land in Vermont presents about as many problems as does power. A short growing season, shallow soil, traditional rockiness of the fields,

Richard M. Klein, "Green Mountains, Green Money," *Natural History*, March 1970, pp. 11–26. Copyright 1970 by the American Museum of Natural History. Reprinted by permission.

and abrupt transitions in elevation all dictate that much of the state is agricul-
turally marginal. Large tracts in and near the Green Mountains were held in
timber, culled to sugar maple, or left alone with occasional selective cutting
of timber. Up to about the end of World War II, land simply wasn't worth
much; it went for less than $20 per acre. Land deeds are so written that acre-
age is casually given as so many acres "more or less" and a 10 percent variation, usually greater than smaller, is expected. Because of depressed valuation,
land assessments and land taxes brought in relatively little money. Even today,
Vermont's Department of Forests and Parks owns over 100,000 acres in the
state and in 1968 paid town taxes of about $.31 per acre. In one town, Groton,
the state's holdings constitute more than 20 percent of the tax listings. These
are fine recreational lands; if they were taxed according to their fair market
value, Groton would be wealthy — and the town knows it.

Four lumber companies — St. Regis, Brown, Atlas Plywood, and International Paper — own close to 800,000 acres of land in Vermont. Under sus-
tained-yield forest management, profit on an acre of timberland is about $1.50
per year. When land is assessed at its fair market value, the taxes on such land
can easily be higher than the timber income. Landowners and towns realized
that there is both immediate and long-term money in developing the land for
recreation. With this realization, some towns are raising land taxes to force
owners to sell for development, and many towns are under pressure to sell
off their municipal forests for both immediate cash and long-term tax gains.
The land boom is definitely on.

Land development and land speculation are old hat in the United States,
and Vermont is no exception. The state's founding fathers, Ethan and Ira Allen,
pushed their Onion River Land Company between bouts with the British. The
first governor of Vermont, Thomas Chittenden, speculated in real estate while
in office. Small-scale developers came and went for a hundred years or so —
their avarice or their honesty had small effect on the over-all stability of the
environment.

Today's activities are, however, on a scale several orders of magnitude
greater than anything ever seen before. The affluence of at least part of the
population, the decreased livability of the eastern seaboard's megalopolis, the
extension of superhighways and the cars that use them, and the desire of many
people to breathe fresh air at least part of the year — all these factors mesh
neatly with the situation in Vermont where agricultural and forested lands are
economically unprofitable, and where the towns and the state are desperately
searching for a firmer, broader tax base to meet the spiraling desire for government services. It is no longer a question of whether Vermont land will serve as
the environmental safety valve for city people and as the economic salvation
of the towns, but rather of who will provide the developmental services and
how will such development be controlled.

Vermont is divided into fourteen counties. Windham County, my focus
of attention, includes the southeastern part of the state with the Connecticut
River forming its eastern margin. Brattleboro, population 13,000, is the only
community of any size, with small towns, villages, and hamlets dotting the
rest of the county. The county is very lovely. It boasts eight ski areas, including
the renowned Mount Snow-Carinthia-Haystack complex and Stratton Moun-

tain. Thousands of well-heeled visitors (a pair of skis can cost $200; boots, $150) receive their first taste of Vermont through skiing visits. Green Mountain National Forest, several reservoirs, excellent trout streams, and a series of tranquilizing vistas have stimulated the desire of many people to own a piece of Windham County.

Local officials thought that they were knowledgeable about summer people. In 1968 there were 3,246 vacation homes (called "camps" by real Vermonters) in the county; Vermonters owned less than 20 percent of these. People from Connecticut, Massachusetts, and New York owned the rest. About $600,000 was realized from property taxes; the average tax bill per camp was less than $200, and none of the towns got rich on that. Of course, purchases and services brought in additional money. At the end of 1968, there was greater appreciation of summer residents since they accounted for one-quarter of all revenue. As of the fall of 1969, the situation was very different; it can best be evaluated by focusing on two townships in Windham County, Dover and Stratton. The situation in these towns is atypical only because things have moved faster here than elsewhere in the state.

The town of Dover is just a few miles from the Mount Snow-Carinthia-Haystack Mountain ski complex. There are 23,000 acres in Dover Township with 2,000 acres tied up as national forest. Four hundred people are registered voters. Up to about 1955, Dover's economy was agricultural with considerable lumbering, but today only one farm is operative and lumbering is minimal. In keeping with its location, its facilities, and its economic position, the annual town expenditures and the decisions involved in disbursing its funds were not onerous for the town clerk and three unpaid selectmen. The spectacular success of the ski areas resulted in additional revenue; ski patrons and ski bums were in, but not of, the town during the winter and generally disappeared with the snow. There were 300 summer residents as of 1968, and the possibility of an increased number of camp owners in colonies surrounding the ski areas was viewed with interest. The Mount Snow Development Corporation owned and planned to develop several moderately sized areas, and other ski companies were also considering this prospect to provide year-round use of their facilities.

With these possibilities in mind, the town had published a zoning ordinance in January, 1967, to ensure the orderly development of summer homes. The minimum requirements for lot and house size, setback from roads, access, and so on were in keeping with tradition and common sense, but they were just that — minimal. Except for the general statement that there should be no hazards to health and that the creation of unsanitary conditions was to be prevented, health and safety regulations were essentially lacking. Basically, Dover does not have the manpower or the expertise to regulate home development, and the town finessed with the hope that state standards and controls would fill in the gaps.

Including the ski areas, there are now over twenty developers in Dover holding close to 7,000 acres. In 1966, West Virginia Pulp and Paper Company sold 3,400 acres of timberland to the Pineland Realty Company, and this parcel was subsequently sold to the Vermont Lumber Company. Eugene Coleman, an active land buyer, acquired Vermont Lumber shortly thereafter and initiated the development of Dover Hills. He sold out quickly to the Cavanagh Leasing Company of New York and Florida. Cavanagh Leasing and Caveland Equities are both directed by Mr. Coleman; stock, which sold for $9 a share when first issued at the end of 1966, was worth $70 per share in August, 1969.

Vermont Lumber essentially went out of the lumber business in 1968 when they announced that they were going to develop 550 acres of their total acreage. If we eliminate land already in homes and discount roads and land that is too steep or otherwise unsuitable, Vermont Lumber owns one-sixth of the land area and controls about one-half of the future of Dover. Decisions affecting the future of the town are out of the hands of the people themselves.

In the spring of 1969 an attempt by the townspeople to restrict building height, control road frontage, and regulate building permits was countered when urban developers swamped the town meeting with company lawyers, a company planning consultant, and $600 in slick publications. The tidal wave of talk by this outside talent effectively packed the meeting, and the local residents — who are the only voters — didn't have a chance. One townsman, Jack Veller, has said that those who will determine the nature of the environment have no sense of Vermont history, no love of land, and no permanent interest because they will never live in Dover.

Of Vermont Lumber's six planned developments, Dover Hills and Dover Hills West are the biggest and are being pushed the hardest. Although lots of one to twelve acres are for sale, the average lot size is just over one acre and the average price is between $5,000 and $6,000. Even at these prices which, incidentally, have greatly inflated the base for tax assessments at "fair market value," about three-quarters of the lots were sold by August, 1969. Assuming that just Vermont Lumber sells all of its acreage, a town of 400 voters will include 3,000 additional homes. Camp owners cannot vote, but their impact on the town and their just demands for road clearing in winter, police and fire protection, and administrative services cannot fail to create severe strains in this community.

Dover Hills is being marketed by the hard sell. My letter from their marketing director, Paul Thibert, was accompanied by a slick brochure with pictures of beautiful people lounging before roaring fireplaces, golfers, pretty girls on horseback, trout streams, and uncrowded ski-lift lines (probably taken on a Monday morning). Dover Hills is "close to convenient shopping, schools, houses of worship, theaters, medical facilities." It depends on what you mean by convenient; furthermore, the public schools of Dover just meet the state standards for room volume per pupil, and hospitals are 25 miles away in Bennington or Brattleboro. Vermont Lumber is using telephone contacts straight from the Connecticut telephone directories; they have not had to extend their area of sales pitch. If a prospect is at all interested, the company sends a "sit-salesman" to the prospect's home to sit down with the family, present a slide show, and discuss the matter. If still interested, the client (no longer a prospect) is invited up for an all-expense weekend where considerable pressure is employed to get a 10 percent refundable down payment. Questions about who wears what pants in which family, appeals to sympathy for the salesman's children, discussions of the value of land as a hedge against inflation, and downright rudeness limit the percentage of returned down payments.

The company has gone to some expense to give the client a good show for his weekend visit. New roads run pleasantly through the development. They have cleared the brush and groomed the woods for about one hundred feet back from the roads, most effective for giving the impression of a mature forest. Sales pitches are replete with promises of things to come, including a 70-acre lake, a golf course, stables, a village shopping center, and (affluent society, indeed!) an airport. As of this writing, none of these extras has materialized. Their promotion speaks of "exclusive Ellis Park," but this is a one-acre site with a picnic table and a children's section containing slides and swings like those in many backyards. Because of a weird loophole in Vermont law, salesmen don't have to be licensed by the state, or even be residents, and their promises beyond the contract are as reliable as snow in June. In an effort to allay the town's concern over schools, one of Vermont Lumber's officials indicated that they would consider donating land, but would assume no responsibility beyond this. Fortunately, there has been little cutting in Dover Hills, and a restrictive covenant under consideration may prohibit extensive tree removal, as well as set broad limits of house size, color, and area. One model home, priced at about $23,000, is completed. It is carpeted, but its imitation wood paneling is apparently nailed to bare studs, for the walls give with gentle finger pressure. Few of the owners have erected homes, but those that have been built are unimaginative, out of keeping with the land, or downright ugly. They are mostly precut or modular units ranging in price from approximately $12,000 up to about $45,000 for the more ornate A-frames.

The major entrance road into both Dover Hills and Dover Hills West comes off the main road in the village of Dover Hills West. It has a fairly steep grade and it might be exciting to see some 8,000 people trying to get in or out on a snowy weekend; snowbound vehicles have already overtaxed road maintenance crews. The local fire department is composed of volunteers whose equipment is adequate for present needs, but the new homes and open woods present a fire hazard (no hydrants, for example) that is likely to be reflected in insurance rates. Vermont Lumber has apparently given no thought to rubbish disposal, even though new state laws drastically limit expansion of town dumps.

Although population pressures, taxes, aesthetics, and other problems exist in Dover Hills, the basic worries are water and sewerage. Vermont gets 35 to 40 inches of rain per year, and a good share of this percolates into the ground. With Dover Hills' 550 houses, about 3,000 square feet of land per housing unit will be covered by houses and roads, effectively sealing off about 1,650,000 square feet of land surface. Thus, over 3,000 gallons of water per housing unit for each inch of rain will have to be carried off instead of entering the ground water supply; erosion, silting, and minor flooding can result. Dover Hills will not have a consolidated water supply; each house must have its own well. This may be fine for the man at the bottom of the hill, but the man on the top may find that his well will run dry. The valley householder may not be too well off either, because runoff from the top can flood his property.

In a report to the governor's Commission on Environmental Control, my colleagues Hub Vogelmann, Jim Marvin, and Max McCormack discussed the ecology of upper-elevation land in Vermont, defined as areas above 2,500 feet. They noted that these lands are the primary sources of abundant, clean water in the state because forested land holds rain and collects fog moisture. The soils are generally shallow and rocky, and road construction — or even extensive foot traffic — severely alters infiltration and percolation of water. It is enough to note that a fair proportion of Dover Hills is located at about 2,500 feet; indeed, lots with breath-taking views, which command the highest prices, are at 3,000 feet.

Dover Hills will not have a consolidated sewage system; each house will have its own septic tank. Assuming that each person in each house uses 50 gallons of water per day and that there will be five people in a house, the septic tank must handle 250 gallons of effluent daily. You can multiply this by 550 (the number of homes) to get an idea of the volume of waste to be disposed of.

Bruce Watson, the state soils man, has surveyed in the Dover area. The mountain soils are thin, allowing relatively little soil volume and drainage for a leach field. Raw or partly digested sewage from such a field, plus seepage from the septic tanks, may eventually get into the ground-water and contaminate the wells, particularly those on the lower slopes. Septic tanks used sporadically in vacation homes function more poorly and break down sooner than those servicing year-round homes because they become less efficient. Since bacterial action is depressed by cold weather in areas where soils are shallow, overflow of undigested sewage can be expected. A "sniff test" in several developments indicates that health hazards are already accompanied by aesthetic insults. A Public Health Service team has reported that about one-third of all water systems examined in Vermont were contaminated with sewage. Indeed, well pollution in southern Vermont developments has already been reported by distraught vacation home-owners. Undigested effluents can kill trees, compounding the damage.

Before detailing the reactions of the state to such a development as Dover Hills, a look a few miles up the road might be interesting. In neighboring Stratton township there is a major ski resort that may soon have clusters of vacation homes around the slopes. In 1968 Stratton had only 94 vacation homes paying a bit over $6,000 in taxes. The township has well over 23,000 acres of timbered land ripe for conversion into vacation homes, and virtually all of it is owned by the International Paper Company; International Paper owns 60 percent of the town of Stratton.

The company has been under fire from both Vermont and New York because of a paper mill at Ticonderoga, New York, at the lower end of Lake Champlain. This mill has for many years made a cesspool of the adjacent segment of the lake. A new plant may reduce insults to the eye and nose, not to mention the lake, but pending its completion, sulfite sludge keeps pouring into the water. International Paper's local reputation as a conservation-minded organization is minimal.

IPC has excellent corporate administrators. They recognized that their holdings in southern Vermont were Green Mountain "gold," not because of spruce for pulp or yellow birch for cabinet veneers, but for land development. They realized that IPC had no knowledge of land development and that it would be useful to acquire a company with such experience. Thus, in 1968 IPC put out $12 million to acquire American Central Company, a Michigan-based firm that had developed about seventy tracts in nine states. According to *Fortune,* IPC incidentally generated a tax write-off by transferring land to their wholly owned subsidiary. The president of IPC, Edward Hinman, said, "American Central has had an impressive record in its ten years of operation for selecting, planning and developing recreational areas of this type." To round out their entrance into land development, IPC purchased Spacemakers, Inc., a Massachusetts firm specializing in the construction of leisure homes ("eight weeks from start to completion") and the interdigitation of IPC land, IPC forest products, and IPC land development was complete.

No one is sure how IPC's development plans for Stratton leaked out, and it is possible that the light of understanding dawned only when bulldozers began clearing the land. Residents became alarmed in late June about the instant community and transmitted their fears to state senator Edward Janeway and Governor Davis. Davis immediately telegraphed Hinman, IPC president, for a meeting. A local officer of the company first presented the over-all plan to a state commission in late June, 1969. Asked what would be done about water and sewerage, the IPC official replied that each lot owner would drill his own well and install his own septic tank. Asked by a representative of the Vermont Water Resources Department about tests for septic tank feasibility, the official said that no tests had been made. Asked about open space, the official replied that some land would be left undeveloped, but admitted that some of this is "rather on the steep side." Asked about building restrictions, he replied that none were contemplated. Asked what responsibility his company would assume for sewage treatment plants and a community water supply, he replied that a council of citizens might be formed to study community problems. Asked if IPC or American Central would ante up a bond to pay for emergencies brought about by the development, he replied that he couldn't speak for the company. At the end of this meeting someone passed around a brochure of an American Central development in Wisconsin that showed a lake completely surrounded by 60- by 150-foot building lots. Senator Janeway later admitted that he shuddered.

Shortly after this interesting session, the Stratton Planning Commission met with a citizens' group, the Vermont Natural Resources Council, to point out that tiny Stratton was unequal to the task of controlling the mammoth IPC combine. One commissioner said that the company was able to hire all the lawyers around and had even invited local selectmen to go on the company's payroll as consultants. One local conservationist reported that he was warned to get out of the way or he'd be run over when he tried to take pictures of operating bulldozers, but he hired a plane and took his photographs from the air. According to people who attended the meeting, the pictures show a hunk of land cut by roads from bottom to top, with virtually no thought of water flow or other ecological considerations.

Hinman and Governor Davis met on July 12 in a closed-door session with the Environmental Control Commission, but by the end of the session the state was no closer to learning any details of the plans than it had been two weeks earlier. Hinman did say, in a press release, that his company had only the best interests of Vermont at heart and that American Central would work closely with local and state officials during the development of its 23,000 acres. On the basis of this meeting, the governor said the relationship was starting off as one of the finest cooperative ventures ever undertaken with a developer.

Over the weekend, however, a completely new view of American Central came to light. Elbert Moulton, special assistant to the governor, made an incognito visit to Tamworth, New Hampshire, where American Central is developing a ski and beach club on a small lake. Moulton was greeted at the entrance by a full-dressed clown, complete with balloons and streamers, who waved and beckoned to drivers. Posing as a prospect, Moulton got the hard sell, with a "weekend-after-the-Fourth-of-July special," promises of no lower limit on cost of home building, favorable financing, and all the rest. The company advertised in Boston newspapers that there was a lake with a natural sand beach, but the saleswoman admitted that they had been hauling in sand for the past week. Moulton, no slouch as a salesman himself — he worked out the "Vermont, the Beckoning Country" campaign — admitted that he beat a hasty retreat. In a report to the governor, he concluded that if American Central were to develop in Stratton as it has been developing in New Hampshire, Vermont should not allow it. At the press conference the Friday before, neither the president of IPC nor the president of American Central admitted that they even knew that American Central was developing in New Hampshire.

Within two days, things really began to pop. On Wednesday, Governor Davis announced that development of Stratton by American Central had ceased pending revision of its plans, that the IPC vice president for public relations would meet forthwith with the governor to establish closer communications, that aides of the governor would visit other American Central projects within a week, and that the president of IPC had expressed concern over the type of development being done by his firm in New Hampshire. Local newspapers printed unattributed stories saying that International Paper was not aware of the building habits of American Central prior to its infolding into the corporate bosom, and that IPC now realized that it had misjudged public reaction to its Stratton development and had erred both in its public relations and in its reluctance to discuss things frankly with the Environmental Control Commission the previous week. Although IPC admitted that the New Hampshire operation is tawdry, they stated that it is not the best example of American Central's work. Unfortunately, reports are already filtering in that American Central developments on Cape Cod and elsewhere are at the same level.

On July 25, Stratton residents finally learned officially that much of the township would soon become a community of one-acre lots — 10 percent down and seven years to pay. The meeting got off to a bad start because American Central didn't show up and a messenger had to be sent up to the mountain to bring a representative down to the meeting. When the townspeople asked for some assurance that American Central would do right, they were told that the development would be a "welcome addition to your town," and that "our company's past record is spotless." It didn't allay their fears to be told that any jump in school-age population would be the concern of the local school board, that the township would double or triple its population in a few years, that 12 miles of roadway are being built for the town to take care of, or that expansion is virtually certain within the next three to five years.

At about the same time, Governor Davis asked a professional planning consultant to meet with American Central to insure that Stratton would be a quality development. By the end of the week, all work was halted pending extensive review and evaluation of the entire operation by state advisers, and by the end of the month, it was announced that plans for the development would be shelved until at least the spring of 1970. The governor hinted that IPC may decide that the development might simply not be worthwhile because of the unfavorable publicity and the adverse reactions of local citizens.

The purchase of large tracts during 1969 has not been restricted to Southern Vermont. Interstate highways will soon complete the network between Massachusetts, Montpelier, the state capital, and the Canadian border. It is a short drive through lovely country into the whole northern part of the state, including the hitherto neglected "northeast kingdom." In one of the kingdom's counties, Essex, 90 percent of all land is owned by lumber companies. Caveland Equities, Inc., also directed by Eugene Coleman (who started Dover Hills), purchased close to 3,000 acres in the kingdom for about $100 per acre — a dirt cheap price. Mr. Coleman, a busy man who keeps his money working hard, also purchased 800 acres on yet-unspoiled Lake Seymour, and 2,700 acres in Greensboro. Some undisclosed group apparently took the trouble to look at a recent state highway map (free from the Vermont Development Commission) and purchased 1,600 acres near Interstate 89 in the town of Sharon. A parcel of about 30,000 acres was sold by a financially depressed lumber company to Laird Properties and Laird's New England Land syndicate added about 40,000 acres within a few weeks. Names like the "Great Northern Land Corporation," "Triton Investments" (a California combine), and several ". . . and Associates" are beginning to crop up on the list of purchasers of large acreages.

An interesting sociopolitical note to the burgeoning land speculation in the northeast part of the state is the separatist movement in Quebec. Many of the Anglo-Saxons (anyone who is not French) have money, and this is part of the reason for the agitation. They are beginning to hedge their finances by heavy buying in those areas of Vermont and New Hampshire within 75 miles of the border and are paying not only inflated land prices but also an unfavorable exchange rate of 7 percent.

Many townships have no zoning regulations and, of those with zoning, many have either interim regulations or, as in the case of Dover and Stratton, minimal zoning. Mere zoning doesn't insure sewerage systems, adequate road construction and maintenance, school sites, a municipal water supply, or even conservation of open space. These are the functions of subdivision regulations, and very few towns have even started arguing about them. Ultimately, direction, power, and nay-saying rests at the state level because the towns haven't the money, men, experience, or hometown power to cope with the situation.

One official of a prominent development company noted that Vermont is a Mecca for his and other companies just because of this.

The realization that something had to be done immediately caused some soul and law searching in state offices. The secretary of state revealed that a 1917 law gave him the power (hitherto unused) to refuse to license any foreign corporation if the refusal would "promote the general good" of the state. Foreign corporation is defined as a firm whose principal place of business is outside Vermont. It was also suggested that municipalities could refuse to take over the roads put in by developers. This would certainly hurt sales because a potential buyer would understandably be loath to purchase property knowing the roads would not be plowed and maintained in the winter. A simple amendment to existing law would require only that the street or transportation portion of the master plan require approval before any work can start.

Up to this year, Vermont really didn't have an integrated system for regulation, not because previous administrations were unaware of the dangers, but because there was real citizen resistance to imposition of state control. This past summer several local boards informed the state in no uncertain terms to keep its nose out of their communities — they could handle their own problems, thank you very much.

Archaic practices worked against effective control. The tax department was not permitted to inform other state agencies when a large tract of potential development land changed hands. Fish and Game, Forests and Parks, Water Resources, Health, Planning and Development were separate and unrelated. Central Planning could act only when requested by Development. Highways, responsible for many winter road services, could assist a town only when invited. The list could be extended for another half column.

Vermont does have laws regarding pollution, but like those in many other states, they are ambiguous, full of loopholes, and subject to "interpretation." It hasn't helped that two involved departments, Health and Water Resources, were independent and not especially cooperative. A key section of the Water Pollution Control Act states that the Water Control Board may take action against any person who permits wastes to enter water so as to reduce the water below the classification set for it. Another law provides that any person who diverts water (such as drilling a well) and either corrupts it or renders it impure is liable to the municipality. At a hearing last year the water resources commissioner stated that he didn't believe (but didn't know) that the board could press a case against a mass developer. When asked what would happen if he did seek an injunction, he stated that he thought (but didn't know) that the law allowed him to act only after pollution has set in. He was challenged to determine the legal extent of his power, but he didn't try. The commissioner knew that he could assist in design and had to approve town plans for both sewerage and water, but he didn't believe (but didn't know) he could regulate a development's plans unless they were submitted by the town.

The health commissioner admitted that Vermont has many laws that provide for regulation, but he noted that he doesn't have the staff or the money for environmental control. Some time back the commission won an injunction forbidding construction of additional homes on a site that couldn't support more septic tanks, but it hasn't taken advantage of this precedent. Health officers said they really don't get complaints until after damage has been done, but I can show you water and health hazards a half hour from my home that are older than I am. Obviously, money is a factor, but the prime considerations are motivation and some sense of urgency, and both have been conspicuously lacking. Up to now the people haven't leaned hard on the state because they haven't been aware of the situation.

With the citizens now aroused, these deficiencies are being cleared up by an extensive reorganization of state agencies. Concern for the quality of the environment, shouted for years by the conservation-minded, is now as Vermontish as white rat-trap cheese or maple sugar on snow with dill pickles. We now have an Inter-agency Council on Natural Resources embracing Forest and Parks, Fish and Game, and several others. In September, a Planning and Community Services Commission was organized to umbrella housing, poverty programs, local affairs, the Central Planning Agency and several others. Not incidentally, it is headed up by Ted Riehle, who fought for and eventually secured the passage of an antibillboard law, only the second in the United States, which will allow all of us to see our mountains without eyeball pollution.

The capstone in any concerted program is an environmental control commission; Vermont established one last summer. Chaired by a legislator with a record of intelligent conservation policy, the commission was charged with making recommendations on new laws, on integration among departments, and on coordination with local governments. Among its first recommendations was one for a 90 percent increase in funds allotted to regional planning groups on the county level, a fiscally, politically, and environmentally sound idea. The commission serves now as an evaluative center for other far-reaching plans. The health commissioner requested the Environment Control Commission to seek legislation that would require all land developers to submit plans to his department for approval prior to any work. He also asked for legislation to give the health department specific authority to move against developers.

Should the state set standards for approving or disapproving certain lands for development? Should Health and Water Resources hire engineers to help towns control land development? Can taxes be scaled to provide advantages if land is not used for development, and what effect will this have on state and local financing? What about pesticide controls, responsibility of town and state for highway construction, protection for lands above 2,500 feet? An important and delicate question is how much authority the state can assume without infringing on local communities. Many argue that local officials cannot be trusted with authority over land development because they have been put on the payrolls of developers, may be in a position to profit personally from development, or are snowed by the high-priced talent at the command of the developer.

In late June, the governor announced that the Environmental Control Commission will form Development Technical Advisory Teams to provide assistance and advice to communities and planning commissions. Happily, the commission was flooded with volunteer expertise, including nationally known regional planners, a professor of zoning laws, and others who are either "instant Vermonters" or "sunshiners" (owners of vacation homes). Economists, ecologists, and other academic types are also available to the communities — not that they weren't before, but few ever asked for their help.

Apparently, the response has been excellent. The town of Wilmington, just south of Dover, asked for a Technical Advisory Team within a week or so after the teams had been set up. A few days later the Stratton Planning Commission sent in an SOS. There are indications that at least some of the developers will avail themselves of these services. In fact, the promulgation of new health-safety regulations that require testing for percolation, ground-water levels, and other basic data will provide, for the first time, a basis for the teams to work effectively. A proposed revision of the sanitary engineering regulations, subchapter on subdivisions, provides the teeth to bite off the outstretched fingers of greedy developers.

I am usually unsatisfied by upbeat endings. Lovers wending their way into the sunset to swelling chords leave me cold. And yet, a colleague who has been deeply involved in Vermont conservation recently told me that he has never been so optimistic about the cause, and I respect his judgment; he has more battle scars than a Roman gladiator. If there is light at the end of this long environmental tunnel, it is the result of the long-overdue realization by Vermont citizens that the "beckoning country" must exist for the future. In a lecture about two years ago, William O. Douglas, a mean infighter for conservation, said that only the people can save their environment, and only if they will support those who have long cried in the wilderness, and only if their wishes are made clear to their elected representatives. These case histories in Vermont tend to support his contention. But public opinion and public support are fickle things. . . .

Chapter 4

Winnie
fitch

Generation of wastes:
unclosed materials cycles

The second chapter began with a discussion of the balance of oxygen and carbon dioxide in the atmosphere. This will now be extended to a short description of the carbon cycle, for the elements and compounds of the universe interact with one another in cycles. The chemical and physical reactions of carbon, oxygen, hydrogen, nitrogen, phosphorus, and sulfur — the most important elements — have been studied in this way.

Man's relation to his food can be shown by a simple combination of cycles: green plants in the land and water use energy from the sun to produce food from carbon dioxide and water. Then animals, including man, use these plants as fuel for their bodily processes and excrete the wastes. These wastes are then broken down by bacteria into the elements to be used again.

Man is interfering with this cycle at every stage. He is limiting the water supply from the ground by not returning used water; he is augmenting the amounts of nitrogen and phosphorus by adding chemicals; he is limiting bacterial action; and he is producing synthetic non-biodegradable compounds which do not fit into the cycle. It should be noted that it is not that a material is laboratory-made that makes it unacceptable to the natural cycle; it is the principle of biodegradation that is important. Some synthetic materials cannot be broken down into elements to rejoin the cycle and will therefore always be antithetical. This is equally true for a hydrocarbon pesticide and for a poly-vinyl chloride plastic. Also, toxicity is not related to a compound's ability to biodegrade, for there are natural toxins in many plants and animals.

This chapter will extend the cyclic concept beyond the chemical elements and compounds to show the materials cycles that man is dealing with at present. These include natural resources of the earth with its minerals and fuels, agricultural products of land and sea, and manufactured goods of industrial society. The articles in this chapter show where there is a closed natural cycle man is opening and where man has built an incomplete cycle that needs to be closed. The article by James O. Evans shows how man can add his organic wastes to the natural cycle by com-

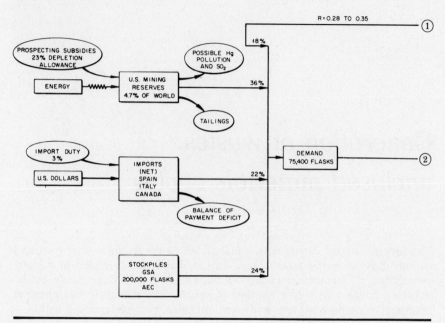

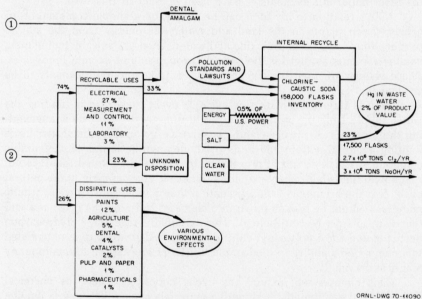

Figure 1.   Mercury flow through U. S. society (1968)**

* R is defined as the fraction of the annual demand which is presently supplied by recycle divided by the maximum possible fraction of demand which technologically could be supplied by recycle.

** Source: "Materials Resources and Recycling," Progress Report of Summer Study (1970) Interdisciplinary Research Relevant to Problems of Our Society, Oak Ridge National Laboratory–National Science Foundation, p. 25.

Y-102167
ORNL-DWG 70-11203

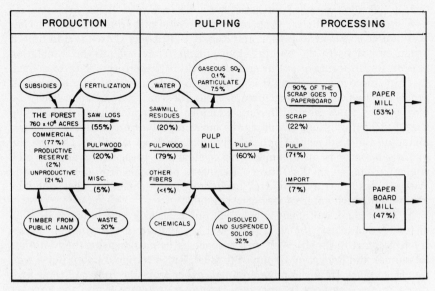

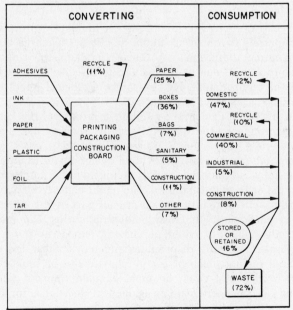

Figure 2.   Schematic flow sheet for paper products

Source: "Materials Resources and Recycling," Progress Report of Summer Study (1970) Interdisciplinary Research Relevant to Problems of Our Society, Oak Ridge National Laboratory–National Science Foundation, p. 29.

bining engineering technology with the natural mechanism of the soil system. In this way, sewage is an asset, not a waste.

In the next article, "Gaseous Sulfur Pollutants from Urban and Natural Sources," Elmer Robinson and Robert C. Robbins show the addition of urban emissions to the natural environment. They include the circulation pattern for all forms of sulfur and show where these forms tend to collect.

In true cyclic systems it is difficult to find entry, but in the chemical process industries it is not common to find a true cyclic system. The next two articles show very different examples of chemical processes. "Who Pays for Plastic Litter?" explains the most important properties of plastics, including their inherent disposal problems, such as stability. The electroplating industry is an example of a system not presently cyclical which could become so in the future. "Recovery of Metals from Electroplating Wastes" describes a method of cyclic recovery where the cost could be offset by the high value of recovered metals.

But it is not sufficient to speak of one process in one industry or even of just one industry, for what is needed is a picture of the complete industry from start to finish. Such an approach is being taken by the Materials Resources and Recycling Group of the Oak Ridge National Laboratory, who traced mercury from the mine and also paper from the forest to their final dispositions. The flow for mercury is shown in Figure 1, and the flow for paper is shown in Figure 2.

But cyclic systems are not limited to industrial processes; they include all materials involved as inputs or outputs, such as air, water, and heat. In "Thermal Pollution — A Cause for Concern," John Cairns, Jr., relates the problem of energy production to the discharge of heated waste water into the environment. He shows the biological effect of this waste material and suggests ways to manage it.

When all these cycles are put into a structure, the result is a materials flow throughout the whole of society, such as that shown in "The Flow of Materials" by Allen V. Kneese, Robert U. Ayres, and Ralph C. d'Arge. Here one can see how individual cycles relate to one another, and how all non-recycled materials end as residuals in the total system.

From the articles in Chapter 4, one might believe the actual consumer is unimportant, but in reality he is a crucial part of the decision. First, he must help by participating in closing industrial cycles. This means he might think of biodegradability when purchasing goods; he must, where warranted, separate trash into disposables and recyclables; and he must consider the final resting place of his purchases. But he must do more than just return bottles and cans; he must acquaint himself with ecological problems so he can participate in ecological decisions, for it is the consumer who pays this bill.

JAMES O. EVANS
The Soil as a Resource Renovator

"That which is used develops — that which is not used wastes away."
Hippocrates, 4th century BC

Horticulturists, foresters, and agronomists view briars, bush, and weeds not just as nuisance vegetation but, more generously, as plants growing out of place — plants occurring where not wanted. Goats, however, reveal no intellectual bias among plants, and, as they pursue their hungry objectives, do not pause to segregate weeds from their bluegrass and clover neighbors. An analogy can be drawn concerning certain discarded residues and effluents. By way of illustration, an earth specialist-ecologist or a soil scientist-sanitary engineer, in contrast to most disposal engineers, can be expected to view treated sewage and many other wastes not as refuse but as valuable resources which happen to be at the wrong place, or in the wrong form, or in the wrong amount, or at the wrong time. Indeed, all resources, whether animate or inanimate, are of limited value to man unless activated and properly utilized. For example, long ago the observation was made that muscles should be used for them to develop; otherwise, they atrophy — a wasteful process.

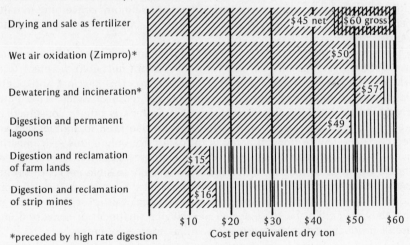

*preceded by high rate digestion

Source: Metropolitan Sanitary District of Greater Chicago

Figure 1. Costs of disposal methods for activated sludge

James O. Evans, "The Soil as a Resource Renovator," *Environmental Science and Technology*, vol. 4, no 9 (September 1970), pp. 733–735. Copyright 1970 by the American Chemical Society. Reprinted by permission of the copyright owner.
The author is a research hydrologist with the Watershed and Aquatic Habitat Research Branch, Division of Forest Environment Research, U. S. Department of Agriculture, Washington, D. C.

The value of human excreta and other animal wastes has been recognized — if not understood — for many centuries. Historically, the Chinese and other early civilizations applied human organic wastes to the land to improve or maintain soil fertility. And there are numerous documented accounts of the common use of "night soil" in European countries. The following quote taken from Victor Hugo's immortal *Les Miserables*, published in 1862, is remarkably accurate, descriptive, and up-to-date:

> *Do you know what these piles*
> *of ordure are, collected at the*
> *corners of streets, those carts of*
> *mud carried off at night from*
> *streets, the frightful barrels of*
> *the nightman, and the fetid*
> *streams of subterranean mud*
> *which the pavement conceals*
> *from you? All this is a*
> *flowering field, it is green grass,*
> *it is mint, thyme, and sage;*
> *it is game, it is cattle, it is the*
> *satisfying lowing of heavy kine;*
> *at night it is perfumed hay, it is*
> *gilded wheat, it is bread on your*
> *table, it is warm blood in your*
> *veins, it is health, it is joy, it is*
> *life.*

Little can be said to supplement such eloquent testimony concerning a material that many people usually describe with a single, common, four-letter word.

A more ancient quote from the Old Testament, Eccles. 1:7, is instructive: *All the rivers run into the sea. Yet the sea is not full; unto the place from whence the rivers come, thither they return again.* This succinct and poetic description of the hydrologic cycle — the eternal reuse of water — illustrates a well-known but little appreciated fact that nothing is utterly consumed or wasted. Instead, substances simply change from one form to another and are recycled. The law of the conservation of matter not only is true — it must be lived by. An understanding of what this implies suggests that every effort should be made by man to: • develop economically feasible means of salvaging waste materials for reuse as salable products; • isolate particularly obnoxious, toxic, or otherwise troublesome industrial wastes at their origin so that they may either be subjected to neutralizing treatment or converted into useful products; • put the wastes to work as sources of energy.

THE SOIL — A MULTIFUNCTIONAL SYSTEM

All of our metals are derived from the earth, and the earth mantle is essential to the existence of land plants and animals. Any soil which promotes the growth and well-being of plants must be amply supplied with air, water, nutrients, and living soil organisms. A given soil may serve in a variety of roles — as a receptacle or absorbing agent, a storehouse or reservoir, a screening or filtering agent, a purifier or renovator, a vehicle for transmission and recharge, or as a foundation or supporting agent. Furthermore, a body of soil conceivably may serve each role simultaneously. Consider only one role for the moment. From the beginning of life on this planet, soil has served as a cleansing and renovating agent. It is no wonder (and no accident) that the microorganisms responsible for biological purification (i.e., degradation and stabilization) in sewage treatment plants have soil as their common origin.

WATER RECYCLING — A NATURAL PHENOMENON

As implied by the hydrologic cycle, all water eventually is recirculated and re-used by various processes and organisms. So-called waste waters, including all the dissolved and undissolved substances they harbor, are likewise recycled, gradually by nature and chance or more rapidly by man and design. Indeed, "waste water" treatment and reuse differ from natural water recycling only in dissimilarities in the rapidity and intensity of the time-treatment processes involved, the former being subjected to a compressed timetable. In our modern, extremely complex society — largely urban and industrial in orientation — no single waste treatment or disposal process is best suited to all conditions, and no perfect system will ever be devised. It is possible, however, through known treatment plant techniques to renovate completely waste waters into potable water. Advanced waste treatment processes have been developed and are being used by the Federal Water Quality Administration to allow effluent discharges from which absolutely no pollution would enter our surface or groundwaters. There is a cost consideration, of course, and proper disposal is required of the quantities of organic and inorganic sludge and ash materials separated from the effluent water during treatment.

Through treatment,* sewage can be separated into two major components: • so-called sludge "solids," an inorganic and organic fluidized sludge material, almost all of which can be useful for fertilizing and soil conditioning, and • a liquid or water fraction. This liquid is not pure water, of course, and contains an appreciable amount of dissolved nutrients which also are available for plant use and growth. Not without reason, this nutrient content is viewed as excessive and undesirable when discharge to streams or lakes produces profuse aquatic growth and the resultant oxygen depletion, fish kills, and hastening of the eutrophication of lakes. And, until recently at least, most of the attention concerning treated sewage has been focused on the liquid por-

---

* Generally a municipal sewerage system will comprise several treatments: the primary will consist of separating the solids or sludge from the liquid, and the secondary will then treat the liquid fraction. Chlorine will be added and certain parameters measured such as the pH (the degree of acidity or basicity), the temperature, the DO (dissolved oxygen), the BOD and/or the COD, and other specific chemicals present. The BOD which is the biochemical oxygen demand, a measure of the amount of oxygen required for biological oxidation of biodegradable material in five days; and the COD, which is the chemical oxygen demand, a measure of the amount of oxygen needed for chemical oxidation of the material are often used as a test of the water quality. If it is not up to certain standards, tertiary treatment must be considered — Editor.

tion. Furthermore, the importance of the water resource for industrial and domestic reuse in some areas is unquestioned, providing ample justification for use of the most advanced waste treatment techniques. There are many situations, however, where the disposal of solids, sludges, and effluents by land spreading or irrigation may offer the ultimate solution to waste disposal problems.

LAND DISPOSAL

Land disposal can serve a variety of useful purposes. In an ecological sense, the partial restoration of the nutrient cycle afforded by land disposal of wastes in itself is a worthy endeavor. Although commercial fertilizers are relatively cheap and fertilizer application to crops and soils is accomplished, generally, with comparative ease, sewage and feedlot wastes usually are free of charge to farmers. And land disposal often is less expensive than any of

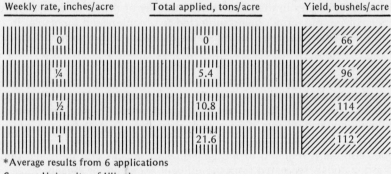

Weekly rate, inches/acre	Total applied, tons/acre	Yield, bushels/acre
0	0	66
¼	5.4	96
½	10.8	114
1	21.6	112

*Average results from 6 applications
Source: University of Illinois

Figure 2.   Sludge application increases corn yields

the advanced waste treatment and disposal alternatives. Land disposal can be viewed if one prefers, strictly as a waste water treatment process. The method can be employed primarily for the irrigation water it supplies, for ground-water replenishment, for soil enrichment and improvement, or as a combination of each.

Modern-day disposal of treated sewage and other wastes (both raw and processed) by application to land surfaces is practiced in many technically advanced countries — England, France, Poland, Germany, and the United States, for example. The practice appears to be increasing in popularity in the United States. A survey made in 1967 revealed at least 29 municipalities in Pennsylvania alone were applying liquid digested sludge onto rural lands; whereas, in June 1963, there were one third fewer Pennsylvania municipalities using this disposal method. A survey made in 1965 by Bendixen revealed over 2400 land-waste disposal systems in use in the United States. (Disposal of solid wastes in landfills was not covered.)

Disposal of organic wastes to the land by industries is commonplace. Of the over 2400 systems mentioned above, about 900 were serving the food processing industry. In this category, at least two installations are worthy of specific reference. Every year, Seabrook Farms Co. in New Jersey successfully sprays tremendous amounts of cannery wastes from a food-processing plant onto forested lands. Campbell Soup Co. in northwestern Ohio disposes of liquid discharges from tomato processing operations by application to land surfaces. In spite of soils of poor natural drainage, a combined spray irrigation –grass filtration system has been used successfully by the Campbell plant. The disposal of papermill waste water by crop irrigation and irrigation of forest lands is an established practice. Disposal of wastes from dairy plants through irrigation or other land application methods has been successfully used in several states including Wisconsin and Minnesota. Even hydrocarbons and oily sludge wastes can be effectively degraded by soil microorganisms in an aerobic environment and assimilated within the soil matrix. An industrial firm in France produces and sells protein synthesized by microorganisms growing on waste low grade petroleum. And since 1951, at the Houston, Texas, refinery of Shell Oil, almost all of the petroleum sludges and stable emulsion from tank bottoms, oil–water separators, sewer boxes, and ship ballast water has been consumed by a land disposal system.

Few would dare deny that the deliberate and orderly return by man of organic and inorganic wastes to the lands from whence they came is a good conservation practice. No one objects to the idea of systematic waste removal to areas where full utilization is possible without contamination of the environment or intrusion on the sensitivity of some group or individual; indeed, all will agree that this disposal practice is good whereas disposal to streams, lakes, open dumps, the air, the ocean, or even to so-called useless wastelands and deep underground cavities is either not so good or is unacceptable. Why then is time wasted talking about what is best rather than taking concerted action to make it a universal practice?

NEGATIVE FACTORS

There are two major factors or obstacles to a more widespread application of what might be termed a wastes conservation-and-utilization concept. One obstacle is a lack of dedication or desire by too many people to see such a practice become universal. This is due mostly to ignorance and unfounded fears — ignorance of the necessity for useful waste disposal and of its benefits, and muddled fears involving aesthetics (such as unpleasant odors or unsightly appearances) and disease or poisoning effects (i.e., contamination of animals, plants, soils, and groundwater with pathogens, excess minerals, or chemical poisons). Although these are valid and highly important considerations, my research investigations indicate such dangers are precluded if reasonable or commonsense precautions are used.

For example, deactivation, neutralization, effective incineration, or safe burial of certain highly toxic, obnoxious, or dangerous wastes may be necessary whenever such wastes occur in sufficient quantities or concentrations. Also, pasteurization or disinfection of human and livestock wastes prior to land disposal may become a recommended practice in some situations. In all cases, waste loading rates onto land areas must be adjusted to local soil, topographic, climatic, and land use conditions so that the soil environmental system is never overtaxed or loaded beyond its assimilative capacity. Continuing research, education, demonstration, and training are possible means by which the first obstacle may be overcome.

The second factor is more complex, but economics is at its core. Although it has been shown that some wastes can be hauled by truck or rail or piped economically over fairly long distances, and suitable disposal sites exist within a distance of 100 miles of almost all of our municipalities, costs must always be competitive with other treatment and disposal alternatives. Bouwer observed in 1968 that ultimate treatment and disposal of conventionally treated sewage by land application is considerably less expensive than costs of the most advanced waste treatment (tertiary) techniques available today. However, beneficial effects of the inexpensive replenishment which soils and land areas accrue from useful organic and inorganic waste materials must be compared with the relative cheapness and ease of application of commercial fertilizers to good agricultural land. And, of course, not all wastes can or should be applied to the land whatever the economic considerations. No intelligent and responsible individual would advocate discarding radioactive wastes, pesticide residues, or used car bodies onto the landscape. (Although such wastes as these also are either degradeable or reclaimable, they require special treatment and handling.)

SUMMATION

Digested sewage sludge and sewage effluent are outstanding examples, however, of so-called waste products for which land disposal is a "natural." They are not useless, are not wastes, strictly speaking, and should not be wasted. They should be considered as resource materials and consequently as assets rather than liabilities.

Whenever agricultural land and crops are mentioned, one perhaps is apt to think of those common crops such as corn, soybeans, grain, or hay and the cultivated soils in which they are grown. Although the response of such crops to sewage application can be dramatic, cultivated soils need not be favored as disposal sites. Vast areas of range and forest lands also are available for waste disposal and utilization. Of course, transport distance would be a determining factor in some cases. A fact worthy of note is that forest soils, in general, exhibit superior water absorbing capabilities and can serve as excellent receptacles for the assimilation and utilization of fluid wastes. And, because of the high evapotranspiration rates exhibited by trees, forests can be very effective in removing excess soil moisture resulting from large waste water applications.

As an awareness of the usefulness, simplicity, finality, economy, and subsequent productivity associated with or resulting from the disposal of sewage and of many other processed "wastes" by application to land becomes more commonplace, a significant increase in the popularity of the practice can be expected. Conceivably, this popularity could be shared by everyone involved with disposal activities — by those needing to get rid of the waste substance and by those needing to get it, i.e., with treatment plant operators or disposal engineers and with land treatment operators or farm managers. Resource or refuse? It is what man makes of it.

Additional reading

Bendixen, T. W., Hill, R. D., DuByne, F. T., Robeck, G. G., "Cannery Waste Treatment by Spray Irrigation-Runoff," J. Water Pol. Contr. Fed. 41 (3), 385–391 (1969).

Bouwer, H., "Returning Wastes to the Land, A New Role for Agriculture," J. Soil Water Conserv., 164–168, September–October 1968.

Dalton, F. E., Stein, J. E., Lynam, B. T., "Land Reclamation — A Complete Solution to the Sludge and Solids Disposal Problem," J. Water Pollut. Contr. Fed. 40 (5), 789–804 (1958).

Evans, J. O., "Ultimate Sludge Disposal and Soil Improvement," Water Wastes Eng., 45–47 (June 1959).

Mihursky, J. A., "On Using Industrial and Domestic Wastes in Aquaculture," Agricultural Engineering, 667–669 (November 1969).

Stephan, D. G., Weinberger, L. W., "Waste Water Reuse — Has It 'Arrived'?," J. Water Pollut. Contr. Fed., 529–539 (April 1968).

ELMER ROBINSON & ROBERT C. ROBBINS

Gaseous Sulfur Pollutants from Urban and Natural Sources

The atmosphere is a complex chemical system in which the emissions from urban pollution sources mix with emanations from the natural environment. By considering both the pollutant and the natural sources, it is possible to improve our understanding of the impact of air pollutants on the atmospheric environment. The sulfur pollutants are responsible for a significant fraction of both past and present air pollution problems. The total environmental impact of the sulfur pollutants is thus an important consideration in the field of air pollution technology.

This discussion covers the common atmospheric sulfur pollutants: SO_2 and H_2S, and also the H_2S and sulfate from the natural environment. These compounds are considered as to their sources, their atmospheric concentrations, their reactions, and available scavenging mechanisms.

Elmer Robinson and Robert C. Robbins, "Gaseous Sulfur Pollutants from Urban and Natural Sources," *Journal of the Air Pollution Control Association,* vol. 20, no. 4 (April 1970), pp. 233–235. Reprinted by permission.

The authors are with the Stanford Research Institute, Menlo Park, California.

SO₂ SOURCES

The sulfur compounds in the atmosphere come from both the natural environment and air pollution emissions. Natural sulfur compound emissions are SO_4 aerosols produced in sea spray, and H_2S from the decomposition of organic matter in swamp areas, bogs, and tidal flats. (In this presentation SO_4 will denote the sulfate ion present as a compound such as $(NH_4)_2SO_4$ or H_2SO_4.) Areas of volcanic activity are a minor source of H_2S. The emissions of SO_2 come almost exclusively from pollution sources. Some H_2S is also of industrial origin.

Annual worldwide pollution emissions of SO_2 have been estimated to be 146×10^6 tons. Of this total, 70 percent is estimated to result from coal combustion and 16 percent from the combustion of petroleum products, mainly residual fuel oil. As Table I shows, the remaining tonnage is accounted for by

Table I. Hemispheric SO₂ pollutant emissions (10^6 tons)

Source	Total SO₂	Northern Hemisphere	Southern Hemisphere
Coal[a]	102	98 (96%)	4 (4%)
Petroleum[a] Comb. and Refin.	28.5	27.1 (95%)	1.4 (5%)
Smelting[b]			
Copper	12.9	8.6 (67%)	4.3 (33%)
Lead	1.5	1.2 (80%)	0.3 (20%)
Zinc	1.3	1.2 (90%)	0.1 (10%)
Total	146	136 (93%)	10 (7%)

[a] United Nations Statistical Papers — World Energy Supplies 1963–1966, Series J, No. 11, Tables 2 and 9.
[b] U. S. Bureau of Mines, Mineral Trade Notes Vol. 64, Nos. 9 and 12 (1967).

petroleum refining and nonferrous smelting. These estimates are based on 1965 world data (U.S. Stat. Abs.[1] and other sources) and standard emission factors (Mayer[2]).

Table I shows the total SO_2 emissions divided according to sources into northern and southern hemispheres. On a total basis, 93 percent of the SO_2 emitted by pollutant sources is emitted in the northern hemisphere. The total is estimated at 136×10^6 tons from northern hemispheric sources out of a total of 146×10^6 tons.

Table II shows the estimated hemispheric emissions of sulfur in its various emission forms — SO_2, H_2S, and sulfate, to total 215×10^6 tons of sulfur. In this estimate H_2S emissions have been prorated over the warmer land and ocean, those areas between 0 and 65° in both hemispheres, whereas sea spray sulfates have been prorated according to total ocean areas. This tabulation shows that the atmosphere of the northern hemisphere receives over twice as much sulfur as does the southern hemisphere. The ratio is 149×10^6 tons or 69 percent of the global total in the northern hemisphere compared with 66×10^6 tons or 31 percent in the southern hemisphere. Details of how

Table II. Total hemispheric sulfur emissions (10^6 tons S)

Source	Total	Northern Hemisphere	Southern Hemisphere
Pollutant			
SO_2 Sources	73	68	5
Biological H_2S (Land)	68	49[a]	19[a]
Biological H_2S (Marine)	30	13[b]	17[b]
Sea Spray	44	19[c]	25[c]
Total	215	149 (69%)	66 (31%)

[a] Based on ratio of land area between 0 and 65°N and S.
[b] Based on ratio of ocean areas between 0 and 65°N and S.
[c] Based on ratio of ocean areas in both hemispheres.

the data on natural H_2S and SO_4 were obtained are presented in the subsequent discussion of the sulfur cycle.

Previous estimates of world SO_2 emissions have been made by Katz.[3] For the years of 1937 and 1940, total emissions were about 69×10^6 tons and 78×10^6 tons, respectively. Thus, SO_2 emissions have roughly doubled in the period between 1940 and 1965.

ATMOSPHERIC REACTIONS AND SCAVENGING PROCESSES

Hydrogen sulfide is rapidly oxidized to SO_2 in the troposphere by ozone in a heterogeneous reaction on surfaces (e.g., aerosol particles). The lifetime of H_2S in the atmosphere ranges from about two hours in urban areas to about two days in remote unpolluted areas (Robinson and Robbins[4]).

There has been considerable interest in SO_2 scavenging reactions for many years, and much research has centered around the need for specific catalysts to promote SO_2 oxidation in liquid droplets. However, a more realistic process for foggy atmospheres involves ammonia. Junge and Ryan[5] found that SO_2 had low solubility in water droplets of low pH, but that ammonia that could be absorbed from the atmosphere promoted the solubility of SO_2 by neutralizing the acid in the droplets formed by the absorbed SO_2. Extrapolation of laboratory experiments to realistic atmospheric conditions indicates that SO_2 lifetimes in foggy conditions might be as short as one hour. The fact that ammonium sulfate is commonly identified in atmospheric particulate samples lends support to this scavenging reaction.

Rainout processes within clouds and washout resulting from falling rain may also be quite effective in scavenging SO_2, as Bielke and Georgii[6] have shown.

Sulfur dioxide oxidation is not confined to fog or rain conditions. While direct oxidation by molecular oxygen has been shown to be insignificant, photochemical oxidation of SO_2 in mixtures with NO_2 and hydrocarbons is probably one of the more significant scavenging systems for SO_2. The resultant aerosol formed by this system is H_2SO_4. The reaction can proceed with very low concentrations of the constituents (Renzetti and Doyle[7]).

An integrated system to explain the reaction of SO_2 in the atmosphere is not now available. Under daytime low humidity conditions, the photochemical processes that form H_2SO_4 or sulfate aerosols seem to be most important. With high humidity and fog or rain, absorption into water drops with subsequent oxidation to SO_4 is probably the most important process.

Sulfur dioxide is also scavenged from the atmosphere by vegetation. In vegetation scavenging it is possible to consider the rate of deposition by using Chamberlain's[8] concept of a deposition velocity. On the basis of chamber studies of SO_2 intake by vegetation (Katz and Ledingham[9]), the calculated deposition velocity for SO_2 is about 1 cm/sec. For a concentration of 1 ppb this deposition velocity predicts an SO_2 deposition rate of 2.5 $\mu g/m^2/day$.

Once SO_2 and H_2S are in aerosol form as SO_4, precipitation scavenging by clouds and rain is an effective removal process. Particles are also removed from the atmosphere as dry fallout. For precipitation processes, the rate of scavenging is dependent upon intensity of precipitation activity and on the size of the aerosol.

SO_2 BACKGROUND CONCENTRATIONS

Sulfur as SO_2 and SO_4 has been measured in polluted atmospheres for many years, and voluminous statistics are available. However, in our analysis of the total cycle of sulfur in the environment concentration data are needed for the clean ambient atmosphere. These data are very sparse.

Vertical profiles taken over Nebraska indicate values of less than 0.3 ppb SO_2 in the upper portions of the troposphere (Georgii[10]). These are in line with the few other available measurements of surface SO_2 in very remote places, such as the 0.3 ppb found in Hawaii and 1 ppb found on the southeast coast of Florida by Junge.[11] Similar values, of 0.3–1 ppb SO_2, were recently found by Cadle et al.,[12] in Antarctica and by Lodge and Pate[13] in the Panama Canal Zone. Over wide areas of the Central Atlantic, Kühme[14] found no SO_2 above the limit of detection, which was about 0.3 ppb. From these values we have tentatively concluded that the average tropospheric SO_2 concentration on a global basis is about 0.2 ppb.

Table III summarizes our present best estimates of background concentrations for SO_2 and the other important atmospheric sulfur compounds.

THE ENVIRONMENTAL SULFUR CYCLE

Our present calculations, along with additional data from the literature, permit us to estimate the circulation of sulfur in various compound forms through our environment. Figure 1 shows our estimate of this sulfur circulation. Some of the values used in this calculation are reasonably well known, i.e., pollutant emissions and total depositions, but some data must be considered very speculative and have been adjusted reasonably to balance the cycle, e.g., land and sea emissions of H_2S.

Table III. Average tropospheric concentrations of sulfur compounds

Compound	Average Concentration	Average Concentration as Sulfur μg/m³
SO₂	0.2 ppb	0.25
H₂S	0.2 ppb	0.14
SO₄	2μg/m³	0.7

To understand this circulation better, we can examine its various components. The sulfur annually discharged to the sea by the world's rivers is 73×10^6 tons: this results from sulfur accumulated from weathering rocks, 14×10^6 tons; sulfur applied to the soil as fertilizer, etc., 11×10^6 tons; and sulfur deposited on the soil by precipitation or dry deposition, 48×10^6 tons. These amounts were estimated by Eriksson.[15a]

The atmosphere-land portion of the cycle contains 70×10^6 tons of pollutant sulfur as SO_2 and H_2S emitted to the atmosphere; 90×10^6 tons of sulfur, mostly as SO_4, deposited from the atmosphere to the land; a loss of 68×10^6 tons of sulfur as H_2S from decaying vegetation; and an intake of sulfur by vegetation from the atmosphere of 26×10^6 tons. The 90×10^6 tons deposited includes 80%, or 70×10^6 tons, in rain and the remainder as dry deposition (Junge[11]). As indicated, 48×10^6 tons of this deposited sulfur is carried off by rivers, and 42×10^6 tons is absorbed by vegetation and then released as H_2S. The intake of sulfur by vegetation is estimated to be 26×10^6 tons based on calculations using a deposition velocity of 1 cm/sec and an ambient concentration of 0.4 ppb (0.5 μg/m³). This is twice the average tropospheric concentrations listed in Table III, which are based on the argument that ground level concentrations over land would be higher than the average concentration for the whole troposphere. The 68×10^6 tons estimated for the emission of sulfur as H_2S from vegetation decay results from a summation of

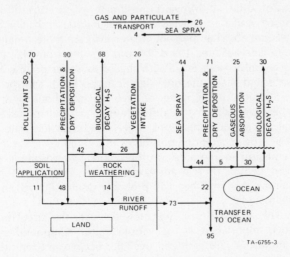

Figure 1.   Environmental sulfur circulation. Units: 10⁶ ton/yr sulfur

the atmospheric vegetation intake, 26×10^6 tons, and the excess of deposition over river carryoff, 42×10^6 tons. This assumes that there is no net accumulation in the surface soils, which seems reasonable. This value is close to Eriksson's[15a] estimate of 77×10^6 tons for H_2S emissions from land areas; however, no data are available with which to check this value. Land areas also gain 4×10^6 tons of sulfur from sea spray (Eriksson[15b]).

The net result of this land circulation is an excess of 26×10^6 tons of sulfur, which must be deposited in the ocean if there is to be no net accumulation in the atmosphere.

Deposition of sulfate in the ocean in rain and as dust is 71×10^6 tons (Junge[11]). The ocean also absorbs 25×10^6 tons of gaseous sulfur calculated on the basis of an average SO_2 concentration of 0.2 ppb and a deposition velocity of 0.9 cm/sec (Eriksson [15ab]). The ocean surface is the source of 44×10^6 tons of sulfur in sea spray (Eriksson[15a]) and 30×10^6 tons of sulfur as H_2S from vegetation decay. There is a tropospheric transfer of 4×10^6 tons of sulfur from the ocean to the land. The H_2S emission of 30×10^6 tons is obtained on the basis of what is needed to balance the 100×10^6 tons of gaseous and solid pickup by the ocean and the transfer from sea to land. There are no data that would provide a check as to whether or not this is reasonable. It is a significantly smaller value than the approximately 200×10^6 tons estimated by Eriksson[15a] and Junge[11] for similar calculations.

The end result of this cycle is an accumulation of sulfur in the oceans of 95×10^6 tons, which is the sum of pollutant emissions, sulfur applied to the soil, and rock weathering.

CONCLUSIONS

This compilation of facts and discussion about sulfur in the environment points up a number of interesting things especially relative to pollutant and natural sources of sulfur. With regard to estimates of gaseous sulfur emissions, our evaluation of available data indicates that natural emissions of sulfur, in the form of H_2S, are about 30 percent greater than are the estimated industrial emissions of SO_2 and H_2S, i.e., 100×10^6 tons as sulfur from H_2S, compared to 76×10^6 tons as sulfur from SO_2. With regard to sulfur pollutants, the most significant fact is that SO_2 is the only significant pollutant and the transformation of SO_2 to SO_4 occurs in a matter of days, perhaps about four. Most of the emitted SO_2 becomes SO_4 in the atmosphere as a result of several possible photochemical or physical reactions. This rapid reaction rate plus ready absorption of SO_2 by vegetation contributes to a rapid decrease in concentration outside emission source areas. In the ambient troposphere, most of the sulfur is present as SO_4. Thus, if any large-scale environmental effects are to result from sulfur emissions, they will probably result from adverse effects of SO_4 particulate material.

It is unlikely that we can adequately evaluate the circulation of sulfur and the relative importance of the various sulfur compound sources until considerably more data are gathered over the oceans and remote land areas of the world.

Acknowledgments

This discussion is a brief summary of a portion of the research carried out for the American Petroleum Institute at Stanford Research Institute. Substantiating calculations and additional discussion for much of the material presented in this paper are given in the basic research report published by the API (see Robinson and Robbins[4]).

References

1. U.S. Statistical Abstracts, U.S. Government Printing Office (1967).

2. Mayer, M., "A compilation of air pollution emission factors," U.S. Public Health Service, Division of Air Pollution, Cincinnati, Ohio (1965).

3. Katz, M., in *Air Pollution Handbook,* P. L. Magill, F. R. Holden, and C. Ackley, Eds., McGraw-Hill Book Company, Inc., New York (1958).

4. Robinson, E. and Robbins, R. C., "Sources, abundance, and fate of gaseous atmospheric pollutants," Final Report SRI Project PR-6755, for American Petroleum Institute, New York (Feb. 1968).

5. Junge, C. E. and Ryan, T., "Study of the SO_2 oxidation in solution and its role in atmospheric chemistry," *Quart. J. Roy. Meteorol. Soc.,* 84, 46–55 (1958).

6. Bielke, S. and Georgii, H.-W., "Investigation on the incorporation of sulfur dioxide into fog and rain droplets," *Tellus,* 20, 431–41 (1968).

7. Renzetti, N. A. and Doyle, D. J., "Photochemical aerosol formation in sulfur dioxide-hydrocarbon systems," *Intern. J. Air Poll. (London),* 2, 327–45 (1960).

8. Chamberlain, A. C., "Aspects of the deposition of radioactive and other gases and particles," *Intern. J. Air Poll.* (London), 3, 63–88 (1960).

9. Katz, M., and Ledingham, G. A., National Research Council of Canada, in *Effect of Sulfur Dioxide on Vegetation,* NCR No. 815, Ottawa (1939).

10. Georgii, H.-W., personal communication to C. F. Junge, (1967).

11. Junge, C. E., *Air Chemistry and Radioactivity,* Academic Press, New York (1963).

12. Cadle, R. D., Fischer, W. H., Frank, E. R., and Lodge, J. P., Jr., "Particles in the Antarctic atmosphere," *J. Atmos. Sci.,* 25, 100–3 (1968).

13. Lodge, J. P., Jr. and Pate, J. B., "Atmospheric gases and particulates in Panama," *Science,* 153, 408–10 (1966).

14. Kühme, H., private communication to C. E. Junge (1967).

15. (a) Eriksson, E., Part II. "The yearly circulation of chloride and sulfur in nations; meteorological, geochemical, and pedological implications," *Tellus,* 12, 63–109 (1960); (b) Eriksson, E., Part I. *Tellus,* 11, 375–443 (1959).

ROGER LEWIN

Who Pays for Plastic Litter?

Society has a problem. Each year in Britain over 10,000 tons of waste plastic are carelessly tossed away to litter the streets and countryside. According to the Staudinger report ("Disposal of plastic waste and litter," SCI Monograph no 35) the output of plastic wrapping will increase fourfold by 1980. Clearly, unless something drastic is done soon the unsightly mess of plastic litter and

Roger Lewin, "Who Pays for Plastic Litter?" *New Scientist: International Review of Science and Technology,* vol. 49, no. 740 (February 25, 1971), pp. 440–441. Reprinted by permission.

its attendant hazard to rural animal life will become intolerable. But how has this situation arisen? What scientific solutions are on offer? Where does this problem fit in the social, technical and economic context?

So far, polymer chemists have exercised all their energies on enhancing the durability of plastic material. Their very success now presents us with the problem of persistent litter. One might have hoped that, in studying the stability of polymers to physical and biological degradation, scientists would have collected together enough basic knowledge to allow them to produce a conveniently degradable plastic.

The real crunch here lies with the qualification "conveniently." It is no good having a material which starts to decay at embarrassing or dangerous moments. The ideal plastic is one which starts to degrade as soon as it is tossed on the rubbish heap. In other words, some sort of trigger is needed. With paper the trigger is the absorption of water, which is rapidly followed by bacterial attack. Such a trigger clearly is useless with plastics, since they are used so widely simply because they do not absorb water.

SUNLIGHT-INITIATED BREAKDOWN

Gerald Scott of Aston University has been investigating the possibility of sunlight-initiated breakdown (see "Vanishing plastics," New Scientist, vol 47, p 293). A highly photosensitive ethylene-carbon monoxide copolymer has recently been developed in the United States to be used for such things as disposable drinking cups. Light-initiated breakdown is certainly an approach worth exploring, but the problem of the degradation of plastics normally exposed to sunlight has to be tackled.

The bacterial attack of plastic polymers has received relatively little serious fundamental study. The central problem is: why are bacterial enzyme systems unable to split the carbon-carbon bonds of the polymer chain? After all, cellulose — the main constituent of paper — is also an extensive polymer on which enzymes will happily operate. The sad truth is that no one knows. Such an admission is cogent commentary on the paucity of fundamental knowledge.

In his talk at the recent Plastics Institute's conference, John Fendley described the Science Research Council's interests in the bacterial degradation of plastic. The SRC's Biological Sciences Committee sees its job not as solving the specific social and technical problems, but as contributing to the general background of basic research upon which technological advances may be built.

In May 1970, a number of university workers met representatives from the major industrial companies at the SRC's London Office to discuss what approaches could be made to the problem at a basic level. With no pretensions to solving the scientific problems of producing a biodegradable polymer — let alone the more tricky business of finding a trigger — the meeting agreed on three main approaches. If preliminary results are encouraging, some of the ideas may be followed up by those people involved at the meeting, and possibly also by other interested parties.

MOLECULAR ACROBATICS

The first approach involves an exercise in molecular acrobatics in an attempt to find what sort of structures bacteria have a taste for. It is known, for instance, that straight chain hydrocarbons containing up to 30 carbon atoms are degraded by some types of micro-organisms; very long hydrocarbon chains, however, are more resistant to degradation. Making the chain branched also tends to reduce the susceptibility to attack. It may be possible, however, to attach a small biodegradable group to a long chain so as to form a locus for attack, thus leading to the breakdown of the chain into smaller, manageable proportions.

The stereochemistry of the polymer backbone is very probably important in resisting bacterial digestion. What is planned, therefore, is to assemble a whole series of small polymer chains which differ slightly in basic structure from conventional plastics. By careful experiment it should be possible to identify those structures which form the molecular armour plating of the polymer and those that would constitute weak points. The way would then be clear for designing a plastic having loci along its chain vulnerable to bacterial attack.

The second approach discussed was the use of finely comminuted material on which bacteria might operate. There is evidence that normally recalcitrant materials — such as crystals of aromatic molecules — are susceptible to attack when in a finely divided form. Furthermore, Howard Eggin's group at the Biodeterioration Information Centre, Aston, has shown that the state of division is a significant factor in the degradation of cellulose-based materials. It was argued, therefore, that finely divided plastics may also be vulnerable to degradation. Clearly, finely ground plastic is irrelevant in the context of litter, but the rationale of such work is to provide model systems on which the possible mechanisms of bacterial attack could be studied.

The last, and possibly most fertile, approach suggested was the study of the biodegradation of materials added to the polymer. Many polymers require the presence of anti-oxidants to prevent the main chain breaking up. If the anti-oxidant could be selectively degraded, the polymer structure would undergo oxidation and then disintegrate. Other additives include colorizers, materials to strengthen the plastic or to confer special properties such as those needed in the photographic industry. It might be possible to develop additives which carry out these functions but which would also break down and, either allow the polymer to oxidize, or initiate biodegradation which would spread to the polymer. Additives with no other functions than to initiate destruction of the plastic at some time in its life would also be worth investigating.

All these approaches demand close collaboration with industrial laboratories, and the SRC was encouraged by industry's willingness to help by supplying essential materials. Fendley stressed the fundamental nature of these studies and expressed the hope that any results forthcoming might contribute to the basic background of knowledge on which might be built any subsequent, more direct, attack on this serious social problem.

Doomwatch fans should note that no plans were made to cultivate bacteria with a penchant for devouring plastics. A strong case can be made, however, for selecting as research tools, already existing micro-organisms which can make a brave attempt at breaking down polymer chains. The use of such organisms would allow the study of the mechanisms by which their enzyme systems attack the polymer chain.

THE ELUSIVE "THROW-AWAY TRIGGER"

As the SRC is aware, the big problem remains the trigger to initiate degradation and it is from this that many real difficulties and dangers spring. The ideal plastic with the "throw-away trigger" will probably remain elusive for a long time. We are left, therefore, with a material of limited life — or, rather, many materials with different life-spans. What happens when a forgotten pile of plastic degrades in the warehouse? More seriously, who is to blame when food becomes contaminated with partially degraded plastic wrapping which has been kept too long? The problems would be widespread and frightening.

A glance at the economic implications are also chastening. A not unreasonable guess for the cost of developing a new plastic and setting up its production would be about £100 million. Many types of disposable plastics (with different life-spans) would be needed to serve the disparate functions demanded of plastic material — plastic cups, sacks for fertilizers, food wrappers, to list only the more obvious. Economies of scale in the production of plastic militates strongly against the manufacture of material on a small scale. Inevitably, the production of a range of plastics with different life-spans would involve low-tonnage economics. The total bill to solve the plastic litter problem by this method would therefore probably be far in excess of the £100 million already mentioned. Is the community prepared to commit this much to avoid the accumulation of 10,000 tons of plastic litter per year?

The economics look even worse if one considers that plastic litter represents only three percent of the total output of plastic wrappings (the other 97 percent finishes up in municipal refuse trucks, from where it is either burnt or dumped). The development of a degradable plastic would, therefore, be designed to cope with the fate of a tiny fraction of the total output. It could be argued that this would be a lop-sided solution of the first order.

What is the real problem anyway? Is it that plastic persists after people throw it in the gutter, or is it that people throw plastic in the gutter? It is widely agreed that industry will be slow to act in producing conveniently degradable plastics unless it has the stimulus of legislation behind it. Maybe a better solution to the litter problem is to use firmer legislation to discourage people from dropping the stuff in the first place. Improvement of refuse-collecting systems would also be timely.

A good deal of useful scientific work could be done on devising ways of recycling plastic waste; this makes good economic and social sense. Any basic work which flows from the SRC initiative would certainly be valuable in this area.

The whole area of plastic litter is a mass of scientific, technological, social and economic problems. It is important to identify in this morass what the real problem is, and then solve that. Leaping to tackle a challenging scientific problem just because it exists should be avoided.

L. C. GEORGE & A. A. COCHRAN
Recovery of Metals from Electroplating Wastes

This research report shows an example of recovery where two potential wastes are mixed to allow maximum economy and reuse of materials.

The lack of technology in treating wastes, including those generated by the electroplating industry, for the recovery of the metal values has resulted in the disposal of spent electroplating solutions and other electroplating wastes to sewers and streams. The solutions not only contain large tonnages of scarce, costly metals, but also contribute to stream and ground water pollution. For example, the consumption and estimated loss of nickel by the plating industry in the recent past is given in Table I. Table I shows that there was a decrease in nickel consumption in 1952; this was due to the stockpiling of nickel brought about by the Korean War. Table I also shows a marked increase in nickel consumption and loss since 1952, and this trend is continuing in recent years.

The nickel losses shown in Table I are due to the discarding of spent or poisoned plating baths by industry, dragout losses from rinse solutions, and the discarding of rack-stripping solutions as waste. When small articles are electro-

---

Table I. Consumption and assumed loss of nickel by the electroplating industry

Nickel consumed or lost	Yearly totals, thousand short tons					
	1948	1952	1956	1960	1964	1968
Anodes	14	7	16	16	19	22
Soluble Ni	7	0.3	1	1	2	4
Total	21	7	17	17	21	26
Loss[1]	4	1	3	3	4	5

[1] Losses are based on the assumption that Ni plating is 80 percent efficient.

Reprinted by permission of the authors and the Office of Mineral Information, Bureau of Mines, from pp. 85–91 of "New Directions in Solid Wastes Processing," Proceedings of an Institute held at Framingham, Massachusetts, May 12–13, 1970. The report is a publication of the Technical Guidance Center for Industrial Environmental Control, University of Massachusetts, Amherst.
The authors are associated with the Bureau of Mines, U. S. Department of the Interior, Rolla, Missouri.

plated they are supported on racks, and during the plating operations metal is also deposited on these racks. Builtup metal must be removed periodically from the racks by various solutions, which are known as rack-stripping solutions. The annual metal losses in discarded rack-stripping solutions from only two electroplating companies are given in Table II. The HNO_3 waste is hot,

Table II. Annual loss of metal values from two industrial electroplating companies

Company	Waste	Quantity discarded, gallons	Metal loss, short tons				
			Ag	Cu	Cr	Fe	Ni
A	HNO_3[1]	12,000	—	3.0	—	0.1	6.5
A	NB[2]	50,000	—	3.9	—	.7	1.7
B	NB	6,000	0.03	.2	—	—	.9
B	Ag-NB	4,000	.92	1.0	—	—	< .1
B	Cr	4,000	—	.9	.9	—	< .1
Total Discarded		76,000	.95	9.0	.9	.8	9.1

[1] Based on values obtained with four waste samples.
[2] Based on values obtained with five waste samples.

concentrated nitric acid, which is used until it will not dissolve any more metal from the racks. Upon cooling, a large amount of precipitate (largely nickel nitrate plus some iron and copper nitrates) appears. NB is an abbreviation of sodium m-nitrobenzene-sulfonate, which contains cyanides, and Cr stands for a chromic acid solution used to etch printed circuits. These five wastes from only two companies represent annual losses of approximately 9 tons of nickel, 9 tons of copper, 1 ton of silver, and 1 ton of chromium. As there are approximately 20,000 electroplating plants in the U. S., it is evident that significant amounts of metals are lost from these industrial operations. The concentrations of several metals in the same five wastes are given in Table III. The high concentrations of silver, copper, chromium, and nickel given in Table III make these wastes interesting from an economic point of view as well as from their potential contribution to pollution problems.

HNO₃ RACK-STRIPPING WASTE

The initial test work was carried out on HNO_3 rack-stripping solutions. Lime was added to adjust the pH of the solution to 2.3 to 2.7, which caused the precipitation of ferric hydroxide. The precipitate, after filtering and drying at 100°C, contained 36.8 percent iron, 2.4 percent copper, and 0.15 percent nickel. In some tests the copper and nickel in the iron precipitate were re-covered by re-solution and re-precipitation. After precipitating iron, the copper was recovered almost quantitatively by controlled potential electrolysis at 0.1 to 0.3 volts. The recovered copper was highly pure; spectrographic analysis revealed only a trace amount of silicon. In other tests, copper was recovered by selective precipitation; additional lime was used to adjust the

Table III. Composition of industrial electroplating wastes in grams per liter

Company	Waste	Ag	Cu	Cr	Fe	Ni
A	HNO₃	—	47–65	—	1.4–3.1	96–188
A	NB'	—	16–20	—	<.1–17	6–9
B	NB	1.3	8.1	—	—	3.7
B	Ag-NB	5.5	5.9	—	—	.2
B	Cr	—	52	51	—	< .1

' NB is the abbreviation of m-Nitrobenzenesulfonate.

pH of the solution to 5.5. This precipitate, after being converted to copper sulfate, analyzed 26.6 percent copper and 0.01 percent nickel; no iron was detected. The remaining solution of nickel nitrate was treated by either of two different methods: (1) Additional lime was added to adjust the pH of the solution to 9.5, which caused nickel hydroxide to precipitate. The filtrate from this precipitation was an approximately 1.5 molar solution of calcium nitrate which has some value as plant food. (2) The solution was treated with concentrated sulfuric acid and heated to 100°C to evolve nitric acid and precipitate calcium sulfate, leaving a nickel sulfate solution that was sufficiently pure to recycle to nickel plating baths. This solution was evaporated to dryness, and the residue analyzed 21.8 percent nickel, 0.05 percent iron, and 0.01 percent copper.

WASTE-PLUS-WASTE METHOD

While these procedures are technically feasible, methods of reducing the cost of such treatments were continually sought. As the organic-cyanide (NB) rack-stripping waste is strongly alkaline, the addition of the nitric acid waste to the NB waste was considered as an inexpensive first step to neutralize both wastes before proceeding to recover the metal values. This procedure would be very dangerous if the order of addition were reversed (if NB waste was added to HNO₃ waste) or if too much HNO₃ waste was added to an NB waste with a high cyanide content, because in either case highly poisonous HCN gas would be evolved. A nitric acid waste was added slowly with stirring to an NB waste until the pH of the solution was approximately 4.5. In a number of tests, this caused almost quantitative precipitation of all the metals as cyanides. During the neutralization, the evolved gas was collected in a 0.1 molar NaOH solution to determine if any HCN was produced. After neutralization, the NaOH solution was analyzed. No cyanides were detected, and the detection limit of the analytical method is 0.08 ppm of cyanides. This indicates that essentially no HCN was evolved under our test conditions.

After the precipitated metal cyanides were filtered off, the filtrate also analyzed less than 0.08 ppm of cyanides and was acceptable for discharge to streams. X-ray diffraction analysis, chemical analysis, and differential thermal analysis revealed that the precipitate was $CuCN$, $Ni(CN)_2$, and $Cu_2Fe(CN)_6$. The mixed cyanide precipitate analyzed 24.0 percent nickel, 23.6 percent copper, and 0.9 percent iron.

The change in the concentrations of copper and nickel during the addition of one waste to another are shown in Figure 1. The concentration of each ion goes through a minimum, and these minima occurred at almost the same point which, in Figure 1, is approximately 66 or 67 ml of HNO_3 waste added to 200 ml of NB waste. Further additions of HNO_3 waste introduced

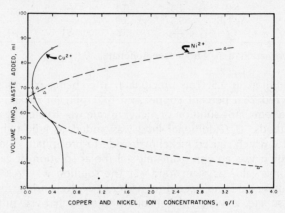

Figure 1. Copper and nickel ion concentrations versus volume of HNO₃ waste added to 200 ml of NB waste

metal ions that were not precipitated and excess acid. However, the evolution of HCN was still negligible, apparently because all of the cyanides were precipitated. Nickel and copper products were recovered from the mixed cyanide precipitate by a few additional steps. The precipitate was heated in air at 250°C to convert the metal cyanides to oxides which were identified by X-ray diffraction as NiO, CuO, and FeO. When heated in air, the mixed cyanides ignite and undergo a self-sustained oxidation reaction during which local temperatures may rise far above the furnace temperature. The mixed metal oxides were digested for 2 hours at 100°C with 10 percent sulfuric acid which converted about 95 percent of the oxides to sulfates. The sulfates were dissolved in water, ferric hydroxide was precipitated with lime as described before, and copper was recovered by controlled potential electrolysis as described before. The remaining nickel sulfate solution was found to be sufficiently pure for direct recycling to a plating bath.

Although only negligible amounts of HCN were produced in these tests, means for removing or destroying HCN would be mandatory for industrial applications.

To summarize, the waste-plus-waste recovery method described has the following advantages: Reagent costs are low, the filtrate is essentially free of cyanides and could be safely discharged to streams, substantial amounts of nickel and copper are precipitated and recovered by simple procedures, and practically no HCN was evolved. As most electroplating plants that use racks to support small objects use both nitric acid and NB solutions to strip the racks, the described process could easily be applied at the source of the two wastes.

JOHN CAIRNS, JR.

Thermal Pollution — A Cause for Concern

Society cannot continue to expand production of electric power and increase discharge of heated wastewater into the aquatic environment indefinitely without causing a major ecological crisis. Except in hydroelectric plants, the source of energy is locked in fossil fuel — coal, oil, or gas — or in nuclear fuel. This energy is transformed into heat by burning or by nuclear reactions. The heat then changes water into high pressure steam. As the steam turns the rotor in a turbine, the heat is transformed into mechanical energy. The turbine motor is connected with a generator where the mechanical energy is converted into electrical energy. But the amount of electrical energy that emerges from the plant is far less than the energy that went into it in the form of fuel. At present most of this heat is "thrown away," as with many other waste products, and it is capable of polluting the environment, just as surely as domestic wastewater, industrial waste, and agricultural waste. Some of the waste heat goes up the smokestack in hot gases; some is disposed of in a nearby stream or lake where it may be a more serious problem. After the steam passes through the turbine, it goes into a condenser. There cooling water circulates through tubing and cools the steam until it condenses into water. It then can be returned to the boiler to begin the cycle all over again. Meanwhile, the cooling water is returned to the river, lake, or coastal waters of the sea from where it came, carrying the waste heat with it.

Like many other industrial wastes, this one was small at first (Figure 1). Early steam electric generating plants were much smaller than those of today. Less waste heat was discharged into waterways, and it could be dispersed quite rapidly. Its effects on the various forms of plant and animal life in the water were therefore possibly quite small. There were few studies made, so little is known about actual effects.

But today the rapid growth of population, the even more rapid growth in the demand for electric power, and the trend toward power grids rather than many small, self-contained electric systems are all leading in the direction of larger and larger generating plants. Fossil-fueled plants are now being built to produce 4 or 5 times the electricity of those built 20 years ago. Further strengthening the trend to enormous generating capacity is the entrance of nuclear power into the field. Nuclear plants are not yet economically feasible in small sizes. Nuclear generating plants are therefore built to produce even more electricity than the new conventional fossil fuel plants. They also pro-

John Cairns, Jr., "Thermal Pollution — A Cause for Concern," *Journal of the Water Pollution Control Federation*, vol. 43, no. 1 (January 1971), pp. 55–66. Reprinted by permission. This paper was presented at the 23rd Annual Meeting of the Virginia Water Pollution Control Association, Natural Bridge, Virginia, April 28–29, 1969.
The author is Professor, College of Arts and Sciences, Virginia Polytechnic Institute.

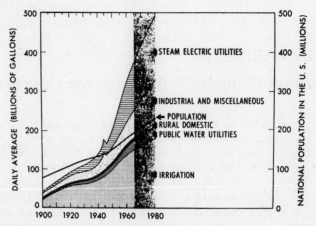

Figure 1. Water use in the United States (based on Picton, W. L., "Water Use in the United States" 1960)

duce electricity less efficiently. That is, less of the energy is transformed into electricity; more of it becomes waste heat. Nuclear energy power generation requires about 50 percent more cooling water than comparable power output by conventional methods (1).

WATER BALANCE

The total average rainfall in the U. S. is 30 in./yr (76 cm/yr) of which about 70 percent is returned to the atmosphere through evaporation and from trees and other plants that lose water to the atmosphere by a process called transpiration. This leaves about 1,200 bil gpd (4,540 mil cu m/day) for surface and subsurface water supplies. Singer estimates that steam-electric power generators will pass 25 percent of this through their cooling systems by 1985 (2). A single power plant now in existence requires up to 0.5 mil gpm (1,892 cu m/min) for cooling purposes; running at full capacity around the clock, this would mean 720 mgd (2,725,000 cu m/day).

Some of this is "consumed." That is, it evaporates and is lost, at least temporarily, to other uses and users. The amount "consumed" has been estimated as averaging 20 acre-ft (24,700 cu m) for each megawatt of electricity generated (3). A large (1,000-megawatt) plant would consume 20,000 acre/ft/yr (24.7 mil cu m/yr) of water. Most of the cooling water, however, is not consumed, but is returned — at a higher temperature — to the waterway from which it was drawn.

Unfortunately, the distribution of water is geographically uneven and it also varies seasonally. In certain watersheds, a major portion of the water available may be required by the local power plant during low flow periods. To make matters worse, this period of maximum use may coincide with the warmest period of the year when surface waters are already at or near maximum temperatures. For example, the Monticello nuclear generating plant (without cooling towers) would use about 65 percent of the entire flow of the upper Mississippi River at times and could raise the river's temperature in that region as much as 16°F ($\cong$9°C). How far the water would flow before returning to its normal temperature is not known (4).

As the cooling water returns to the stream or other source, it may carry with it very small amounts of heavy metals from corrosion of the tubes in the condenser or chlorine which is sometimes used to clean those tubes. Minute aquatic organisms, drawn through the system along with the water, have been subjected to increased temperatures and may be affected. Water drawn from an estuary, for example, may include fish eggs and larvae, and the microscopic plants (phytoplankton) and animals (zooplankton) that abound in these waters. Some investigators feel that few of these will survive the shock of passing through the condenser (5). Unfortunately, little research has been carried out on organisms drawn through cooling systems, and results of the research that has been done are not in agreement. Even if all the organisms that pass through the condenser are killed, the effect on the ecosystem is difficult to predict. It would probably vary from one area to another. Preliminary results from research in the author's laboratory indicate that these effects are not particularly severe.

The effect of the heat is not limited to the water actually drawn through the generating plant and the forms of life contained in that water. When the heated water returns after it has flowed through the power plant, the entire aquatic ecosystem — the interrelated system of living things in the larger body of water — may be affected even though only a portion of the water was used. This added heat may then change the character of both the system of living things and the receiving water, which together make up the aquatic ecosystem.

Man is a simplifier of complex ecosystems and a creator of simple ecosystems. What makes a natural ecosystem is the multitude of interactions such as predation, parasitism, and competition, which occur between the many species of organisms, both plant and animal, that make up the biological part of an ecosystem. Seasonal changes occur, and species have good periods and bad periods, but over the long run the important thing is the relative constancy in number of species present and in their relationships. This functional stability is the mark of a healthy natural ecosystem.*

Corn fields and fermentation vats are good examples of simplified ecosystems. These are notoriously unstable and require constant care and maintenance. Large amounts of pesticides are used each year to keep insect populations at low levels in the cornfield, and brewers must carefully measure their ingredients and control the environmental conditions so that the desired end-product is obtained. Simple ecosystems are not necessarily "bad" nor are complex systems necessarily "good," but they do have different characteristics.

---

* This explanation is necessarily oversimplified. For readers who would like to learn more about ecosystems, "Ecology" by Eugene F. Odum, published by Holt, Rinehart and Winston, New York, N. Y. (1963), is recommended.

ENVIRONMENTAL STRESSES

Each technological advance has produced increased stress on the natural environment. As stress increases and more and more species are eliminated, the many biological interactions that maintain ecosystem stability are short-circuited. "Weed" species (those able to tolerate the stress) flourish as their more sensitive competitors and predators are removed. With the sudden application of a stress factor to an ecosystem, only those species with a pre-existing ability to cope with the new conditions will survive. Populations can accommodate to gradual change (i.e., spread out over many generations) by the process of natural selection. In fact, that is how species and ecosystems evolve.

Even with a relatively rapid change in conditions, species are rarely eliminated *en mass*. As stress is applied to an ecosystem, the first response is a reduction in the number of individuals of the more sensitive species. At the same time, numbers of individuals of the more tolerant species may increase so that the total number of individuals has hardly changed. If the stress increases, species begin to disappear as conditions exceed their tolerance levels. For example, in a small watershed in eastern Pennsylvania, 23 species of fish were found in the main stream. In a polluted tributary three pollution-resistant species, goldfish, creek shiners, and killfish, were the only species found. The total pounds per acre of fish in the clean water stream and in the polluted tributary were quite comparable. The three pollution-tolerant species can survive and reproduce in the stressed environment free from competition with or predation from the other 20 species (6). This is typical of polluted waters, whether the pollution is from heat or from other forms of waste.

Although in terms of geologic time, man's modification of the environment must be considered sudden, to an observer trying to document the changes as they occur, it is a very gradual process. The replacement of individuals of sensitive species with those of more tolerant species is also a biological accommodation that masks change. Such a change is often not obvious even to a trained observer unless he has studied the area sufficiently well over a period of time to have statistically reliable data. Eventually, if an increase in stress continues, a point will be reached where the ecosystem collapses. The fish are gone, the water smells, industrial and municipal wastes are not degraded as well as they formerly were, and one does not need to be an ecologist to know that things have changed.

Discharge of heated wastewater seems to have the same effects as other types of stress in that there are three levels of biological response:

1. A range within which no abnormal response to change is noted;
2. A zone of graded response — increased stress produces increased response (more dead fish and fewer species);
3. A threshold beyond which further increases elicit no further response (because the system is incapable of further response — not because further increase is suddenly harmless).

Most aquatic organisms can withstand the effects of heat only within very narrow limits. They are further handicapped by not having regulatory mechanisms (such as sweating) which buffer effects of increased heat in the environment. It is true that some can move to cooler areas, but this is avoidance rather than regulation and is possible only when a cooler area exists. Moreover, the discharge of heated water into a stream can create a hot water barrier which effectively blocks the spawning migrations of many species of fish, as well as other, less spectacular movements. The temperature an aquatic animal can tolerate depends greatly on the conditions in the normal environment — tropical fishes are adapted to warm waters that would kill a brook trout. Sometimes in areas with very stable temperatures the margin of safety is very slight. The polyps that build coral reefs are killed by temperatures only 2° or 3°F (2.2° to 6.4°C) above those at which they carry out a normal existence.

Though abrupt application of heat can kill bacteria and other microorganisms (pasteurization is an example) the probable result of gradual changes in a natural environment is exclusion of nontolerant species by resistant species. That is, those species more tolerant of the new conditions outperform the others and reproduce more rapidly while the less tolerant reproduce slowly or not at all. The result is a qualitative shift in kinds of species present which may or may not be accompanied by a change in total numbers of individuals. Diatoms, green algae, and blue-green algae, each group including a number of species, may all be found together in an aquatic ecosystem. However, Figure 2 shows how the species relationships, in one experiment, shifted as the temperature rose from 68°F (20°C) to 104°F (40°C). The number of species of diatoms dropped sharply; the trend among blue-greens was the opposite — there were more species present in the warmer water. Species of greens increased with rising temperature until it passed 86°F (30°C) and then dropped off again. Present evidence suggests that blue-greens are not as suitable as diatoms to the organisms dependent on algae as a food supply. Many blue-greens produce unpleasant odors, and some are toxic to shellfish and other organisms.

The major effects of heat pollution on higher aquatic organisms are:

1. Death through direct effects of heat;
2. Internal functional aberrations (changes in respiration, growth);

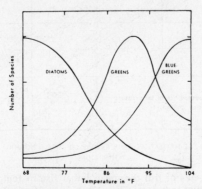

Figure 2. How the relationship between three groups of algae shifts as the water temperature rises (°F − 32) 0.555 = °C

3. Death through indirect effects of heat (reduced oxygen, disruption of food supply, decreased resistance to toxic substances);
4. Interference with spawning or other critical activities in the life cycle; and
5. Competitive replacement by more tolerant species as a result of the above physiological effects.

Experiments suggest that some aquatic organisms can become acclimated to higher temperatures than those to which they are normally accustomed. But even in the laboratory, gradual acclimation to much higher temperatures has limitations. The experiments of Alabaster (7) have shown that for three species of fish, the mean lethal rise in temperature decreases as acclimatization temperature increases (Figure 3). Of course, one should be quite cautious about using results even from carefully controlled laboratory experiments to develop standards for use in natural environments. Some organisms survive higher temperatures in natural situations than in laboratory tests. The reverse may also be true. In the laboratory, an organism may have near optimal conditions with the exception of the changing temperature being studied. Many organisms in the natural environment already live under less than optimal conditions and are often subject to other kinds of stress at the same time the temperature is changing. Another form of stress is a secondary effect of heated water. Heating water decreases the solubility of oxygen (Figure 4) and, within certain limits, increases bacterial activity. These events lower the amount of oxygen available to the higher aquatic organisms.

The problems caused by heated wastewater discharge into lakes probably are as complex as those in rivers, though data on lakes is quite scarce. Shallow lakes are mixed by the wind and may therefore have little temperature variation throughout, but deep lakes are quite different. The most dramatic ecological events for deep lakes in the temperate zone are the seasonal turnovers. In the spring, surface waters warm to 39°F (4°C) (the temperature

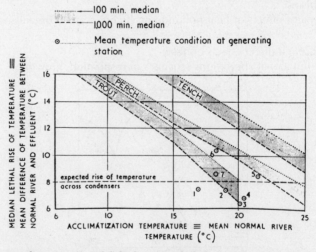

Figure 3. **For three species of fish the mean lethal rise in temperature decreases as acclimatization temperature increases. (°F − 32) 0.555 = °C**

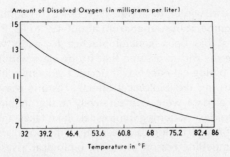

Figure 4. **As water is heated, its ability to hold dissolved oxygen (DO) decreases, making less oxygen available for respiration by aquatic organisms. °C = 0.555 (°F − 32)**

at which water has its greatest density) and sink to the bottom, bringing the nutrient-rich bottom water to the surface. In the fall, the surface waters cool, and again a turnover occurs. The algal blooms which often follow these turnovers are well known. The ecology of temperate zone lakes is largely determined by turnovers and by the stratification of the water into layers with varying temperatures during the intervening periods. The chemical, physical, and biological structure of lake ecosystems is keyed to these events. A power plant that places a layer of warm water on a lake surface may disrupt the circulation pattern and prevent turnovers from occurring or change the season at which they take place. The effects of this on lake ecology might be drastic and possibly disastrous.

When the New York State Electric and Gas Corporation proposed construction of a nuclear generating plant on Lake Cayuga, near Ithaca, N. Y., a group of Cornell scientists pointed out that during the summer, the plant would withdraw from the lower, cooler layer of the lake roughly 10 percent of its average volume. Seven hundred seventy mgd (2.9 mil cu m/day) of water heated to 65° to 70°F (18° to 21°C) would be added to the top, warmer layer. The scientists predicted that this would substantially delay the usual cooling and mixing of the lake in the fall. The addition of heated water in the winter might cause the summer stratification to begin earlier. The lake's growing season would therefore be extended at both ends, with a higher rate of biological production (8). In other words, discharge of heated wastewater might increase the growth of algae and speed the eutrophication or aging process in the lake. It should be noted that these comments apply primarily to smaller lakes. The Great Lakes pose a unique situation that will require particular attention and probably a set of standards that are different from those of ordinary lakes.

One might think that the vast oceans would be immune to effects of heat pollution and that therefore electric generating plants could best be placed along the coasts, but since marine life is frequently concentrated in coastal areas, this may not be the easy solution it seems to be on first inspection. For example, it has recently been reported that a combination of heat and salt pollution caused by waste discharge from the Point Loma saline water conversion plant near San Diego, Calif., has affected intertidal marine life (9). Temperatures taken at a power station in South Wales ranged from about 73°F (22°C) in winter to about 99°F (37°C) in summer in an estuary where mean sea temperatures range from about 45° to 63°F (7° to 17°C) (10).

Historically, it has been general practice to assess water pollution in purely chemical terms and to assume that if one stays within certain arbitrary limits, no harmful biological effects will occur. Frequently, little or no effort is spent directly assessing the biological effects. Historic reasons for this seem to be that chemical data were comparatively easily acquired and could be gathered more rapidly. Acquiring biological data takes far less time today because many improved biological assessment methods are available. However, the most compelling reason for using biological assessment methods is that knowing the chemical or physical characteristics of a waste or receiving water makes possible only an estimate of the effects on living organisms. These effects may be accurately determined only by a direct biological assessment. Biological study seeks to understand environmental interactions, but it does not indicate the exact substances or conditions involved. Rather than rely on any single approach, biological, chemical, and physical assessments should all be used in studying pollution.

Initial attempts to avoid biological problems resulting from the discharge of heated wastewater were primarily directed toward avoiding lethal temperatures. However, because temperature changes often act to time the occurrence of biological events, it is quite possible to disrupt biological systems fundamentally while staying within nonlethal temperatures by changing the pattern of temperature change. Gardeners know that certain bulbs and seeds require cooling in order to produce plants. The temperature pattern during the cooler months also affects the life cycles of many aquatic organisms so that where heated water is discharged, the receiving water may not get cold enough for many species. The emergence pattern and reproductive cycle of some aquatic insects depends on seasonal temperature cycles. A population of insects emerging in March when it would normally appear in May would surely meet with disaster. Further, its absence in May would be likely to affect other animals that depend on it for food. A whole chain of events that would seriously disrupt normal biological interactions could be set into motion by the mistiming of seasonal temperature changes.*

The related and complementary problems of increased energy production and population growth are forcing man to make a choice between a complex environment with considerable functional stability and a simplified

---

* Documenting the effects of temperature in the aquatic environment in detail is clearly outside the scope of this article. Kennedy and Mihursky (11) recently prepared a superb bibliography of 1,220 key references on this subject. The increase in literature on temperature effects in recent years is quite dramatic. More papers on this subject were produced in a single year in the sixties than in all the years from 1900 to 1920. Raney and Menzel (12) have an extremely useful 34-page bibliography primarily devoted to the effects of heated discharges on fish. For those interested in the physiology of temperature adaptation, "Molecular Mechanisms of Temperature Adaptation" by Prosser (13) will provide an excellent starting point. A general discussion of all phases together with an impressive selected bibliography are included in "Temperature and Aquatic Life" by Holdaway et al. (14). The excellent pair of books edited by Parker and Krenkel (15) furnish much valuable information on heated wastewater problems. Anyone interested in further information may consult these source materials.

environment with increased management costs. A good example of a stable environment is a complex forest consisting of a great variety of plants and animals that will persist year in and year out with no interference from man. This ecosystem is a complex mixture of biological, chemical, and physical interactions, many of which cancel each other out. For example, if there are several predators regulating a population of rodents and one disappears, the effect often is reduced by a population expansion of other predators also feeding on the rodents. Therefore, the system is one of dynamic equilibrium, with the system itself being stable but with many of its components under-going change. A simple system such as a corn field produces a quantity of material immediately useful to man but is notoriously unstable. Without constant care and attention it would cease to be useful and would disappear. So the history of civilization has been one of widespread simplification of the environment with consequent increased management requirements.

THE EFFECTS OF TECHNOLOGY

When man simplifies an ecosystem, he creates numerous ecological problems. When a complex natural area is cleared and planted with corn, a single type of food is concentrated in a limited area and it requires protection against insects and other pests. To reduce the number of these pests, pesticides are applied and the diversity of life in the soil and in the field is further reduced. Because certain of the pests may become resistant to the insecticides after repeated application, there is a gradual escalation of concentrations of these which may further simplify the ecosystem. At the same time, other organisms including man are beginning to have substantial amounts of these pesticides incorporated into their own tissues. For example, concentrations of DDT in the fat deposits of human tissues in the U. S. average 11 ppm and Israelis have been found to have as much as 19.2 ppm (16). So the overall question is whether not only thermal pollution but also all the other problems producing the environmental crisis can be controlled. Gershinowitz (17) summed up the problem rather succinctly, "As soon as one becomes involved in any one of the specific problems of the pollution of the environment it becomes apparent that no one problem can be treated in isolation. Methods for waste disposal, whether they are concerned with gases, liquids or solids, interact with each other; incineration of solids can cause contamination of the air, sanitary fills can cause contamination of water supplies, substitutes for incineration, such as maceration, can increase the load on water purification systems." To create a workable method for a single form of stress without considering the others will only cause a slight delay in the inevitable catastrophe. Only with total environmental planning, including population control, will a meaningful pro-gram to insure a harmonious relationship with the environment be possible.

The carrying capacity of the earth usually has been estimated by calcu-lating the number of people and the food resources to feed them at certain nutritional levels. In short, food supply was thought to be the ultimate limita-tion on the size of the human population. However, it may well be that the ultimate limitation on the number of people the earth can support will be the capacity of the environment to transform wastes into acceptable or useful materials. Somehow the cyclic nature of useful things has been forgotten, possibly because man talks of a consumer society. Actually, it is a user society which temporarily uses consumer goods and then discards them in forms such as domestic wastewater, carbon dioxide, and tin cans into the environment. Because man depends on the environment as a life support system, an attempt should be made to understand its waste transforming capacities which are as integral a part of the life-support system as is the food supply. Man can no longer afford merely to insure the survival of the ecosystems which provide oxygen and transform wastes. He must also determine the conditions required for optimal function, because, with the predicted increase in rate of loading with wastes, nothing less than optimal function will prevent disaster.

PRIORITIES

There are four basic alternatives that are open with regard to the heated wastewater problem, which may be chosen singly or in various combinations:

1. Placing all heated wastewater in streams, lakes, and oceans without regard to the effect and considering the environmental damage as a necessary consequence of the increased power demand;
2. Using, but not abusing, present ecosystems. This means regulating the heated wastewater discharge to fit the receiving capacity of the ecosystem;
3. Finding alternative ways to dissipate or beneficially use waste heat; and
4. Modifying ecosystems to fit the new temperature conditions.

Using, but not abusing, present ecosystems would entail determining the receiving capacity of each ecosystem for all the wastes being discharged into it. This would include insecticide runoff, domestic wastewater, silt from road building, and heavy metals, as well as heated wastewater. Without a doubt, the receiving capacity of an ecosystem would vary seasonally. Therefore, adjusting waste discharge to fit the needs of the system would require either (a) limitation of the population at something near its present size and improving waste treatment facilities in areas where serious environmental degradation has occurred, or (b) if the population is to increase, toleration of a lower quality environment or drastically changed waste disposal practices. Both of these are going to be quite difficult to achieve and may be virtually impossible under present circumstances. There are two positions taken by a few power company spokesmen that are outdated in today's complex society in which single purpose use of a major natural resource is virtually impossible:

1. The company has a legal obligation to supply safe and adequate electric service and any attempt to regulate wastes from this process is contrary to public interest;
2. Criteria for controlling heated wastewater discharge are needlessly restrictive and not based on scientific fact.

There are major weaknesses in these positions that fortunately are realized by many electric power company spokesmen. The first weakness is that the human race depends not only on electricity but on the total ecosystem including the water, the soil, and the air. The second point that the criteria are not based on sufficient scientific fact probably means that biologists cannot tell the precise death point for each and every species in the environment. This is true and will probably remain true for generations to come; however, it is known that substantial changes in temperature will have major effects on the functioning of an ecosystem including its ability to transform and degrade wastes. One should remember to distinguish between standards and criteria. Standards can be changed without changing criteria.

On the other hand, if a power company has demonstrated that the ecological quality of an area will not be degraded by the proposed heat wastewater discharge and is prepared to provide an ecological monitoring program to show that environmental quality is being maintained, requiring further treatment for its own sake seems irrational. In essence, this latter requirement would mean applying economic resources where no significant results will be produced, and very likely diverting resources from other areas where they are badly needed. The basic question that society faces is what are the most beneficial uses of a nonexpandable resource, the environment, which will permit it to survive as a vigorously functioning, dependable system available for future beneficial uses. Neither conservationists who refuse to recognize the need for rational industrial use of natural resources nor industrial representatives who feel that industrial use of the environment should never be questioned are contributing to the solution of a common pressing problem. Both positions are untenable in the present circumstances. Unrestricted industrial use would so damage the ecosystems that the life support capacity would be either destroyed or seriously degraded. The extreme conservationists' attitude would not permit the type of industrial society to which the U. S. is accustomed. If the kind of harmonious working relationship that will permit full beneficial use of the environment is to be achieved, less extreme positions will have to be taken by spokesmen on both sides.

The third alternative — that of finding other ways of dissipating heat or using it for other beneficial purposes, such as heating greenhouses in the north — deserves more attention than it has received in the past. One alternative to the open-cycle system (in which the water is passed through the condensing units and returned to the stream or lake from which it was taken at a considerably higher temperature) is the use of cooling towers. Wet-type hyperbolic cooling towers have been used in Europe for the past 50 years and have been used widely enough in the U. S. so that their operational characteristics are fairly well understood. Dry-type cooling towers are a relatively recent development and are less well understood. The first dry-type tower was erected at the Rugeley Station in Great Britain serving a unit rated at 120,000 kw and went into service in December 1961. There seems to be no question even from the relatively small amount of information available on dry-type cooling towers that the cost of operating these will be considerably greater than the wet towers; estimates run as high as four times as much. On the other hand, the wet-type cooling towers do cause a considerable loss of water through evaporation, and makeup water is required periodically as well as the discharge of the nonevaporative portion of the water used in cooling which would contain a rather large dissolved solids load. An aesthetic objection might also be raised to the use of all cooling towers because for some typical power generating units now being constructed, the requirement would be five wet-type hyperbolic towers, each tower being several hundred feet high and several hundred feet in diameter. Obviously in most areas these would be difficult to hide. It is quite evident that some means of making social decisions, which include the aesthetic as well as the other factors, must be developed. One of the most common objections to the installation of cooling towers is that they are quite expensive and that the public is unwilling to pay the additional cost for electric power. However, the results of a recent Gallup poll (18) indicate that this may be a fallacious generalization. About half (51 percent) of all persons interviewed said they are "deeply concerned" about the effect of air and water pollution, soil erosion, and destruction of wildlife. About one-third (35 percent) said they are "somewhat concerned." Only 12 percent said they are "not very concerned." Even more important, about three out of every four people interviewed backed up their concern by stating that they would be willing to pay additional taxes to improve natural surroundings. Because people are never eager to pay additional taxes, these figures indicate a strong desire on the part of the American people to protect the environment and a willingness to pay directly for the cost of this protection. Senator Henry M. Jackson of Washington, Chairman of the Senate Interior Committee, summed up this viewpoint as follows: "A new attitude of concern for values which cannot be translated into the language of the market place or computed in cost-benefit ratios is being felt and seen in citizen efforts to save parks, open spaces, and natural beauty from freeways, reservoirs, and industry." Senator Jackson further stated, "People are no longer complacent about the quality of their surroundings, about the use of the environment, and the way public resources are being administered." It seems quite clear that there is both public interest in the development of alternative uses of heated discharge waters (such as heating greenhouses) and a willingness to pay for treatment that would not introduce dangerous quantities of heated wastewater into the natural environment. Man depends on a life support system that is partly industrial and partly ecological. Unfortunately, he has reached a stage of development where the nonexpandable portion of the life support system, the ecological part of the environment, is endangered by the expanding industrial portion of the environment. Developing a balanced life support system that serves the greatest variety of beneficial uses will not be possible unless narrow discipline-oriented, single-purpose views toward environmental management and use are abandoned. Optimal use and management of such a complex system will only be possible with the full cooperation of engineers, ecologists, congressmen, economists, urban and regional planners, regulatory agencies, businessmen, geologists, to mention just a few of the many sources of critical points of view. The decisions are too important to be left to a single group — too complex to be solved by a single discipline.

Finally, waste discharge regulations that cause needless expense without protecting the receiving ecosystem must be revised. Failure to do so will undoubtedly alienate industrial representatives and divert energy and money from areas where improved waste control practices will have marked benefits.

Acknowledgments

The author is grateful to *Scientists & Citizen* (now *Environment*) for giving permission to quote parts of the author's article "We're in Hot Water" which appeared in Vol. 10, No. 8, pp. 187–198, 1968.

References

1. Koldat, T., Testimony in "Thermal Pollution — 1968." Hearings before the Subcommittee on Air and Water Pollution of the Committee on Public Works, U. S. Senate, 90th Congress, 2nd Session, U. S. Govt. Printing Office, Washington, D. C., 63 (Feb. 1968).

2. Singer, S. F., "Waste Heat Management." *Science,* 159, 3820, 1184 (1968).

3. Bennett, N. B., Jr., Address to Western Water and Power Symposium, Los Angeles, Calif., April 9, 1968.

4. Abrahamson, D. E., and Pogue, R. E., "Some Concerns about the Environmental Impact of a Growing Nuclear Power Industry: I. The Discharge of Radioactive and Thermal Wastes." *Jour. Minn. Acad. Sci.* (In press.)

5. Mihursky, J., Testimony in "Thermal Pollution — 1968." Hearings before the Subcommittee on Air and Water Pollution of the Committee on Public Works, U. S. Senate, 90th Congress, 2nd Session, U. S. Govt. Printing Office, 102 (Feb. 1968).

6. Trembley, F. J., Testimony in "Thermal Pollution — 1968." Hearings before the Subcommittee on Air and Water Pollution of the Committee on Public Works, U. S. Senate, 90th Congress, 2nd Session, U. S. Govt. Printing Office, 94 (Feb. 1968).

7. Alabaster, J. S., "Effects of Heated Effluents on Fish." *Air & Water Poll.,* 7, 541 (1963).

8. Arnold, D. E., *et al.,* "Thermal Pollution of Cayuga Lake by a Proposed Power Plant." Citizens Committee to Save Cayuga Lake, Ithaca, N. Y. (1968).

9. Leighton, D., *et al.,* "Effects of Waste Discharge from Point Loma Saline Water Conversion Plant on Inter-Tidal Marine Life." *Jour. Water Poll. Control Fed.,* 29, 1190 (1967).

10. Naylor, E., "Biological Effect of a Heated Effluent in Docks at Swansea, South Wales." *Proc. Zoological Society of London,* 114, 253 (1965).

11. Kennedy, V. S., and Mihursky, J. A., "Bibliography on the Effects of Temperature in the Aquatic Environment." Natural Resources Inst., Univ. Maryland, College Park, mimeo, (1967). Reprinted in "Thermal Pollution — 1968." Hearings before the Subcommittee on Air and Water Pollution of the Committee on Public Works, U. S. Senate, 90th Congress, 2nd Session, U. S. Govt. Printing Office (1968).

12. Raney, E. C., and Menzel, B. W., "A Bibliography: Heated Effluents and Effects on Aquatic Life with Emphasis on Fishes." Fernow Hall, Cornell Univ., Ithaca, N. Y. (1967).

13. Prosser, C. L., "Molecular Mechanisms of Temperature Adaptation," AAAS, Pub. No. 84, 390 pp. (1967).

14. Holdaway, J. L., *et al.,* "Temperature and Aquatic Life." Tech. Advisory and Investigations Branch, Tech. Serv. Progr., FWPCA, U. S. Dept. of Int., Lab. Investigations Series, No. 6, Washington, D. C. (1967).

15. Krenkel, P. A., and Parker, F. L., "Biological Aspects of Thermal Pollution." Vanderbilt Univ. Press, Nashville, Tenn. (1969) and Parker, F. L., and Krenkel, P. A., "Engineering Aspects of Thermal Pollution." Vanderbilt Univ. Press, Nashville, Tenn. (1969).

16. Ehrlich, P. B., "The Population Bomb." Ballantine Books, New York, N. Y. (1968).

17. Gershinowitz, H., "The Environmental Studies Board." Presented at the An-

nual Meeting of the National Research Council in Washington, D. C. (March 1969).
    18. Cahn, R., *Christian Science Monitor,* 5 (March 11, 1969).

Additional reference

Raney, E. C., and Menzel, B. W., "Heated Effluents and Effects on Aquatic Life with Emphasis on Fishes." Cornell Univ., Water Resources and Marine Sciences Center and Ichtyological Associates, Ithaca, N. Y., Bull. No. 2, 470 pp. (1969).

ALLEN V. KNEESE, ROBERT U. AYRES & RALPH C. D'ARGE
The Flow of Materials

[W]e find it useful to view environmental pollution and its control from the perspective of a materials balance problem for the entire economy.[1] The inputs of the system are fuels, foods, and raw materials which are partly converted into final goods and partly become residuals. Except for increases in inventory, final goods also ultimately enter the residuals stream. Thus, goods which are "consumed" really only render certain services. Their material substance remains in existence and must be either reused or discharged to the natural environment.

In an economy which is closed (no imports or exports) and where there is no net accumulation of stocks (plants, equipment, inventories, consumer durables, or buildings), the amount of residuals which is inserted into the natural environment must be approximately equal to the weight of basic fuels, food, and raw materials entering the processing and production system, plus oxygen taken from the atmosphere.[2] This result, while obvious upon reflection, leads to the at first rather surprising corollary that residuals disposal involves a greater tonnage of materials than basic materials processing, although many of the residuals, being gaseous, require comparatively little physical "handling."

Chart 1 shows a materials flow of the type we have in mind and relates it to a broad classification of economic sectors which is convenient for our later discussion and which is generally consistent with the Standard Industrial Classification used by the Census Bureau of the U. S. Department of Commerce. In an open (regional or national) economy, it would be necessary to add flows representing imports and exports. In an economy undergoing stock or capital accumulation, the production of residuals in any given year would be less by that amount than the basic inputs. In the entire U. S. economy, accumulation accounts for about 10–15 percent of basic annual inputs, mostly in the form of construction materials, and there is some net importation of raw and partially processed materials, amounting to 4 or 5 percent of domestic

Allen V. Kneese, Robert U. Ayres, and Ralph C. D'Arge, "The Flow of Materials," from *Economics and the Environment: A Materials Balance Approach,* Resources for the Future, Inc., 1970, pp. 7–15. Reprinted by permission.

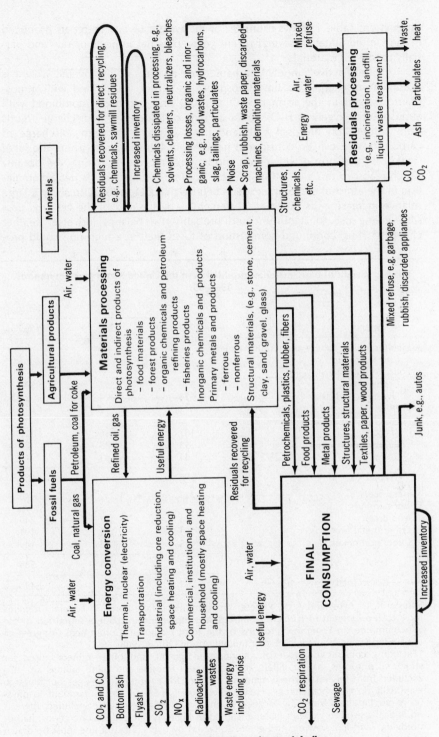

Chart 1. **Schematic depiction of materials flow**

production. Table 1 shows estimates of the weight of raw materials produced in the United States in several recent years, plus net imports of raw and partially processed materials.

Of the "active" inputs,[3] perhaps three-quarters of the overall weight is eventually discharged to the atmosphere as carbon (combined with atmospheric oxygen in the form of CO or CO_2) and hydrogen (combined with atmospheric oxygen as H_2O) under current conditions. This discharge results from combustion of fossil fuels and from animal respiration. Discharge of carbon dioxide can be considered harmless in the short run. There are large "sinks" (in the form of vegetation and large water bodies, mainly the oceans) which reabsorb this gas, although there is some evidence of its net accumulation in the atmosphere. Some experts believe that CO_2 is likely to show a large relative increase — as much as 50 percent — by the end of the century, possibly giving rise to significant and probably, on balance, adverse weather changes.[4] Thus, continued combustion of fossil fuels at a high rate could pro-

Table 1. Weight of basic materials production in the United States plus net imports, 1963–65

			$(10^6$ tons)
Material	*1963*	*1964*	*1965*
Agricultural (incl. fishery and wildlife and forest) products:			
Food and fiber:			
Crops	350	358	364
Livestock and dairy	23	24	23.5
Fishery	2	2	2
Forestry products (85% dry wt. basis):			
Sawlogs	107	116	120
Pulpwood	53	55	56
Other	41	41	42
Total	576	596	607.5
Mineral fuels	1,337	1,399	1,448
Other minerals:			
Iron ore	204	237	245
Other metal ores	161	171	191
Other nonmetals	125	133	149
Total	490	541	585
Grand total[a]	2,261	2,392	2,492

Source: R. U. Ayres and A. V. Kneese, "Environmental Pollution," in *Federal Programs for the Development of Human Resources,* a compendium of papers submitted to the Subcommittee on Economic Progress of the Joint Economic Committee, Congress of the United States, Vol. 2 (U.S. Government Printing Office, 1968).
[a] Excluding construction materials, stone, sand, gravel, and other minerals used for structural purposes, ballast, fillers, insulation, etc. Gangue and mine tailings are also excluded from this total. These materials account for enormous tonnages but undergo essentially no chemical change. Hence, their use is more or less tantamount to physically moving them from one location to another. If this were to be included, there is no logical reason to exclude material shifted in highway cut and fill operations, harbor dredging, land-fill, plowing, and even silt moved by rivers. Since a line must be drawn somewhere, we chose to draw it as indicated above.

duce externalities affecting the entire world. The effects associated with most residuals will normally be more confined, however, usually limited to regional air and water sheds.

The remaining residuals are either gases (like carbon monoxide, nitrogen dioxide, and sulfur dioxide — all potentially harmful even in the short run), dry solids (like rubbish and scrap), or wet solids (like garbage, sewage, and industrial residuals suspended or dissolved in water). In a sense, the dry solids and gases are the irreducible, limiting forms of residuals. By the application of appropriate equipment and energy, most undesirable substances can, in principle, be removed from water and air streams,[5] but what is left must be disposed of in solid form, transformed, or reused. Looking at the matter in this way clearly reveals a primary interdependence between the various residuals streams which casts into doubt the traditional classification of air, water, and land pollution as individual categories for purposes of planning and control policy.[6]

Material residuals do not necessarily have to be discharged to the environment. In many instances it is possible to recycle them back into the productive system. The materials balance view underlines the fact that the throughput of new materials necessary to maintain a given level of production and consumption decreases as the technical efficiency of energy conversion and materials utilization increases. Similarly, other things being equal, the longer cars, buildings, machinery, and other durables remain in service, the fewer new materials are required to compensate for loss, wear, and obsolescence — although the use of old or worn machinery (e.g., automobiles) tends to increase other residuals problems. Technically efficient combustion of (desulfurized) fossil fuels would leave only water, ash, and carbon dioxide as residuals, while nuclear energy conversion need leave only negligible quantities of material residuals, although pollution from discharge of heat — an energy residual — and of radiative materials cannot be dismissed by any means.

Given the population, industrial production, and transport services in an economy (a regional rather than a national economy would normally be the relevant unit), it is possible to visualize combinations of social policy which could lead to quite different relative burdens placed on the various residuals-receiving environmental media. And, given the possibilities for recycle and less residual-generating production processes, a lighter overall burden can be placed upon the environment as a whole. To take one extreme, a region which went in heavily for electric space heating and wet scrubbing of stack gases (from steam plants and industries), which ground up its garbage and delivered it to the sewers and then discharged the raw sewage to watercourses, would protect its air resources to an exceptional degree. But this would come at the sacrifice of placing a heavy residuals load upon water resources. On the other hand, a region which treated municipal and industrial liquid residuals streams to a high level but relied heavily on the incineration of sludges and solid residuals would protect its water and land resources but at the expense of discharging residuals predominantly to the air. Finally, a region which practiced high-level recovery and recycle of residuals and fostered low residuals production processes to a far-reaching extent in each of the economic sectors might discharge very few residuals to any of the environmental media.

Further complexities are added by the fact that sometimes it is possible to modify an environmental medium through investment in control facilities so as to improve its assimilative capacity. The clearest, but far from only, example is with respect to watercourses where reservoir or groundwater storage can be used to augment low river flows which ordinarily are associated with critical water quality levels (high external cost situations).[7] Thus, internalization of external costs associated with particular discharges by means of other restrictions, even if done perfectly, cannot guarantee Pareto optimality. Investments involving public good aspects must enter into an optimal solution.[8]

CONCLUSION

Air and water used to be the economist's favorite examples of "free goods" (goods so abundant that their marginal value to any user, or potential user, is zero). It was historically fortunate for conventional economic theorizing about the efficiency of market processes that this was approximately true in fact. These media served the function of "infinite sinks" for most of the residuals which are, as the materials balance view so clearly shows, an inevitable accompaniment of production and consumption activities.

What is appearing now, however, is a vast asymmetry in the adequacy of our property institutions (which, of course, underlie all private exchange) to handle resources allocation problems. On the one hand, in the production of basic natural resources commodities, property institutions with some controls and adjustments, in general, serve quite well to lead production into highest productivity channels now and in the future. On the other hand, the flow of residuals back to the environment is heavily weighted to media where private property institutions can function imperfectly, if at all. Once these media become overloaded on a significant scale, they are free goods no more but, rather, *natural resources* of ever increasing value as economic development proceeds.

To recapitulate briefly our main points so far:

(1) Technological external diseconomies are not freakish anomalies in the processes of production and consumption but inherent and normal parts of them.
(2) These external diseconomies are quantitatively negligible in a low-population economically undeveloped setting, but they become progressively (nonlinearly) more important as the population rises and the level of output increases (i.e., as the natural reservoirs of dilution and assimilative capacity become exhausted).[9]
(3) They cannot be properly dealt with by considering environmental media such as air and water in isolation.
(4) Isolated and ad hoc taxes and other restrictions are not sufficient for their optimum control, although such policy instruments are essential elements in a more systematic and coherent program of environmental quality management.
(5) Public investment programs, particularly including transportation systems, sewage disposal, and river flow regulation, are intimately related to the amounts and effects of residuals and must be planned in light of them.

In view of this it is important to develop not only improved measures of the external costs resulting from differing concentrations and durations of residuals in the environment, but more systematic methods for projecting emissions of external cost producing residuals, technical and economic trade-offs among them, and the effects of recycle on environmental quality. . . .

References

1. As far as we know, the idea of applying materials balance concepts to waste disposal problems was first expressed by Smith. F. A. Smith, "The Economic Theory of Industrial Waste Production and Disposal," draft of a doctoral dissertation, Northwestern University, 1967. We also benefited from an unpublished paper by Joseph Headley in which a pollution "matrix" is suggested. We have also found suggestive references by Boulding to a "spaceship economy" ("The Economics of the Coming Spaceship Earth," pp. 3–14). One of the authors has previously used a similar approach in ecological studies of nutrient interchange among plants and animals; see R. U. Ayres, "Stability of Biosystems in Sea Water," Technical Report No. 142, Hudson Laboratories, Columbia University, 1967. As we note later, residual energy is another major source of external costs and could be analyzed analogously in terms of "energy balance."

2. To simplify our language, we will not repeat this essential qualification at each opportunity, but assume it applies through the following discussion. In addition, we must include residuals such as NO and NO_2 arising from reactions between components of the air itself but occurring as combustion by-products.

3. See footnote to Table 1.

4. *Implications of Rising Carbon Dioxide Content of the Atmosphere,* Conservation Foundation, New York, 1963. There is strong evidence that discharge of residuals has already affected the climate of individual cities. W. P. Lowry, "The Climate of Cities," *Scientific American,* Vol. 217 (Aug. 1967), pp. 15–23. The other side of the coin of CO_2 production is oxygen consumption, which some experts also regard as a potential problem. In the United States in 1965 about 1.3 billion tons of fossil fuels were consumed for all purposes along with 2.74 billion tons of atmospheric oxygen, to yield 3.77 billion tons of CO_2 plus immense tonnages of assorted by-products. In comparison, human respiration requires about 60 million tons of atmospheric oxygen (for the population of the United States) and produces 98 million tons of CO_2. Based on biomass, the sum total of all animals — mainly cattle — would require less than five times as much oxygen as the human population alone, or somewhere in the neighborhood of 0.3 billion tons, and produces 0.5 billion tons of CO_2 at most.

5. Except CO_2, which may be harmful in the long run, as noted.

6. Water pollution on the federal level is presently the province of the Federal Water Pollution Control Administration (Department of the Interior); air pollution, of the National Air Pollution Control Administration (Department of Health, Education, and Welfare); and solids, of the Bureau of Solid Wastes Management (also DHEW). Similar divisions are usually present at the state and local levels.

7. Careful empirical work has shown that this technique can fit efficiently into water quality management systems. See R. K. Davis, *The Range of Choice in Water Management* (Johns Hopkins Press for RFF, 1968).

8. A discussion of the theory of such public investments with respect to water quality management is found in J. H. Boyd, "Collective Facilities in Water Quality Management," appendix to Kneese and Bower, *Managing Water Quality.*

9. Externalities associated with residuals discharge may appear at certain threshold values which are relevant only at some stage of economic development and industrial and population concentrations. This may account for their general treatment as "exceptional" cases in the economics literature. These threshold values truly would be exceptional cases for less developed agrarian economies.

Chapter 5

Values: the best ecosystem

An environmental manager ultimately faces the questions of what output to seek in the management operations and for whose benefit resources should be managed. To maximize one goal may require minimizing other desired objectives. So, to manage a forest for the greatest production of one species may result in the decline of others. A similar problem is faced if a multiple-use philosophy is employed in forest management. Maintaining a stand of timber for recreation, wood production, and wildlife preservation requires understanding who is to benefit over what time period. Some uses are incompatible and some are compatible; unless a policy articulates benefits for particular users over a certain time period, real management is not being done.

Regulation of fisheries poses similar problems. The famed Maine lobster is now being overfished, so supply is falling behind demand and natural growth of the stock is being arrested. Will we give this generation of fishermen and gourmets the benefit, or will we manage the stock on a sustained yield basis so that lobsters will be available for generations? These are questions of values. Leaving the decision to marketplace economics usually leads to overfishing and the decline of species. Current practice has led to moving from one species to another: overfishing until the stock is depleted, then going on to new stocks. Indeed a technology of mobile fisheries has made it economically attractive to roam the world's oceans, with continued depletion of fish stocks. As long as there are more stocks, the frontier of the sea can be mined as past frontiers have been.

However, in such practices is an implicit set of values based on a first-come, first-served policy. The tremendous growth in population and protein demand, with the understanding that the earth has finite resources, means values will have to be better articulated and examined. Investment decisions will have to be made to see if aquaculture technology can improve the earth's stock of fish at a greater rate than present fisheries policy. Cultural evaluation of the tastes of certain populations will have to determine if fish stocks are to be classified as trash or tasty. People will have to choose between the costs of sewage treatment plants and the availability of shellfish. Shellfish and municipal sewage are not often linked in the management decision process, but environmental management requires the decision be made in a full rather than a narrow context.

René Dubos's "The Genius of the Place" helps us recognize that value decisions cannot simply be made on man's wishes. The earth itself requires our attention, and the value of it to man is related to the responsibility we take. His concept of "the genius of place" would have us recognize that value decisions must be made in a larger context than present thinking might otherwise encompass.

The solution to conflicts of values by happy coexistence becomes more and more difficult as the world population rises. Just how many more people the earth can tolerate, while men tolerate each other, is still an open question. However, most environmentalists now agree we are headed for disaster and anything short of curbing births is merely an illusory measure to buy a little more time for a lot more people. At some point, nature — in the form of disease or other ravaging and mindless disasters — will cut the top off the human growth curve. Nature is an effective, but unsympathetic, manager of the environment.

Economic development as a worldwide policy has been the response to the population growth and man's desire to live better. The best ecosystem has, until now, been thought one in which all men's living standard approached that of the Western nations. However, that decision was not made in a context which included natural resource limitations. Early reactions to an eco-aware posture resulted in advice to curb economic development. Open confrontation between growth and ecology seemed inevitable. It was believed men would have to make a value choice between environmental preservation and economic well-being as we measure it today. While this formulation will no doubt hold sway for some time, the real issue is more complex.

From the point of view of value choices, Max Nicholson's article on international economic development illustrates there really is no choice. The consequences of short-term victory for man, in a man versus nature posture, is in fact economically degrading in the long run. If we want economic growth, we will also have to be good environmental protectors. That level of awareness goes beyond mere antimaterialism and gets to the core of an internationally applicable environmental policy.

A related point is made in Gerhard Kade's criticism of the current tools of economists and planners. This article should be read twice, for it requires changes in the way men regulate their relations to other men. Without paying close attention to the reasoning in his article, we may all be doomed to ficticious success.

Perhaps no one can make this point more tellingly than Jay W. Forrester, whose article makes us acutely aware of the bind we are in. Ameliorative solutions are possibly disastrous solutions; without considering the broad implications of our actions, we may solve problems only by creating new and bigger ones. The reader may quibble with the data and equations in Forrester's model. However, some such analysis is absolutely necessary if the scientist and the politician are to achieve their goals.

Herman E. Daly's article makes this point tellingly. The value choices are difficult. However, ignorance of consequences may make current problems even more difficult to deal with later. As we will discuss in the last chapter, we are currently saddled with a short-run culture, so that entrepreneurs of the future and officials with the public interest in mind will face decisions which require far more knowledge and skills than are available today.

RENÉ JULES DUBOS
The Genius of the Place

The word environment now evokes nightmares. It calls to mind the exhaustion of natural resources, the accumulation of waste products, the various forms of pollution, crowding, noise, and the thousand devils of the ecological crisis. But while it is true that environmental degradation is now almost as widespread and as traumatic in the country as in the city, there is danger in thinking about the environment only in such negative terms. If we limit our interest to the correction of environmental defects, we shall behave like hunted creatures, trying to escape from one danger after another, taking shelter behind an endless series of protective devices — today afterburners on our cars and complicated sewage treatment systems, tomorrow gas masks over our faces and filters on our water faucets. Such technological fixes will have temporary usefulness, but they will increasingly complicate our life and ruin its quality. The real solution to the ecological crisis will have to come from a change in our ways of life and from the development of positive values relating human nature to external nature. I had these positive values in mind when I selected "The Genius of the Place" as a title for my presentation.

Positive values can at times be introduced from the outside. But almost universally, the values most likely to be successful in a given system are those which are inherent in the system itself and which are part of its "genius" or "spirit" — using these words in the sense they had in the classical Greco-Roman tradition.

Ancient peoples personified a locality with a particular god or goddess who symbolized its qualities and potentialities. We no longer believe in dryads, nymphs, or genii. But rationalists as we may be, we still respond to phrases such as "the genius of New England" or "the spirit of the Far West." These phrases imply the acknowledgement that each place is characterized by a set of attributes that makes it different from others, and that gives it uniqueness.

René Jules Dubos, "The Genius of the Place," *American Forests,* September 1970, pp. 16–19, 61–62. Reprinted by permission. This article is condensed from the Tenth Horace M. Albright Lecture of the School of Forestry and Natural Resources, University of California.

The visitor can perceive in a few minutes the spirit of London in a pub, or the spirit of Paris on the crowded terrasse of a student café. He need only cross the frontier between Italy and Switzerland to apprehend at a glance the contrasting geniuses of these two countries. Much as I am tempted to do it, I shall not discuss the differences between city and city or country and country — even though this topic would provide telling examples of the genius of the place. Suffice it to point out that the word genius, as used here, does not imply a judgment of values or some measure of superiority. It refers only to the array of attributes which give its unique characteristics to a place and enable it to evolve in such a manner that, while changing, it retains its uniqueness.

One of Aldo Leopold's famous aphorisms is that conservation shows us what a land can be, what it should be, what it *ought* to be. In my opinion, this statement implies a questionable philosophy of nature, because it seems to assume that some invisible hand guides nature to the one perfect path of ecological harmony among its different parts. In reality, as we shall see, it is possible in most areas of the world to find several safe roads to ecological salvation. Leopold's aphorism implies furthermore a defeatist view of man's relation to nature. It regards man as an intruder whose inventions almost inevitably dislocate the ecological order and are likely thereby to cause nature's destruction.

Leopold's type of pessimism has taken the curious form among many conservationists and ecologists of making Biblical teachings responsible for the destructive influence of man on nature. I shall devote some space to this peculiar assertion, not only because it is unwarranted by historical facts and present practices, but also because its widespread acceptance threatens to distract attention from the real problems of the relationships between the earth and mankind.

THE JUDEO-CHRISTIAN TRADITION

The ecological crisis in the Western world, so the saying goes among ecologists and conservationists, has its origin in the first chapter of *Genesis,* where man is given dominion over creation. Finding a ready excuse in this passage of the Scriptures, the peoples of Judeo-Christian origin have had no scruples — so it is stated — in exploiting nature for their selfish benefit. The outcome has been a variety of ecological disasters — from erosion of the land to exhaustion of natural resources. Oddly enough, conservationists and ecologists who certainly know better, hardly ever mention that many peoples outside the Judeo-Christian tradition have also been ruthless with nature, in many cases even before the Bible was written. Erosion resulting from human activities has occurred in ancient China and it probably caused the end of the Teotihuacan civilization in ancient Mexico. Plato explicitly stated in the dialogue *Critias* his belief that Greece was eroded before his time as a result of deforestation and overgrazing. The noble groves of cedars and cypresses in Lebanon were massively exploited not only by Solomon but also by the Assyrian kings and the Roman emperors.

The Judeo-Christian civilization has been no worse and no better than others in its relation to nature. Throughout history, men have disturbed the ecological equilibrium, almost universally out of ignorance and chiefly because they have been more concerned with immediate advantages than with long-range goals. The goat has helped countless human beings to survive by its ability to derive nourishment from poor lands, but it has probably contributed even more than modern bulldozers to the destruction of the land and the creation of deserts.

The view that Biblical teachings have been responsible for the exploitation and raping of nature by modern man has recently led to the advocacy of a return to the humble attitude of the early Franciscans. Because Francis of Assisi worshipped all aspects of nature, it has been suggested that we should try to follow in his footsteps and abandon our aggressive attitude toward nature. In a fascinating and often-quoted article, Professor Lynn White has suggested that Francis of Assisi be made patron saint of ecologists. Even the early Franciscans, however, soon abandoned the romantic and unworldly attitude of the saint. Man has never been just a worshipper of nature or a passive witness of natural events. Indeed, he developed his humanness in the very act of interacting constructively with the world around him and while molding nature by his will to make it better suited to his needs, wishes, and aspirations. Stonehenge, Angkor Wat, the Parthenon, and the countless other temples created by man before the Judeo-Christian era represent expressions of man's will which exacted as much from nature as did the construction of Gothic cathedrals or of the George Washington Bridge.

Among religious leaders, Saint Benedict of Nubia is much more relevant to the human condition than Saint Francis. Saint Benedict and his followers taught and practiced a doctrine based on the second chapter of *Genesis* in which it is stated that the Lord instructed man to tend the Garden of Eden and dress it. Their attitude toward nature was one of active intervention, but their wise management of the land has proved compatible with the maintenance of environmental quality.

The concepts of Saint Benedict

When Saint Benedict established the first great monastery of Western Europe on Monte Cassino in Italy during the sixth century, he decided that the monks should not only pray to God, but should also work; he recommended furthermore that their monasteries be self-sufficient. In order to achieve self-sufficiency, the Benedictine monks developed skills pertaining to agriculture and architecture. They learned to manage their holdings on such sound ecological principles that their land retained its productivity despite intensive cultivation and thus continued for long periods of time to provide the monasteries with food, clothing, and wealth. The monks also developed an architecture well suited not only to their religious and lay activities, but also to the type of country in which they lived; Benedictine architecture thus achieved such great functional beauty that it constitutes one of the major achievements of early medieval civilization.

The Benedictine order was so successful that during the Middle Ages, it established numerous monasteries over most of Europe, and thereby greatly contributed to the creation of European agriculture and landscape in the form we know them today.

Most influential from this point of view was the Cistercian branch of the Benedictine order which established its monasteries in wooded river valleys and marshes. The Cistercians rapidly became masters in the art of drainage, developed the use of water power, and converted malarious forests into habitable and fertile land. They achieved such great fame in the control of malaria that a Pope gave them the responsibility of draining the Campagna Romana.

The conversion of forest into farmland by the Benedictine monks is just one among the many historical examples that could be quoted to illustrate that man has great latitude in determining the face of nature. Before the Christian era, the Celtic populations of Britain lived almost exclusively on the calcareous plateaus, such as the Salisbury Plain, probably because the low, wooded areas were unhealthy and too difficult to cultivate. In contrast, the Romans, and then the Saxons, who had a more advanced technology, succeeded in colonizing the malarious forest of the Thames Valley and thus prepared the ground for one of the greatest centers of civilization. The Pennsylvania Dutch country provides another striking example of the fact that land created from the forest can long be maintained in a healthy, productive state. Thus, the transformation of the land by man need not be destructive; in many cases indeed it has been a creative act.

The ecological crisis in our times has nothing to do with the Judeo-Christian tradition but rather comes from the tendency now prevalent all over the world to use land and waters, mountains and estuaries for short-range economic benefits. The solution to the ecological crisis will not be found in a retreat from technological civilization, but rather in an enlightened transformation of it based on ecological understanding. We must learn to recognize the limitations and potentialities of the land and to manipulate it in such a manner that it remains a productive and desirable place for human life.

THE "VOCATIONS" OF A REGION

Successful management of the earth demands that we identify the "vocations" of its various parts. In Latin the word *vocatio* refers to the divine call for a certain kind of function. Similarly, each part of the earth has, so to speak, one or several vocations, which it is the duty of scholars to identify and of practical men to develop.

Certain parts of the earth, like certain persons, may have only one vocation. For example, there may be only one thing that can be done with certain arctic areas, with tropical lands, or with desert regions. But in general most places, like most persons, have several potential vocations; the inde-terminacy resulting from these several options adds much to the richness of life.

Consider for example what has happened to the primeval forest in the temperate countries. Much of it has been transformed into farmlands, each area developing its own agricultural specialization, social structure, and esthetic quality. But the temperate forest can have other fates. In Scotland and Eastern England, it was progressively transformed into moors by lumbering activities and sheep grazing. These moors are not productive from the agricultural point of view, but their charm has enriched the life of Great Britain and its literature. In North America, most of the forest was transformed into prairies as a result of the fires set by the pre-agricultural Indians. Even though the prairies have now been replaced by agricultural lands, they have left a lasting imprint on American civilization.

Utilitarian considerations are only one aspect of man's relation to the earth. The widespread interest in the preservation of wildlife and of primeval scenery is sufficient evidence that man finds in wilderness a kind of satisfaction that transcends economic usefulness — perhaps because he wants to retain some contact with his distant origins.

In practice, however, the only chance most people have to experience and enjoy nature is in its humanized aspects — cultivated fields, parks, gardens, and human settlements. This is true all over the world, even in the United States, where so much is made of wilderness preservation. For this reason, it is not sufficient to save the Redwoods, the Everglades, and as much of the wilderness as possible; it is equally essential to protect the esthetic quality of farmlands and to improve Coney Island.

There are many different kinds of beautiful landscapes. Some derive their appeal from their majestic scale, their uniqueness, or their splendor. The national parks in the United States provide many varied examples of scenery to which man's presence does not add anything. In most cases, however, the quality of the landscape consists in a sense of fitness between man and his surroundings. This fitness accounts for most of the charm of ancient settlements, not only in the Old World but in the New World as well. The river settlements of the Ivory Coast, the Mediterranean hill towns, the pueblos of the Rio Grande, the village greens of New England, and the old cities organized along peaceful rivers throughout the world, are as many different types of landscapes which derive their quality not so much from topographical or climatic peculiarities, as from the intimate association between man and nature.

Living as we do in an industrial mercantile society, we are inclined to overemphasize the role of technological and economic factors in determining the quality of the environment. But there are many other environmental factors that have a pervasive influence on human life. History and the climate, for example, play creative roles in determining the architecture and materials of dwellings and churches, the shape and botany of gardens and parks.

The formal gardens of Italy and France did not just happen through the caprice of wealthy men or the genius of a few landscape architects. They were successful because they fitted in the physical, biological, and social atmosphere of Italy and France at the time of their creation. Formal gardens and parks also flourished in England but the English school achieved its distinction by creating an entirely different kind of park better suited to the local conditions. The great English parks of the seventeenth and eighteenth centuries are characterized by magnificent trees grouped in meadows and in vast expanses of lawn. This style was suited to the wet climate of the British Isles. In France, many attempts were made in the eighteenth century to create gardens and parks in the English style, but with limited success. As Horace Walpole remarked in a letter giving an account of his visit to the continent: "In short, they [the French] can never have as beautiful a landscape as ours, til they have as bad a climate."

Walpole's witticism expresses the biological truth that a given landscape style can be lastingly successful only if it is compatible with the ecological imperatives of the country. This is what Alexander Pope summarized in his famous line, "In everything respect the genius of the place."

Just as the climate in most parts of France is almost incompatible with the green magnificence of the English parks, so is the atmosphere in many American cities unsuited to certain types of plants. This does not mean that plant life is out of place in urban conglomerations, only that more effort should be made to identify and propagate for each particular city the kinds of trees, flowers, and ground cover that can best thrive under its set of climatic and other constraints. Ordinary grass looks so pathetic in most cities, and the rows of plane trees so monotonous, that botanists and foresters should be encouraged to discover or create other plants congenial to urban environments. Studies of plant ecology may become more urgent in the city than in the wilderness.

Ecology and the genius of the place

The genius of the place is thus made up of the physical, biological, social, and historical forces which together give its uniqueness to each locality or region. All great cities have a genius of their own which transcends geographical location, commercial importance, and size. And so is it for each region of the world. Man always adds something to nature, and thereby transforms it, but his interventions are successful only to the extent that he respects the genius of the place.

Man's transformations of the land from one ecological state to another have not always been successful. As already mentioned, the famous stands of cedars and cypresses in Lebanon have all but disappeared and much of the Mediterranean basin has been disfigured by erosion. Ecologic changes have given desirable results chiefly in situations where they occurred so slowly that they were compatible with adaptive processes of biological and social nature. Deforestation yielded beautiful farmland and romantic moors in Great Britain where it occurred progressively over several centuries. But, in contrast, deforestation resulting from massive and hasty lumbering has been responsible for ghost towns and eroded land in many parts of North America.

Because most transformations of the earth's surface will now occur rapidly, a new kind of ecological knowledge is needed to predict the likely consequences of technological interventions and to provide rational guides as substitutes for the empirical adjustments that time used to make possible.

Ecology will provide the scientific basis for understanding and developing the genius of the place.

But orthodox ecological knowledge is not enough. In the final analysis, all decisions concerning the environment involve matters of taste and therefore value judgments.

During the eighteenth century, tastes concerning landscape architecture were profoundly influenced by the artistic style of a few painters, in particular Salvadore Rosa, Claude Lorrain, and Nicholas Poussin. Each in his own way, these painters used Italian scenery to create an idealized picture of the pastoral ways of life, and this ideal rapidly found its way into the design of parks and gardens all over Europe, especially in England.

Nature and the climate in England are far different from what they are in Italy. But the English landscape architects succeeded nevertheless in using the genius of their land to develop a new kind of scenery expressing the emotional and esthetic values that they had acquired from seventeenth-century painting. By so doing, they created the scenic beauty of England which we still enjoy today.

The successes of the English school of landscape architecture illustrate that man's intervention in the environment can generate new values. It can take the form of creative interplay resulting in the progressive flowering of the potentialities hidden in human nature and in external nature.

GERHARD KADE

Introduction: The Economics of Pollution and the Interdisciplinary Approach to Environmental Planning

The following reflections are intended as a critical review of the theory of planning on the eve of a new and important challenge to planning sciences. The decade to come will be marked by efforts to solve various problems of man's environment. At a time when, all over the world, scientists, politicians and administrators have begun to draw attention to the multiple threats to the survival of mankind stemming from the scientific, technological and economic development of our industrial civilization, planners will face the question whether the tools they have developed are adequate or at all useful to tackle the problems of environmental planning.

These critical reflections on the "state of the art" will be supplemented

Gerhard Kade, "Introduction: The Economics of Pollution and the Interdisciplinary Approach to Environmental Planning." From the *International Social Science Journal,* vol. 21, no. 4, 1970. Reproduced with the permission of Unesco.

by what seems to us an improved conceptual framework for solving planning problems. Our analysis will thus primarily be methodological; however, problems of application will be touched upon, especially whenever we encounter questions pertaining to the economics of environment. Such problems and certain strategies for their solution have become fashionable ever since the social cost concept became a basic idea in economics.[1]

Since it is highly questionable whether the concepts and models of problem-finding and problem-solving in contemporary economics are conducive to tackling problems of long-term conservation and the improvement of man's environment and since the prevailing conception of planning is closely tied to the development of economic science, it would seem that a parallel treatment, i.e. a critical review of planning techniques combined with some highlighting of the economics of environment may bring out certain new aspects which might prove useful in the practical attack on environmental problems.

SOURCES OF THE PREVAILING THEORY OF PLANNING

Planning as a specific approach towards decision-making is the last consequence of the rationalistic ideology incorporated in the economic doctrines of the eighteenth and nineteenth centuries. This may seem surprising but it is none the less true, despite the extent to which the traditional dualism of competition versus planning has been a pet theme in discussion about functioning social systems in economics to date.

Due to social conditions in the eighteenth century and to the dominating influence of Western rationalism, economics at the time of its foundation was primarily concerned with an operation model of a free enterprise economy. The basic concepts in the design of this model were those of equilibrium and optimum. The over-all optimum of the system was conceived as resulting from the individually rational behavior of the different economic agents.

If, however, rational behavior was the essential prerequisite for the attainment of optimum results — both for the individual and for the social system as a whole — then it is not surprising that economics as a science contributed powerfully to the shaping of economic and rational behavior, so that economic behavior was defined as rational behavior with "economic" parameters of action.

This, more or less, was the background against which the modern ideology of planning developed. The essential components of the free enterprise model were transformed into concepts of modern planning: the economic reward-punishment mechanism, which is the basic idea of the price mechanism, appears in the shape of the various cost-benefit concepts in modern planning; the postulate of rational behavior develops into the more general idea of optimizing behavior, and the model of economic decisions implying the dichotomy of means and ends already proclaimed by J. S. Mill[2] which, in the nineteenth century, was transformed into the concept of "pure economics."

The development of the modern theory of planning from the basic ideas of liberal economics was supported by the following trends: (a) introduction of mathematical methods into economics; (b) the general theory of decisions; and (c) the amalgamation of rationalism and interventionism.

An important step in the development of the dominant ideology of planning was the introduction of mathematical methods into economics in the course of the nineteenth century. The methods of the calculus seemed suitable to derive the necessary and sufficient conditions for the optimal position of an economic system. The optimizing technique used in the nineteenth-century calculus was considered to be a direct representation of rational behavior, and the language of mathematics to reveal the formal structure of optimizing behavior: economic behavior is rational decision-making which can be mathematically represented by maximizing or minimizing an objective function under certain constraints.

The formation of modern planning theory took place at a time when, through the convergence of different disciplines the special model of rational behavior adopted by neoclassical economics developed into a general theory of rational decision-making which, despite its more general scope and applicability, is basically framed by the definition of economic rationality.

Finally, the historical circumstances under which the transition from *laissez-faire* to economic planning took place are responsible for the general view of planning problems in social systems or sub-systems: the combination of the formal schemes of rational decision-making with the idea of State intervention gave rise to an ideology of planning which is at once rationalistic and interventionistic. Thus, planning is conceived as an act of influencing the operation of a social system by intervention through policy based on a model of rational decision.

Consequently, in modern economics, and especially in the theory of quantitative economic policy, there are two types of planning models which reflect the concept of rational-interventionistic decision-making, viz. the so-called fixed-target policy models,[3] i.e. macro-economic models with target variables the values of which are fixed by policy-makers, and optimizing techniques (flexible-target policy models)[4] which utilize explicit objective functions and constraints.

THE GENERAL MODEL OF PLANNING AND THE DICHOTOMY OF ENDS AND MEANS

In order to elaborate the socio-political implications of the traditional planning concept it is useful to make explicit reference to the general model of rational decision. Action is defined as the transformation of an initial situation S into a final situation S', i.e. mapping the set of relations describing S on another set of relations S' where some maximum M is the correlator producing the mapping of S on S'.[5] The traditional concept of planning implies a certain phasing of the process of transformation of S into S' which reveals the dichotomy of ends and means. The following steps are taken into consideration: (a) target

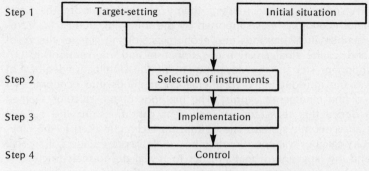

Figure 1.   General model of planning

setting; (b) description of the initial situation S; (c) selection of instruments; (d) implementation; and (e) control. (See Fig. 1 below.)

If the initial situation is given by $[Z_1, Z_2, \ldots, Z_n; X_1, X_2, \ldots, X_m]$, the set of targets by $[Z_1^*, Z_2^*, \ldots, Z_n^*]$, where Z_j are targets and X_i instruments of the planning problem, then the program is given by $[X_1^*, X_2^*, \ldots, X_m^*]$ which is the set of instrument variables. In this context, planning is nothing more than the selection of set $[X_1^*, X_2^*, \ldots, X_m^*]$ compatible with a given set of targets $[Z_1^*, Z_2^*, \ldots, Z_n^*]$.

It is obvious that by reducing the planning process to a functional process of transformation the planner would require information about all possible alternatives and their consequences as well as a consistent order of preference; this is equivalent to saying that the well-defined set of instruments $[X_1^*, X_2^*, \ldots, X_m^*]$ is optimal with respect to a given target or set of targets. The model is "artificially" closed which leads to a more or less deductive process of rational decision with centralization of diagnosis, valuation, and selection; all relevant information is supposedly simultaneously at the disposal of the decision-maker, an assumption called the "synoptic ideal" of planning.[6] Planning problems are defined as "well-structured" ones which can be solved by suitable mathematical techniques. This is why most of the planning literature of the past two decades has concentrated on formal models and mathematical techniques which all fit into the pattern described above.

THE FAILURES AND FALLACIES OF THE PREVAILING CONCEPT OF PLANNING

No matter under what social, economic and political conditions the traditional planning concept has been applied the failures were much too obvious to be ignored. The results of economic and other types of social planning in market economy and socialist countries as well as in the under-developed parts of the world are so disappointing that a mere reorganization of the planning procedure should be out of question. However, traditional planning theory mostly reacted to these obvious failures by advocating more refined techniques rather than by a critical review of the whole planning ideology.

Planning problems are in fact ill-structured problems which can be tackled by heuristic procedures,[7] but not by formal models and mathematical techniques. Instead of logical elements it is pragmatic criteria which must determine the process of planning. The main features of decision-making are no longer the conditions necessary and sufficient for the derivation of a mathematical solution to an optimizing problem but the organizational, motivational and informational components of a process[8] which defines planning as a combination of adaptive and learning processes.

The main illusion implicit in the prevailing ideology of planning has its roots in the positivistic theory of knowledge or logic of scientific discovery. The dichotomy of values and facts has its "political" counterpart in the dichotomy of ends and means or targets and instruments. If target-setting is left to the political decision-makers and the analysis of a consistent set of instruments is declared to be the realm of research then we have a dangerous ideology of objectivity, the political implications of which are anything but democratic. The clear-cut distinction between the rational selection of instruments and the political irrationality of decisions on targets or goals of action prevents an analysis of the power structure, repression manipulation, the play of interests, etc. Objectivity has proved to be a very easily manageable ideology by which the influence of the power elite is best concealed.

The complexity of social planning problems cannot be reduced to technical solutions. The process of target-setting must be institutionalized and the prevailing dichotomy of ends and means must be replaced by a valuation process of combined clusters of targets and instruments.

The second basic problem in the modern theory of planning is the question of implementation. As long as we continue to adopt a separate-function model of communication between experts and decision-makers[9] we shall perpetuate the frustrating situation of a growing amount of expert opinion in ever-thicker planning reports piled up on the shelves of public administrators. The idea is basic to the line of thought in economics and other social sciences and is implicit in the dichotomy of planning (or rather programming and implementation); it is the *ceteris paribus* clause of a discipline-oriented approach. The economic adviser, for example, thinks of himself as the provider of a certain amount of expertise to the political decision-maker who will in turn have to think about what further advice and administrative arrangements he will need to implement, say, a programme of optimal growth. Thus, the programme is always good; if it fails in the process of implementation it is not the fault of any particular discipline which designed the programme on the basis of available knowledge.

There is no royal road from research to planning, and the existing gap can not be bridged by improved mathematical techniques. Any attempt to diminish the failures of present planning procedures by more complicated mathematical methods is an attempt to avoid the solution of social problems which can only be brought about by making the process of target-setting explicit and by abolishing the dichotomy between the subjects and objects of planning.

The last stage of the planning process, the control of operation, finally, is not operational in a model of planning based on the dichotomy of means and ends. Any control within a social system must be directed towards a simultaneous transformation of instruments and of goals and unless we find the proper approach to an integrated cluster of targets and instruments, there can be no possibility of control.

The pollution of the natural environment is not an isolated problem brought about by the application of certain technologies to be controlled by introducing different technologies. It is a social problem affecting the very base of our socio-economic system. The application of traditional planning techniques will not solve the problems we are facing because all there is to offer is a set of technical solutions in a social system which is basically assumed to be functioning soundly. During the past twenty years economists have been trying to develop an economics of pollution which claims to embrace the social aspects of environment. That most famous textbook, Samuelson's *Economics,* contains a chapter on pollution in its latest edition.[10] But can we expect economics to change the predominantly technical discussion of environmental problems?

THE POLITICAL ECONOMY OF THE RAVAGED ENVIRONMENT

The economics of pollution is not in a very promising state. The poisoning of the natural environment with noxious garbage, chemicals, sewage, heat, noise and fumes which confronts mankind with the latest threat of self-destruction has become the personal experience of many inhabitants of highly industrialized countries; it has brought up a number of promising if not already operational recommendations. New technologies have been suggested in various fields and more general technical solutions were recently put forward at the 136th meeting of the American Association of the Advancement of Science, where recycling was suggested as a cure to further environmental decay.

Yet economics has not been greatly disturbed by the growing destruction of the environment. As usual, when new social problems arise and require analysis in terms of their economic implications, the traditional corpus of economic theory was not challenged to such an extent that some of its basic postulates, dating back to the days of Adam Smith and David Ricardo, be subjected to critical analysis. Much rather the new problem was assimilated to the existing body of economic theory.[11]

Thus, liberal economics as a science has increasingly reached the point where the causal analysis of socio-economic processes has been displaced by functional models primarily designed to prove that the free enterprise system represents the best of all possible economic worlds. There are, of course, some admitted minor deficiencies; the price mechanism is not in all cases capable of automatically producing the social optimum, though basically it guarantees the functioning of the system.

Thus, when economics acknowledged the problems of the human environment, it was not surprising at all that there was a handy concept in the box of tools which had merely to be produced: the concept of externalities which played its role in neoclassical price theory.

It is well known that the concepts of external economies and diseconomies or, what amounts to largely the same in our context, the divergence of private and social costs, are key instruments in the attempt to defend the free enterprise system against attack.

When the first systematic treatment of the phenomenon of social costs appeared twenty years ago[12] ecological damage was already so obvious that, in two chapters on air and water pollution, the concept of social costs was revitalized in order to make an assessment of the social loss due to the destruction of the environment. This line of thought has been kept up during the past two decades and it is hardly surprising that Arrow, during last year's annual meeting of the American Economic Association used the same conceptual and analytical framework in his paper on "Externalities and Public Policy."

Like other departures from the market mechanism as the universal steering device of the economy which always and under all conditions allocates resources to their socially most efficient uses, the economics of pollution, by reliance on a purely economic frame of reference, have resorted to the empty formula: as much market mechanism as possible and as much non-market mechanism as necessary.

While scientists keep offering new technologies to repair the damage done by the old, economists, in a sense, also rely on technological solutions when they offer their functional models of externalities and social versus private costs. Thus, the technical solutions are more or less translated into economic terms, into cost-benefit calculations, and the entire discussion is conducted as if economics were still dominated by the marginal utility school. The concepts of the rational allocation of resources and of rational calculation within a given economic system, fashionable in the first decades of this century[13] come up again and lay claim to being adequate frameworks for the solution of contemporary socio-political problems. It is not surprising, therefore, that policy recommendations derived from these hollow categories are proving inadequate to restore the environment and prevent its further destruction.

What emerges from the functional models of traditional economics is developed by scientists and technicians when they suggest new technologies to replace the old or recommend some system of recycling. As a result, we have by now a number of what seem quite reliable estimations of the costs of technological change to avoid water and air pollution, and other consequences of waste. But when economists, by and large, try to develop some scheme of imputation and to suggest tax and subsidy policies to solve the waste problem, it is obvious that they rely on the operation of that same steering device which is itself responsible for environmental decay.

No doubt the problems we are facing must be related to the motivations and attitudes which the industrial system has introduced and/or supported. Man's attitude towards his environment is determined by religious traditions which placed him in an elevated position within the hierarchical order of the universe. The historical development of this attitude led from an exploratory to an exploitative perspective leading to risk of self-destruction.[14]

Pollution as a threat to mankind is but a variation on the theme of Protestantism (or rather Judeo-Christian tradition) and the rise of capitalism. The principal elements of the economic model of the free enterprise system, the profit motive, competition, the best use of available resources, etc., produced a very specific view of the environment. Nature was the object of exploitation, and it is not surprising that in economics water and air were defined as "free goods." No wonder either that *entrepreneurs* felt free to make so much use of these resources as to contribute enormously to the contamination of the human environment.

In the course of industrial development the prime mover of the capitalist system, the profit motive, geared the system to affluence and waste, so that pollution of the environment seems to be the price of a high continuous rate of economic growth.

The villain of the piece is sought in different parts of the system, preferably, however, on the consumer side. The consumers are those "who demand (or at least let themselves be cajoled into desiring) new, more, faster, bigger, cheaper play-things without counting the cost in a dirtier, smellier, sicklier world."[15] Economics has usually, during the past two centuries, been apologetic and it is not surprising that nowadays, under conditions of affluence and waste, the victim is made the villain of the piece.

The pollution of the natural environment is, however, a social and political problem which cannot be solved unless we transcend the traditional categories of plausibility wherein the putative solutions of scientists and economics are generated. Our damaged environment can only be saved from further destruction and possibly restored when we stop allowing our imagination to be confined by technicalities. If we are not ready to enter into a causal analysis of the problems of environmental decay we shall not be able to develop long-term plans to prevent the self-destruction of mankind. Pollution cannot be attributed to mistaken technologies, population growth, consumption habits and economic growth as such, these superficial phenomena are symptoms, not causes. We must overlook the interests in avoiding causal analysis by dwelling on such superficial phenomena. The specific interests of certain social groups have always been well served by reducing social conflicts to superficial problems which can be solved by minor technical rearrangements.

TOWARDS A NEW STRATEGY OF PLANNING

Any examination of the scientific and technical analyses of different forms of pollution shows a number of interdependences of which scientists are aware, and it is not surprising that these interrelations often arouse the general expectation that the solution will have to come from a more thorough analysis of the motives and attitudes, the patterns of behaviour in the social system. This vague feeling of the insufficiency of a discipline-oriented approach may be the point of departure for an attempt to develop an interdisciplinary approach to environmental planning.

The basic idea for a revised strategy of planning is not to start with goal-setting and to forget the traditional boundaries of scientific disciplines. To start by fixing certain targets usually implies, as we have seen, that the solution is a purely technical problem. Any attempt to set certain targets at the very beginning of a planning process will fail to identify the problem in all its ramifications. Members of a social system have a certain idea of the operation of that system according to their personal background. What they have to offer when defining a problem is a certain plausibility, not the identification of a complex problem. We all tend to have a quick idea of what is wrong, and in formulating it hardly realize that we have at the same time given the solution because plausible problems usually have merely technical solutions.

Thus, the first phase of a planning process has nothing to do with goal-setting, value systems or implicit solutions. Planning is a process of problem-identification and problem-solving, of which the first phase requires interdisciplinary co-operation and the later phase is organizational problem with motivational and informational components.

If we wish to develop long-term programmes for the conservation and restoration of our damaged environment it is necessary in the first instance to provide an over-all view of the disturbances within the system. Now, some of us will be aware of what is going on. In the United States, for instance, there are each year 360 million tons of garbage, 1,500 million tons of solid waste from mines and factories, 142 million tons of air pollutants, 50,000 million gallons of polluted water; we know about the thermal threat of power plants, the growing noise and so on. But there is one thing wrong with this type of information: only a minority is aware of it and the experts producing it are much too ready to sell it together with a number of quick solutions. Hence we have started to introduce new technologies to solve certain problems in detail before we know all the interrelations. This will result in a number of very costly solutions to discrete problems if we stop short of analysing the whole catastrophe before us.

Since the entire earth is affected by a number of interrelated pollutants the over-all problem must be structured and the public must be made aware of what is going on. This includes an analysis of the historical development of environmental decay in order to determine which processes have contributed to contamination. It also includes an investigation into social and economic systems which by concentrating on the exploitation of the natural surroundings, by profit-oriented technical and economic progress have created conditions of affluence and waste which raise the question of whether mankind will accelerate its own destruction for the sake of high rates of growth and profit.

If the pending environmental catastrophe is given adequate publicity then the possible alternatives will be much clearer than they are on the basis of purely technological information. Only when all the threats are well known can the process of planning for better environments be undertaken.

The next step, after identifying the disturbances in the system, is the organization of the planning process. This is not a very simple problem since it implies changes in administration and legislation and is further affected by international arrangements. What must be achieved is the participation of different interest groups in planning organizations, which in turn raises the whole problem of organizing public opinion for political decision-making.

Only after the organizational problem has been solved can the process of goal-fixing begin. By departmentalizing the over-all problem, by identifying variables, constraints and parameters a set of rules of action must be established, which in turn must be tested for consistency. Then priorities can be determined and, after some test runs, the detailed plan of implementation will result.

This process is variously interconnected by organizational arrangements and rearrangements, by information flows, and by continuous changes in rules of action. It can be practised in a number of smaller fields, in delimited planning spheres which, however, can only be segmented after the total problem has been identified. The main advantage of this new strategy of planning is to bridge the gap between goals and instruments since it allows for constant interrelations of means and ends, and to bridge the gap between programme and implementation, since the planners are also the implementors. There is a process of identification so that the old problem of divergences between the subject and the object of planning no longer exists.[16]

It is true that we have become more and more aware of the pending environmental catastrophe. A change in perspective from the purely technical to the social implications is under way. Even scientists and technicians now refer to major changes in the social system, changes in attitudes and motivations. This cannot be brought about by moral persuasion as some seem to believe. Nor can we expect much fruitful advice from traditional economics. The solution may be found in a combination of political economy and planning, an examination of the causes of pollution and the use of an interdisciplinary — that to say problem-oriented — approach for curing the ills.

References

1. W. Kapp, *The Social Costs of Private Enterprise*, Cambridge, 1950.

2. J. S. Mill, *Essays on Some Unsettled Questions of Political Economy*, London, 1844; reprinted London, 1948.

3. J. Tinbergen, *On the Theory of Economic Policy*, 4th ed., Amsterdam, North-Holland Publishing Co., 1966; J. Tinbergen, *Centralization and Decentralization of Economic Policy — Principles and Design*, 3rd ed., Amsterdam, North-Holland Publishing Co., 1966.

4. H. Theil, *Optimal Decision Rules for Government and Industry*, Amsterdam, North-Holland Publishing Co., 1964.

5. J. Kempski, "Handlung, Maxime, Situation", in: H. Albert (ed.), *Theorie und Realität*, p. 233, Tübingen, Mohr & Siebeck, 1964.

6. D. Braybrooke and C. E. Lindblom, *A Strategy of Decision — Policy Evaluation as a Social Process*, New York, The Free Press, 1963.

7. D. W. Taylor, 'Decision Making and Problem Solving', in: J. G. March (ed.), *Handbook of Organization*, p. 73, Chicago, Ill., Rand McNally, 1965; G. A. Miller, E. Galanter and H. K. Pribram, *Plans and the Structure of Behavior*, New York, Holt, Rinehart & Winston, 1963.

8. E. Neuberger, 'Libermanism, Computopia and Visible Hand', *American Economic Review*, Vol. 56, 1966, p. 131.

9. C. W. Churchman and A. H. Schainblatt, 'The Researcher and the Manager: A Dialectic of Implementation', *Management Science*, Vol. 11, 1965, p. 69.

10. P. Samuelson, *Economics*, 8th ed., New York, McGraw-Hill, 1970.

11. Compare the analysis in terms of social costs by W. Kapp, op. cit., with the latest Swedish publication of E. Dahmén, *Sätt pris p a miljön*, Stockholm, 1968.

12. W. Kapp, op. cit.

13. F. A. Hayek (ed.), *Collectivist Economic Planning,* London, 1935.

14. This idea is developed in greater detail in the article by William Leiss on 'Utopia and Technology' page 576.

15. *Newsweek,* 26 January 1970, p. 26.

16. For a detailed view of the structure of the planning process see the Appendix overleaf.

MAX NICHOLSON

International Economic Development and the Environment

I

From an ecologist's standpoint — one likely to influence deeply the perspective of future judges — the first quarter century of international development programs has been characterized by a crass and almost total disregard of the true nature of the environment destined to be developed. That environment has been wrongly assumed to be static and passive, inexhaustibly productive in the face of ignorant and injurious practices, and relatively invulnerable as a permanent asset.

This essay will seek to demonstrate that any sound and enduring development programs of the future will have to be carefully held within the limits imposed by considerations of biological productivity and natural resource conservation, limits which must be ascertained in advance for each site to be subjected to development processes. Important questions arise concerning the proper selection and treatment of sites which, on scientific or other grounds, ought to be withheld from development as protected natural areas.[1] Such questions, however, are assumed to fall outside the scope of the present discussion, which is directed to the pursuance of development processes upon sites taken as properly chosen for such purposes according to the principles of sound land use, ecology, and care of the capital asset formed by the environment. The main consideration of the present discussion will be to show how land which is to be developed may be safeguarded against abuse and injury of types which have hitherto too often accompanied the development process and have eventually caused the depreciation or even the destruction of the basis of investment.[2]

Max Nicholson, "International Economic Development and the Environment." Permission to reprint is acknowledged to the *Journal of International Affairs,* vol. 24, no. 2 (1970), pp. 272–287.
The author is Chairman of Land Use Consultants, London. He was previously a member of the U. K. Advisory Council on Scientific Policy and was Director-General of The Nature Conservancy of the U. K.

II

Perhaps the best introduction is provided by consideration of the accompanying diagram demonstrating the interplay of the *Biosphere* and the *Technosphere*. These two terms are used to indicate that the total activities of nature and of man respectively are being viewed specifically in terms of the physical processes involved in their operation, divested of any philosophical, ethical, economic, social, aesthetic, or other value judgments. The biosphere converts solar radiation and inorganic elements into a world of living matter, or biomass, maintained by continuous processes of biological productivity. It is primarily responsible for the creation of vegetable matter and secondarily, through vegetation, for growth of animal matter. The technosphere extracts from, or crops, the biosphere by mining, farming, fishing, hunting, and other methods, to acquire elements which are processed into "usable" products. Most of these are immediately distributed to human consumers or users,

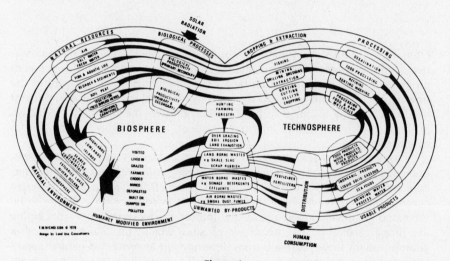

Figure 1

while a few, such as pesticides and fertilizers, are channelled back into the biosphere by being spread on the land. In addition to these "usable" products, however, vast quantities of wastes, effluents, and gases are either leaked or dumped back into the biosphere. These latter processes, like extraction and cropping, convert the land and natural resources affected from a natural into a humanly modified environment.

The merit, if any, of such a diagram is that it displays the basic natural *and* artificial processes currently discernible upon this planet in terms of continuous flows in the course of which innumerable transformations and diversions occur both within the natural and artificial spheres and at the interfaces between the two. These flows can be rated according to their energy, their efficiency or productivity, their partial absorption or rejection of inputs, and their capability of running indefinitely upon a sustained yield basis. In the present context it is feasible to reproduce only a single highly simplified and conventionalized global model, but regional, local, functional, or other more specialized models could be used to represent, for example, the inputs of particular industries or the situations on particular sites. The essential point to be made, however, is that there is always a dynamic inter-relation — whether it is recognized or not — between natural and techno-logical processes. The use of crude terms such as "waste," "pollution," and "raw materials" tends to obscure the fact that "pollution," for example, is one of the normal products of many modern technological processes and can, like other products, be produced in different forms and quantities within broad limits set by considerations of cost and physical practicability. If we view the market as the positive destination of the end products of technical and economic activity, then pollution, in the widest sense, represents their negative destination. Pollution is the negative counterpart of usable produc-tion, and, at a price, switching is possible between the two.

A useful complementary approach to the environmental problem which has been developed takes the form of a *Chart of Human Impacts* on the environment. It covers activities ranging from land reclamation, drainage, and dam-building through forestry, agriculture, mineral extractions, and fisheries and water abstraction, to construction on the land for various purposes, the use of the land for activities such as recreation and tourism, and the with-holding of land from use in wilderness areas. This approach makes it possible to list every relevant activity or operation, showing the area or land-type which it affects, its incidence in time, space, and degree, the nature of the effects, the main interested parties, and typical documented examples showing vari-ous analyses of the problem and suggesting some possible lines of treatment. With only a minimal effort, such a chart was constructed for Great Britain in 1963.[3] One could and should be prepared for any territory affected — or threatened — by large-scale development in order to provide checks and guidelines for action.

A particular value of the Biosphere-Technosphere and Human Impacts approaches is that they facilitate the forecasting, analysis, and appropriate treatment of environmental issues by non-ecologists, that is, by executives and specialists totally unfamiliar with such problems. At present, many of those making decisions on land use and land management are too ignorant to know how ignorant they are or to know when and where to seek advice before irrevocable mistakes are made. As a result, there has been a wide-spread failure to commission the surveys and research which could indicate how to diagnose and treat such chronic problems as deforestation, over-grazing, destructive burning, and the triggering of erosion and siltation. Cer-tain enlightened countries have had maps prepared indicating areas of actual and potential soil erosion. In Tunisia, for example, the Secretariat of Planning and National Economy recognized in 1964 that sound economic planning in rural areas called for the systematic study of key ecological factors in the form of phyto-ecological maps of fairly large scale (basically 1:200,000) accom-panied by explanatory handbooks. These were prepared and published in 1967 and 1968 in the *Annales de l'Institut National de la Recherche Agro-nomique de Tunisie*. Few other territories can so fully illustrate the value of the thorough coordination of ecological and conservation studies and development plans.

Land capacity classification is the third and final tool to be mentioned here as essential for relating development plans to the potentialities and the limitations of the environment.[4] Probably the best example of the application of this technique in a developing country is to be found in West Malaysia, where an *Explanatory Handbook* was published in 1967 by the National Resource Capability Section of the National Development Planning Committee. The five main classes of land defined in the supplement to the handbook were a) land possessing a high potential for mineral development, b) land possessing a high potential for agricultural development with a wide range of crops, c) land possessing a moderate potential for agricultural development with some limitation of the range of crops, d) land possessing a high potential for productive forest development, and e) land processing little or no mineral, agricultural, or productive forest development potential, but possibly suitable for development for protective forest reserves, water catchment areas, game reserves, or recreation areas.

Summing up, it will be necessary in all future development planning to recognize that:

a. natural systems are highly complex, dynamic, and vulnerable, and that the relationship of any major proposed development to the future workings of the biosphere must be studied and taken fully into account as a precondition to sound project design; that
b. there is a large fund of information available on how best to develop, and that repetitions of known and avoidable errors will be less and less tolerated or overlooked from now on; and that
c. although largely unknown or neglected by economists, engineers, and others concerned with project planning, techniques of assessing environmental factors are readily available and have been tested under relevant developmental conditions.

III

Development as such inevitably imposes strains upon the limited adaptability of the natural environment. These unavoidable strains are greatly aggravated when development projects are rushed through without adequate surveys, consultations, or expert advice, when they are designed and executed in ignorance of significant environmental factors, or when excessive demands are placed upon inadequate natural resources through greed, misjudgment, or political pressures.

Certain contemporary trends tend to increase the incidence of such unfortunate errors. One of the most universal is the disastrously rapid increase of rates of population growth, which now indicates a doubling of the world's population within thirty-seven years, and in extreme national cases — the Philippines, Costa Rica, and Libya, for example — within twenty years or less. A glance at the population based problems even of advanced countries such as Italy, the United Kingdom, and West Germany, which will require a century or more to double their populations, shows that the average rate of population increase in many developing countries is at least five times higher than that consistent with orderly and environmentally bearable improvements in living standards. Accelerated population growth, apart from all its other well known evils, means intensified exploitation and more and bigger mistakes in land use.

The liability to error in decision-making is increased not merely by the haste which population growth and political pressures impose, but by the failure hitherto to make provision for ecological and environmental surveys and advice within the structure of development agencies, and by the frequently inadequate, local, and patchy coverage of such consideration as may be given to these aspects of development planning. Even such relevant knowledge as exists may be unduly difficult to locate and interpret owing to the fragmentary and disorganized pattern of piecemeal specialized studies. Furthermore, it is often true that awareness of these background pressures and these difficulties in assembling a sound body of facts and advice on environmental questions leads to an *a priori* psychological block against giving them any serious consideration at all. This, in turn, tends to perpetuate attitudes antipathetic to the creation of a comprehensive network of environmental information and advisory services. What is needed, therefore, is a new style of project design, one better able to ensure that *all* the main factors relevant to the viability and sustained success of any development project are ascertained, evaluated, and integrated *before commitments are made.*

The problem of minimizing damage to the environment arising from development programs and projects may therefore be considered under three heads. *First,* it is important that everything possible should be done to relieve the *underlying world-wide pressures* which have recently demanded unduly intensified and hasty efforts for the exploitation of natural resources. A reduction in rates of population growth, an increase of crop yields and of primary production on existing cultivated areas, the minimization of waste and pollution, and the encouragement of tendencies to view improvements in standards of living in less exclusively material terms are the kinds of issues involved here. *Second,* it is urgently necessary to eliminate the many weaknesses and omissions manifest in the *search for facts and advice* concerning the environment. The technical, administrative, and financial problems involved present no serious obstacles. The widespread absence of the will or the interest to take the necessary action on the part of most of the international and national agencies responsible for development, however, is a major impediment to progress. *Third,* there is a need for the *training and deploying of capable people* to carry out necessary studies and evaluations, to make practical recommendations, and to ensure that the proper environmental data are integrated into the process of development in the right way and at the right stages as future development programs and projects are shaped. This is not a matter of awaiting the emergence of new types of experts not yet in existence, but rather of a flexible resolution to ensure that somehow, perhaps differently in each project, some person or persons or bodies able to contribute or employ the relevant environmental material and advice are given full opportunity to do so. The right man may be an ecologist, a landscape architect, a physical planner, or a land capability specialist. Or the project may require men of two or more specializations or a full consultancy team. In any case, of course, the proper breadth and depth of environmental approach, enough practical experience and capacity for give-and-take in teamwork, and resourcefulness in learning what one does not already know are more important requirements than any particular degree or diploma.

As the 1960's ended, it became increasingly clear that world affairs were no longer dominated by concepts and prejudices opposed to recognizing and acting upon the need for urgent and drastic measures to bring human reproduction rates into some reasonable relation to the earth's natural resources — including living space. Nevertheless, the ill effects of the past twenty years of neglect and evasion of this problem, particularly on the part of leading developmental policy-makers, will aggravate political, social, and economic difficulties at least until well into the twenty-second century. Unfortunately, while there has been a marked reduction of activity on the part of those engaged in earlier successful efforts to keep this subject off the international agenda and to embarrass and discredit those who sought to raise it, propaganda and suppression continues. The small dedicated minority of family planners and their voluntary allies have lately won forthright support from the World Bank and some encouragement from such organizations as the Food and Agriculture Organization of the United Nations (FAO), but the new message is not yet pressed home with anything approaching the pertinacity, clarity, and universality which characterize the dissemination of the negative viewpoint.

In the 1970's, conservationists must hope for a far more massive and convincing campaign to bring home to all the *impossibility* of solving the problems of development without much faster and better directed progress toward the control of human reproduction in all countries. Many dogmatic opponents of birth control have long gained comfort from overly optimistic promises of what could be achieved by enlightened development policies and programs. In response to this, the tacit assumption that development can in some way constitute a substitute for serious efforts at population control needs to be clearly and effectively repudiated. The antithesis, that development is doomed to failure without control of reproduction, needs to be reiterated in the plainest terms.

The 1950's and the early 1960's exhibited the painful contrast which exists between high expectations of science and technology "solving the world food problem," for example, and a dearth of practically applicable new discoveries and techniques in this field. Food production failed even to keep pace with population growth in many regions. Among the few technological techniques to be adopted on a massive scale was the use of pestcides and herbicides, but in dosages and situations which most advanced countries have now found it necessary to regulate or to prohibit. Nevertheless, the net future additional contributions to world food supplies from such sources are unlikely to go far toward feeding the two billion people to be added to the earth's population by the year 2000. Authoritative assessments of the potential of other food sources — the oceans and artificial, laboratory-bred means of food production, for example — offer little hope that any really major new food source will appear within the next two or three decades. We return therefore to the conclusion, clearly stated fifteen years ago in the Political and Economic Planning Institute's *World Population and Resources,* that efforts and hopes must be concentrated primarily on increasing the production of established food crops in already cultivated regions.[5] The Institute stated then that in terms of increasing yields from cultivated land, genetic advance had far to go in most countries and especially in the underdeveloped ones. This judgment has been borne out by recent spectacular productivity improvements, notably in rice yields. Even here, however, progress still relies on a number of favorable factors, and conservative growers can make a case that in their actual conditions it is best for them to stick to traditional lower-yield strains. Nevertheless, genetic and other biological improvements, coupled with the spread of better agricultural techniques, can go far toward meeting world food requirements *provided that the necessary accompanying measures for social and environmental amelioration are taken.*[6] Above all, the pressing requirement for environmental conservation should not be treated as yet another separate compartmental activity. It can and should be fully integrated into a pattern of agriculture and forestry, modernized with the aid of intensive social studies, and made viable through effective measures of population planning, agrarian reconstruction, and community adaptation and revival. It is in this context that the detailed consideration of environmental conservation should be undertaken.

In addition, returning to a more explicit consideration of population problems, more research is needed in order to perfect inexpensive, reliable, and culturally acceptable methods of birth control. The dilatory progress made in freeing "the pill" of suspicion on health grounds and in eliminating undesirable side effects is largely a function of underinvestment and of covert opposition to the main objective. Since development unaccompanied by family planning is a principal factor in massive and lasting damage to the environment, there will be a serious impediment to progress in the improvement of environmental care until those concerned with development begin fully to do their duty in the sphere of population control. In terms of dollars, of manhours, and of honest effort, the disparity between the backing accorded family planning and that lavished on development is indefensible.

Almost equally serious is the sluggish rate of development of training, research, and pilot projects directed toward a fuller understanding of social patterns and motivations relevant to the modernization of social attitudes which must occur as people of differing traditional cultures experience the impact of the modern world. That the technosphere is hardly a pliant slave of its creators is demonstrated by the fact that its creators are encountering ever greater difficulty in avoiding the admission that they themselves have become the slaves of its blind momentum and of the painful psychological and environmental sacrifices which it exacts. Prime Minister Indira Gandhi has spoken feelingly of the dangers for developing countries of unwittingly importing this phenomenon along with technical advances, and of thus sacrificing more in true values than is intended or acceptable.[7] A world-wide program of social studies and experimental projects to evaluate the full cost implications of injecting crude doses of western technology into western as well as other mature cultures is the essential bridge between the aid concepts of the 1950's and the 1960's and the comprehensive and balanced forms of mutual aid which we must hope to develop during the 1970's.

The creation of this sort of program would offer three great advantages. *First,* since this is an area of inquiry in which no nation can claim to be "advanced," it would offer unique opportunities for a mutuality of learning and an exchange of methods of a different order from those to be found in purely technological exchanges. *Second,* it would provide training and practical experience for service in their own countries to many talented young men and women who are presently offered no suitable place in the excessively technological complex of existing aid programs. By creating a series of relevant social science positions, the program would provide a mechanism for the constructive harnessing of many creative drives which are currently frustrated. It would furnish countries without a mature middle class with a means for responsible and informed public opinion to make itself felt. The arithmetic of current demography and development plainly demonstrates the need for a population of trained and responsibly employed social scientists many times greater than that which has as yet been envisaged by most governments. Such a population could direct more specialized and timely attention to areas of tension and misunderstanding, could provide many hitherto nonexistent opportunities for valuable voluntary work, and could feed back to the technological, administrative, and political elements in world development processes an invaluable stream of information for tailoring each project and program more sensitively to conditions at the receiving end. And *third,* such a program, as an ostensibly constructive and idealistic expression of international cooperation, could contribute toward tackling the world-wide problem of replacing crudely materialistic notions of "progress" with much more sophisticated concepts involving perhaps fewer automobiles and washing machines and a less shoddy quality of life for more and more human beings. This problem will certainly not be resolved by infantile and aggressive "demonstrations" on the one hand or by complacent denial of its existence on the other.

IV

It has been necessary to discuss the background factors of population growth, failures of social research and provision, and disappointing progress in improving world food production from conventional sources because each of them greatly aggravates the pressures on the natural environment and multiplies the number and seriousness of the errors committed against it. The mere laying down of ground rules for safeguarding the environment will have little effect as long as those responsible for the adequacy of development policies in general continue to default so heavily on their primary obligations.

Although much more could be done on the basis of existing knowledge, the culpable failure to identify and support research into major conservation problems logically represents the first such deficiency. For example, the present and future productivity of immense areas is being rapidly deteriorated by land use practices related to grazing and browsing by livestock which have been conclusively demonstrated during a full half-century to be indefensible. The Sahara, for instance, is increasing its desert area by tens of thousands of hectares annually without any serious effort being made to check the loss to world production. Recently, when the scientific authorities concerned unanimously agreed upon an international project to tackle this problem and found a suitable program site in Tunisia with strong governmental backing and financial support in dinars, the United Nations Development Program (UNDP) calmly declined to recognize it as anything more than a national project of Tunisia, thus ensuring that it be deprived of any significant United Nations funding. In this way the UNDP has ensured that the Sahara will win further large territories before the long and difficult task of recovery can begin. In a similar way, at the Serengetti Research Station in Tanzania where highly important research on the carrying capacity of arid lands is in progress, a devoted group of ecologists is working with virtually hand-to-mouth financial support from individual governments and foundations, with the result that key posts for the study of basic vegetation problems cannot be established.

It is clear that the world needs a small network of international ecological stations to do for the various great "biomes" — tundra, grassland, desert, tropical savanna, tropical forest, and coniferous forest — what leading marine stations such as those at Naples and Woods Hole, Massachusetts, have long since done for the oceans. Efforts currently being made to establish the nucleus of this essential research network are crippled by the total absence of effective interest and support on the part of United Nations agencies and of most of the great private foundations. It is now practicable to cover the earth with a series of key stations where most ecologically significant conditions could be adequately recorded on a standard basis and where changes could be regularly monitored on land safeguarded for the permanent interests of science and development. One of the goals of the International Biological Program is to create the necessary conditions for such a network and, with the backing of an international data bank and a processing center using modern computer facilities, to bring a nucleus of it into operation immediately.[8] As this paper was being written, progress was stalled while efforts were being made to raise $2,300 to pay for the necessary first stage of computer programming. Despite the fact that the main problems of development are biological, total United Nations contributions to the International Biological Program over the past five years have been insignificant, and even national subventions have been disappointingly inadequate. Nevertheless the effort goes on, with more than twelve thousand survey check sheets already distributed to national committees for data returns on key sites in all continents.

It is essential to create within the main agencies concerned liaisons to bridge the gap between the conduct of surveys and decision-making and the available expertise which needs to be harnessed into the development planning framework. Economic, engineering, agricultural, and other forms of expertise are already admitted to planning's "magic circle," but not ecology or other environmental professions. After some encouraging discussions at the headquarters of the International Bank for Reconstruction and Development a year ago, the present writer submitted a brief memorandum suggesting that high-level publicity should be used to emphasize the World Bank's concern that environmental resources be adequately protected in development projects and programs; that the land-linked professions should modernize their thinking in order to meet that need; and that suitable provision for environmental expertise should be included in appropriate project teams sponsored by the Bank itself. It is understood that the Smithsonian Institution, the Conservation Foundation, and the United States National Committee for the International Biological Program have been holding discussions with the Bank along similar lines. The fact that corresponding requirements exist in other agencies concerned with the funding and planning of development at both the international and national levels is at least encouraging and may augur substantial progress in meeting the challenge of preserving the earth's environment in the midst of rapid international economic and technological development.

Studies have been made in some countries of the relationship of legislative and administrative practice to modern environmental problems. The Legislation Commission of the International Union for the Conservation of Nature and Natural Resources has undertaken far-reaching research in this field, but, at both international and national levels, out-of-date and faulty legislation, regulations, and codes of practice are daily causing pointless and seemingly easily avoidable damage to the environment. In any review of legislative principles and practice concerning development, the need for modernizing the environmental aspects of law will clearly have to be fully reckoned with. At present, only a handful of countries are equipped with central governmental mechanisms capable of grasping and acting upon environmental requirements as a whole. The Netherlands structure of physical planning is the most well-rounded program.[9] Among advanced countries, Sweden, the United Kingdom, and the United States have been active in parts of the field, and among developing nations, Malaysia, Kenya, and Tunisia have taken interesting initiatives, especially in the field of land capacity classification. Even the best of the new-style consortia which have been formed in some places to attempt comprehensive coverage of all aspects of specific development projects, however, still fall far short of modern requirements. They are usually dominated by long-established and financially strong anti-conservationist interest groups such as public works contractors, civil engineers, or architects. In addition, there are no organized recruitment, training, or operations centers in the world where the best means of smoothly and rapidly assimilating the contributions of all the relevant professions can be sought. Consequently, if environmental expertise or the social sciences are included at all at the present time in planning procedures, their role is marginal.

V

More generally, the time is long overdue for development interests to cease thinking, writing, and behaving as if interests for care of the environment did not exist. Even in the excellent recent report of the Commission on International Development, *Partners in Development*,[10] we find no indication that the vast environmental problems which so acutely trouble so many have come to the notice of the eminent Commissioners. Despite the many inescapable evidences of recognition of other failings of development programs, recognition of their failures in terms of land use and care of environment is still only in its nascent stages. The growing body of scientifically based conservationists view with dismay this blind complacency, and look, as yet in vain, for some recognition that development, like conservation, deals with land and with natural resources, that the handling of land and natural resources can be scientifically monitored, and that the record shows much development to have been misconceived or wrongly executed in terms of conserving basic natural assets as capital for future generations.

In view of inadequate understanding and contact on the development aspect of the great modern problems of man's environment, this essay has inevitably been preoccupied more with global problems of policy and organization than with the infinitely varying forms which they assume on the land itself, territory by territory and site by site. Before concluding, however, it is necessary to sketch a few of the environmental impacts of development as examples of items for an agenda of reconciliation between development and the needs of the environment.

The choice of unsuitable sites — abandoned after being badly damaged — has been the most conspicuous type of environmental problem created by development. Such cases have rarely attained public prominence, but the write-offs of development are of special significance as quantifiable wastes of resources which could frequently have been avoided by a better appraisal of environmental factors in the first place. A less readily identifiable type of wrong site decision occurs when land reasonably well suited to several alternative uses is allocated not to the one for which its advantages are unique, but to one the requirements of which could equally readily be satisfied elsewhere. The erection of a factory on a coastline with greater earning capacity for tourism, or of housing facilities on a rich deposit of minerals are simple examples. Only the kind of land capability classification already indicated can minimize such mistakes. An even more common problem is that of choosing sites which, although not entirely suitable for the desired development, are only able to sustain it with more continuous, more skilled, and often more expensive maintenance than was foreseen or can be assured. Such sites often display run-down or damaged facilities which are blamed upon poor maintenance when they should actually be attributed to over-optimistic or unrealistic site selection based on insufficient environmental knowledge.

Reference has already been made to the world-wide loss of arable land due to unsound practices of pastoralism. It is clear that in many wild areas the cropping of wild herbivores can yield more protein than their replacement by domesticated livestock. The discovery of the precise scope of such possible cropping and the drawing of appropriate ecological lines between the two land uses, however, await the funding of additional research. Other related and vastly extensive problems are created by burning and deforestation. In some cases the resulting unforeseen loss of water yields terminates local cultivation and even deprives cities of natural water supplies. Where new reservoirs are constructed in forested uplands to replace these supplies, local people take advantage of construction roads to strip the tree cover. This opens the slopes to rapid erosion which may in turn silt up a reservoir to such an extent that a substantial part of its rated capacity must be written off as useless. The exent to which current development generates such indirect repercussions on "waste" lands which may be needed for development later on or throws open hitherto unused lands to destructive practices is one of the graver disregarded problems of present policies. All unused land should be conserved as a bank for the future, and any access fortuitously provided to it should be controlled with that object in mind.

The needs of long-term development call for a world-wide survey of existing, threatened, and potential erosion and for the adoption of plans which will end the insane wastefulness of permitting fertile topsoils and water-yielding catchments to be converted into bare sterile surfaces producing nothing except occasional devastating floods. In the case of large man-made lakes, some progress has been made in arranging for comprehensive ecological surveys in advance and for providing appropriate measures of conservation and environmental management during and after dam construction. Even here, however, displacement of human populations without adequate provision for resettlement can inflict heavy ecological damage elsewhere. On a lesser scale but similarly, the apparently beneficial provision of water holes in arid lands can so distort patterns of grazing and temporary or permanent settlement that vegetation within easy reach of the water holes is destroyed by the livestock attracted.

Such are a very few examples of the kinds of impact on the environment which need to be watched, studied, and prevented or remedied. Some indication that the reality of such problems is appreciated will do much to give reassurance that those responsible for development do not wish to be ranked among the unheeding destroyers of mankind's natural environment. A well-prepared joint meeting between leading exponents of development and leading conservationists is urgently needed to produce an authoritative and comprehensive report on the problems arising on the interface between their respective activities and interests. Having signally failed fifteen years ago to get the message about the world population explosion, world development interests must not equally fail to get the environmental message now. Conservationists who are already fairly well briefed on points of contact and of stress and who are willing to cooperate in the great tasks of development, can be relied upon to do all in their power to help build the necessary interdisciplinary bridges.[11]

References

1. International Union for the Conservation of Nature. *Liste des Nations Unies des Parcs Nationaux et Réserves Analogues* (Brussels: 1967).

2. Max Nicholson, *The Environmental Revolution: A Guide for the New Masters of the Earth* (London: Hodder and Stoughton Ltd., 1970).

3. Max Nicholson and A. W. Colling, "Chart of Human Impacts on the Countryside" (prepared for the Countryside in 1970 Study Conference of 1963), in Nicholson, *op. cit.*, pp. 308–335.

4. Commonwealth Scientific and Industrial Research Organisation Symposium, Canberra (1968), *Land Evaluation* (Melbourne: 1968).

5. *World Population and Resources: A Report of Political and Economic Planning* (London: Allen and Unwin Ltd., 1955).

6. N. W. Pirie, *Food Resources, Conventional and Novel* (Baltimore: Penguin Books, 1969).

7. Opening Speech by the Prime Minister of India to the General Assembly of the International Union for Conservation of Nature and Natural Resources, New Delhi, November 24, 1969.

8. See various publications of the International Biological Programme, Central Office, Marylebone Road, London, N.W. 1.

9. *Second Report on Physical Planning in the Netherlands* (The Hague: Government Printing Office, 1966).

10. Lester B. Pearson *et al., Partners in Development: Report of the Commission on International Development* (New York: Praeger Publishers, 1969).

11. Since this paper was first presented at the Columbia University Conference on International Economic Development, the International Bank for Reconstruction and Development has announced its decision to provide for specialist advice to be taken for the ecological validation of projects submitted to the Bank. Following this welcome action in pursuance of the kind of approach here advocated, arrangements have been made for a Working Group of specialists in development and in conservation to meet at the headquarters of the Food and Agriculture Organization in Rome on the lines suggested above.

JAY W. FORRESTER

Alternatives to Catastrophe—
Understanding the Counterintuitive Behavior
of Social Systems

This paper addresses several issues of broad concern in the United States: population trends; the quality of urban life; national policy for urban growth; and the unexpected, ineffective, or detrimental results often generated by government programs in these areas.

The nation exhibits a growing sense of futility as it repeatedly attacks deficiencies in our social system while the symptoms continue to worsen. Legislation is debated and passed with great promise and hope. But many programs prove to be ineffective. Results often seem unrelated to those ex-

Dr. Jay W. Forrester, "Alternatives to Catastrophe — Understanding the Counterintuitive Behavior of Social Systems," in *Technology Review*, vol. 73, no. 3 (January 1971), pp. 52–68. Reprinted by permission of the author.

This paper is copyright 1971 by Jay W. Forrester. It is based on testimony for the Subcommittee on Urban Growth of the Committee on Banking and Currency, U. S. House of Representatives, on October 7, 1970. This text has appeared in the January 1971 issue of the *Technology Review* published by the Alumni Association of the Massachusetts Institute of Technology.

The author is Professor of Management, Sloan School of Management, Massachusetts Institute of Technology. In 1968 he was named Inventor of the Year by George Washington University, and he has received many other awards for his work.

pected when the programs were planned. At times programs cause exactly the reverse of desired results.

It is now possible to explain how such contrary results can happen. There are fundamental reasons why people misjudge the behavior of social systems. There are orderly processes at work in the creation of human judgment and intuition that frequently lead people to wrong decisions when faced with complex and highly interacting systems. Until we come to a much better understanding of social systems, we should expect that attempts to develop corrective programs will continue to disappoint us.

The purpose of this paper is to leave with its readers a sense of caution about continuing to depend on the same past approaches that have led to our present feeling of frustration and to suggest an approach which can eventually lead to a better understanding of our social systems and thereby to more effective policies for guiding the future.

A NEW APPROACH TO SOCIAL SYSTEMS

It is my basic theme that the human mind is not adapted to interpreting how social systems behave. Our social systems belong to the class called multi-loop nonlinear feedback systems. In the long history of evolution it has not been necessary for man to understand these systems until very recent historical times. Evolutionary processes have not given us the mental skill needed to properly interpret the dynamic behavior of the systems of which we have now become a part.

In addition, the social sciences have fallen into some mistaken "scientific" practices which compound man's natural shortcomings. Computers are often being used for what the computer does poorly and the human mind does well. At the same time the human mind is being used for what the human mind does poorly and the computer does well. Even worse, impossible tasks are attempted while achievable and important goals are ignored.

Until recently there has been no way to estimate the behavior of social systems except by contemplation, discussion, argument, and guesswork. To point a way out of our present dilemma about social systems, I will sketch an approach that combines the strength of the human mind and the strength of today's computers. The approach is an outgrowth of developments over the last 40 years, in which much of the research has been at the Massachusetts Institute of Technology. The concepts of feedback system behavior apply sweepingly from physical systems through social systems. The ideas were first developed and applied to engineering systems. They have now reached practical usefulness in major aspects of our social systems.

I am speaking of what has come to be called industrial dynamics. The name is a misnomer because the methods apply to complex systems regardless of the field in which they are located. A more appropriate name would be *system dynamics*. In our own work, applications have been made to corporate policy, to the dynamics of diabetes as a medical system, to the growth and stagnation of an urban area, and most recently to world dynamics representing the interactions of population, pollution, industrialization, natural resources, and food. System dynamics, as an extension of the earlier design of physical systems, has been under development at M.I.T. since 1956. The approach is easy to understand but difficult to practice. Few people have a high level of skill; but preliminary work is developing all over the world. Some European countries and especially Japan have begun centers of education and research.

Computer models of social systems

People would never attempt to send a space ship to the moon without first testing the equipment by constructing prototype models and by computer simulation of the anticipated space trajectories. No company would put a new kind of household appliance or electronic computer into production without first making laboratory tests. Such models and laboratory tests do not guarantee against failure, but they do identify many weaknesses which can then be corrected before they cause full-scale disasters.

Our social systems are far more complex and harder to understand than our technological systems. Why, then, do we not use the same approach of making models of social systems and conducting laboratory experiments on those models before we try new laws and government programs in real life? The answer is often stated that our knowledge of social systems is insufficient for constructing useful models. But what justification can there be for the apparent assumption that we do not know enough to construct models but believe we do know enough to directly design new social systems by passing laws and starting new social programs? I am suggesting that we now do know enough to make useful models of social systems. Conversely, we do not know enough to design the most effective social systems directly without first going through a model-building experimental phase. But I am confident, and substantial supporting evidence is beginning to accumulate, that the proper use of models of social systems can lead to far better systems, laws, and programs.

It is now possible to construct in the laboratory realistic models of social systems. Such models are simplifications of the actual social system but can be far more comprehensive than the mental models that we otherwise use as the basis for debating governmental action.

Before going further, I should emphasize that there is nothing new in the use of models to represent social systems. Each of us uses models constantly. Every person in his private life and in his business life instinctively uses models for decision making. The mental image of the world around you which you carry in your head is a model. One does not have a city or a government or a country in his head. He has only selected concepts and relationships which he uses to represent the real system. A mental image is a model. All of our decisions are taken on the basis of models. All of our laws are passed on the basis of models. All executive actions are taken on the basis of models. The question is not to use or ignore models. The question is only a choice among alternative models.

The mental model is fuzzy. It is incomplete. It is imprecisely stated. Furthermore, within one individual, a mental model changes with time and even during the flow of a single conversation. The human mind assembles a few relationships to fit the context of a discussion. As the subject shifts so does the model. When only a single topic is being discussed, each participant in a conversation employs a different mental model to interpret the subject. Fundamental assumptions differ but are never brought into the open. Goals are different and are left unstated. It is little wonder that compromise takes so long. And it is not surprising that consensus leads to laws and programs that fail in their objectives or produce new difficulties greater than those that have been relieved.

For these reasons we stress the importance of being explicit about assumptions and interrelating them in a computer model. Any concept or assumption that can be clearly described in words can be incorporated in a computer model. When done, the ideas become clear. Assumptions are exposed so they may be discussed and debated.

But the most important difference between the properly conceived computer model and the mental model is in the ability to determine the dynamic consequences when the assumptions within the model interact with one another. The human mind is not adapted to sensing correctly the consequences of a mental model. The mental model may be correct in structure and assumptions but, even so, the human mind — either individually or as a group consensus — is most apt to draw the wrong conclusions. There is no doubt about the digital computer routinely and accurately tracing through the sequences of actions that result from following the statements of behavior for individual points in the model system. This inability of the human mind to use its own mental models is clearly shown when a computer model is constructed to reproduce the assumptions held by a single person. In other words, the model is refined until it is fully agreeable in all its assumptions to the perceptions and ideas of a particular person. Then, it usually happens that the system that has been described does not act the way the person anticipated. Usually there is an internal contradiction in mental models between the assumed structure and the assumed future consequences. Ordinarily the assumptions about structure and internal motivations are more nearly correct than are the assumptions about the implied behavior.

The kind of computer models that I am discussing are strikingly similar to mental models. They are derived from the same sources. They may be discussed in the same terms. But computer models differ from mental models in important ways. The computer models are stated explicitly. The "mathematical" notation that is used for describing the model is unambiguous. It is a language that is clearer, simpler, and more precise than such spoken languages as English or French. Its advantage is in the clarity of meaning and the simplicity of the language syntax. The language of a computer model can be understood by almost anyone, regardless of educational background. Furthermore, any concept and relationship that can be clearly stated in ordinary language can be translated into computer model language.

There are many approaches to computer models. Some are naive. Some are conceptually and structually inconsistent with the nature of actual systems. Some are based on methodologies for obtaining input data that commit the models to omitting major concepts and relationships in the psychological and human reaction areas that we all know to be crucial. With so much activity in computer models and with the same terminology having different meanings in the different approaches, the situation must be confusing to the casual observer. The key to success is not in having a computer; the important thing is how the computer is used. With respect to models, the key is not to computerize a model, but instead to have a model structure and relationships which properly represent the system that is being considered.

I am speaking here of a kind of computer model that is very different from the models that are now most common in the social sciences. Such a computer model is not derived statistically from time-series data. Instead, the kind of computer model I am discussing is a statement of system structure. It contains the assumptions being made about the system. The model is only as good as the expertise which lies behind its formulation. Great and correct theories in physics or in economics are few and far between. A great computer model is distinguished from a poor one by the degree to which it captures more of the essence of the social system that it presumes to represent. Many mathematical models are limited because they are formulated by techniques and according to a conceptual structure that will not accept the multiple-feedback-loop and nonlinear nature of real systems. Other models are defective because of lack of knowledge or deficiencies of perception on the part of the persons who have formulated them.

But a recently developed kind of computer modeling is now beginning to show the characteristics of behavior of actual systems. These models explain why we are having the present difficulties with our actual social systems and furthermore explain why so many efforts to improve social systems have failed. In spite of their shortcomings, models can now be constructed that are far superior to the intuitive models in our heads on which we are now basing national social programs.

This approach to the dynamics of social systems differs in two important ways from common practice in social sciences and government. There seems to be a common attitude that the major difficulty is shortage of information and data. Once data is collected, people then feel confident in interpreting the implications. I differ on both of these attitudes. The problem is not shortage of data but rather our inability to perceive the consequences of the information we already possess. The system dynamics approach starts with the concepts and information on which people are already acting. Generally these are sufficient. The available perceptions are then assembled in a computer model which can show the consequences of the well-known and properly perceived parts of the system. Generally, the consequences are unexpected.

Counterintuitive nature of social systems

Our first insights into complex social systems came from our corporate work. Time after time we have gone into a corporation which is having severe and well-known difficulties. The difficulties can be major and obvious such as a falling market share, low profitability, or instability of employment. Such difficulties are known throughout the company and by anyone outside who reads the management press. One can enter such a company and discuss with people in key decision points what they are doing to solve the problem.

Generally speaking we find that people perceive correctly their immediate environment. They know what they are trying to accomplish. They know the crises which will force certain actions. They are sensitive to the power structure of the organization, to traditions, and to their own personal goals and welfare. In general, when circumstances are conducive to frank disclosure, people can state what they are doing and can give rational reasons for their actions. In a troubled company, people are usually trying in good conscience and to the best of their abilities to solve the major difficulties. Policies are being followed at the various points in the organization on the presumption that they will alleviate the difficulties. One can combine these policies into a computer model to show the consequences of how the policies interact with one another. In many instances it then emerges that the known policies describe a system which actually causes the troubles. In other words, the known and intended practices of the organization are fully sufficient to create the difficulty, regardless of what happens outside the company or in the marketplace. In fact, a downward spiral develops in which the presumed solution makes the difficulty worse and thereby causes redoubling of the presumed solution.

The same downward spiral frequently develops in government. Judgment and debate lead to a program that appears to be sound. Commitment increases to the apparent solution. If the presumed solution actually makes matters worse, the process by which this happens is not evident. So, when the troubles increase, the efforts are intensified that are actually worsening the problem.

Dynamics of urban systems

Our first major excursion outside of corporate policy began in February, 1968, when John F. Collins, former mayor of Boston, became Professor of Urban Affairs at M.I.T. He and I discussed my work in industrial dynamics and his experience with urban difficulties. A close collaboration led to applying to the dynamics of the city the same methods that had been created for understanding the social and policy structure of the corporation. A model structure was developed to represent the fundamental urban processes. The proposed structure shows how industry, housing, and people interact with each other as a city grows and decays. The results are described in my book *Urban Dynamics*, and some were summarized in *Technology Review* (*April, 1969, pp. 21–31*).

I had not previously been involved with urban behavior or urban policies. But the emerging story was strikingly similar to what we had seen in the corporation. Actions taken to alleviate the difficulties of a city can actually make matters worse. We examined four common programs for improving the depressed nature of the central city. One is the creation of jobs as by bussing the unemployed to the suburbs or through governmental jobs as employer of last resort. Second was a training program to increase the skills of the lowest-income group. Third was financial aid to the depressed city as by federal subsidy. Fourth was the construction of low-cost housing. All of these are shown to lie between neutral and detrimental almost irrespective of the criteria used for judgment. They range from ineffective to harmful judged by their effect on the economic health of the city or by their long-range effect on the low-income population of the city.

The results both confirm and explain much of what has been happening over the last several decades in our cities.

In fact, it emerges that the fundamental cause of depressed areas in the cities comes from *excess* housing in the low-income category rather than the commonly presumed housing shortage. The legal and tax structures have combined to give incentives for keeping old buildings in place. As industrial buildings age, the employment opportunities decline. As residential buildings age, they are used by lower-income groups who are forced to use them at a higher population density. Therefore, jobs decline and population rises while buildings age. Housing, at the higher population densities, accommodates more low-income urban population than can find jobs. A social trap is created where excess low-cost housing beckons low-income people inward because of the available housing. They continue coming to the city until their numbers so far exceed the available income opportunities that the standard of living declines far enough to stop further inflow. Income to the area is then too low to maintain all of the housing. Excess housing falls into disrepair and is abandoned. One can simultaneously have extreme crowding in those buildings that are occupied, while other buildings become excess and are abandoned because the economy of the area cannot support all of the resi-dential structures. But the excess residential buildings threaten the area in two ways — they occupy the land so that it cannot be used for job-creating buildings, and they stand ready to accept a rise in population if the area should start to improve economically.

Any change which would otherwise raise the standard of living only takes off the economic pressure momentarily and causes the population to rise enough that the standard of living again falls to the barely tolerable level. A self-regulating system is thereby at work which drives the condition of the depressed area down far enough to stop the increase in people.

At any time, a near-equilibrium exists affecting population mobility be-tween the different areas of the country. To the extent that there is dis-equilibrium, it means that some area is slightly more attractive than others and population begins to move in the direction of the more attractive area. This movement continues until the rising population drives the more attractive area down in attractiveness until the area is again in equilibrium with its surroundings. Other things being equal, an increase in population of a city crowds housing, overloads job opportunities, causes congestion, increases pollution, encourages crime, and reduces almost every component of the quality of life.

This powerful dynamic force to re-establish an equilibrium in total at-tractiveness means that any social program must take into account the eventual shifts that will occur in the many components of *attractiveness*. As used here, attractiveness is the composite effect of all factors that cause population move-ment toward or away from an area. Most areas in a country have nearly equal attractiveness most of the time, with only sufficient disequilibrium in attrac-tiveness to account for the shifts in population. But areas can have the same composite attractiveness with different mixes in the components of attractiveness. In one area component A could be high and B low, while the reverse could be true in another area that nevertheless had the same total composite attractiveness. If a program makes some aspect of an area more attractive than its neighbor's, and thereby makes total attractiveness higher momentarily, population of that area rises until other components of attractiveness are driven down far enough to again establish an equilibrium. This means that efforts to improve the condition of our cities will result primarily in increasing the population of the cities and causing the population of the country to concentrate in the cities. The overall condition of urban life, for any particular economic class of population, cannot be appreciably better or worse than that of the remainder of the country to and from which people may come. Programs aimed at improving the city can succeed only if they result in eventually raising the average quality of life for the country as a whole.

On raising the quality of life

But there is substantial doubt that our urban programs have been contributing to the national quality of life. By concentrating total population, and especially low-income population, in urban locations, undermining the strength and cohesiveness of the community, and making government and bureaucracy so big that the individual feels powerless to influence the system within which he is increasingly constrained, the quality of life is being reduced. In fact, if they have any effect, our efforts to improve our urban areas will in the long run tend to delay the concern about rising total population and thereby contribute directly to the eventual overcrowding of the country and the world.

Any proposed program must deal with both the quality of life and the factors affecting population. "Raising the quality of life" means releasing stress and pressures, reducing crowding, reducing pollution, alleviating hunger, and treating ill health. But these pressures are exactly the sources of concern and action aimed at controlling total population to keep it within the bounds of the fixed world within which we live. If the pressures are relaxed, so is the concern about how we impinge on the environment. Population will then rise further until the pressures reappear with an intensity that can no longer be relieved. To try to raise quality of life without intentionally creating compensating pressures to prevent a rise in population density will be self-defeating.

Consider the meaning of these interacting attractiveness components as they affect a depressed ghetto area of a city. First we must be clear on the way population density is, in fact, now being controlled. There is some set of forces determining that the density is not far higher or lower than it is. But there are many possible combinations of forces that an urban area can exert. The particular combination will determine the population mix of the area and the economic health of the city. I suggest that the depressed areas of most American cities are created by a combination of forces in which there is a job shortage and a housing excess. The availability of housing draws the lowest-income group until they so far exceed the opportunities of the area that the low standard of living, the frustration, and the crime rate counterbalance the housing availability. Until the pool of excess housing is reduced, little can be done to improve the economic condition of the city. A low-cost housing program alone moves exactly in the wrong direction. It draws more low-income people. It makes the area differentially more attractive to the poor who need jobs and less attractive to those who create jobs. In the new population equilibrium that develops, some characteristic of the social system must compensate for the additional attractiveness created by the low-cost housing. The counterbalance is a further decline of the economic condition for the area. But as the area becomes more destitute, pressures rise for more low-cost housing. The consequence is a downward spiral that draws in the low-income population, depresses their condition, prevents escape, and reduces hope. All of this is done with the best of intentions.

My paper, "Systems Analysis as a Tool for Urban Planning" from a symposium in October, 1969, at the National Academy of Engineering, suggests a reversal of present practice in order to simultaneously reduce the aging housing in our cities and allocate land to income-earning opportunities. The land shifted to industry permits the "balance of trade" of the area to be corrected by allowing labor to create and export a product to generate an income stream with which to buy the necessities of modern life from the outside. But the concurrent reduction of excess housing is absolutely essential. It supplies the land for new jobs. Equally important, the resulting housing shortage creates the population-stabilizing pressure that allows economic revival to proceed without being inundated by rising population. This can all be done without driving the present low-income residents out of the area. It can create *upward economic mobility* to convert the low-income population to a self-supporting basis.

The first reaction of many people to these ideas is to believe that they will never be accepted by elected officials or by residents of depressed urban areas. But some of our strongest support and encouragement is coming from those very groups who are closest to the problems, who see the symptoms first-hand, who have lived through the failures of the past, and who must live with the present conditions until enduring solutions are found.

Over the last several decades the country has slipped into a set of attitudes about our cities that are leading to actions that have become an integral part of the system that is generating greater troubles. If we were malicious and wanted to create urban slums, trap low-income people in ghetto areas, and increase the number of people on welfare, we could do little better than follow the present policies. The trend toward stressing income and sales taxes and away from the real estate tax encourages old buildings to remain in place and block self-renewal. The concessions in the income tax laws to encourage low-income housing will in the long run actually increase the total low-income population of the country. The highway expenditures and the government loans for suburban housing have made it easier for higher-income groups to abandon urban areas than to revive them. The pressures to expand the areas incorporated by urban government, in an effort to expand the revenue base, have been more than offset by lowered administrative efficiency, more citizen frustration, and the accelerated decline that is triggered in the annexed areas. The belief that more money will solve urban problems has taken attention away from correcting the underlying causes and has instead allowed the problems to grow to the limit of the available money, whatever that amount might be.*

Characteristics of social systems

I turn now to some characteristics of social systems that mislead people. These have been identified in our work with corporate and urban systems and in more recent work that I will describe concerning the world-wide pressures that are now enveloping our planet.

First, social systems are inherently insensitive to most policy changes that people select in an effort to alter the behavior of the system. In fact, a social system tends to draw our attention to the very points at which an attempt to intervene will fail. Our experience, which has been developed from contact with simple systems, leads us to look close to the symptoms of trouble for a cause. When we look, we discover that the social system presents us with an apparent cause that is plausible according to what we have learned from simple systems. But this apparent cause is usually a coincident occurrence that, like the trouble symptom itself, is being produced by the feedback-loop dynamics of a larger system. For example, as already discussed, we see human suffering in the cities; we observe that it is accompanied (some think caused) by inadequate housing. We increase the housing and the population rises to compensate for the effort. More people are drawn into and trapped in the depressed social system. As another example, the symptoms of excess population are beginning to overshadow the country. These symptoms appear as urban crowding and social pressure. Rather than face the population problem squarely we try to relieve the immediate pressure by planning industry in rural areas and by discussing new towns. If additional urban area is provided it will temporarily reduce the pressures and defer the need to face the underlying population question. The consequence, as it will be seen 25 years hence, will have been to contribute to increasing the population so much that even today's quality of life will be impossible.

A second characteristic of social systems is that all of them seem to have a few sensitive influence points through which the behavior of the system can be changed. Those influence points are not in the location where most people expect. Furthermore, if one identifies in a model of a social system a sensitive point where influence can be exerted, the chances are still good that a person guided by intuition and judgment will alter the system in the wrong direction. For example in the urban system, housing is a sensitive control point but, if one wishes to revive the economy of a city and make it a better place for low-income as well as other people, it appears that the amount of low-income housing must be reduced rather than increased. Another example is the world-wide problem of rising population and the disparity between the standards of living in the developed and the underdeveloped countries, an issue

---

* Our continuing examination of urban behavior has been made possible through a grant to M.I.T. from the Independence Foundation of Philadelphia.

arising in the world system to be discussed in the following paragraphs. But it is beginning to appear that a sensitive control point is the rate of generation of capital investment.

And how should one change the rate of capital accumulation? The common answer has been to increase industrialization, but recent examination suggests that hope lies only in reducing the rate of industrialization. This may actually help raise quality of life and contribute to stabilizing population.

As a third characteristic of social systems, there is usually a fundamental conflict between the short-term and long-term consequences of a policy change. A policy which produces improvement in the short run, within five to ten years, is usually one which degrades the system in the long run, beyond ten years. Likewise, those policies and programs which produce long-run improvement may initially depress the behavior of the system. This is especially treacherous. The short run is more visible and more compelling. It speaks loudly for immediate attention. But a series of actions all aimed at short-run improvement can eventually burden a system with long-run depressants so severe that even heroic short-run measures no longer suffice. Many of the problems which we face today are the eventual result of short-run measures taken as long as two or three decades ago.

A global perspective

I have mentioned social organizations at the corporate level and then touched on work which has been done on the dynamics of the city. Now we are beginning to examine issues of even broader scope.

In July, 1970, we held a two-week international conference on world dynamics. It was a meeting organized for the Club of Rome, a private group of about 50 individuals drawn from many countries who have joined together to attempt a better understanding of social systems at the world level. Their interest lies in the same problems of population, resources, industrialization, pollution, and world-wide disparities of standard of living on which many groups now focus. But the Club of Rome is devoted to taking actions that will lead to a better understanding of world trends and to influencing world leaders and governments. The July meeting at M.I.T. included the general theory and behavior of complex systems and talks on the behavior of specific social systems ranging from corporations through commodity markets to biological systems, drug addiction in the community, and growth and decline of a city. Especially prepared for this conference was a dynamic model of the interactions between world population, industrialization, depletion of natural resources, agriculture, and pollution. A detailed discussion of this world system will soon appear in my book *World Dynamics*, and its further development is the purpose of the "Project on the Predicament of Mankind" being sponsored by the Club of Rome at M.I.T. for a year under the guidance of Professor Dennis Meadows. The plan is to develop a research group of men from many countries who will eventually base their continuing efforts in a neutral country such as Switzerland. The immediate project will reexamine, verify, alter, and extend the preliminary dynamic study of the world system and will relate it to the present world-wide concern about trends in civilization.

The simple model of world interactions as thus far developed shows several different alternative futures depending on whether population growth is eventually suppressed by shortage of natural resources, by pollution, by crowding and consequent social strife, or by insufficient food. Malthus dealt only with the latter, but it is possible for civilization to encounter other controlling pressures before a food shortage occurs.

It is certain that resource shortage, pollution, crowding, food failure, or some other equally powerful force will limit population and industrialization if persuasion and psychological factors do not. Exponential growth cannot continue forever. Our greatest immediate challenge is how we guide the transition from growth to equilibrium. There are many possible mechanisms of growth suppression. That some one or combination will occur is inevitable. Unless we come to understand and to choose, the social system by its internal processes will choose for us. The natural mechanisms for terminating exponential growth appear to be the least desirable. Unless we understand and begin to act soon, we may be overwhelmed by a social and economic system we have created but can't control.

Figure 1* shows the structure that has been assumed. It interrelates the mutual effects of population, capital investment, natural resources, pollution, and the fraction of capital devoted to agriculture. These five system "levels" are shown in the rectangles. Each level is caused to change by the rates of flow in and out, such as the birth rate and death rate that increase and decrease population. As shown by the dotted lines, the five system levels, through intermediate concepts shown at the circles, control the rates of flow. As an example, the death rate at Symbol 10 depends on population P and the "normal" lifetime as stated by death rate normal DRN. But death rate depends also on conditions in other parts of the system. From Circle 12 comes the influence of pollution that here assumes death rate to double if pollution becomes 20 times as severe as in 1970; and, progressively, that death rate would increase by a factor of 10 if pollution became 60 times as much as now. Likewise from Circle 13 the effect of food per capita is to increase death rate as food becomes less available. The detailed definition of the model states how each rate of flow is assumed to depend on the levels of population, natural resources, capital investment, capital devoted to food, and pollution.

Individually the assumptions in the model are plausible, create little disagreement, and reflect common discussions and assertions about the individual responses within the world system. But each is explicit and can be subjected to scrutiny. From one viewpoint, the system of Figure 1 is very simplified. It focuses on a few major factors and omits most of the substructure of world social and economic activity. But from another viewpoint, Figure 1 is comprehensive and complex. The system is far more complete and the theory described by the accompanying computer model is much more explicit than the mental models that are now being used as a basis for world and governmental planning. It incorporates dozens of nonlinear relationships.

* All figures are taken from the manuscript for *World Dynamics* by Jay W. Forrester, Wright-Allen Press, 238 Main Street, Cambridge Mass. 02142, available about February, 1971.

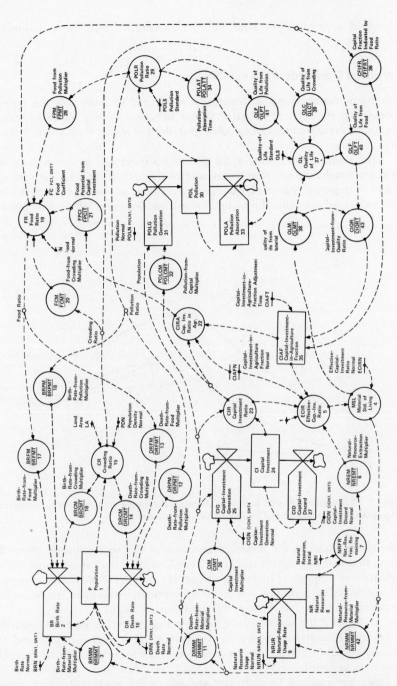

Figure 1. Upon this world model are based the author's comments on the effects of changing population and economic growth factors in the next 50 years. It shows the interrelation of population, capital investment, natural resources, pollution, and the fraction of capital devoted to agriculture on which is based the following discussion.

The world system shown here exhibits provocative and even frightening possibilities.

Transition from growth to equilibrium

With the model specified, a computer can be used to show how the system, as described for each of its parts, would behave. Given a set of beginning conditions, the computer can calculate and plot the results that unfold through time.

The world today seems to be entering a condition in which pressures are rising simultaneously from every one of the influences that can suppress growth — depleted resources, pollution, crowding, and insufficient food. It is still unclear which will dominate if mankind continues along the present

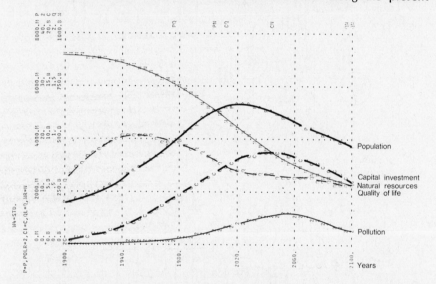

Population

Capital investment
Natural resources
Quality of life

Pollution

Years

Figure 2.   Basic world model behavior showing the mode in which industrialization and population are suppressed by falling natural resources.

path. Figure 2 shows the mode of behavior of this world system given the assumption that population reaches a peak and then declines because industrialization is suppressed by falling natural resources. The model system starts with estimates of conditions in 1900. Adjustments have been made so that the generated paths pass through the conditions of 1970.

In Figure 2 the quality of life peaks in the 1950's and by 2020 has fallen far enough to halt further rise in population. Declining resources and the consequent fall in capital investment then exert further pressure to gradually reduce world population.

But we may not be fortunate enough to run gradually out of natural resources. Science and technology may very well find ways to use the more plentiful metals and atomic energy so that resource depletion does not intervene. If so, the way then remains open for some other pressure to arise within the system. Figure 3 shows what happens within this system if the resource shortage is foreseen and avoided. Here the only change from Figure 2 is in the usage rate of natural resources after the year 1970. In Figure 3, resources are used after 1970 at a rate 75 percent less than assumed in Figure 2. In other words, the standard of living is sustained with a lower d ain on the expendable and irreplaceable resources. But the picture is even less attractive! By not running out of resources, population and capital investment are allowed to rise until a pollution crisis is created. Pollution then acts directly to reduce birth rate, increase death rate, and to depress food production. Population which, according to this simple model, peaks at the year 2030 has fallen to one-sixth of the peak population within an interval of 20 years — a world-wide catastrophe of a magnitude never before experienced. Should it

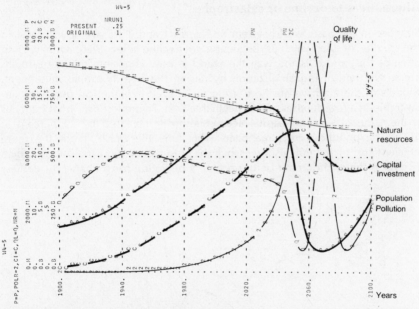

Figure 3. Pollution crisis precipitated by lower usage rate of natural resources. In 1970 natural resource usage is reduced 75 percent by more effective technology without affecting material standard of living.

occur, one can speculate on which sectors of the world population will suffer most. It is quite possible that the more industrialized countries (which are the ones which have caused such a disaster) would be the least able to survive such a disruption to environment and food supply. They might be the ones to take the brunt of the collapse.

Figure 3 shows how a technological success (reducing our dependence on natural resources) can merely save us from one fate only to fall victim to something worse (a pollution catastrophe). There is now developing throughout the world a strong undercurrent of doubt about technology as the savior of mankind. There is a basis for such doubt. Of course, the source of trouble is not technology as such but is instead the management of the entire technological-human-political-economic-natural complex.

Figure 3 is a dramatic example of the general process discussed earlier wherein a program aimed at one trouble symptom results in creating a new set of troubles in some other part of the system. Here the success in alleviating a natural resource shortage throws the system over into the mode of stopping population caused by industrialization which has been freed from natural resource restraint. This process of a solution creating a new problem has defeated many of our past governmental programs and will continue to do so unless we devote more effort to understanding the dynamic behavior of our social systems.

Alternatives to decline or catastrophe

Suppose in the basic world system of Figures 1 and 2 we ask how to sustain the quality of life which is beginning to decline after 1950. One way to attempt this, and it is the way the world is now choosing, might be to increase the rate of industrialization by raising the rate of capital investment. Models of the kind we are here using make such hypothetical questions answerable in a few minutes and at negligible cost. Figure 4 shows what happens if the "normal" rate of capital accumulation is increased by 20 percent in 1970. The pollution crisis reappears. This time the cause is not the more efficient use of natural resources but the upsurge of industrialization which overtaxes the environment before resource depletion has a chance to depress

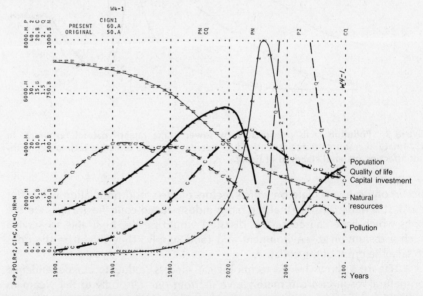

Figure 4.   In 1970 the rate of capital accumulation is increased 20 percent in an effort to reverse the beginning decline in quality of life. The pollution crisis occurs before natural resources are depleted.

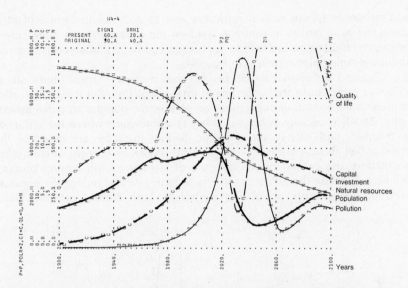

Figure 5. **In 1970 the 20 percent increase in capital accumulation of Figure 4 is retained and "normal" birth rate is reduced 50 percent. Capital investment continues to grow until the pollution crisis develops. After an initial decline, population is again pushed up by the rapid rise in quality of life that precedes the collapse.**

industrialization. Again, an "obvious" desirable change in policy has caused troubles worse than the ones that were originally being corrected.

This is important, not only for its own message but because it demonstrates how an apparently desirable change in a social system can have unexpected and even disastrous results.

Figure 4 should make us cautious about rushing into programs on the basis of short-term humanitarian impulses. The eventual result can be anti-humanitarian. Emotionally inspired efforts often fall into one of three traps set for us by the nature of social systems: The programs are apt to address symptoms rather than causes and attempt to operate through points in the system that have little leverage for change; the characteristic of systems whereby a policy change has the opposite effect in the short run from the effect in the long run can eventually cause deepening difficulties after a sequence of short-term actions; and the effect of a program can be along an entirely different direction than was originally expected, so that suppressing one symptom only causes trouble to burst forth at another point.

Figure 5 retains the 20 percent additional capital investment rate after 1970 from Figure 4 but in addition explores birth reduction as a way of avoiding crisis. Here the "normal" birth rate has been cut in half in 1970. (Changes in normal rates refer to coefficients which have the specified effect if all other things remain the same. But other things in the system change and also exert their effect on the actual system rates.) The result shows interesting behavior. Quality of life surges upward for 30 years for the reasons that are customarily asserted. Food-per-capita grows, material standard of living rises, and crowding does not become as great. But the more affluent world population continues to use natural resources and to accumulate capital plant at about the same rate as in Figure 4. Load on the environment is more closely related to industrialization than to population and the pollution crisis occurs at about the same point in time as in Figure 4.

Figure 5 shows that the 50 percent reduction in "normal" birth rate in 1970 was sufficient to start a decline in total population. But the rising quality of life and the reduction of pressures act to start the population curve upward again. This is especially evident in other computer runs where the reduction in "normal" birth rate is not so drastic. Serious questions are raised by this investigation about the effectiveness of birth control as a means of controlling population. The secondary consequence of starting a birth control program will be to increase the influences that raise birth rate and reduce the apparent pressures that require population control. A birth control program which

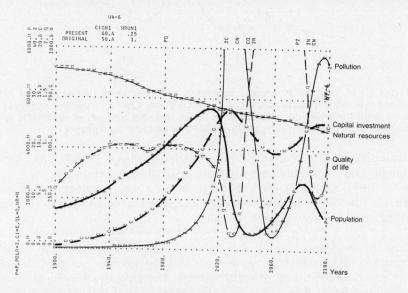

Figure 6.   The 20 percent increase of capital investment from Figure 4 and the 75 percent reduction of natural resource usage from Figure 3 are combined.

would be effective, all other things being equal, may largely fail because other things will not remain equal. Its very incipient success can set in motion forces to defeat the program.

Figure 6 combines the reduced resource usage rate and the increased capital investment rate of Figures 3 and 4. The result is to make the population collapse occur slightly sooner and more severely. Based on the modified system of Figure 6, Figure 7 then examines the result if technology finds ways to reduce the pollution generated by a given degree of industrialization. Here in Figure 7, the pollution rate, other things being the same, is reduced by 50 percent from that in Figure 6. The result is to postpone the day of reckoning by 20 years and to allow the world population to grow 25 percent greater before the population collapse occurs. The "solution" of reduced pollution has, in effect, caused more people to suffer the eventual consequences. Again we see the dangers of partial solutions. Actions at one point in a system that attempt to relieve one kind of distress produce an unexpected result in some other part of the system. If the interactions are not sufficiently understood, the consequences can be as bad as or worse than those that led to the initial action.

There are no utopias in our social systems. There appear to be no sustainable modes of behavior that are free of pressures and stresses. But there are many possible modes and some are more desirable than others. Usually, the more attractive kinds of behavior in our social systems seem to be possible only if we have a good understanding of the system dynamics and are willing to endure the self-discipline and pressures that must accompany the desirable

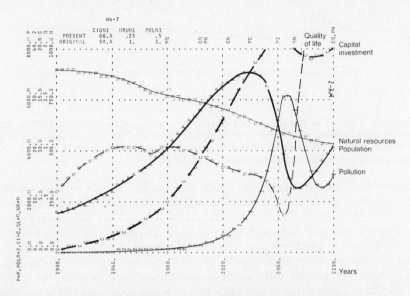

Figure 7. Increased capital investment rate and reduced natural resource usage from Figure 6 are retained. In addition in 1970 the "normal" rate of pollution generation is reduced 50 percent. The effect of pollution control is to allow population to grow 25 percent further and to delay the pollution crisis by 20 years.

mode. The world system of Figure 1 can exhibit modes that are more hopeful than the crises of Figures 2 through 7. But to develop the more promising modes will require restraint and dedication to a long-range future that man may not be capable of sustaining.

Figure 8 shows the world system if several policy changes are adopted together in the year 1970. Population is stabilized. Quality of life rises about 50 percent. Pollution remains at about the 1970 level. Would such a world be accepted? It implies an end to population and economic growth.

In Figure 8 the normal rate of capital accumulation is *reduced* 40 percent from its previous value. The "normal" birth rate is reduced 50 percent from its earlier value. The "normal" pollution generation is reduced 50 percent from the value before 1970. The "normal" rate of food production is *reduced 20*

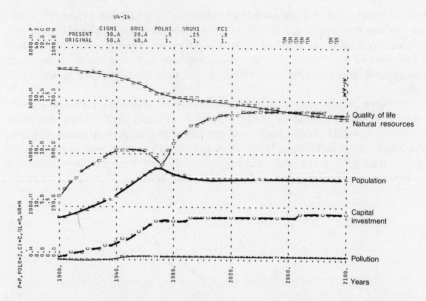

Figure 8.   One set of conditions that establishes a world equilibrium. In 1970 capital investment rate is reduced 40 percent, birth rate is reduced 50 percent, pollution generation is reduced 50 percent, natural resource usage rate is reduced 75 percent, and food production is reduced 20 percent.

percent from its previous value. (These changes in "normal" values are the changes for a specific set of system conditions. Actual system rates continue to be affected by the varying conditions of the system.) But reduction in investment rate and reduction in agricultural emphasis are counterintuitive and not likely to be discovered or accepted without extensive system studies and years of argument — perhaps more years than are available. The changes in pollution generation and natural resource usage may be easier to understand and to achieve. The severe reduction in world-wide birth rate is the most doubtful. Even if technical and biological methods existed, the improved condition of the world might remove the incentive for sustaining the birth reduction emphasis and discipline.

Future policy issues

The dynamics of world behavior bear directly on the future of the United States. American urbanization and industrialization are a major part of the world scene. The United States is setting a pattern that other parts of the world are trying to follow. That pattern is not sustainable. Our foreign policy and our overseas commercial activity seem to be running contrary to overwhelming forces that are developing in the world system. The following issues are raised by the preliminary investigations to date. They must, of course, be examined more deeply and confirmed by more thorough research into the assumptions about structure and detail of the world system.

- Industrialization may be a more fundamentally disturbing force in world ecology than is population. In fact, the population explosion is perhaps best viewed as a result of technology and industrialization. I include medicine and public health as a part of industrialization.
- Within the next century, man may be facing choices from a four-pronged dilemma — suppression of modern industrial society by a natural resource shortage, collapse of world population from changes wrought by pollution, population limitation by food shortage, or population control by war, disease and social stresses caused by physical and psychological crowding.
- We may now be living in a "golden age" where, in spite of the world-wide feeling of malaise, the quality of life is, on the average, higher than ever before in history and higher now than the future offers.
- Efforts for direct population control may be inherently self-defeating. If population control begins to result as hoped in higher per capita food supply and material standard of living, these very improvements can generate forces to trigger a resurgence of population growth.
- The high standard of living of modern industrial societies seems to result from a production of food and material goods that has been able to outrun the rising population. But, as agriculture reaches a space limit, as industrialization reaches a natural-resource limit, and as both reach a pollution limit, population tends to catch up. Population then grows until the "quality of life" falls far enough to generate sufficiently large pressures to stabilize population.
- There may be no realistic hope for the present under-developed countries reaching the standard of living demonstrated by the present industrialized nations. The pollution and natural resource load placed on the world environmental system by each person in an advanced country is probably 10 to 20 times greater than the load now generated by a person in an underdeveloped country. With four times as much population in underdeveloped countries as in the present developed countries, their rising to the economic level of the United States could mean an increase of 10 times in the natural resource and pollution load on the world environment. Noting the destruction that has already occurred on land, in the air, and especially in the oceans, no capability appears to exist for handling such a rise in standard of living for the present total population of the world.
- A society with a high level of industrialization may be nonsustainable. It may be self-extinguishing if it exhausts the natural resources on which it depends. Or, if unending substitution for declining natural resources is possible, the international strife over "pollution and environmental rights" may pull the average world-wide standard of living back to the level of a century ago.
- From the long view of a hundred years hence, the present efforts of underdeveloped countries to industrialize along Western patterns may be unwise. They may now be closer to the ultimate equilibrium with the environment than are the industrialized nations. The present underdeveloped countries may be in a better condition for surviving the forthcoming world-wide environmental and economic pressures than are the advanced countries.

When one of the several forces materializes that is strong enough to cause a collapse in world population, the advanced countries may suffer far more than their share of the decline.

A NEW FRONTIER

It is now possible to take hypotheses about the separate parts of a social system, to combine them in a computer model, and to learn the consequences. The hypotheses may at first be no more correct than the ones we are using in our intuitive thinking. But the process of computer modeling and model testing requires these hypotheses to be stated more explicitly. The model comes out of the hazy realm of the mental model into an unambiguous model or statement to which all have access. Assumptions can then be checked against all available information and can be rapidly improved. The great uncertainty with mental models is the inability to anticipate the consequences of interactions between the parts of a system. This uncertainty is totally eliminated in computer models. Given a stated set of assumptions, the computer traces the resulting consequences without doubt or error. This is a powerful procedure for clarifying issues. It is not easy. Results will not be immediate.

We are on the threshold of a great new era in human pioneering. In the past there have been periods characterized by geographical exploration. Other periods have dealt with the formation of national governments. At other times the focus was on the creation of great literature. Most recently we have been through the pioneering frontier of science and technology. But science and technology are now a routine part of our life. Science is no longer a frontier. The process of scientific discovery is orderly and organized.

I suggest that the next frontier for human endeavor is to pioneer a better understanding of the nature of our social systems. The means are visible. The task will be no easier than the development of science and technology. For the next 30 years we can expect rapid advance in understanding the complex dynamics of our social systems. To do so will require research, the development of teaching methods and materials, and the creation of appropriate educational programs. The research results of today will in one or two decades find their way into the secondary schools just as concepts of basic physics moved from research to general education over the past three decades.

What we do today fundamentally affects our future two or three decades hence. If we follow intuition, the trends of the past will continue into deepening difficulty. If we set up research and educational programs, which are now possible but which have not yet been developed, we can expect a far sounder basis for action.

The nation's real alternatives

The record to date implies that our people accept the future growth of United States population as preordained, beyond the purview and influence of legislative control, and as a ground rule which determines the nation's task as finding cities in which the future population can live. But I have been describing the circular processes of our social systems in which there is no unidirectional cause and effect but instead a ring of actions and consequences that close back on themselves. One could say, incompletely, that the population will grow and that cities, space, and food must be provided. But one can likewise say, also incompletely, that the provision of cities, space, and food will cause the population to grow. Population generates pressure for urban growth, but urban pressures help to limit population.

Population grows until stresses rise far enough, which is to say that the quality of life falls far enough, to stop further increase. Everything we do to reduce those pressures causes the population to rise farther and faster and hastens the day when expediencies will no longer suffice. The United States is in the position of a wild animal running from its pursuers. We still have some space, natural resources, and agricultural land left. We can avoid the question of rising population as long as we can flee into this bountiful reservoir that nature provided. But it is obvious that the reservoirs are limited. The wild animal usually flees until he is cornered, until he has no more space. Then he turns to fight, but he no longer has room to maneuver. He is less able to forestall disaster than if he had fought in the open while there was still room to yield and to dodge. The United States is running away from its long-term threats by trying to relieve social pressures as they arise. But if we persist in treating only the symptoms and not the causes, the result will be to increase the magnitude of the ultimate threat and reduce our capability to respond when we no longer have space to flee.

What does this mean? Instead of automatically accepting the need for new towns and the desirability of locating industry in rural areas, we should consider confining our cities. If it were possible to prohibit the encroachment by housing and industry onto even a single additional acre of farm and forest, the resulting social pressures would hasten the day when we stabilize population. Some European countries are closer to realizing the necessity of curtailing urban growth than are we. As I understand it, in farm land surrounding Copenhagen, the severest of pressures forces the government to rezone small additional parcels. When land is rezoned, the corresponding rise in land price is heavily taxed to remove the incentive for land speculation. The waiting time for an empty apartment in Copenhagen may be years. Such pressures certainly cause the Danes to face the population problem more squarely than do we.

Our greatest challenge now is how to handle the transition from growth into equilibrium. Our society has behind it a thousand years of tradition that has encouraged and rewarded growth. The folklore and the success stories praise growth and expansion. But that is not the path of the future. Many of the present stresses in our society are from the pressures that always accompany the conversion from growth into equilibrium.

In our studies of social systems, we have made a number of investigations of life cycles that start with growth and merge into equilibrium. There are always severe stresses in the transition. Pressures must rise far enough to suppress the forces that produced growth. Not only do we face the pressure that will stop the population growth; we also encounter pressures that will stop the rise of industrialization and standard of living. The social stresses will rise. The economic forces will be ones for which we have no precedent. The psychological forces will be beyond those for which we are prepared. Our studies of urban systems demonstrated how the pressures from shortage of land and rising unemployment accompany the usual transition from urban growth to equilibrium. But the pressures we have seen in our cities are minor compared to those which the nation is approaching. The population pressures and the economic forces in a city that was reaching equilibrium have in the past been able to escape to new land areas.

But that escape is becoming less possible. Until now we have had, in effect, an inexhaustible supply of farm land and food-growing potential. But now we are reaching the critical point where, all at the same time, population is overrunning productive land, agricultural land is almost fully employed for the first time, the rise in population is putting more demand on the food supplies, and urbanization is pushing agriculture out of the fertile areas into the marginal lands. For the first time demand is rising into a condition where supply will begin to fall while need increases. The crossover from plenty to shortage can occur abruptly.

The fiscal and monetary system of the country is a complex social-economic-financial system of the kind we have been discussing. It is clear the country is not agreed on behavior of the interactions between government policy, growth, unemployment, and inflation. An article by a writer for *Finance* magazine in July, 1970, suggests that the approach I have been discussing be applied in fiscal and monetary policy and their relationships to the economy. I estimate that such a task would be only a few times more difficult than was the investigation of urban growth and stagnation. The need to accomplish it becomes more urgent as the economy begins to move for the first time from a history of growth into the turbulent pressures that will accompany the transition from growth to one of the many possible kinds of equilibrium. We need to choose the kind of equilibrium before we arrive.

In a hierarchy of systems, there is usually a conflict between the goals of a subsystem and the welfare of the broader system. We see this in the urban system. The goal of the city is to expand and to raise its quality of life. But this increases population, industrialization, pollution, and demands on food supply. The broader social system of the country and the world requires that the goals of the urban areas be curtailed and that the pressures of such curtailment become high enough to keep the urban areas and population within the bounds that are satisfactory to the larger system of which the city is a part. If this nation chooses to continue to work for some of the traditional urban goals, and if it succeeds, as it may well do, the result will be to deepen the distress of the country as a whole and eventually to deepen the crisis in the cities themselves. We may be at the point where higher pressures in the present are necessary if insurmountable pressures are to be avoided in the future.

I have tried to give you a glimpse of the nature of multi-loop feedback systems, a class to which our social systems belong. I have attempted to indicate how these systems mislead us because our intuition and judgment have been formed to expect behavior different from that actually possessed by such systems. I believe that we are still pursuing national programs that will be at least as frustrating and futile as many of the past. But there is hope. We can now begin to understand the dynamic behavior of our social systems. Progress will be slow. There are many cross-currents in the social sciences which will cause confusion and delay. The approach that I have been describing is very different from the emphasis on data gathering and statistical analysis that occupies much of the time of social research. But there have been breakthroughs in several areas. If we proceed expeditiously but thoughtfully, there is a basis for optimism.

Suggested readings

Jay W. Forrester, *Industrial Dynamics*. Cambridge: The M.I.T. Press, 1961.
Jay W. Forrester, *Principles of Systems*. Cambridge (238 Main St.): Wright-Allen Press, 1968.
Jay W. Forrester, *Urban Dynamics*. Cambridge: The M.I.T. Press, 1969.
Jay W. Forrester, *World Dynamics*. Cambridge (238 Main St.): Wright-Allen Press, forthcoming.
Dennis L. Meadows, *Dynamics of Commodity Production Cycles*. Cambridge (328 Main St.): Wright-Allen Press, 1970.

HERMAN E. DALY

National Economy: How High Is Up?

What is meant by a "stationary-state" economy? Why is it necessary? How might it be attained? The first two questions are easy, the third is extremely difficult.

The stationary-state is defined as an economy in which the total population and the total stock of *physical* wealth are both constant. For the population this implies that the birth rate is equal to the death rate. For the stock of physical wealth it implies that the rate of physical production is equal to the rate of physical consumption. In both instances the rate of input equals the rate of output and is thus also equal to the rate of throughput. Stocks can be maintained constant by high or by low rates of throughput.

Our definition of stationary-state is not complete until we specify the rate of maintenance throughput. Generally speaking we want the rate of throughput to be as low as possible. For the equilibrium population, low birth and death rates imply high life expectancy. For the stock of wealth, low rates of production and consumption imply high "life expectancy" or durability of physical wealth. If it is desirable for people to live longer and for goods to last longer, then it is desirable to maintain stocks with lower rates of throughput.

Herman E. Daly, "How High Is Up?" *Consulting Engineer*, vol. 36, no. 3 (March 1971), pp. 107–111. Reprinted by permission.
The author is Associate Professor of Economics, Louisiana State University.

The stationary-state is not a new concept. The main idea comes straight from classical economics, where it received its best formulation from John Stuart Mill in 1857. But it has been an unpopular idea whose time is only now arriving. The accompanying diagram and explanatory text summarize the basic concepts and relations of the modern notion of stationary-state.

Why is the stationary-state necessary? In a finite world nothing physical can grow forever. All demographers agree that zero population growth is necessary at some point. The differences among them concern the size of the optimum population and the speed with which we should try to bring

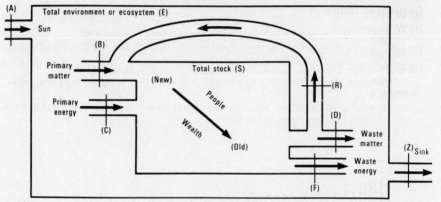

Figure 1

Rectangle (E) is the total ecosystem which contains the total stock (S) of wealth and people as one of its mutually dependent components. The ecosystem imports energy from outer space (sun) and exports waste heat to outer space (sink). (E) is a stationary-state system. Its material cycles form a closed loop turned by the energy throughput from the sun.

(S) is maintained in a steady-state ($\Delta S = 0$) by the total throughput, which consists of environment depleting raw material inputs (B) and energy inputs (C), and of environment polluting waste material outputs (D) and waste energy outputs (F). We know that the change in stock equals inputs minus outputs; i.e., $\Delta S = (B + C) - (D + F)$. Since $\Delta S = 0$, $(B + C) = (D + F)$. For an equilibrium stock, input equals output equals throughput.

From the first law of thermodynamics (conservation of matter and conservation of energy) and the postulated steady-state of (S) we know that (B = D) and (C = F) (neglecting matter-energy transformation).

From the second law of thermodynamics we know that energy cannot be recycled. Matter may be recycled (R), but only by using more energy (and matter) to do it. In the diagram energy moves only from left to right, while matter moves in both directions. Recycling does not eliminate pollution and depletion. But it does allow a trade-off between material and thermal forms of pollution and depletion.

For a constant (S) the lower the rate of throughput the more durable or longer-lived is the total stock. For a given throughput, the lower the rate or recycling (R), the more durable are the individual commodities. The optimum durability of an individual commodity is attained when the marginal production cost of increased durability equals the marginal recycling cost of not increasing durability further. "Cost" is total ecological cost and is extremely difficult to measure.

Both the size of the stock and rate of maintenance throughput must not be so large relative to the total environment that they obstruct the natural ecological processes which form the biophysical foundations of life and wealth, or the total stock (S) and its associated throughput become a cancer that kills total organism (E).

our present population (up or down) to the optimum level. Likewise all economists should agree that zero growth in the stock of physical wealth is necessary at some point, though they may differ on the optimum level and the optimum speed of adjustment to it. The analogy between physical stocks of wealth and people is very close. Both take up space. Both require low entropy inputs from the environment (depletion) for their maintenance, and both must return high entropy outputs back to the environment (pollution). The larger the stocks, the larger the necessary maintenance flows of depletion (production) and pollution (consumption). As long as these flows are negligible relative to the material and energy exchanges of the total ecosystem then we are protected by our own impotence. But with large and growing stocks of wealth and people, and with ever more powerful technologies for transforming material and energy inputs in ways and in quantities never before experienced in the aeons of biophysical evolution of our planet — we begin to resemble a growing bull in a China shop of fixed dimensions.

A PHYSICAL NECESSITY

Ultimately the stationary-state is a physical necessity. The only disagreements that can exist among reasonable men are at what levels of population and wealth to stop, and how fast to decelerate to zero growth. To choose optimum stocks of wealth and population implies the choice of an optimum ratio of wealth to people or an optimum standard of living. With whole species of animals and plants unable to survive the increasing encroachment of man and his products, it becomes increasingly difficult to classify as "reasonable men" those who do not suspect that we may have overshot the optimum and who do not feel a sense of urgency about beginning deceleration now. The sooner we begin our deceleration to zero growth the longer we can take and the less painful and disruptive that adjustment will be.

But have we not overlooked technology, that marvelous bag of tricks for confounding the pessimists? Technology can certainly help by increasing the durability of the stocks — by raising the maintenance efficiency of the throughput so that the same stock can be maintained with a smaller throughput, or a larger stock with the same throughput. This actually is what medical technology seeks to do; it increases life expectancy making it possible to maintain a given population with a smaller number of annual deaths and births. There probably are limits to how long people should or do wish to live, but so far no one advocates decreasing life expectancy. But production technology generally aims at maximizing the flow of physical production rather than minimizing it. The result is that the stock must grow. But if the stock grows too large people will not need more goods and there will be no market for the production flow that we are maximizing. Therefore the rate of physical consumption (wearing out) must increase to make room for the new production. Durability or life expectancy of commodities tends to be minimized — exactly the opposite of what is desirable. Technology is indeed wonderful, but not when it pushes in the wrong direction. Production is the *cost* of maintenance of the stock of wealth, and like all costs it should be minimized, not maximized. As Kenneth Boulding has long argued, it is the stock of wealth that satisfies human wants and is therefore valuable. Production is a deplorable and costly activity made necessary because wealth wears out and must be replaced.

The intelligent use of technology, analogous to the use made of medical science, is to increase life expectancy or durability of goods. This can be done in two ways: by increasing the durability of the individual commodity (instead of planning for obsolescence and self-destruction), and designing technologies and distribution channels so that the material "corpse" of commodities can be recycled — either in a natural material cycle (biodegradable), or in a new commodity cycle, thus avoiding the material depletion and pollution inherent in our throw-away technology.

The most exciting technological possibility I have seen for increasing durability is the notion of closing material cycles by use of a "fusion torch," which uses ultra-high temperature plasmas to reduce any material (solid waste) to its basic elements for separation. (See Bernard J. Eastlund and William C. Gough, *Closing the Cycle from Use to Reuse,* U.S. Atomic Energy Commission, May 15, 1969). The high grade heat produced as a by-product could be used to generate electric power, and the waste heat from electric power production could be used, instead of fossil fuels, for heating buildings, so that there apparently need be no increase in thermal pollution. The idea is essentially an imitation of nature's closed loop material cycles powered by the sun. Fusion gives unlimited solar-like energy, and the fusion torch provides the work of decomposition, so that the cycle can be completely closed — no material depletion or pollution, and with unlimited energy we need not worry about energy depletion. Energy or thermal pollution is, of course, still present, but by cascading energy downward to ever lower grade uses it can be kept low. Urban problems of solid waste disposal and electric power would be solved together.

The benefits of such a technological development are potentially immense and should justify high priority for related research and development. It should certainly rank higher than collecting a second generation of moon rocks. It would not allow us to grow forever, or to escape the logic of the eventual stationary-state. It would, however, greatly increase the carrying capacity of our planet and help to extend a decent existence to the poor majority of the world's present population. Great technical problems remain, and there is no assurance that they will necessarily be solved. However, this is an example of the type of technology which is best suited to the stationary-state.

How to attain stationary-state

Now if the concept of the stationary-state is so simple, and its necessity so easily deduced from physical first principles, and if there are so many ecological signs that the time to stop growth is at hand, then why are so few people convinced? Perhaps because the third question, how to attain the stationary-state, is such a hard one to face up to. Minimizing production sounds downright subversive, and indeed it is. Many people prefer to attempt the physically impossible than to question the conventional wisdom of current economic practices. Dr. Johnson divided those who disagreed with him into two categories: fools and knaves. In more diplomatic modern terms we may speak of those who are honestly confused by the issue, and those who have a vested interest in dishonestly confusing the issue. In either situation the point at which confusion arises, or is created, involves a physical-financial schizophrenia.

First let me give an example of this schizophrenia in another context. The budget department of a certain gas-transmission company once budgeted expected revenues which, at the legally fixed price, implied a delivery in excess of the physical capacity of the pipeline. This is an apt paradigm for the world today — businessmen and economists are budgeting revenues and expenditures in blissful ignorance of the physical carrying capacity of environmental "pipelines." Some men speak a pecuniary language, others a physical language. Lack of communication is frequent.

A nice example of this schizophrenia is found in the Chase Manhattan Bank's *Business in Brief* for October 1970. A two-page article on improving the quality of life begins with a reasonable summary of the basic physical and ecological limits to growth. It ends with a call for "continued or accelerated economic growth." In between, financial and political arguments for growth are given top priority, and a pathetic attempt is made to "buy off" the earlier arguments of physical necessity by suggesting that one-fifth of the annual increment of GNP be devoted to cleaning up. How long can a physical magnitude (real GNP) continue to grow at $4\frac{1}{2}\%$ annually, doubling every $15\frac{1}{2}$ years? The Bank considers this "normal growth." One-fifth of this "normal" increment may well be devoted to making the other four-fifths less noxious, but it cannot make one iota of it disappear. Not only does the physical stock continue to increase, but also the inflow is itself increasing by $4\frac{1}{2}\%$ per year. By the law of conservation of matter and energy this means that depletion is also growing at $4\frac{1}{2}\%$ annually, and eventually pollution will have to grow at that rate also. And the Chase Manhattan economists assure us that "only in this manner can we hope to increase the quality of life in America. Can anything more absurd be imagined?

There is no reason why a sum on deposit with Chase Manhattan could not grow at $4\frac{1}{2}\%$ forever; money as a unit of account has no physical dimension. Why cannot GNP grow forever? Because it is physical. Not all of it is physical, of course, and there is no reason why nonphysical goods (leisure and some services) cannot continue to grow. But leisure is not counted in GNP, and the important physical-non-physical distinction is never made. Continued growth in nonphysical GNP, with zero growth in physical GNP, implies a shift away from material-intensive activities toward time-intensive activities.

Defining GNP

The benefits of future technical progress must take the form of reducing the maintenance cost of the stock of wealth (i.e., production). This will mean less time devoted to production (more leisure), and less matter and energy absorbed in production (less depletion and pollution). This is what must happen in reality. Whether GNP goes up or down as this transformation takes place is a matter of secondary importance, and depends mainly on how we choose to define "GNP." Is this how Chase Manhattan sees things? Not at all. The Bank says we should "evaluate the 'product' of the cleanup process as a component of economic growth." Happily for Chase, though apparently unknown to it, this is precisely the current practice in calculating GNP. Nevertheless, from a logical point of view it makes no sense at all.

Purely defensive expenditures designed to protect ourselves from the unwanted side-effects of other production should be subtracted from GNP, not added. They are costs, not benefits. One of the costs of heating with coal is more frequent laundering of shirts, but extra laundry bills increase GNP. One of the costs of the cigarette habit is more doctor bills, which also swell GNP. How nice it is to calculate net revenue by adding costs to revenue rather than subtracting them! But once we recognize that all GNP is basically a *cost* and should be minimized, then these insane contradictions disappear — even though it remains true that some parts of GNP are more cost-like than others.

Economic growth is subject to both the law of diminishing marginal utility and the law of increasing marginal costs. People as consumers satisfy their most pressing wants first, therefore growth satisfies ever less pressing wants; i.e., the marginal utility of growth declines. People as producers first use the qualitatively best (most useful) pieces of the environment as mines, farms, and garbage dumps, and only when these are used up do they resort to qualitatively inferior (more costly) pieces of the environment. Marginal cost or disutility increases. When marginal benefit less marginal cost equals zero, then growth should stop. But our current accounting adds costs and benefits and thus would always have positive net benefits and always more growth seems called for. The rule becomes "grow until it kills you, and then count your funeral expenses as further growth." Environmental degradation and urban decay are "iatrogenic diseases," induced by economic physicians who treat the basic malady of "unlimited wants" by prescribing "unlimited growth." One does not cure a treatment-induced disease by increasing the treatment dosage.

Economists rightly point out that the best solution lies in "internalizing externalities," i.e., in making the cost of all disamenities and unwanted side effects of production fall on the producer responsible for them by taxing whatever productive activity gives rise to them. This raises the marginal cost to the producer and induces him to cut back on production, thus checking growth.

But Chase Manhattan is not without allies. In the November 1970 edition of *The Center Magazine* economist Neil Jacoby of the Center for the Study of Democratic Institutions gives a more lengthy and sophisticated version of the sophistry of growthmania. In "disposing of the partial or superficial diagnoses" of the zero growth school, Jacoby flatly states that "zero growth of population and production is, moreover, impossible to achieve." Taken literally the statement is nonsense. In the long run it is impossible *not* to attain zero growth. What Jacoby has in mind, perhaps, is that given our present institutions and attitudes zero growth is impossible, which is precisely why these institutions and attitudes must change. Chase Manhattan readily admits that "in technical terms it would be perfectly possible to check growth." But Jacoby also feels that "zero growth is undesirable. A rising GNP will enable the nation more easily to bear the costs of eliminating pollution." More of the hair-of-the-dog-that-bit-you and increase-the-dosage philosophy. Jacoby does recognize the necessity of "redirecting growth," but we are not told from what to what. The zero growth or stationary-state position says that growth should be redirected from physical GNP to nonphysical GNP, plus leisure, and to growth in the degree of equality in the distribution of income and wealth.

The ultimate dilemma of physical-financial schizophrenia was posed by a writer in the London *Sunday Telegram*: "In America today 6% of the world's population is consuming 40% of the world's nonrenewable resources . . . The whole world is not just going to sit by and watch America use up irreplaceable resources . . . So President Nixon is faced with the following appalling dilemma . . . If America continues its present demographical and industrial development, with energy consumption increasing by 9% a year, it is faced by ecological disaster . . . On the other hand, if Nixon stops industrial growth, there'll be a slump on Wall Street that will make people think of 1929 with nostalgia." It is not surprising that Chase Manhattan seems more worried about a financial disaster than an ecological disaster. One recalls Bertrand Russell's statement, "Finance, like war, suffers from the fact that almost all those who have technical competence also have a bias which is contrary to the interests of the community."

Needed changes

But if there are irreconcilable conflicts between our current social institutions of finance on the one hand, and the first and second laws of thermodynamics and the laws of ecological balances on the other, then it should be clear to all that the burden of adjustment must fall on the social-financial institutions. How can we change our social and economic institutions so as to restore harmony between the economy of man and the ecology of nature? How can we attain a stationary-state economy?

The first thing to realize is that the change is a radical one. It means using technology to minimize the flow of production, subject to maintenance of some chosen stock of wealth and people. It means designing products to last. It means repairing things rather than throwing them away. But none of this strays too far from the old Protestant Ethic. The radical implication is in terms of distribution: if the annual flow of product is kept small, then how can we help those who are still poor? No longer can we piously hope that growth will take care of them. An increase in wealth for the poor will imply a decrease for the well-off. The focus of attention will be on the distribution of the stock of wealth, rather than on the minimized flow of income. Unlike the distribution of income the distribution of wealth has no theoretical explanation, much less justification. It is a historical datum. How can ethical claims to equal participation in using the stock of wealth be countered? Not, as today, by appealing to the necessity of inequality to provide incentives and to facilitate saving, all in the service of growth. The Chase Manhattan article correctly notes that without growth "any improvement in the lot of those now living at poverty levels could come only at the expense of those with higher levels of income." But to avoid facing up to the moral necessity of sharing, Chase seems willing to attempt the physical impossibility of growing forever.

If we reduce the flow of product we also will reduce the necessary input of labor. Full employment and the income-through-jobs principle of distribution will no longer be feasible. Even a constant flow of production is insufficient today to maintain full employment. Investment must bolster aggregate demand, and investment means growth. The flow of short-lived wealth, e.g. food, will have to be distributed independently of jobs as property income of some kind. A more egalitarian distribution of property rights on the total stock of wealth would be necessary.

If we can make these big adjustments in attitudes and distributive institutions, then we can imagine a number of ancillary policies for furthering the attainment of a stationary-state. Longer minimum writeoff periods for depreciation of physical assets could be imposed. This also would mean that new technologies would not be so quickly embodied, leaving more time to study their total effects and facilitating an escape from our present state of technological drivenness. Longer minimum guarantee periods on consumer durables could be made mandatory. Depletion taxes could replace depletion allowances. Consumer debt could be severely limited.

Workers could be given much more flexibility in the labor-leisure choice. The four-day or three-day week could be made an option for all. Even if a laborer chooses to get a second job instead of leisure he will have at least enriched his working hours with variety. In *spending* our incomes we have fine gradations of choice. But in *earning* his income the worker usually must choose between 40 hours per week on an assembly line or zero hours. In most instances such rigidity is not necessary. The conditions a man faces in earning his income probably have a greater effect on his welfare than the conditions he meets in spending his income. Why must they be so rigid?

The question of population

Recent studies indicate that a stable population in the U.S. might result simply from avoiding all unwanted births, by making contraceptives and voluntary abortions completely legal and easily available. Other incentive schemes for regulating population have been much discussed. In stopping population growth we reduce the problems of sharing and inequality, unlike the case of stopping growth in wealth which exacerbates these problems. Some seem to feel, therefore, that population control is in some way a stingy, selfish, niggardly policy — as Pope Paul puts it, limiting the number of guests at life's banquet rather than increasing the number of places at the table. But what kind of host keeps sending out "invitations" (to people who do not yet exist) when he cannot even feed those already at the table?

By keeping the stock of physical wealth constant we make fewer demands on our environmental resources, but in sharing the constant stock we place much heavier demands on our moral resources. Although stabilizing population will somewhat ease the problem of sharing, great moral resources are needed to achieve a stable population in the first place. Will our moral resources prove sufficient? No one knows, but even if we are doubtful it is obvious we are reaching the limit of the ability of economic growth to substitute for moral growth. One thing at least seems clear — a physically stationary economy must be a morally growing economy. If this means that economists should begin to study ethics and theology, then so be it. That is where economics began.

Chapter 6

Research for environmental management: needed knowledge

Chapter 4 described nature's closed cycles and man's open cycles, and now it is the relationship between them that is important. This chapter explores the kinship in terms of what is basic knowledge and what remains to be learned. All the articles here deal either directly or indirectly with the end problem of water pollution, but it is the research necessary to solve the problem that is under scrutiny in this chapter.

Chapter 6 is divided into two sections. The first starts with an area study, then traces material losses, both particulate and solution, from a forest through an estuary into the sink of the ocean. The second part begins with a case history and ends with the setting of high standards for environmental management.

The first article, "Stagnant Sea" by Stig H. Fonselius, gives an extremely useful picture of the Baltic Sea as it sets the basic parameters of the problem. This area has all the complications of industrial, urban, and maritime activities plus inherent limits in its own structure. It is fortunate there is data available over a rather long time span to show these effects, and the author points out the need for future study. This complex solution, however, is a question for international study, as there are seven nations on the Baltic proper, and several others close enough to affect it and be affected by it.

The next article is about the Hubbard Brook Experimental Forest in West Thornton, New Hampshire, an area maintained and operated by the U. S. Forest Service as an opportunity to experiment on an ecosystem. The authors explain the change mechanisms while demonstrating the stability of a natural environment. The editors' note at the end also shows the effects on the ecosystem of changes which produce an instability exhibited in run-off waters which then go to a river, then to an estuary, and finally to the ocean. "Suspended Matter in Surface Waters of the Atlantic Continental Margin from Cape Cod to the Florida Keys" records the path of material once it has reached the ocean. Max Blumer's article then reminds us that not all the ocean's problems arise from the land; some may originate in the sea.

The case history takes place at Galveston Bay and the first article in the second section of Chapter 6 presents proper background information. The Galveston Bay area is dominated by industry and an increasing population, a situation that threatens fisheries and recreational resources. Many state and local authorities share responsibility for the area, and the Texas Water Quality Board is organizing their efforts. This bureau has initiated an analytical study of the area, as discussed in "Systems Analysis of Galveston Bay," in an attempt to plan for future use. This method of analysis will be discussed in Chapter 7, but it is useful here to see the data available for such a study.

There are always decisions to be made in the solution of water pollution; a trade-off must be made between closed cycles and open cycles. In drawing a line between uses of the estuary which are compatible to the environment and those which are not, a management plan is necessary. There are decisions to be made; the data must be collected to make them, now.

To compound the issue, the note by M. Alexander on possible contamination from outer space indicates how difficult it will be to find information on the contact of one biosphere with another.

Even though it is less formidable — because he specifies our need for information on just this biosphere — the article by Eugene P. Odum indicates it will take a great deal of scientific progress to bring together the information ultimately needed for the job of environmental management.

STIG H. FONSELIUS
Stagnant Sea

This Baltic Sea* is a major shipping highway that serves industrial centers in Northern Europe and the U.S.S.R. Chemical and organic wastes — by-products of industrial, urban, and shipping activities — impede the life-supporting capacity of the Baltic. This threat is heightened by an influx of sewage, much of it untreated, from the millions of persons living along the coast. Modern synthetic detergents and fertilizers have contributed to a sharp rise of phosphate levels in the sea that may strain the critical oxygen balance by feeding algae which then proliferate, die, and cause oxygen depletion during decom-

Stig H. Fonselius, "Stagnant Sea," Reprinted by permission from the August issue of the magazine *Environment,* a publication of the Committee for Environmental Information. Copyright 1970 by the Committee for Environmental Information. For further information, write *Environment,* 438 North Skinker Blvd., St. Louis, Mo. 63130.
The author is Assistant Professor of chemical oceanography at the University of Gothenburg.
* A map of the Baltic is at the end of this article.

position by bacteria. Overfertilization may initially increase the number of commercially valuable fish in some areas, but the long-term result may be a reduction of oxygen that is essential to marine life.

Reduced oxygen content of shallower water already has changed the composition of marine plants and animals in some fjords and archipelagos. Sewage sediment off Gothenburg on Sweden's west coast has contributed to a decrease in the diversity of animal species. Pollution of Öresund, the sound off Copenhagen, has been marked by pollution-indicator organisms, and pollution may have impaired reproduction of certain marine species. Viruses and bacteria harmful to man have been reported in some regions.

Other pollution problems plague the 800-mile long sea. Fibers from cellulose industries suffocate bottom life and destroy fish spawning grounds. Ammunition, poison gas containers, and other military cast-offs disposed of during and after World War II foul fishing gear in the central Baltic and threaten the safety of fishermen. Mercury from compounds in pesticides, agricultural products, and paper manufacturing wastes have often built up to dangerous levels in fish and consequently have forced suspension of commercial fishing in many coastal areas. Another potentially hazardous industrial chemical, polychlorinated biphenyl, or PCB, is at high levels in Baltic fish, sea birds, and seals. DDT concentrations in the seals of the Baltic are up to ten times higher than those in their cousins in the North Sea. Local episodes of oil pollution, though so far minor, are a potentially serious threat in the confined waters of the Baltic, particularly in view of the large modern tankers scheduled to carry petroleum products there.

The pollution threat in the Baltic is similar to that in Lake Erie, although one obvious difference is the scale involved — the Baltic is fifteen times larger than Lake Erie. Another difference is a natural tendency toward stagnation in the Baltic due to heavy influx of salt water, a problem that does not occur in fresh water. This tendency means that this century's sharp decline in dissolved oxygen content in the Baltic must be ascribed to natural as well as to man-made causes. At the same time, the naturally low content of oxygen in the deep basins of the Baltic makes control of pollution even more crucial to protect its marginal life-supporting capacity.

Last year was designated "Baltic Year" to focus the attention of the scientific community on unresolved questions about the state of the sea. Another major result of such activities was a report published in February 1970 as the cooperative research effort of representatives from the seven countries bordering the Baltic. The report was prepared under the auspices of the International Council for Exploration of the Sea (ICES), an oceanographic organization with headquarters in Denmark that established a working group in 1967 to assemble scientific data on the pollution threat to the North Sea. That investigation led to a research report that identified major sources of pollution along the coasts of central and northern Europe and England. The research was carried forward by another working group established in 1969 that helped to gather data for the 1970 Report on the Baltic, entitled "Report of the ICES Working Group on Pollution of the Baltic Sea." I will describe major findings of the report in the course of this article.

STAGNANT BASINS

The Baltic is generally considered to be a stagnant basin, and there has always been an oxygen deficit in the Baltic deep water. The stratification in sediment cores from the Baltic shows dark or black bands, which indicate stagnation periods. These become more frequent towards the top of the core.

A stagnant basin is a semi-enclosed sea area with a restricted oxygen supply to the deep water. This is generally caused by narrow and shallow connections to the ocean and by the occasional or permanent existence of a light surface water layer, which isolates the deep water from oxygen exchange with the atmosphere.

Natural stagnant basins are generally found in areas with a humid climate. In such areas the annual freshwater supply through river discharge and precipitation exceeds the evaporation from the sea surface. The excess of freshwater then forms a brackish layer of light surface water, which impedes the replenishment of oxygen to the deep water by prohibiting the vertical mixing of layers. The existence of a shallow sill (a submerged ridge) in the inlet area restricts the horizontal water exchange. This gives the deep water a long residence time in the basin.

Bacteria utilize oxygen to convert dead organic material to simple inorganic compounds, carbon dioxide, water, phosphate, nitrate, and silicate. If the water exchange in the deep water is very slow and the production of living matter by small plants, or phytoplankton, in the surface layer is relatively high, the dissolved oxygen in the deep water may be completely used up because of the continuous supply of organic matter in the form of dead organisms which sink down from the surface. Then hydrogen sulfide is formed in the deep water through reduction of sulfate by anaerobic bacteria (bacteria that live in the absence of oxygen). In this process, the oxygen from the sulfate ions is used to oxidize organic matter. Ammonia and nitrogen gas are formed during the process. Due to the slow water exchange, inorganic compounds thus formed accumulate in the deep water. Therefore, the concentration of hydrogen sulfide, carbon dioxide, nitrogen, ammonia, phosphate and silicate is extremely high in stagnant basins where the oxygen has been completely exhausted. A stagnant basin thus acts as a kind of nutrient trap. Nutrients are removed from the surface area and accumulate in the stagnant deep water. In spite of the high nutrient concentration in the deep water, the surface water may have a very low nutrient content, often close to zero.

The best known stagnant basin is the Black Sea. The largest stagnant area of the world, it contains enormous amounts of hydrogen sulfide and is known to have been stagnant for at least 6,000 years. The volume of the Black Sea is approximately 538,250 cubic kilometers. The Black Sea is characterized by the absence of coastal features and by very deep shores that give it the shape of a large bowl. The maximum depth is 2,200 meters, and the average depth of the basin is 1,271 meters. The average residence time for the water of the whole Black Sea can be calculated to be around 1,350 years, being much longer in the deep water.

Stagnant basins are not very common in nature, but several Norwegian fjords (narrow inlets of the sea between high cliffs or steep slopes with shallow entrances) and similar formations in Greenland and Canada are known to be naturally stagnant. A fjord has generally a narrow and shallow sill at the entrance, a considerable water depth inside the sill, and a supply of freshwater through a river which discharges its water in the innermost part. Some fjords have an annual water exchange due to autumn storms, but there are fjords with constantly stagnant water which contain large amounts of hydrogen sulfide.

The Baltic is one of the most investigated seas of the world and has been the subject of an extremely long series of observations. Hydrographic measurements have been carried out rather regularly since the beginning of the present century. The first oxygen measurements in the deep basins of the Baltic were made during the 1890s, and from 1904 regular oxygen analyses have been carried out using the Winkler method. The work was interrupted only during the two world wars. A compilation of the results from some main stations during this period shows that the oxygen concentration of the deep water in the northern part of the Baltic proper has decreased from around three milliliters oxygen per liter of water in the beginning of the century to zero in 1969 (Fig. 1). During 1969 hydrogen sulfide was found in

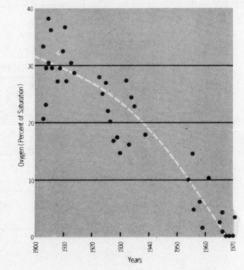

The concentration of oxygen essential to marine life has decreased near the bottom of the Northern Central basin of the Baltic from slightly over 30 percent of saturation in 1900 to zero in January 1970, as is shown in this graph. The depletion of oxygen is due to both stagnant conditions and the burden of pollutants.

Figure 1. Dissolved oxygen in the North Central Basin 1900–1970

all the main deep basins of the Baltic proper. Hydrogen sulfide formation had earlier been observed only occasionally in a few places. The first formation occurred in the large Gotland basin (see map at end of article) in 1932. The water was renewed the following year, and no new hydrogen sulfide formation was observed until after World War II. In December 1951 there occurred an unusually large inflow of salt water through the Belts (the three narrow straits leading into the Baltic). In only a few weeks, more than 200 cubic kilometers of salt water penetrated into the Baltic. This caused a long stagnation period in the Gotland basin, where the water was renewed ten years later, in 1961. The old stagnant water was spread into the deep water north of the Gotland basin, causing unusually low oxygen values in the water there. Since then, six different inflows have occurred, and some of them have been large enough to cause hydrogen sulfide formation in the Gotland basin and in others.

These stagnation periods are turning the entire deep-water area into a large oceanic desert without any kind of life except anaerobic bacteria.

The last stagnation period observed began in the middle of 1966. In 1968, all the deep basins of the Baltic proper contained hydrogen sulfide. Such an enormous hydrogen sulfide poisoning of the Baltic has never been observed in historical time, even though stagnation periods have occurred earlier in geological time in the Baltic. The water of the Baltic was again renewed during 1969 through an inflow of water from Kattegat which began in November 1968 and January 1969. In January 1970 there were only traces of hydrogen sulfide left in some of the deep basins in the northern part of the Baltic proper. The most recent measurements show that the oxygen values in the deep water of the Gotland basin are fast decreasing and that all oxygen will be used up in the near future. A new hydrogen sulfide period will then begin. It seems that the stagnation periods get more and more frequent and that the amount of hydrogen sulfide formed increases each time (see Fig. 2).

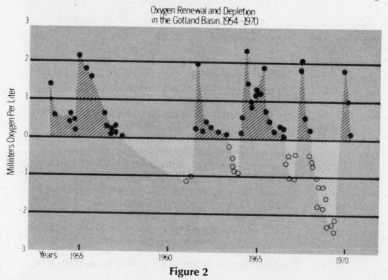

Figure 2

Under normal conditions bodies of water maintain sufficient dissolved oxygen to support ecological cycles. The Baltic, however, undergoes periods of oxygen depletion. The cycle of alternating water (and oxygen) renewal and stagnation periods in the Gotland basin from 1954 to 1970 is shown in this graph. The water renewals are expressed as oxygen increases and are indicated by the black dots and black diagonal lines. The stagnation periods are expressed as oxygen decreases followed by hydrogen sulfide formation; the hydrogen sulfide values are expressed as "negative oxygen" and are indicated on the graph by the circles and white diagonal lines. The most recent measurements show that the oxygen values in the basin's deep water are decreasing fast and have already dropped to zero in some areas. It seems that the stagnation periods are becoming more frequent and that the amount of hydrogen sulfide produced at the depth of the cycle is increasing.

A cycle of alternating stagnation periods and fertilizations has started, and it seems to be very difficult for nature to restore the normal conditions.

COMPLEX CAUSES

One may, of course, ask the reason for this development. It is known that the salinity of the Baltic has increased during the present century. This increase is a natural phenomenon and is caused by changes in the water balance of the Baltic. This may have increased the stability of the water stratification and thus decreased the water exchange through the halocline (a permanent layer which marks the beginning of an increase in salinity and which isolates deep water from the surface). It is also known that the temperature of the deep water has increased more than one degree centigrade during the same period. This has increased the oxidation rate of organic matter. It has been shown in freshwater research that a ten-degree increase of the water temperature will double the oxidation rate. Then it may be assumed that a one-degree increase in the Baltic has increased the oxidation rate by some 10 percent. The increased oxidation rate will, of course, increase the oxygen utilization in the deep water. The reason for the increased temperature is probably the observed increase of the surface temperature in the North Atlantic during the century. This increase is of climatological origin.

These two natural factors may well have caused the observed oxygen deficit in the Baltic deep water. Another phenomenon which is connected with the increased salinity is the fact that in the central Baltic the halocline during the century has risen from 80 meters below the water surface to 60 meters, increasing the volume of the deepwater body by some 200 cubic kilometers. It has also been observed that during the last fifteen years the concentration of dissolved phosphate has increased nearly three times in the deep water. This may be ascribed to the dissolution of phosphate from the sediments during reducing (oxygen consuming) conditions and to mineralization of organic phosphorus from large amounts of dead organisms sinking down from the productive layer. Fertilization and greater growth of algae caused both by natural processes and by sewage and industrial wastes in the surface layer have obviously increased the transport downward of dead matter.

THE POLLUTION PROBLEM

There are, however, other important factors which may have played a role in the eutrophication processes in the Baltic. The water exchange is slow both vertically and horizontally. One has to recall that some twenty million people live around the Baltic. The living standard is generally high, and the area is heavily industrialized. Enormous amounts of urban and industrial wastes are discharged into the Baltic.

The working group of the International Council for Exploration of the Sea made a thorough investigation of the pollution state of the Baltic as discussed above. Members of the working group were from Denmark, Finland, Poland, the Soviet Union, Sweden, and the Federal Republic of Germany. The German Democratic Republic, which is not a member of the ICES, participated as representative from the "Baltic Oceanographers." Most countries have their own methods and rules for pollution control, and it was not easy to find a commonly acceptable way to express pollution values from different countries in a comparable way. It was finally agreed to express the results as biological oxygen demand [the oxygen used by bacteria to convert organic material to inorganic substances] during five days (BOD_5). BOD_5 figures, as a rule, give only part of the real organic load carried by waste waters, and the value of BOD_5 estimations has been discussed many times. Nevertheless, these estimations are considered to give a hint of the pollution load imposed on the oxygen supply of a body of water.

The BOD_5 figures were calculated on the basic assumption of the organic load of discharged sewage per person per year. The organic load was estimated for each country as directly and indirectly (by rivers, for instance) discharged sewage. The phosphorus load of the waste water was estimated in the same way. The phosphorus content was calculated from the basic assumption that the discharge is equivalent to one kilogram per person per year.

In many cases the BOD_5 and phosphorus figures were "corrected" in relation to the degree of sewage treatment or other local circumstances known to be important for the estimations. It has to be stressed that the figures are rough approximations. This is especially true for those figures which refer to indirect discharge. The members of the committee discussed the difficulties of expressing pollution conditions in more exact ways and decided to use the figures in the report as they were. Sewage pollution and industrial pollution were estimated separately in the report.

Sewage pollution

Table 1 shows the sewage BOD_5 and phosphorus content figures for the different countries summarized for the different areas of the Baltic as indirect and direct sewage discharge.

As can be seen, the quantities of sewage discharged into the Bothnian Bay and the Bothnian Sea are small; those released into the Baltic proper, the Belt Sea, and the Kattegat are moderate. Those deposited into the Gulf of Finland and the Öresund are, however, large, due to the dense population, especially in the Leningrad and the Copenhagen-Malmö regions.

Most of the directly discharged sewage is not treated at all or undergoes only primary treatment — separation of liquids and solids. There are some biological treatment plants, but at present no treatment plants for chemical precipitation of phosphorus compounds have been built. In all countries much greater efforts have been made hitherto to avoid pollution of the inland waters.

In some countries pipelines extending out some distance from the shore have been constructed or are planned in order to protect nearshore areas from sewage pollution. The working group agreed that this is generally not a

Table 1

areas	No. of inhabitants (in millions)		BOD$_5$ Tons/year		Phos. tons/year	
	on shore	on river systems	from shore	from river systems	from shore	from river systems
Bothnian Bay	.230	.167	5,600	4,500	290	220
Bothnian Sea	.565	.495	13,650	12,200	780	600
Gulf of Finland	4.868	.797	121,450	19,200	5,050	870
Baltic Proper	3.335	2.065	60,900	30,000	3,880	2,370
Baltic Sea	8.998	3.524	201,600	65,900	9,760	4,060
Belt Sea	1.195	2.600	40,100	21,000	1,240	2,800
Öresund	1.770	.310	40,600	2,600	1,960	350
Kattegat	.625	.360	16,000	5,000	890	400
Total	12.588	6.794	298,300	94,500	13,850	7,610

good way to dispose of sewage or industrial wastes unless they are sufficiently treated beforehand. The heavy load of nutrients carried out by pipelines can eventually influence the conditions so much that they may be harmful to fisheries in areas with restricted water exchange. A number of coastal areas were found to be more or less influenced by sewage discharges, often in combination with local industrial wastes.

Heavy organic loads causing, among other things, reduced oxygen content of the water followed by changes in the marine flora or fauna, have been reported from the fjords of Schleswig-Holstein and the Bay of Lübeck in Germany, the archipelagos of Stockholm in Sweden, and Turku and Helsinki in Finland.

Even if no remarkable oxygen decrease is observed, sewage pollution may contribute to changes in the distribution of some organisms. In the heavily polluted archipelago off Gothenburg there is a good oxygen supply, but a thick sediment layer contributes to a decreased number of hard-bottom animals and the water turbidity seems to prevent the distribution of some fish species. In the same area the number of soft-bottom species has decreased, but the number of individual fish has increased.

Changes in the bottom fauna caused by pollution have been observed in many parts of the Öresund. The increase of some pollution indicator organisms, sludge worms for example, has been established. It has not been possible to show that fish, except perhaps herring, avoid the waters of Öresund, but some scientists consider the reproduction ability of some species to be reduced. The fish population, however, seems to be replenished, mainly from Kattegat.

Heavy blooms of marine algae, caused by eutrophication through pollution, have occurred in some of the coastal areas, including the archipelagos of Stockholm and Helsinki.

Viruses and bacteria harmful to man have been reported from some places. A case of an epidemic caused by an adeno virus from Stockholm sewage has been described in the scientific literature. Different microorganisms which cause epidemics — the *salmonella* species, for example, found in the Öresund area — have been shown to survive for a considerable time in the water. *Salmonella* and viruses have also been shown to be present in the water in rather large quantities in the Puck and Gdansk areas. All countries monitor the content of coliform bacteria in bathing waters.

An anaerobic bacterium, *Clostridium botulinum,* which may be common in sewage and which may render fish products toxic, has been found in both bottom sediments and fish of the Öresund.

Industrial pollution

Table 2 shows the industrial pollution of the Baltic expressed as BOD_5 values.

The coastal waters of all countries around the Baltic area are contaminated with industrial wastes, often in combination with sewage. The worst problems seem to occur on the coasts of Sweden and some of the Finnish coastal areas. This is to a great extent due to the large paper and pulp industries in these countries. The location of a large part of the Finnish paper industry in inland areas has caused severe problems for the inland waters. Plans for discharging the waste water from these industries into the Baltic through a big tunnel or through an open channel have been discussed. The paper and pulp industry along the Baltic coast in the Soviet Union is not of great importance, but it has to be remembered that large amounts of wastes from such industry are discharged into Lake Onega and Lake Ladoga. The Onega discharges into Ladoga through the Svir River, then to the Neva River, and finally to the Gulf of Finland. A great part of the Finnish paper industry discharges its wastes into the Saima water system which also discharges into Lake Ladoga. Opinions differ as to how much waste is broken down in the lakes and how much reaches the Baltic.

Liquors from pulp industries can be toxic and can also taint the flesh

Table 2

areas	BOD_5 tons/year (from shore and river systems)
Bothnian Bay	160,000
Bothnian Sea	385,000
Gulf of Finland	115,000
Baltic Proper	110,000
Baltic Sea	760,000
Belt Sea	10,000
Öresund	10,000
Kattegat	20,000
Total	800,000

of fish. Furthermore, the chemicals may interfere with the assimilation process of phytoplankton. The oxygen content of the water may also be affected since sulfite liquors may contain half of the original content of wood in solution. The breakdown of this amounts to 200 to 500 kilograms BOD_5 per ton of pulp.

Fibers from different kinds of cellulose industries are often discharged in great quantities. They accumulate on the bottom, suffocating the bottom life and destroying spawning grounds for fish. The breakdown of the fibers also contributes to the decrease of the oxygen content of the water. Several examples of this are known from the Swedish coast.

Other toxic substances from industries, such as heavy metals, cyanides, arsenic, and phenols, may be dangerous even though they are discharged in small amounts. This is especially true for almost indestructible compounds such as PCB (polychlorinated biphenyls) [see *Environment*, January-February, 1970] used, for example, in paints.

Industrial wastes have been dumped into the Baltic, but this is now avoided, especially inside territorial waters. It is known that several thousand tons of raw arsenic mixed with concrete have been dumped into the Gulf of Bothnia. Waste products containing mercury have also been dumped there. Sulfuric and hydrochloric acid and chromium compounds are also known to have been dumped into the Baltic. Furthermore, phosphorus compounds, chlorinated hydrocarbons, and heavy metals like mercury are carried through the air from industrial centers in Europe and may fall into the Baltic as dust or with rain or snow. It is believed that part of the PCB found in different offshore organisms in the Baltic is brought there through the air.

Eutrophication through pollution

The direct effect of pollution on the oxygen conditions in the Baltic probably is significant only in semi-enclosed bays and in the archipelagos. A more severe threat is the eutrophication of the surface waters by nutrients discharged in the wastes. The surface water has a very low nutrient content, and it is generally considered that phosphate is the limiting nutrient for the primary production (growth of algae) in the Baltic.

Most of the phosphorus compounds discharged into the Baltic derive from sewage. A minor part comes from industrial wastes. A rough estimation, according to some Finnish figures, suggests that the amount is a maximum of 30 percent. Therefore, most of the phosphorus is discharged in areas with a high population density.

The phosphorus figures given in Table 1 were, as was mentioned above, calculated from the basic assumption that the personal equivalent is one kilogram of phosphorus per year. The figures may be higher for some countries, and for all countries they may be increasing. In Sweden it has been estimated that sewage from communities some ten to fifteen years ago contained about 1.5 grams phosphorus per person per day and that the amount now has increased to about 4 grams per person per day. This increase is believed to depend on the increasing use of synthetic detergents, especially washing powders. These may contain up to 30 percent phosphates. The same trend has been observed in other countries. The use of phosphate-containing fertilizers in agriculture has also increased in some countries.

From Table 1 it can be seen that the total phosphorus supply from sewage and industry (excluding the Belt Sea, the Oresund, and the Kattegat) is estimated to be around 14,000 tons per year. To this amount must be added the natural amount of phosphorus in the river water (about 3,400 tons per year), the airborne phosphorus (this has been measured to be about 3,000 tons per year, a surprisingly high value), and the phosphorus brought in from Kattegat with the inflowing saline water (estimated by the author to be 6,100 tons per year). The total supply of phosphorus to the Baltic will then be 26,500 tons per year. About 8,000 to 10,000 tons are carried out from the Baltic with the outgoing surface current through the sounds. This leaves a surplus of 16,000 to 18,000 tons per year. Most of this phosphorus is taken in by organisms or is deposited directly in the neighborhood of the discharge point. In shallow areas most of the dead organic matter is included in the sediments and thus removed from the biological life cycle. Very small amounts reach the open sea areas. The effect of such eutrophication has, however, been observed in the vicinities of the large cities on the shores of the Baltic.

The increased primary production caused by this fertilization of the surface waters will be beneficial for the fisheries, as has been observed, for example, in the Gulf of Riga. It will, however, influence the deep waters in a negative way by increasing the amount of organic matter there. This may be one of the reasons for the observed increasing oxygen deficit of the deep water. The phosphorus balance of the Baltic is at present not well understood, but the very extensive data from the "Baltic Year" reports may give us a better basis for understanding.

Of the total BOD_5 load of about 1,200,000 tons per year discharged into the Baltic, 580,000 tons enter the Gulf of Bothnia. Here also many of the worst polluted coastal areas are found, especially on the Swedish side. The open parts of the Gulf of Bothnia have a generally good water circulation, and this reduces the pollution effects in the open sea. The small phosphorus supply to this area seems to be unimportant.

The BOD_5 load of the Gulf of Finland is higher than that of the Baltic proper, and in both areas the phosphorus supply has a considerable influence in the coastal areas. The open sea may also be influenced to some degree. In the Belt area and the Öresund, the phosphorus values are higher than in the open sea. It has been shown that the phosphate values of the deep water of the Öresund have increased during the last decades; and a slightly increasing oxygen deficit has been observed there. There are also some signs of the same trend in the Kattegat, but the observations are too few to allow any direct conclusions.

There are a few biological waste-treatment plants around the Baltic, and several are planned. There are, however, no chemical precipitation plants for removing nutrients from the waste water being built or planned. Attempts have been made to replace the phosphate in washing powders by other substances such as nitrilo-tri-acetic acid (NTA). It is, however, not known if NTA may have unknown harmful effects. Extensive research is being carried out on that problem in the Federal Republic of Germany and in Sweden.

Pesticides

Pesticides are used in agriculture, horticulture, forestry, and the textile industry. In the paper and pulp industry, pesticides are used as slimicides and pre-
servatives. DDT probably is still the most used pesticide in the world, despite
increased restrictions. DDT is found in the air and in the thin surface film on
natural waters which consists of fats produced by planktonic organisms.
Through turbulence it is spread downward. It may affect primary production
by inhibiting the photosynthetic assimilation process of phytoplankton.

Chlorinated hydrocarbons such as DDT are soluble in fat and are only
slowly destroyed through oxidation. Therefore, they tend to accumulate in
tissues of living organisms, especially in the fat.

In Sweden, Dr. S. Jensen and his co-workers in 1966 found a formerly
undetected chlorinated hydrocarbon by analyzing trace substances in biological material. This hydrocarbon was a form of polychlorinated biphenyl
(PCB). It was found together with DDT, but it seems to be even more persistent than DDT. Analysis of tissues of marine organisms, mussels, herring,
plaice, picked dogfish, cod, salmon, grey seal, common seal, ringed seal,
guillemot, white-tailed eagle, and heron have shown that organisms from the
Baltic contain eight to ten times higher concentrations of PCB and DDT
than organisms from the Swedish west coast (Kattegat) or from England or
Canada. The eagles (all found dead) contained concentrations 100 times
higher than those found in eagles caught in northern Sweden (Lappland).
The eagles in the Lappland area generally build their nests on the Norwegian
north coast.

The investigation of the Baltic shows that the concentration of DDT
and PCB increases along the food chain and that the animals on the top of
the food chain therefore have the highest concentrations. Since many of the
animals investigated were caught in the open sea, there must be a transport
of pesticides and other toxic substances from land to the open sea. The concentration of chlorinated hydrocarbons seems to be ten times higher in the
Baltic water than in the waters of Kattegat and Skagerrak. The reason for this
certainly is the restricted water exchange through the Danish sounds. The
chlorinated hydrocarbons are brought to the Baltic in river water and through
direct fallout from the air.

Mercury compounds have shown the same tendency to accumulate in
the food chain. Such compounds have been used as pesticides in the agriculture of some countries. In Sweden and Finland they have also been widely
used as slimicides and fungicides in the paper and pulp industry. Wastes containing mercury also derive from many industries, from the burning of household wastes, and from other processes. Some of the mercury wastes themselves are toxic to living organisms. Others may be transformed by organisms
into more toxic forms.

Considerable amounts of mercury have already accumulated in nature.
In many Swedish inland waters and coastal areas the concentrations in fish
are so high that these areas have been closed to fishing. Fish caught from
such areas may not be sold or given to other persons as gifts. The fishermen
themselves are, however, allowed to eat the fish at their own risk. The

threshold value lies at one milligram mercury per kilogram of wet fish weight. About a dozen of the prohibited areas lie in the coastal zones.

It seems that mercury pollution is more restricted to coastal areas than DDT and PCB pollution. German investigations of cod from the open Baltic do not show unusually high concentrations. The use of mercury compounds is now to a great extent forbidden in Finland and in Sweden. New substances have therefore been introduced in the paper and pulp industry. At least one of them (pentachlor phenol) has been shown to have adverse effects on fish, however.

Oil pollution

The oil pollution problem is becoming serious in the Baltic. The oil tanker traffic increases every year, and the tankers are bigger. The seventeen-meter sill of the Baltic limits the size of the tankers to a little more than 100,000 tons, but plans have been discussed to deepen the sill area in order to admit bigger tankers. Most tanker routes go to Danish, Finnish, and Swedish ports. Accidents involving oil tankers have been rare, but the damages of such accidents may be disastrous in narrow waterways. However, illegal flushing of tanks in the open sea and dumping of oil from smaller ships are the main sources of oil pollution in the Baltic. Some oil prospecting has been carried out in the Baltic area, but without success. Some small oil pollution problems exist around areas where oil shale ("burning stone") is exploited in Estonia. Sweden has several refineries in the Baltic area, but most of the other Baltic countries have none.

As an example of the problem from chronic oil pollution, 125 oil discharges from ships are known to have occurred during 1968 along the coasts of Sweden. These originated both from tankers and cargo ships. Even if most of them were rather small, they caused considerable damage to beaches, fishing gear, and marine life. It has been shown that marine algae are very sensitive to oil and oil products, which may cause death of the algae or retardation of cell division.

Radioactive pollution

Radioactive wastes have been dumped into the Baltic, but nowadays the control is rigorous and no dumping seems to occur. The Baltic has, of course, been polluted by radioactive fallout. A slight increase of some radioactive compounds has been reported by Finnish scientists.

The construction of nuclear power plants going on or planned in the Baltic area will cause the release of small additional amounts of radioactive matter. Control measures will, of course, be very stringent, but it has to be remembered that leakages may accidentally occur even if authorities do not admit to such possibilities. Nuclear ships, both submarines and surface vessels, may be a potential danger. If a large leakage occurs in the Baltic, marine life may be damaged for several decades.

Pollution by cooling water from nuclear power plants or from power plants using fossil fuels may cause unpredictable damages. The cooling water will be warmed about 10 degrees C. In Sweden some ten nuclear plants are planned during the next 25 years. Every plant will be using 39,600 gallons of water per second. If it is assumed that the other countries build altogether at least ten plants during the same period, the amount of cooling water will be equal to 20 percent of the freshwater supply from the rivers. The effect on the temperature of the Baltic as a whole will be negligible, but in the vicinities of the plants, the warm water will increase the oxidation rate of organic matter. This may cause oxygen deficits in these areas.

Pollution through wars

During the world wars hundreds of thousands of mines were laid out by the fighting powers and the neutral states. The mines from World War II, especially the magnetic mines, are still a great danger for shipping outside the swept channels. Mine accidents are still known to happen occasionally in the entrance to the Baltic. Drifting mines are not uncommon in Kattegat. More than a hundred ships have been destroyed by mines in the southern Baltic, the Belts, and Kattegat since the war. During the summer of 1969, five mines were found on the Swedish west coast. A Danish fishing vessel was destroyed by a mine almost in sight of the ferries between Rödby and Puttgarden in August 1969. Another problem is that oil leaking from the German cruiser Blücher, sunk in the Oslo fjord, is now a threat to the shores in the Dröbak area.

After World War II ammunition and war gas containers and other kinds of German war material were dumped into the Bornholm basin and other places in the southern Baltic by the Allied occupation forces. Fishermen who have caught corroded mustard gas containers in their trawls have been severely injured. Several such accidents happened during 1969, and one occurred this year. The containers are dragged by the trawls, and when they are discovered, they are generally dumped on the spot where they are found. Other fishermen may them drag them farther away, spreading them over large areas. It has been estimated that around 20,000 tons of mustard gas have been dumped into the Baltic.

Pollution by ships

The ship traffic among the Baltic countries is considerable. The traffic in the Danish waters and in the Öresund is especially heavy. Other areas with concentrated traffic are the ferry routes between Gothenburg and Frederikshavn in Kattegat and between Sweden and Finland in the Åland Sea. It is estimated that more than twenty million passengers travel across the Öresund every year. During the summer season some 500 passenger ships cruise in the Baltic area yielding between 250 to 400 cubic meters of waste per day. Dumping of garbage from the regular ferry boats is forbidden, but in spite of this I have personally seen it happen several times. Garbage is, of course, also dumped from cargo ships and from all kinds of smaller vessels such as fishing boats, motor boats, and sailing yachts.

CONTROL OF WATER POLLUTION

In all Baltic countries there are laws against water pollution. The control is exercised by special national or regional authorities. As a rule the general trend in all countries is to try to prevent the pollution from damaging the environment too seriously. For the most part, however, there is either no or only primary treatment of the sewage and industrial wastes which are discharged into the sea. All of the countries are trying to strengthen the control of coastal pollution. Dumping of wastes from ships, except mud dumping from harbors and treatment plants, is forbidden or at least not recommended within the territorial waters of any of the countries.

The discharge of wastes harmful to the open sea is prohibited from Finnish territory or Finnish ships in accordance with the 1958 Geneva Convention (approved by the U.N. Conference on the Law of the Sea). This convention will probably be ratified in Denmark and the Federal Republic of Germany in the near future. In Germany the discharge of wastes outside territorial waters is now subject only to voluntary control.

All countries except the U.S.S.R. and the German Democratic Republic have ratified the London Oil Pollution Convention. The U.S.S.R. has some special rules for avoiding oil pollution within 50 miles from the coast. The German Democratic Republic uses rules similar to those of the convention.

International research collaboration

Pollution research is carried out in all the countries. International collaboration in the hydrographical and biological field is carried out through different international organizations, such as the International Council for Exploration of the Sea, the Intergovernmental Oceanographic Commission, the Intergovernmental Maritime Consultative Organization, the International Atomic Energy Commission, and others. Important local organizations also carry out pollution research. In the hydrographical field the "Baltic Oceanographers" have worked since 1957. The "Baltic Biologists" was established some years ago. There are also several more local organizations: the Committee on Pollution of the Öresund (Denmark and Sweden), the Committee on Pollution of the Gulf of Finland (Finland and U.S.S.R.), and others.

It is realized that the pollution problems of the Baltic cannot be solved by one country alone. All countries must cooperate in an effort to stop the contamination.

There have been some more or less fanciful suggestions in newspapers about the pollution problems, especially on how to improve the water circulation. It has been suggested that deepening the sills in the entrance area, by using nuclear power, for example, would give a better water exchange through the sounds. The sill area at Darss is very large, and the difficulties would be enormous. It is not at all certain that such an enterprise would improve the conditions. There is a possibility that the salinity of the deep water would increase, thereby increasing the vertical stratification. Another idea is to close the sounds by locks, transforming the whole Baltic to a freshwater lake. This lake could then be used as a freshwater reservoir for Europe. Since the shipping in the sounds is among the densest in the world, however, locks would cause enormous delays for ship traffic. Freshwater freezes more easily than salt water, and freshwater ice is much harder than the porous seawater ice. This may shorten the sailing period and make the ice more compact, causing enormous costs to the shipping industry. There are, of course, also political aspects of such a project. For example, limitations on free and uncontrolled passage through the sound by warships certainly will not be accepted by all countries.

All countries are aware of the pollution problem, and all agree that something has to be done. It is, however, not easy for the scientists to give recommendations which can be accepted by all of the governments. It is not possible to stop all contamination; the costs for communities and industries would be too high. Much can be done, but we do not know enough about the water exchange through the Danish sounds to be able to tell if the oxygen situation in the deep water really will improve if the organic load and the fertilization are diminished. What proportion of the present situation in the deep water is caused by human activity and what part by natural processes? We hope to be able to answer this important question in the near future.

PROFILE OF THE BALTIC

The Baltic separates Scandinavia from the European continent. The entrance to the Baltic is formed by the broad straits of Skagerrak and Kattegat. Skagerrak separates Norway from Denmark. Its continuation, Kattegat, separates Sweden from Denmark. From Kattegat three narrow straits — Lille Belt, Store Belt, and Öresund — lead into the southern end of the Baltic proper. In the northern part of the sea, three large gulfs extend far inland. The Gulf of Bothnia lies between Sweden and Finland; the Gulf of Finland separates Finland from the Estonian Soviet Republic; and the Gulf of Riga thrusts between Estonia and the Latvian Soviet Republic. The distance from the mouth of the Skagerrak at the boundary of the North Sea to the city of Tornio in the northernmost part of the Gulf of Bothnia is about 1,500 miles. The surface area of the Baltic is about 374,000 square kilometers, including Skagerrak and Kattegat.

The Baltic proper is surrounded by seven countries: Denmark, Sweden, Finland, the Soviet Union, Poland, The German Democratic Republic (East Germany), and The Federal Republic of Germany (West Germany). Southern Norway borders on the Skagerrak. Large cities are located in the Baltic area. Oslo, the capital of Norway, lies on the Skagerrak. Gothenburg, the largest port of Sweden, is on the Kattegat. Cophenhagen, the capital of Denmark, lies on the Öresund. The German cities of Kiel, Lübeck and Rostock are also located in the entrance area to the Baltic. At the shores of the Baltic proper and its large gulfs we find the capitals of Sweden and Finland, Stockholm and Helsinki, Leningrad (with a population of more than four million), Tallinn, Riga, Gdansk, and Gdynia. More than 50 smaller cities are located along the coasts.

Many of the coastal areas are heavily industrialized. The coasts of the Baltic with large archipelagos, river mouth, gulfs and bays make for excellent

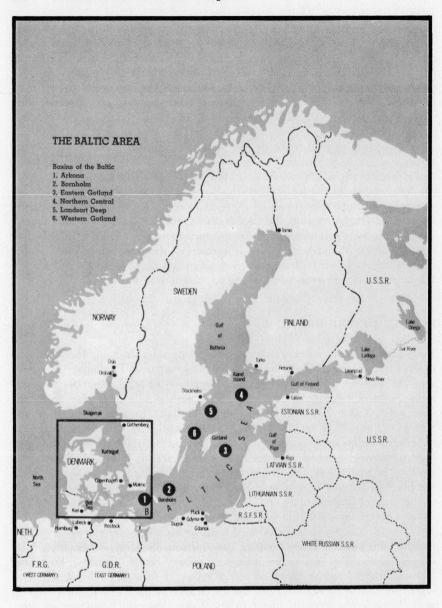

THE BALTIC AREA

Basins of the Baltic
1. Arkona
2. Bornholm
3. Eastern Gotland
4. Northern Central
5. Landsort Deep
6. Western Gotland

harbors, and the shipping in the Baltic plays a very important role in the economies of the surrounding countries. Ship traffic in the Danish sounds is among the densest in the world. It has been estimated that nearly twenty million people live around the Baltic in the coastal areas.

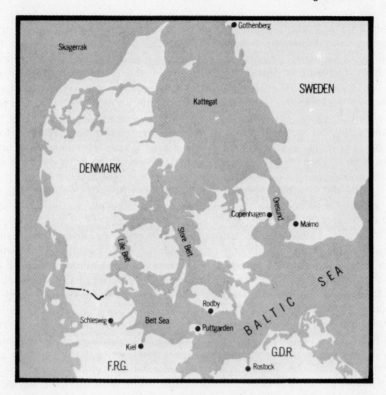

The Baltic is basically shaped like a fjord, which is a narrow inlet between steep ridges with a shallow entrance. The main difference is that the
Baltic is a shallow sea with an average depth of only 60 meters. Therefore the
water volume is only around 22,000 cubic kilometers in spite of the large
surface area of 366,000 square kilometers inside the entrance sills (submerged
ridges). The average river discharge to the Baltic is 472 cubic kilometers per
year, and the average precipitation 200 cubic kilometers per year. The annual
evaporation over the surface is estimated to be close to 200 cubic kilometers.
This gives a net freshwater supply of nearly 500 cubic kilometers per year. The
water of the Baltic is brackish, and therefore there must be a transport of salt
water into the Baltic. This inflow has been computed to be also about 500
cubic kilometers per year. In order to keep the water level of the Baltic constant, the annual excess of water, about 1,000 cubic kilometers, must flow out
through the Danish sounds. These are narrow and shallow. The sill depth to
the Baltic at Darss is only seventeen meters. The outflowing water forms a
surface current called the "Baltic Current" which in Kattegat follows the
Swedish coast, and in Skagerrak the Norwegian coast. Large amounts of salt
water flow into the Baltic below the surface current at Darss. The Baltic therefore has a light surface water layer with a low salinity. The salinity in the

central Baltic is about .7 percent by weight, and the thickness of the surface layer is about 60 meters. Below that layer, the deep water of the Baltic has a salinity of between 1.0 and 1.3 percent and a low oxygen concentration. Although the Baltic is nearly a stagnant basin, the small volume of the deep water (3,500 to 4,000 cubic kilometers) makes it possible for the water to be renewed occasionally. The residence time of the water in the Baltic as a whole is about 22 years. The oxygen content of the deep water is, however, constantly low, but generally hydrogen sulfide is not formed there due to the occasional renewals of the deep water. These renewals are caused by unusually large inflows of salt water along the bottom of the Belts over the sill at Darss.

The topography of the Baltic shows a series of basins connected to each other over shallower sills. The main basins are: the Arkona basin, indicated on the map as (1), at the entrance area west of the island of Bornholm (maximum depth 55 meters) and the Bornholm basin (2) east of Bornholm (maximum depth 105 meters). The sill connecting them is located between Bornholm and the Swedish coast (sill depth 45 meters). East of the Bornholm basin, the large central basin of the Baltic proper begins. The sill depth at the Slupsk Furrow is 60 meters. The central basin may be divided into three main parts. The eastern Gotland basin (3) extends from the Gdansk Deep between the Baltic coast and the island of Gotland. The maximum depth is 249 meters at the Gotland Deep half way between Ostergarn on Gotland and Ventspils in Latvia. This basin is connected to the northern central basin (4) over a 115 meter deep sill. The northern Central basin extends from Hogland in the Gulf of Finland to Landsort at the Swedish coast. There the Landsort Deep (5), the deepest spot of the Baltic, is located (459 meters). South of the Landsort Deep, a 100 meter sill leads into the western Gotland basin (6) (maximum depth 205 meters) located between Gotland and the Swedish coast. Between the southern tip of Gotland and the island of Öland, the water depth decreases to below 50 meters. The Gulf of Bothnia is separated from the Baltic proper through a 40-meter-deep ridge extending between Sweden and the southern part of the Åland archipelago.

When heavy salt water enters over the sill at Darss, it follows the deepest channels along the bottom of the Baltic proper. The Arkona basin is first filled up to the depth of the sill at the Bornholm basin. When the Bornholm basin is filled to the 60 meter level, the salt water may enter the eastern Gotland basin. The deep water thus circulates counter-clockwise around Gotland. The deep water in the western Gotland basin has therefore moved around Gotland and has entered into the basin from the north through the Landsort Deep. No deep water can enter into the Gulf of Bothnia due to the shallow sill at Åland. The deep water is slowly diluted, and the salinity decreases from 1.5 to 1.8 percent in the southern part to 1.0 percent in the western Gotland basin. There the last remains of the inflow are mixed into the surface layer. Due to the great difference in salinity between the surface water and the deep water, a very stable permanent halocline is formed in the Baltic proper. The halocline is a permanent layer that marks the beginning of a sharp, stepwise increase in salinity with depth. It is an impediment to the mixing and effectively isolates the deep water from the surface. Therefore the deep water cannot renew its oxygen content, and the oxygen concentration decreases rapidly and may be close to zero in the bottom water of the Bornholm basin. This is due to the fact that the inflowing water occasionally may be so heavy that it remains for a long time in the basin. The next inflow may consist of water with a lower density. In that case it may float over the heavy bottom water directly to the next basin. If the bottom water stays long enough in the basin, it may completely lose its oxygen and hydrogen sulfide may be formed there. Through diffusion and turbulence in the boundary layer, the density eventually decreases so much that a new inflow may expel the old water from the basin. The hydrogen sulfide disappears and the oxygen concentration increases in the deep basin.

The old water from the basin is displaced northward into the area north of Gotland and from there to the Gulf of Finland and the western Gotland basin. If the water contains hydrogen sulfide, it will react with the oxygen of the water it is mixing into. Therefore the oxygen values will decrease in the northern parts of the Baltic. If the hydrogen sulfide concentration of the expelled water is high, all oxygen in the northern Baltic deep water will be used up in the deepest parts and hydrogen sulfide will be found there. If the inflow is great enough to renew the deep water of the whole Baltic proper, the hydrogen sulfide will, of course, eventually disappear through reacting oxygen below the halocline. No hydrogen sulfide will reach the surface layer.

During stagnant conditions nutrients will accumulate in the stagnant water. These nutrients originate from decaying organic matter. A part of these nutrients is deposited into the bottom sediments. When hydrogen sufide is formed close to the bottom, these nutrients will dissolve in the water, increasing the nutrient concentration of the stagnant water still more.

When the water of the basins is renewed, the nutrients are spread out in the deep water and eventually they are mixed up into the surface water during the winter, when the vertical convection mixes the whole surface layer. This causes an enormous fertilization of the surface water. During the spring, the phytoplankton bloom will increase to a corresponding degree. This again will increase the transport of dead organic matter to the deep water. The oxygen of the deep water will be used up quickly, and hydrogen sulfide will soon be formed close to the bottom. Again nutrients will be accumulated through dissolution from the sediments and mineralization of organic matter in the water. Thus, alternating periods of hydrogen sulfide and oxygen will occur in the deep basins. The hydrogen sulfide periods will become more prolonged until a steady state is reached. This serious development seems to be occurring in the Baltic, at present, as all observations indicate.

Notes

285. "... *inflow* ... *500 cubic kilometers*...." Brogmus, W., "Eine Revision des Wasserhaushaltes der Ostsee," Kieler Meeresforschungen IX, 1., 1952.

286. "... *40 meter-deep ridge* ... *Åland archipelago*." Ibid.

"... *sill at Darss*." Fonselius, S. H., "Hydrography of the Baltic Deep Basins III," Fishery Board of Sweden, Series Hydrography, nr. 23, 1969.

287. "... *hyrogen sulfide is formed close to the bottom* ... *increasing the nutrient concentration*...." Ibid.

"... *hydrogen sulfide periods* ... *steady state is reached*." "On the Stagnant

Conditions in the Baltic," Abstract of Gothenburg Dissertations in Science, nr. 14, 1969.

270. *". . . the concentration of hydrogen sulfide . . . oxygen has become completely exhausted."* Richards, F. A., "Anoxic Basins and Fjords," Chemical Oceanography, J. P. Riley and G. Skirrow, ed., Academic Press, London and New York, 1965.

". . . Black Sea . . . naturally stagnant basin." Caspers, H., "The Black Sea," Treatise on Marine Ecology and Paleoecology, J. W. Hedgpeth, ed., Geol. Soc. America, Memoir 67, 1957.

271. *". . . water was renewed ten years later, in 1961."* "Hydrography of the Baltic Deep Basins I," Fishery Board of Sweden, Series Hydrography, nr. 13, 1962.

272. *". . . January 1970 . . . only traces of hydrogen sulfide. . . ."* "On the Stagnation and Recent Turnover of the Water in the Baltic," Tellus, 1970 (in press).

273. *". . . alternating stagnation periods and fertilizations has started. . . ."* Fonselius, "On the Stagnant Conditions in the Baltic," loc. cit.

". . . one-degree increase . . . has increased the oxidation rate some 10 percent." Kullenberg, G., "On the Oxygen Deficit in the Baltic Deep Water," 7th Conference of the Baltic Oceanographers, Helsinki, May 11–15th, 1970.

". . . increased the transport downward of dead matter." Fonselius, "Hydrography of the Baltic Deep Basins III," loc. cit.

274. *". . . representative from the 'Baltic Oceanographers.' "* International Council for Exploration of the Sea (ICES), "Report of the ICES Working Group on Pollution of the Baltic Sea," Cooperative Research Report, Series A, B. Oybern, ed., no. 15, 1970.

"Table 1. . . ." Ibid.

276. *"Table 2. . . ."* Ibid.

277. *". . . phosphate is the limiting nutrient for the primary production. . . ."* Fonselius, "Hydrography of the Baltic Deep Basins III," loc. cit.

278. *"The total supply of phosphorus . . . 26,500 tons per year. . . ."* Ibid.

". . . increased primary production . . . Gulf of Riga." Lishev, M. N., "Stocks of Baltic Herring in the Gulf of Riga and Prospects for their Utilization 1965–1967," Fish. Res. in the Baltic Coll. 1, Riga, 1966, (in Russian).

". . . signs of the same trend in the Kattegat. . . ." Corin, C., S. H. Fonselius and A. Svansson, "On the Oxygen and Phosphate Conditions in the Kattegat and Öresund 1900–1968," Meddel. Havsfiskelaboratoriet, Lysekil, nr. 62, 1969.

279. *". . . Jensen and his co-workers. . . ."* Jensen, S., A. G. Johnels, M. Olsson and G. Otterlind, "DDT and PCB in Marine Environment," Fauna och Flora 4, 1969, (in Swedish).

F. H. BORMANN, G. E. LIKENS & J. S. EATON

Biotic Regulation of Particulate and Solution Losses from a Forest Ecosystem

Major losses of nutrients from terrestrial ecosystems results from two processes: particulate matter removal accomplished by erosion and transportation in surface drainage water, and solution removal accomplished by dissolution and transportation of solutes by surface and subsurface drainage water. Not only is knowledge of these two types of removal processes important to our understanding of nutrient-energy relationships of the terrestrial ecosystem but it is basic to our understanding of the relationships between interconnected terrestrial and lotic ecosystems. In a larger sense, this information contributes to a more detailed understanding of fluvial denudation of the landscape and the relative importance of removal of solutes and particulate matter in this basic geological phenomenon.

Solution removal occurs in both surface and subsurface drainage water while particulate matter removal is primarily restricted to surface drainage. Consequently, changes within an ecosystem in the relative amounts of surface and subsurface water shift the relative importance of particulate and solution removal. This consideration is of fundamental ecological importance since the relative importance of subsurface drainage often increases as ecological succession proceeds and since human manipulations may shift the pattern of movement in either direction with consequent effects on nutrient removal patterns.

Despite the obvious importance of these processes, we have, with a few exceptions (e.g., Crisp, 1966), little information on the quantitative importance of solution and particulate matter removal as nutrient and energy stripping

F. H. Bormann, G. E. Likens, and J. S. Eaton, "Biotic Regulation of Particulate and Solution Losses from a Forest Ecosystem," *Bioscience*, vol. 19, no. 1 (July 1969), pp. 600–610. Reprinted by permission.

Dr. Bormann is a professor in the School of Forestry, Yale University. Dr. Likens was an Associate Professor and Mr. Eaton a Research Assistant in the Department of Biological Science, Dartmouth College; they are now in the Division of Biological Sciences, Cornell University.

This is contribution No. 9 of the Hubbard Brook Ecosystem Study. Financial support was provided by National Science Foundation Grants GB1144, GB4169, GB6742, and GB6757. Published as a contribution to the U. S. Program of the International Biological Program and the International Hydrological Decade.

This work was done through the cooperation of the N. F. Forest Experiment Station, Upper Darby, Pa. We gratefully acknowledge the use of hydrologic data provided by the Northeastern Forest Experiment Station, USDA Forest Service, chemical data provided by B. Hobbie and D. Fisher, and T. Siccama for important contributions to the mathematical and computational aspects of this study. We appreciate criticisms and comments from N. M. Johnson, R. S. Pierce, and M. Gordon Wolman.

agencies in small ecosystems (i.e., first or second order drainage basins by our definition, Bormann and Likens, 1967). According to Leopold et al. (1964), there are few quantitative data on how the interplay between these processes in first order watersheds is affected by variation in the hydrologic cycle or by natural or man-induced changes in the structure of the biological fraction of the ecosystem.

The functions of this paper are: (1) to discuss the comparative role of solution and particulate matter losses in the nutrient economy of a small undisturbed forested watershed-ecosystem, (2) to examine the effect of variations in the hydrologic cycle on these relationships, and (3) to evaluate the effect of biota on the nutrient-hydrologic interaction.

This study is based on data obtained by measuring solution and particulate matter losses in a small gaged watershed (Bormann and Likens, 1967) in the Hubbard Brook Experimental Forest in West Thornton, New Hampshire. The period reported here covers 2 water years (a water year begins after spring runoff and ends one year later) from 1 June 1965 to 31 May 1967.

Watershed 6, 13.23 ha, is underlain by till of varying thickness and gneiss of the Littleton Formation (Billings 1956: Johnson et al., 1968) and is covered by well developed northern hardwood forest dominated by sugar maple (*Acer saccharum*), beech (*Fagus grandifolia*), and willow birch (*Betula alleghanenses*). Additional details on the site, its biology, ecology, hydrology, and climate are given in Likens et al. (1967).

The watershed-ecosystem covers 245 m of elevation and has an average slope of about 26% (Fig. 1). Because of the high porosity of the soils and the unfrozen conditions of the soils in the winter (Likens et al., 1967), there is

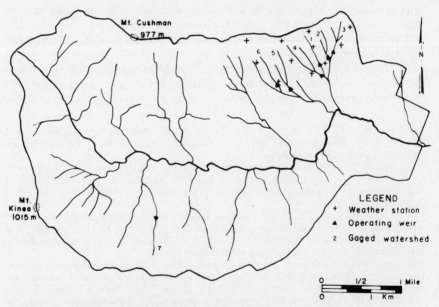

Figure 1. Outline map of the Hubbard Brook Experimental Forest showing location of gaged watersheds, weirs, and weather stations

very little surface runoff over most of the watershed. Except for minor surface flow during the periods of very high runoff, most water percolates into the soil and moves laterally as subsurface flow to the stream channel. The watershed is drained by a first order stream with one intermittent branch (Wisler and Brater, 1965) and has a total channel length of approximately 800 m. The streambed, at bank-full water levels, occupies 1.4% of the area of the watershed and is characterized by a profusion of boulders and cobbles and sizable accumulations of organic debris. Debris dams formed by leaves layered over twigs, branches, or stones create many small pools, approximately one every 1 to 5 m of streambed.

Since deep seepage is not a factor in this watershed (Likens, et al., 1967), all of the water draining from this watershed is measured by a combination San Dimas flume and a 90° V-notch weir anchored in the bedrock (Fig. 2). The flume records stage heights during high flows, while the V-notch records lower flows. At the very highest flow, the water jet from the flume will partially clear the raceway leading to the stilling or ponding basin and thus short circuit the V-notch weir. This did not occur during the water year 1965–66, but it did occur twice during 1966–67. However, the flume minimizes turbulence and heavier materials moving as bed load in the lower half of the water column are probably deposited in the raceway. A supplementary barrier of hardware cloth below the flume structure partially traps material that clears the raceway during very high flows.

Annual precipitation, measured by a network of gages, was 125 cm and 133 cm, while runoff for W-6 was 76 cm and 85 cm in 1965–66 and 1966–67,

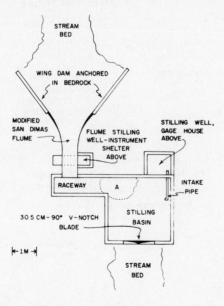

Figure 2.   Diagram of combination San Dimas flume and V-notch blade. The letter "A" shows the principal site of accumulation of inorganic material within the stilling or ponding basin

respectively. The 1965–66 figures are close to the 8-year average for small watersheds of Hubbard Brook, while 1966–67 would be considered a wet year (Likens et al., 1967).

Solution losses in the drainage water consist of ions essential to the metabolism of the biota, nonessential ions, nonionized inorganic compounds, and dissolved organic matter. Particulate matter losses consist of an organic and an inorganic fraction. The organic fraction (consisting of wood, twigs, leaves, bark, fruit, bud scales, invertebrate animals, etc., in all stages of disintegration) represents losses of nutrients and energy tied up in organic compounds. The inorganic fraction may be composed of cobbles, pebbles, granules, or smaller size classes of native rock or weathered fractions such as quartz sand, mica flakes, etc. These output relationships, showing the origin of output in various compartments of the ecosystem, are summarized in Figure 3.

Solution losses are measured following the procedures of Likens et al. (1967) and Fisher et al. (1968). A streamwater sample is collected each week and analyzed for $Ca++$, $Mg++$, $Na+$, $K+$, $Al+++$, NH_4+, $Cl-$, NO_3-, SO_4-, HCO_3-, and SiO_2. Concentration data are fed into a computing system where they are multiplied by the volume of streamflow recorded during the sampling period. This system provides weekly, monthly, and yearly estimates of losses of each substance in terms of kilogram per hectare of watershed-ecosystem. Four years of data covering six small watersheds have been reported (Likens et al., 1967; Johnson et al., 1968; Fisher et al., 1968).

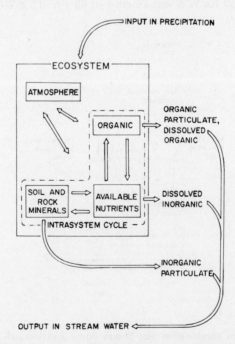

Figure 3. Model showing sites of accumulation and pathways of nutrients in the Hubbard Brook Ecosystem. Model is primarily applicable to elements with sedimentary cycles

Particulate matter is lost from the watershed as suspended load carried by turbulent water and as bed load rolled, bounced, and slid along the stream-bed. All of the bed load and part of the suspended load drops in the settling basin behind the weir (Figs. 2, 4) where the stream loses much of its velocity, or into the barrier constructed to handle exceptional flows. The remaining suspended load is carried over the weir and out of the basin.

Collections of particulate matter in the settling basin are made periodically when the stream is diverted around the weir. Water in the basin is drained through a 1-mm mesh nylon bag, and the remaining debris is removed from the basin. Material from the basin may be collected in two piles. One is composed almost wholly of inorganic debris which settled out at the junction of the flume race and the settling basin (Fig. 2), while the other pile is a mixture of organic and inorganic debris distributed throughout the basin. Occasionally, the collection is limited to a single, small organic-inorganic pile.

If the piles are relatively small, the entire collection is removed to the laboratory for dry and ash weight analysis. This was done for all samples collected during water year 1965–66. If a pile is too large for expeditious handling, its wet weight and volume are obtained in the field by weighing known volumes with a chatillon spring balance. A representative subsample is removed, its wet weight obtained, and transported to the lab for further analyses. Data from 23 September 1966 are based on a 100% sample of the inorganic pile and a 26% sample of the organic-inorganic pile. Data from 16 November 1966 are based on a 100% collection of the inorganic pile and a 13% sample of the organic-inorganic pile. Data for June, 1967, are based on a 100% sample of the inorganic pile and six proportional subsamples (28%) of the organic-inorganic pile. Oven dry weights of total output for each period and various hydrologic data characterizing the period are given in Table 1.

The organic-inorganic material consists of an organic component of leaves, leaf fragments, twigs, small branches, bark, fruits, invertebrates, and other material interspersed with primary and secondary mineral matter. The

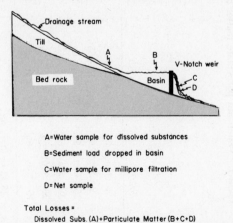

A = Water sample for dissolved substances
B = Sediment load dropped in basin
C = Water sample for millipore filtration
D = Net sample

Total Losses =
Dissolved Subs. (A) + Particulate Matter (B + C + D)

Figure 4. Sampling procedure employed in the study of dissolved and particulate matter losses from a watershed-ecosystem showing the points at which samples are taken

Table 1. Water and particulate matter output and flow rates associated with various ponding basin collections, Watershed 6

	Collection period			Water output		Particulate matter output			Flow rate		
	Start	Finish	Days	10^6 liters	% of Total	Kg	% of Total	Kg output per 10^6 liters	Av. c.f.s.	Highest av. daily c.f.s.	Highest av. c.f.s. for 12 consecutive hr.
(a)	1 June 65	9 Sept 65	101	4.81	2.3	7.6	1.7	1.59	0.02	0.53	1.16
(b)	9 Sept 65	26 Oct 65	47	12.47	6.0	10.8	2.4	0.87	0.11	0.88	1.82
(c)	26 Oct 65	19 May 66	205	76.83	37.0	33.0	7.3	0.43	0.15	1.38	1.74
(d)	19 May 66	23 Sept 66	127	16.70	8.0	20.5	4.5	1.23	0.05	0.68	1.05
(e)	23 Sept 66	16 Nov 66	54	22.17	10.7	324.6	71.4	14.64	0.17	2.88	4.29
(f)	16 Nov 66	2 June 67	198	74.70	36.0	58.2	12.8	0.78	0.15	2.36	2.83

a c.f.s. $\times$ 28.32 = liters/sec.

occurrence of clay-sized particles is negligible as evidenced by the clarity of stream water (Hellige turbidity measurements range from 0 to 0.52 American Public Health Association turbidity units) and by the minor occurrence of clay in the soils of the watershed (B horizon contains 4 to 8% clay). To separate the organic and inorganic contributions, a collection was thoroughly mixed, halved through a riffle, one-half randomly selected, halved again, etc., until a 150-cm³ subsample was drawn. A minimum of eight 150-cm³ subsamples was taken from each collection. The oven-dry weight of each subsample was obtained at 105 C and it was ashed at 500 C + 30 C. Since these samples contained negligible amounts of clay, loss-on-ignition approximates loss of weight due to combustion of organic matter (Wilde et al., 1964).

To calculate the oven-dry weight of organic matter prior to ashing, it is necessary to add to loss-on-ignition the weight of ash attributable to the organic matter. The average ash weight of "clean" debris was determined to be 4% by two separate methods, thus loss-on-ignition values were increased accordingly to give organic matter fractions of ashed subsamples. Average organic matter fractions and inorganic fractions and their standard deviations were calculated for the ash subsamples and multiplied by the oven-dry weights of whole collections to give organic and inorganic weights in the organic-inorganic collection. Inorganic weights were added to those obtained for inorganic piles. Total weights for organic and inorganic materials in each collection are given in Table 2.

Table 2.   Organic and inorganic particulate matter (output) collected during various periods from the ponding basin of Watershed 6, 13.23ha (data are in kilograms of oven-dry weight)

Collection period		Whole watershed			Per hectare of watershed		
Start	Finish	Organic	Inorganic	Total	Organic	Inorganic	Total
1 June 65	8 Sept 65	6.0	1.6	7.6[a]	0.45	0.12	0.5%
9 Sept 65	26 Oct 65	7.2	3.6	10.8[a]	0.55	0.28	0.8%
26 Oct 65	19 May 66	14.8	18.2	33.0[a]	1.12	1.37	2.4%
19 May 66	23 Sept 66	8.4	12.1	20.5[b]	0.64	0.91	1.5%
23 Sept 66	16 Nov 66	136.2	188.4	324.6[b]	10.29	14.24	24.5%
16 Nov 66	2 June 67	32.8	25.4	58.2[a]	2.48	1.92	4.4%

[a] s.c. < ±7% ; [b] s.c. not applicable because of sampling method.

The material that does not settle passes out of the basin over the V-notch weir or, infrequently, over the flume raceway. This particulate matter is measured in two ways. Once a week, a large 1-mm mesh nylon bag is put under the stream coming over the V-notch (Fig. 4*). After about 2 hr, the net is removed, its contents oven dried and weighed. Concentrations per liter are determined by dividing total oven-dry weight by volume of water passing over the notch during the sampling period.

To estimate losses of smaller-sized material passing through the net, once each week 12 liters of water were passed through the net (Fig. 5)* and

* Figure 5 has been omitted.

removed to the laboratory where two 6-liter subsamples were run through 0.45 μ Millipore filters under 40 psi. Each filter and residue was oven dried at 60 C, cooled in a desiccator, and weighed to the nearest 0.02 mg. The original O.D.W. of the filter alone was subtracted to give weight of the residue; this divided by 6 gave concentration in milligrams per liter. Results for the two subsamples were averaged.

Considerable difficulty was experienced in the use of Millipore filters due to their hygroscopicity, static electricity, and their loss of weight, due in part to leaching of detergents (Cahn, 1967). Tests of several kinds ultimately gave rise to the use of double filters, taken from the same batch, weighings made only with a static electricity reducer, and utilization of an equilibration period during which both filters come to equilibrium with ambient humidity (Eaton et al.). This system was instituted in January, 1967. Prior to that time, data were based on weight of residue obtained with a single filter corrected for average weight loss of a filter after passing 6 liters of distilled water. The two methods produced similar data as shown by the distribution of points in Figure 6.

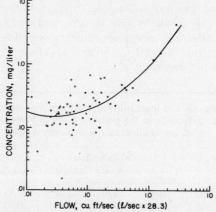

Figure 6. **Curve showing the relationship between concentration of filtered material and flow rate. Open circles show data collected with single filters, solid circles show data collected with double filters**

The relationship between suspended load and discharge in larger streams can often be described by a linear log-log equation (Leopold and Miller, 1956). To establish a similar relationship between both netted and filtered values and flow (cubic feet per second passing over the weir) recorded at the time of collection, curves of various forms were fitted to these data. For filtered data, a curve of the log form of a second order quadratic equation (Log $Y = 1.02$ Log $X + 0.328$ (Log $X)^2 - 0.025$ where $Y =$ milligrams of particulate matter per liter and $X =$ ft^3/sec at time of measurement) gave the best fit, accounting for 47% of the variation. Using this equation, and the recorded flow (in ft^3/sec) for the watershed, the output of filtered material was computed as kilogram of oven-dry weight per hectare per year.

Data for netted matter gave no clear-cut relationship between concentration and cubic feet per second. This is probably to be expected since the stilling basin (Fig. 2) is designed to minimize the velocity of water approaching the weir blade except when flows exceed the capacity of the V-notch (R. Pierce, personal communication). A high proportion of our netted samples were taken at flows less than V-notch capacity. Annual output of netted material was calculated by multiplying weekly concentrations (mg/l) by the volume of water passing over the weir during the week in which the sample was taken. Netted losses during highest storm flows were probably underestimated because few samples were collected during those periods. Data for netted, filtered, and basin material are given in Table 3.

Table 3.   Annual particulate matter from Watershed 6. Kilograms of oven-dry weight of organic and inorganic materials per hectare of watershed (based on a water year, i.e., June 1 to May 31)

Source of data	Organic	Inorganic	Total
	1965–66 Water Year		
Ponding Basin	2.12	1.77	3.89
Net	0.39	0.01	0.40
Filter	2.04	1.61	3.65
Total	4.55	3.39	7.94
	1966–67 Water Year		
Ponding Basin	13.41	17.07	30.48
Net	3.38	0.07	3.45
Filter	4.47	3.51	7.98
Total	21.26	20.65	41.91
	1965–67 Average		
Ponding Basin	7.77	9.42	17.19
Net	1.89	0.04	1.93
Filter	3.26	2.56	5.82
Total	12.92	12.02	24.94

Generally speaking, netted debris seemed relatively free of inorganic contamination, but dissolution of two ash samples with warm 6 N HCl indicated that about one-third of the ash was insoluble. X-ray diffraction of the insoluble part indicated an abundance of quartz, muscovite, and feldspar. Hence, it was assumed that most of the insoluble material (2% of the oven-dry weight of the unashed sample) was primary minerals and computed weights for netted material were presumed to be 98% organic and 2% inorganic.

Examination of the residue on the Millipore filter with a dissecting microscope indicated an amorphous brownish-black material and small lumps of aggregates. Preliminary analyses by John Hobbie, based on volatilization of carbon and measurement of CO_2 by infrared gas analysis, indicate that 56% of the filter residue is organic and 44% inorganic. Filter data were adjusted to reflect these proportions (Table 3).

Values for the export of dissolved substances during the period 1965–67

Table 4. **The gross output of dissolved substances from Watershed 6 in terms of kilograms per hectare of watershed per water year**

Substance	Symbol	Water year 1965–66	Water year 1966–67	Average
Aluminum	Al +++	2.4	2.8	2.60
Ammonium	NH₄ +	0.9	0.4	0.65
Calcium	Ca ++	9.0	10.7	9.85
Magnesium	Mg ++	2.7	2.9	2.80
Potassium	K +	1.3	1.7	1.50
Sodium	Na +	6.3	6.8	6.55
Bicarbonate	HCO₃	0.4	2.0	1.20
Chlorine	Cl	4.3	4.7	4.50
Nitrate	NO₃	6.5	5.9	6.20
Sulfate	SO₄	47.2	51.4	49.3
Silicon dioxide	SiO₂	31.3	36.8	34.05
Dissolved organic Carbon	C	18.9	21.2	20.05
Total		131.2	147.3	139.3

(Table 4) were taken from Likens et al., 1967, Fisher et al., 1968, and unreported data. Although the list given in Table 4 is not complete, it includes the great bulk of material exported in dissolved form.

Comparative losses of individual elements in dissolved or particulate form (Table 7) were estimated as follows: losses of dissolved substances were taken from Table 4. Losses in particulate matter were estimated in three categories: organic matter, inorganic particulate matter > 0.105 mm in size, and inorganic particulate matter < 0.105 mm in size. Two organic debris samples were analyzed for Fe, Ca, Mg, Na, and K and six samples were analyzed for Kjeldahl nitrogen (Table 6). These percentages (Table 6) were then applied to average total organic matter output for 1965–67 (Table 3) to give losses in organic matter (exclusive of dissolved organic matter). Inorganic matter collected in the basin was separated by sieving into two classes — 0.105 mm (97%) and < 0.105 mm (3%). New measurements suggest that 3% is a low estimate. Two subsamples of the < 0.105 mm class were analyzed for Ca, Mg, Na, K, and Fe (Table 6). Three percent of the average inorganic material in the basin collection plus the inorganic material attributable to the average netted and filtered categories shown in Table 3 (2.88 kg/ha) were multiplied by the percentage for the < 0.105 mm class in Table 6 to give losses of

Table 5. **Annual losses of dissolved substances and particulate matter from Watershed 6**

Water year	Dissolved substance kg/ha	Total particulate matter kg/ha	Percent dissolved substances	Annual runoff cm
1965–66	131.2	7.94	94	76
1966–67	147.3	41.91	78	85
Average/yr	139.3	24.93	85	81

Table 6. Percentage content of selected elements in various forms of particulate matter (average rock and till data are from Johnson et al., 1968)

Element	Organic matter	Inorganic matter > .105 mm in size	Average rock and till
Aluminum	*	*	8.3
Calcium	0.54	1.57	1.4
Iron	0.07	3.28	4.4
Magnesium	0.46	0.51	1.1
Nitrogen	0.94	*	*
Potassium	0.10	1.79	2.9
Sodium	0.01	1.55	1.6
Silicon	*	*	30.7
Sulfur	0.1[a]	*	< 0.1

* not measured
[a] estimated

individual elements in the < 0.105 mm inorganic category. The remaining material in the basic collections, 9.14 kg/ha, was multiplied by the percentage composition for various elements in average rock-till of the watershed (Table 6). The average total losses for the 2-year period are presented in Table 7.

DISCUSSION

1. Variations in particulate matter output

This study allows a preliminary analysis of seasonal variations in basin output of particulate matter. With the exception of an unusual storm in November 1966, 70% of the bulk of material is moved downstream during the late

Table 7. Average annual gross losses of individual elements as dissolved substance and as particulate matter (based on 2 years of data)

Element	Kilograms per hectare				Percent of total		
	Organic part. matter	Inorganic part. matter	Dissolved substance	Grand total	Organic part. matter	Inorganic part. matter	Dissolved substance
Aluminum	***	1.00[a]	2.60	3.60	***	27.7	72.3
Calcium	0.07	0.18	9.85	10.10	0.7	1.8	97.5
Iron	0.01	0.49	**	0.50	2.0	98.0	**
Magnesium	0.06	0.11	2.80	2.97	2.0	3.7	94.3
Nitrogen	0.12	**	1.90	2.02	5.9	**	94.1
Potassium	0.01	0.32	1.50	1.83	0.5	17.5	82.0
Sodium	0.00	0.19	6.55	6.74	0.0	2.8	97.2
Silicon	***	3.69[a]	15.92	19.61	***	18.8	81.2
Sulfur	0.01	0.01[a]	16.42	16.44	0.1	0.1	99.8

[a] rock and till per cent (Table 6) used in calculation of 0.105 mm fraction.
** not measured but very small.
*** not measured.

winter-spring runoff period (c + f vs. a + b +d, Table 1). It is interesting to note, however, that on the average, the spring runoff period moves only 0.59 kg of basin material per 10^{6} liters of hydrologic output, while remaining flows (excluding e.g. Table 1), move 1.10 kg/10^{6} liters. This is not wholly related to the occurrence of high flows during the various periods (Table 4) but implies instead that hydrologic discharge during the spring snowmelt period is less effective in removing sediment (Leopold et al., 1964, p. 72) than simple levels of discharge during the summer and fall. In this regard, it is interesting to note that in the White Mountains debris avalanches following heavy rains occur from June through November and that none has been reported for the snowmelt period or following heavy spring rains (Haccus, 1958a; 1958b).

Although the above discussion indicates an underlying seasonal pattern of particulate matter export with lower concentrations and maximum export associated with the spring runoff period, unusual hydrologic events leading to peak runoffs can greatly alter this pattern. This is shown by the data for the 16 November 1966 collection. A single storm on 3 November 1966, with high intensity runoff, deposited 64% of the particulate materials in the stilling basin during the 2-year measurement period. This storm will be discussed more fully in Section 5.

The relative proportions of organic and inorganic material in the different ponding basin collections are quite variable, ranging from 21 to 59% inorganic material (Table 2). Some of this variation is probably due to inadequacies of measurement techniques, but some is to be expected since organic-inorganic proportions are no doubt influenced by numerous factors such as (1) seasonal input of organic matter (e.g., leaves) into the streambed, (2) seasonal biologic activity that leads to weakening of debris dams or disintegration of leaves and twigs, and (3) a disproportionate effect of runoff in moving inorganic materials during high-velocity flows or during the various seasons of the year. High flows may result in a higher proportion of inorganic matter in ponding basin collections as indicated by the 16 November 1966 collection (58% inorganic). This effect may have two roots. First, the relative effectiveness of the stream in moving inorganic materials increases with increasing velocity and, second, increasing flow rates may increase turbulence within the ponding basin resulting in proportionally more lighter organic material passing out of the ponding basin and over the weir at higher flows. This latter artifact of weir design may influence the relationship proposed for filtered material output (Fig. 6).

2. Losses of particulate water and dissolved substances from the watershed-ecosystem

Average annual losses of particulate matter are about 25 kg/ha/yr (Table 3), shale losses of dissolved substances are 139 kg/ha/yr (Table 4). According to our model (Fig. 3), about equal proportions of exported particulate matter are drawn from the organic compartment (52%) and the soil and rock compartment (48%) of the ecosystem. A comparison of 1965–66 data with 1966–67 indicates how a single intense rainstorm can shift the proportion toward the inorganic side.

Average annual organic matter losses are 53 kg/ha, of which 13 kg/ha are particulate (Table 3) and 40 kg/ha are dissolved organic matter (Table 4, dissolved carbon multiplied by 2 to estimate dissolved organic matter). This material represents an export of energy and nutrients from the forest ecosystem to the lotic ecosystem. Considering that the material from the watershed is concentrated in the stream, an average of 700 kg of organic matter is exported from Watershed 6 to the lower stream. This allochthonous material must play a major role in supporting aquatic food webs in these heavily shaded streams.

Data in Table 3 indicates an average total particulate matter loss (organic + inorganic) of about 2.5 metric tons/km^2 (7 tons/square mile). This value is far below Langbein and Schumm's (1958) predicted value of 140 metric tons/km^2 (400 tons of suspended and bed load per square mile) for forested areas in the United States with about 127 cm (50 inches) of effective precipitation, or for the few available records of sediment yield for northeastern rivers which range from about 14 metric tons (40 tons) for Scantic River in Connecticut to 130 metric tons/km^2 (370 tons/square mile) for the Lehigh River in Pennsylvania (Langbein and Schumm, 1958). The difference between our estimate of particulate matter losses and those of Langbein and his coworkers may represent differences in size and order of streams, and in part, a measure of the effect of human manipulation of watersheds on particulate matter output (e.g., agriculture, forestry, etc.). Judson (1968) reports that utilization of the central Italian landscape has resulted in increased erosion.

The export of dissolved substances from our undisturbed forest ecosystem averaged 14 metric tons/km^2 (40 tons/square mile). This is about one-quarter of the dissolved load predicted by Langbein and Dawdy (Leopold et al., 1964, p. 78) for regions with about 75 cm (30 inches) of runoff, or for the North Atlantic Slope (Durum et al., 1960). The relative differences between our data and those cited above would be even greater if the contributions from dissolved substances in precipitation were taken into consideration (e.g., approx. 8 metric tons/ha/yr of dissolved substances were added to our watershed-ecosystem (Likens et al., 1967; Fisher et al., 1968).

Bricker et al. (1968) found that 0.7 metric tons of particulate matter and 3.7 metric tons of dissolved substances were removed by drainage water from a small watershed in Maryland. The significance of their data is difficult to evaluate, however (1) because sizable quantities of water may have left their watershed as deep seepage, (2) vegetational disturbance on the watershed may have upset ionic concentrations (Bormann et al., 1968), and (3) insufficient data are provided on hydrologic parameters.

A comparison of losses indicates an average of 85% of all material is lost as dissolved substances (Table 5). The 16% difference between percent dissolved substance in 1965–66 and 1966–67 is related to the 3 November 1966 storm and indicates that the percentage is somewhat sensitive to the occurrence of relatively infrequent storms during a water year.

This proportion of solution losses, 85% of total losses, is greater than those reported by Leopold et al. (1964, p. 76) for comparable climatic areas but is intermediate between those reported by Corbel (1959) for *lowlands* with cold winter climates and intermediate maritime climates. It is far greater than any percentage solution losses reported by Corbel (1959) for mountainous areas with cold climate.

In terms of a general spectrum of terrestrial ecosystems, the undisturbed forest ecosystem at Hubbard Brook is very stable. This view is justified on the bases of comparatively low losses of dissolved substances and particulate matter and the low ratio of particulate matter to dissolved substances (Table 5) and the low probability of debris avalanches to be discussed in Section 4. The equilibrium of the Hubbard Brook ecosystem is also reflected in the population structure of the forest which will be reported elsewhere.

3. Pattern of export for individual elements

Data in Table 7 illustrate export of individual elements according to the three routes shown in Figure 3, i.e., via organic particulate matter, inorganic particulate matter, and dissolved substances exclusive of dissolved organic matter. In all cases, with the exception of iron, major losses occur via the dissolved substance route, and it is clear that the relative importance of the three routes shifts from element to element. This is no doubt a function of the geochemistry of the element, its utilization by the biological fraction of the ecosystem, and its differential accumulation within the ecosystem. For example, both magnesium and potassium accumulate within the ecosystem as secondary minerals (Johnson et al., 1968) and a comparison of the aluminum, iron, and silicon contents of bedrock and till (Table 6) and their total export (Table 7) indicates that the same is true for these elements. The pattern for nitrogen and sulfur is related to their primary roles in metabolism and their lack of importance in the bedrock-till (Table 6). The pattern for sodium is influenced by its relative unimportance as a constituent of plant materials which constitute the bulk of the organic export.

Chemical elements that circulate within the ecosystem must at some time be in a soluble form. Our data indicate that the bulk of material capable of intrasystem circulation (Fig. 3) leaves the ecosystem as dissolved substance (inorganic + organic) rather than as particulate organic matter. Assuming that the bulk of the elements removed from the ecosystem in inorganic particulate matter is tied up in rock particles and was never solubilized prior to export, the solubilized material is removed either as dissolved substances or as part of the particulate organic matter. Data in Table 7 indicate that for all elements that have once been solubilized, with the single exception of iron, the great bulk is lost as dissolved substance; generally losses as particulate organic matter constitute 2% or less of this total.

4. The role of debris avalanches

Our data suggest that first-order watersheds with their well-developed forest are gradually lowered in place by the action of solution coupled with slow mass movements both of which deliver materials to the stream whence it is removed by erosion and transportation. The possibility that infrequent debris avalanches play an equal or greater role in moving material downslope in first-order watersheds should also be considered. For example, Hack and

Goodlett (1960) have shown in the Appalachian Mountains of Virginia and West Virginia that infrequent but catastrophic landslides play a major role in removing material from first-order watersheds and that this activity is independent of any restraining influence by the biota. Flaccus (1958a, 1958b) has shown essentially the same thing for the White Mountains of New Hampshire. Our data on stream losses allow a rough comparison of these very different denudational processes.

Flaccus (1958a, 1958b) mapped six debris avalanches on aerial photos of the White Mountains. His study area, much of which is heavily forested, is adjacent to Hubbard Brook and contains extensive stretches of the Littleton Formation which underlies our watershed. The mapped avalanches occur in about equal proportions on slopes of the Littleton Formation and slopes underlain by plutonic rocks. Flaccus examined in detail a range of avalanches, thought to be a fair sample of the total, and calculated the average weight of material moved downslope as 21,800 metric tons (24,000 tons). In those slides fresh enough to permit location of the topmost elevation it was found that 100% occurred above the 610 m elevation contour. Within his study we have calculated an area of about 128,000 ha above 610 m elevation. Flaccus was able to accurately date 136 slides, all of which occurred after 1773. Since slides revegetate rapidly, it is probable that the 543 slides mapped on aerial photos occurred within the last 200 years (Flaccus, personal communication). Based on the above data, we estimate that 462 kg/ha/yr are moved downslope by debris avalanches occurring above 610 m.

Limiting considerations to elements common to unaltered bedrock and till (Al, Ca, Mg, K, Na, sulfate, silica, Table 4), average net losses in dissolved substances during 1965–67 are about 60 kg/ha/yr after correction for input of these same substances in precipitation (Fisher et al., 1968; Johnson et al., 1968). Added to this are 12 kg/ha/yr of inorganic particulate matter (Table 3), giving an average total net loss of about 72 kg/ha/yr by removal in first order streams.

This estimate (72 kg/ha/yr) is approximately an order of magnitude less than the 462 kg/ha/yr estimated for debris avalanches. This suggests that debris avalanches are a more important mechanism in lowering the surface of first-order watersheds in the White Mountains than are the combined actions of solution and slower mass movements. However, two additional factors must be considered: (1) Disturbances that destroy the biotic stability of the ecosystems, such as fire and wind, could lead to greatly increased losses by mass wasting and erosion. (2) The incidence of avalanches per unit area increases sharply with increasing elevation and with increasing slope (Flaccus, 1958a; 1959b). In the White Mountains, only 18% of the avalanches recorded by Flaccus occur wholly below 909 m.

At Hubbard Brook, it seems unlikely that debris avalanches have occurred within the immediate area. Except for a few sites of very restricted area, our slope does not meet Flaccus' minimum slope requirement of 25°, nor is there any evidence of recent or old debris avalanches. It seems safe to conclude that debris avalanches have not played a significant role in the denudation of the relatively gentle slopes of the Hubbard Brook watershed, at least during the last millennium.

Apparently, denudation in the Hubbard Brook area is primarily a result of the less dramatic action of solution and erosion in combination with slower mass movements such as creep which may deliver materials to the stream beds. This, in turn, suggests that the weathering rind in our watersheds is fairly old. Locally, this is shown by well-developed soil profiles, however, in some places the surface is subject to shallow stirring by wind throws, animal burrows, etc.

5. Hydrologic relationships governing losses of dissolved substances and particulate matter

The Hubbard Brook study emphasizes the fundamental difference between the relationship of losses of dissolved substances and of particulate matter to the flow rate of the stream draining the watershed-ecosystem.

Our study of dissolved substances indicates that ionic concentrations vary somewhat, but are *relatively* independent of flow rate (Likens et al., 1967; Johnson et al., 1968; Fisher et al., 1968; Johnson et al., 1969). Harcombe and Woodwell (unpublished data) show about the same relationship between dissolved substances and drainage water for shrub microcosms of the Long Island pine-oak ecosystem. On the other hand, Johnson and Needham (1966) have shown a strong inverse relationship between ionic concentration and stream discharge in a mountain stream in California. Leopold et al. (1964, p. 74) report that, in general, concentrations of dissolved material in river channels decrease with increasing magnitude of flow.

Causes of decreased concentration of dissolved substances with increased flow rates of first-order streams may be twofold. First, there is a dilution effect when there is an insufficient reserve of exchangeable cation in the soil mass to maintain the same ionic concentration at all levels of drainage water passing through the soil. Second, as flows increase, proportionally more water may reach the stream channel without contact with the exchange surfaces of the soil (e.g., Johnson and Needham, 1966). For nitrogen and potassium, cessation of biological activity results in increased concentrations during the dormant season.

At any rate, it seems safe to conclude that for our watershed-ecosystems, and probably for most others, concentrations of dissolved substances in drainage water are probably independent of flow rate or inversely related to it.

On the other hand, both basin and filter collections gave evidence that particulate matter concentrations (wt/vol of water) were strongly positively correlated with flow rate of the stream draining the ecosystem. This relationship is shown for filtered material (Fig. 6), but is less obvious for basin data where individual collections represent fairly long periods of time. For basin collections, if we assume that concentration is independent of flow rate (i.e., concentration = total wt in mg over the 2-year period ÷ total water output in liters) and estimate output during the various collections periods by multiplying average concentration by the amount of water output during each collection period, there is little correlation with actual amounts of particulate matter output measured during the collection period. On the other hand, plots of total basin output during a collection period against either total water output

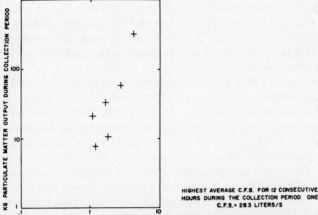

Figure 7. Periodic collections of basin particulate matter plotted against the highest flow rate for 12 consecutive hours during the collection period

or average f³/sec during that period (Table 1) suggest a curvilinear fit on log-log paper. A plot of total particulate matter output per collection period against highest average daily f³/sec or the highest average f³/sec for any consecutive 12 hours during the period (Fig. 7) gave a surprisingly linear or slightly curvilinear arrangement of points. This is in line with the general observation on rivers that suspended load increases with increasing magnitude of flow (Leopold et al., 1964, p. 74).

Our data (Fig. 7) suggest that individual storms with high intensity runoff are very important in determining particulate matter output from this ecosystem. This point was dramatically shown by a storm on 3 November 1966. The basin had been cleaned on 23 September 1966 and was observed to have minor collection of debris prior to the storm. The storm, 8.6 cm (3.4 inches) of rain on a saturated watershed, produced an average runoff of 2.88 f³/sec for the day or a total of 7×10^6 liters. However, 74% of this water came out during a 12-hr period with a range of 1.9 to 7.4 f³/sec. Runoff from Watershed 6 exceeded 2.0 f³/sec only 0.26% of the time during 4.5 years of record (Table 8). Trap efficiency was probably lower than normal during this flow, still the

Table 8. Frequency of flow rates in Watershed 6 over a 4½ year period, 1 January 1963 to 31 August 1967 (flow rates in cubic feet per second)

Range in c.f.s.	Percent of total time in class	Range in c.f.s.	Percent of total time in class
0. –0.5	95.779	3.5–4.0	0.018
0.5–1.0	2.918	4.0–4.5	0.015
1.0–1.5	0.728	4.5–5.0	0.002
1.5–2.0	0.311	5.0–5.5	0.002
2.0–2.5	0.097	5.5–6.0	0.000
2.5–3.0	0.099	6.0–6.5	0.002
3.0–3.5	0.023	6.5–7.0	0.000
		7.0–7.5	0.004

storm filled about three-quarters of the ponding basin (Fig. 2) with debris. If we assume that 90% of the 16 November collection is attributable to the 12-hr runoff period on 3 November, then 64% of the particulate matter collected in the ponding basin over the 2-year period can be attributed to 2.5% of the runoff during the period.

Leopold et al. (1964, p. 71) suggest that in larger streams the bulk of the sediment is moved by more modest but relatively frequent floods rather than rarer catastrophic floods. They also suggest (p. 84) that this concept may not apply to mountain streams where required competence (maximum size of a particle that a stream can move) increases upstream, in steep valleys (p. 83), or in small drainage basins (p. 74). Under these circumstances, a larger percentage of the load (i.e., particulate matter by our definition) may be contributed by relatively infrequent storms. Our data, where one 12-hour event in a 2-year time span (0.07% of the total time) apparently accounts for 54% of the basin + filter output, confirm this point of view.

The pattern of behavior of our stream may be linked, in part, to the action of organic materials in the streambed. At moderate and low flows the stream is essentially a stair-step of small pools. These pools lie behind hydrodynamically stable debris dams formed by leaves layered over twigs, branches, or stones. The dams are quite resistant to hand pressure exerted in a downstream direction but collapse under much less pressure exerted in an upstream direction. At modest and low flows, the pools act as a series of settling basins connected by rivulets of water running over, around, and seeping through the dams. It seems likely that at most flow rates the dams act as effective filtering and settling mechanisms. However, these dams are not wholly impervious to the pressure exerted by the stream and at higher flows they begin to be washed out, setting the debris formerly contained in and behind the dam in motion. Thus, debris dams act somewhat like large boulders in the streambed, in that only large discharges provide the necessary stress to move them (Leopold et al., 1964, p. 84).

Since we have no direct measurements of concentrations of basin output versus flow rate, a curve of rough estimate was developed by trial and error following these criteria: (1) The curve would be a straight line on log-log paper. This is in accordance with sediment-discharge curves developed for many kinds of streams by Leopold and Miller (1956). (2) The bulk of the work is done at the highest flow rate, therefore use of the curve in combination with flow rate data from the hydrograph should predict accurately output from our 3 November storm (i.e., 292 kg in 12 hr), and (3) the curve should predict within ±20% output over the 2-year period (445 kg). The curve, Log $Y = 0.069 + 2.374$ Log X predicted 317 kg for 3 November and 521 kg for the 2-year period (y = m of basin output per liter of discharge, X = f³/sec). The concentration curve for filtered material (Fig. 6) was added to this curve plus a constant 0.246 mg/l for netted material to give the summation curve shown in Figure 8.

A graphic comparison of the effects of flow rate on concentration of dissolved substances and particulate matter is shown in Figure 8. The curve for dissolved substances is based on the observation that concentrations do not change appreciably over the range of flow rate observed, hence total output

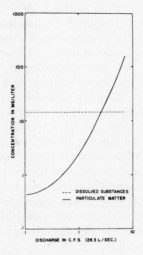

Figure 8. Curves showing the relationship of the concentration of dissolved substances and particulate matter to flow rate in a mature northern hardwood forest ecosystem

of all substances (Table 4), in milligrams divided by total water output in liters equals the y intercept, 14.8 mg/l. A dilution effect reported by us for some ions and by other authors (Johnson and Needham, 1966; Leopold et al., 1964) may occur at highest flows, but it is not shown on the figure.

6. Biotic control of the hydrologic cycle and its effects on nutrient cycling and ecosystem stability

The relationship shown in Figure 8 is basic to understanding the indirect role that the biota plays in regulating nutrient losses from the ecosystem. This control manifests itself through regulation of the hydrologic cycle, i.e., the total volume of water passing out of the system, and the pattern of discharge rates, and erodibility of the system.

Annual losses of dissolved substances are dependent upon the total volume of liquid water passing through the ecosystem (Fig. 8). Thus, the proportion of water lost from the ecosystem as runoff has a direct effect on the quantity of nutrients lost as dissolved substance. In humid forested ecosystems, the biota, through its effect on transpiration, detention storage, and interception, can have a very considerable effect on the proportion of water lost as runoff or streamflow (Lassen et al., 1951; Coleman 1953). The magnitude of this effect was demonstrated at Hubbard Brook where clear-cutting of all the vegetation in one watershed resulted in a 68% decrease in evapotranspiration and a 40% increase in runoff (Bormann et al., 1968). Similar drastic reductions in evapotranspiration and increases in runoff have been demonstrated in western North Carolina (Hibbert, 1967) and in West Virginia (Reinhart et al., 1963) following severe reductions in forest cover.

Annual losses of particulate matter from an ecosystem are primarily a function of discharge rate and erodibility rather than total volume. The shape of the curve of particulate matter concentration versus discharge rates (Fig. 8) reflects both the capacity of moving water to do work as its velocity increases (Leopold et al., 1964, p. 183) and erodibility or the rate at which moving water of a given velocity can remove material from the ecosystem.

It is well known that the biota of an ecosystem and its organic debris tend to damp high discharge rates through partial control of snow melt and/or the conversion of soil surface flow to subsurface flow. The latter effect is achieved through direct and indirect effects on detention and retention storage and on infiltration and percolation rates (Lassen et al., 1951; Coleman 1953). The effect of the climax ecosystem on the pattern of discharge rate at Hubbard Brook is not known. With time, we will be able to establish this effect through a comparison of discharge records from our cut-over watershed with our undisturbed forested watershed. Data from Lassen et al. (1951) are presented in Figure 9 to illustrate potential changes in discharge rate resulting from a lessening of biotic control.

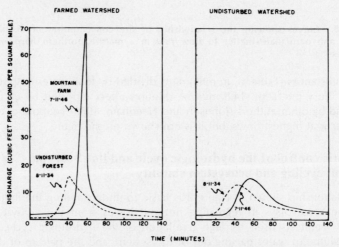

Figure 9.   The effect on discharge rate of conversion of an undisturbed forest to mountain farm (after Lassen et al., 1951)

Often, following a severe reduction in the biomass of an ecosystem, the effect of increased frequency of high discharge rates on particulate matter losses cannot be separated from the effect of a change in erodibility. For example, the particulate matter curve shown in Figure 8 would shift to the left following a severe disturbance that increased the erodibility of particulate materials in the ecosystem. Erodibility of the soil mantle is influenced by biomass and its organic debris through (1) protection of the soil from the energy of falling rain drops, (2) binding action of the roots, and (3) promotion of aggregation of soil particles (Coleman, 1953). All of these factors are operative in the undisturbed ecosystems of Hubbard Brook as well as other factors that reduce the erodibility of the first-order stream channel such as binding effects of roots on stream banks and bottoms, organic debris dams described earlier, and leaf coating effects, where leaves form a protective shield against erosion of exposed banks. The importance of the biotic control over discharge rates and erodibility and consequently over particulate matter losses has been dramatically shown in a hardwood ecosystem converted to a mountain farm at the Coweeta Hydrologic Station in western North Carolina (Hursh, 1951).

All of the biotic effects discussed above might be thought of as direct or indirect functions of biomass, a conveniently measurable attribute of terrestrial ecosystems. Severe reductions in biomass resulting from clear-cutting, windstorms, or fire would tend to negate the above effects, while sharp increases in biomass associated with secondary succession would enhance them. It is through biomass accumulation that ecological succession contributes to a tightening of some biogeochemical cycles within the ecosystem (i.e., net losses of some elements decrease as secondary succession proceeds). This is in accord with Margalef's view (1963) that biomass is the "keeper of organization" and that the amount of biomass is proportional to the influence that an ecosystem can exert over future events.

Secondary succession in humid forested ecosystems following destruction of the forest is marked by an increase in biomass. If the destructive force (e.g., fire or agriculture) removed or reduced the organic layers of the soil, increases in biomass will be accompanied by increases in organic debris. Biomass and organic debris together compose the organic compartment of our ecosystem model (Fig. 3). The increase in biomass is directly linked in some nonlinear fashion to an increase in water leaving the ecosystem as a vapor (evapotranspiration) and to a reduction in water leaving the system as a liquid (deep seepage and/or surface and subsurface runoff). Increases in biomass and organic debris are also inversely related to the frequency of high discharge rates and to the erodibility of the ecosystem.

The above factors operate to reduce material losses (both dissolved and particulate) associated with hydrologic losses. Thus, secondary succession would be accompanied by a reduction in dissolved matter output achieved through a diminished liquid water output, and a reduction in particulate matter achieved through a lower frequency of high discharge rates and a decrease in erodibility of the ecosystem.

The effect of secondary succession on nutrient conservation, however, may be still greater. Evidence from several studies indicate marked increases in the concentration of dissolved substances in stream water following clear-cutting (Bormann et al., 1968; Likens et al., 1969; unpublished data). Increased concentrations coupled with increased runoff result in substantially greater net chemical losses from recently disturbed sites as compared with undisturbed sites. With time, these losses are reduced by secondary succession which brings the ecosystem back to the undisturbed condition.

Conclusions

1) Particulate matter losses from the Hubbard Brook watershed-ecosystems show seasonal variations, with the bulk of the material being exported dur-

ing the spring runoff period. However, a single autumnal storm of unusual intensity accounted for 54% of the total particulate matter output during a 2-year period.

2) Total particulate matter losses amounted to 2.5 metric tons/km²/ year. This value is appreciably less than values reported for other similar regions.

3) Total output of dissolved substances was 14 metric tons/km²/yr. This is about 25% of the dissolved load predicted for such areas by Langbein and Dawdy (Leopold et al., 1964).

4) The relatively small losses of dissolved substances and particulate matter indicate that the Hubbard Brook ecosystem is very stable. This conclusion is also supported by the biotic structure of the ecosystem.

5) Chemicals may be exported from various compartments of the ecosystem as (1) particulate or dissolved organic material from the organic compartment, (2) dissolved inorganic substances from the available nutrient compartment, and (3) inorganic particulate matter from the soil and rock mineral compartment. The route of export an element follows is a function of its geochemistry, its utilization by the biological components, and its differential accumulation within the ecosystem.

6) Although debris avalanches are not an important consideration at Hubbard Brook, our data suggest that at higher elevations in the White Mountains avalanches are probably a·more important denudational force by an order of magnitude than solution and slower mass movements.

7) Secondary ecological successions following severe disturbance of forest ecosystems result in significant "conservation" of nutrients lost from the ecosystem. This effect is achieved by a complex interaction of biomass accumulation, alteration of the hydrologic cycle, reduction of erodibility of the system, and changes in concentration of dissolved substances in drainage waters.

References

Billings, M. P. 1956. The geology of New Hampshire. Part II. Bedrock geology. New Hampshire State Planning Commission, Concord, N.H.

Bormann, F. H., and G. E. Likens. 1967. Nutrient cycling. *Science*, 155: 424–429.

Bormann, F. H., G. E. Likens, D. W. Fisher, and R. S. Pierce. 1968. Nutrient loss accelerated by clear-cutting of a forest ecosystem. *Science*, 159: 882–884.

Bricker, O. P., A. E. Godfrey, and E. T. Cleaves. 1968. Mineral-water interaction during chemical weathering of silicates. *Advan. in Chem. Ser.*, 73: 128–142.

Cahn, R. D. 1967. Detergents in membrane filters. *Science*, 155: 195–196.

Coleman, E. A. 1953. *Vegetation and Watershed Management*. Ronald Press Co., New York, 412 p.

Corbel, J. 1959. Vitesse de l'erosion. *Z. Geomorphol.*, 3: 1–28.

Crisp, D. T. 1966. Input and output of minerals for an area of Pennine moorland: the importance of precipitation, drainage, peat erosion and animals. *J. Appl. Ecol.*, 3: 327–348.

Durum, W. H., S. G. Heidel, and L. J. Tison. 1960. World-wide runoff of dissolved solids. Intern'l Assoc. of Scientific Hydrology, General Assembly of Helsinki, Publ. No. 51, p. 618–628.

Eaton, J. S., G. E. Likens, and F. H. Bormann. The use of membrane filters in gravimetric analyses of particulate matter in natural waters. (Submitted for publication)

Fisher, D. W., A. W. Gambell, G. E. Likens, and F. H. Bormann. 1968. Atmospheric contributions to water quality of streams in the Hubbard Brook Experimental Forest, New Hampshire. *Water Resources Res.*, 4 (5): 1115–1126.

Flaccus, E. 1958a. Landslides and their revegetation in the White Mountains of New Hampshire. Ph.D. dissertation. Duke University, Durham, N.C., 186 p.

————. 1958b. White Mountain landslides. *Appalachia*, 32: 175–191.

Hack, J. T., and J. C. Goodlett. 1960. Geomorphology and forest ecology of a mountain region in the central Appalachians. U.S. Geol. Survey Prof. Paper 347, 66 p.

Hibbert, A. R. 1967. Forest treatment effects on water yield. In: *International Symposium on Forest Hydrology*, W. E. Sopper and H. W. Lull (eds.), Pergamon Press, New York, p. 527–543.

Hursh, C. R. 1951. Research in forest-stream-flow relations. *Unasylva*, 5 (1): 2–9.

Johnson, C. M., and P. R. Needham. 1966. Ionic composition of Sagehen Creek, California, following an adjacent fire. *Ecology*, 47: 636–639.

Johnson, N. M., G. E. Likens, F. H. Bormann, and R. S. Pierce. 1968. Rate of chemical weathering of silicate minerals in New Hampshire. *Geochim. Cosmochim. Acta.* 32: 531–545.

Johnson, N. M., G. E. Likens, F. H. Bormann, and D. W. Fisher. 1969. Factors regulating the ionic composition of stream water in the Hubbard Brook Experimental Forest, New Hampshire. (Manuscript)

Judson, J. 1968. Erosion rates near Rome, Italy. *Science*, 160: 1444–1446.

Langbein, W. B., and S. A. Schumm. 1958. Yield of sediment in relation to mean annual precipitation. *Amer. Geophys. Union Trans.,* 39: 1076–1084.

Lassen, L., H. W. Lull, and B. Frank. 1951. Some fundamental plant-soil-water relations in watershed management. USDA Forest Service, Div. of Forest Influences, Washington, D.C. July, 1951.

Leopold, L. B., and J. P. Miller. 1956. Ephemeral streams — hydraulic factors and their relation to the drainage net. U.S. Geol. Survey Prof. Paper 282-A.

Leopold, L. B., M. G. Wolman, and J. P. Miller. 1964. *Fluvial Processes in Geomorphology.* W. H. Freeman & Company, San Francisco, Calif.

Likens, G. E., F. H. Bormann, N. M. Johnson, and R. S. Pierce. 1967. The calcium, magnesium, potassium and sodium budgets for a small forested ecosystem. *Ecology*, 48: 772–785.

Likens, G. E., F. H. Bormann, and N. M. Johnson. 1969. Nitrification: importance to nutrient losses from a cut-over forested ecosystem. *Science*, 163 (3872): 1205.

Margalef, R. 1963. On certain unifying principles in ecology. *Amer. Naturalist*, 97: 357–374.

Reinhart, K. G., A. R. Eschner, and G. R. Trimble, Jr. 1963. Effect on streamflow of four forest practices in the mountains of West Virginia. U.S.F.S. Res. Paper NF-1. N.E. For. Expt. Sta., Upper Darby, Pa.

Wilde, S. A., G. K. Voigt, and J. G. Iyer. 1964. *Soil and Plant Analysis for Tree Culture.* Oxford Publishing House, New Delhi.

Wisler, C. O., and E. F. Brater. 1965. *Hydrology.* John Wiley & Sons, Inc., New York. 408 p.

SUPPLEMENTARY EDITOR'S COMMENT

It should be noted that this last article is but one of many such studies from the Hubbard Brook Ecosystem Study. It is appropriate here to include some discussion of a later report entitled "Effects of Forest Cutting and Herbicide Treatment on Nutrient Budgets in the Hubbard Brook Watershed-Ecosystem."* In this report all of the vegetation in one of the watersheds was cut and then treated with the herbicides

* Likens et al, *Ecological Monographs*, Vol. 40, No. 1, Winter 1970 pp. 23–47.

Bromacil ($C_9H_{13}BrN_2O_2$) and 2,4,5-trichlorophenoxyacetic acid in an attempt to determine the effect on the stream water from the watershed.

The conclusions are startling in the abrupt changes noted: for example, the deforestation resulted in much larger runoffs with very different nutrient concentrations. Nitrate ion was found to have increased 41-fold the first year and 56-fold the second, showing a significant change in the nitrogen cycle within the watershed. Also, the pH of the drainage stream went from 5.1 to 4.3, along with a change in temperature and electrical conductivity of the stream water.

This combination of higher nutrient concentrations, higher water temperature and greater solar radiation due to the loss of forest cover produced the first sign of eutrophication, an algal bloom. The beginning of eutrophication was a signal that a change in the ecosystem of the watershed had occurred, and no longer was the nitrogen cycle closed. The increased plant productivity could then lead to a decrease in the dissolved oxygen in the water, with the result that the effect of cutting and the use of herbicides which started in the forest would be transferred to the outgoing water.

FRANK T. MANHEIM, ROBERT H. MEADE & GERARD C. BOND

Suspended Matter in Surface Waters of the Atlantic Continental Margin from Cape Cod to the Florida Keys

We have studied the distribution and composition of suspended matter from about 600 stations covering a large part of the Atlantic continental margin of the United States. Samples were taken during coastal cruises of the Woods Hole Oceanographic Institution vessels *Asterias* (inshore) and *Gosnold* (offshore). Although the samples represent surface waters almost exclusively, they were obtained during a limited period (May and June of 1965) and hence give a nearly synoptic view of the area.

Our data, briefly reported earlier (1, 2), show a rapid decrease with dis-

Frank T. Manheim, Robert H. Meade, and Gerard C. Bond, "Suspended Matter in Surface Waters of the Atlantic Continental Margin from Cape Cod to the Florida Keys," *Science*, vol. 167 (January 23, 1970), pp. 371–376. Copyright 1970 by the American Association for the Advancement of Science. Reprinted by permission.
Frank T. Manheim and Robert H. Meade are with the U. S. Geological Survey, Woods Hole Oceanographic Institution, Woods Hole, Massachusetts. Gerard C. Bond is a member of the Department of Geology, Williams College.

tance from shore of terrigenous influence on suspended matter in surface waters. Our seawardmost samples contain lower concentrations of total suspended matter than the 0.1 to 1 mg/liter range that has been reported for the Atlantic Ocean by many previous workers (3) (Table 1). Our results agree within analytical error with those of Krey and co-workers, Folger and Heezen, with the average of Jacobs and Ewing and with the maximum value of 0.050 mg/liter for inorganic detritus in the world oceans calculated by Kullenberg (4) from data collected by N. G. Jerlov. The large proportion of combustible organic matter that we found in surface waters outside the direct influence of rivers, estuaries, or nearshore sediments disagrees with some previous observations on the general proportions or total amounts of organic detritus in oceanic surface waters (5). The absolute values of organic matter, however, agree with those that others have found in Atlantic waters (6).

In our study, surface waters were collected by lowering buckets over the sides of the vessels and immediately filling one or two 1-liter sampling bottles. In inshore waters, salinity samples, Forel color, Secchi-disk, and temperature measurements were usually taken simultaneously. On offshore cruises, only water samples were taken; these were collected in clean polyethylene buckets on polypropylene rope lowered from the bow of the moving vessel and poured immediately into precleaned polyethylene sampling bottles. We were careful to check for and avoid soot and other sources of shipboard contamination, but the small water samples and the relative crudity of our sampling technique give doubtful accuracies at concentrations of total suspended matter less than 0.1 mg/liter.

The technique for obtaining and analyzing suspended matter is based on micropore filters, which have been used extensively in suspended-matter studies by Lisitsin and others (7). We filtered the water samples on board ship through preweighed Millipore R filters having nominal pore size of 0.45 μ and a diameter of 47 mm. A vacuum pump and a special stainless steel filter holder were used in this operation. The filters were then washed five times (with filter funnel removed) with filtered distilled water. Residual salt retained by the filters proved to be the most serious single source of error and was a potential source of erroneously large concentrations of suspended matter. Some filters, therefore, required further washing in the shore laboratory (8). All filters were stored in individual plastic petri dishes.

For original and subsequent weighings, the dried filters were allowed to equilibrate for several days in a room where temperature and humidity were controlled. They were then weighed, along with control filters, to the nearest 0.01 mg on a microbalance. A fresh 500-pc polonium source reduced electrostatic attraction. Approximately every tenth petri dish contained two filters that were carried through the operation as one (9). The lower filter receives virtually no suspended matter during filtration, and it provides a means of evaluating the losses and gains of weight that are due to seawater filtration, washing, humidity, absorption, or other influences. Systematic weight variations among the control filters of given batches were usually reproducible within about 0.05 mg, and appropriate corrections were applied to the uncontrolled filters.

To determine the composition of the suspended matter, the reweighed

Table 1. Total suspended sediment concentrations in open Atlantic waters. Sources cited in (3). Nearshore studies, studies involving particle counts (22), or optical studies only (23) are not included here. "Membrane" filters refer to filters with pore size of 1 μ or less

Area	Depth	Dominant conc. range (mg/liter)	Source	Remarks
Mid-Atlantic Ridge about 52°N	Surface	0.32 (SiO$_2$)	Murray and Irvine (1891)	Single sample; paper filter
North Atlantic	Variable	0.05–1.0	Armstrong (1958)	Membrane filter
Cape Farewell to Flemish Cap	Variable	.02–15	Krey et al. (1959)	Paper filter
Northern North Atlantic	Surface	.5 (av.)	Krey (1964)	1.8-μ filter
	Deeper water	.1 (av.)		
North and South Atlantic	Variable	.1–1.0	Klenova et al. (1962)	Membrane filter; higher conc. near bottom
North Atlantic	Variable	.3–3.0	Vikhrenko and Nikolaeva (1962)	Membrane filter
East of Blake Plateau	4030 m	2.5	Groot and Ewing (1963)	Single sample; continuous centrifuge
Eastern North and South Atlantic	Surface	.7 (av.)	Gordeev (1963)	Membrane filter
		.1–3	Gordeev (1963)	Continuous centrifuge
Western North Atlantic	Surface	.2–1.0	Vikhrenko (1964)	Membrane filter
Central Gulf Stream	Surface	.13	Krey (1961)	Membrane filter
	Deeper water	.06		
Tropical Atlantic	Surface	.1–2	Hagmeier (1964)	Membrane filter
	Deeper water	.02–08		
Tropical Atlantic	Variable	.2–1.0	Klenova and Vikhrenko (1965)	Membrane filter
North Atlantic	Just below surface	.04–14	Folger and Heezen (1968)	Membrane filter
Subtropical western North Atlantic	Variable	.001–25 (mean 0.05)	Jacobs and Ewing (1969)	Continuous centrifuge
Western North Atlantic	Surface	≤.1	This report	Membrane filter

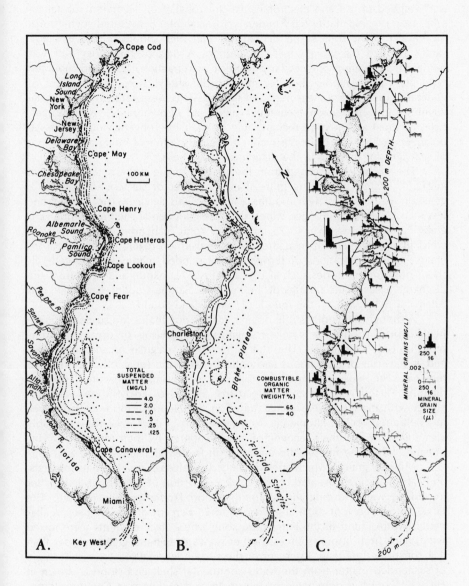

Figure 1. Composition and grain size of suspended sediments in surface waters along the Atlantic continental margin, May and June 1965. (A) Total suspended matter. In the area off New Jersey, obvious pollutants such as soot and fly ash were subtracted wherever possible, from the total concentrations portrayed. (B) Combustible organic matter. (C) Grain-size distribution of recognizable minerals; note the hollow histograms represent concentrations that are 100 times smaller than those represented by solid histograms

filters were carefully halved. One half of each filter was ashed, after preliminary charring with alcohol, in a crucible made of 2.5-μ platinum foil. The ash was weighed on a Cahn electrobalance (microbalance). Hydrated substances other than organic matter (clay minerals, for example) constituted such a small proportion of the total suspended matter that they should not have significantly affected the weight loss on ignition. A part of the other half was rendered transparent with cedar oil (index of refraction, 1.51) and mounted on a glass petrographic slide for microscopic study. Sizes of the grains of mineral particles were measured, and their weights were estimated by special counting and conversion techniques described elsewhere (2). Mineral particles as small as 4 μ were recognizable by their birefringence under crossed polarizers. All weight estimates were converted to units of milligrams per liter of seawater for plotting in the diagrams shown here.

The main results gained from the analysis of the suspensates are shown in Fig. 1. Waters containing more than 1 mg/liter of suspended matter are generally restricted to river mouths, estuaries, and a narrow nearshore zone less than 10 km wide. Surface waters over the continental shelf and slope generally contained less than 0.125 mg/liter of total suspended matter, most of which (60 to 90 percent) consisted of combustible organic matter. Local increases in concentrations of terrigenous suspended matter were noted offshore from promontories such as capes Hatteras, Lookout, and Fear, from the discharge areas of the mouths of the Pee Dee, Santee-Cooper, Savannah, and Altamaha rivers, and off the mouth of Long Island Sound.

Although the combustible organic matter dominates the suspended particulates in the offshore waters, recognizable organisms or organic remains make up only a small part. The bulk is present as irregular organic aggregates and as particles of amorphous and optically isotropic (or faintly birefringent) material. The most commonly recognized organisms were dinoflagellates, diatoms, silicoflagellates, and radiolarians. Masses of coccolithophorids, together with diatoms, were concentrated in the Georgia-Florida-Bahama area in a belt a few tens of kilometers from shore. Soft-bodied algae were probably also abundant, but their recognition was hampered by their tendency to disintegrate when the filters were flushed with fresh water (8).

Mineral grains, which included quartz, feldspar, micas, clay minerals, and carbonates, represented only a small proportion of the suspended matter in surface waters during the sampling period [Table 2; see also (2)]. The largest proportions of mineral grains (10 to 25 percent of the total suspended matter) were found in the long-shore zone where river effluents were mixed with grains from littoral sources. Farther seaward, mineral grains coarser than 4 μ constitute less than 3 percent of the suspended matter. A typical sample of suspended matter from the outer continental shelf and slope is shown in Fig. 2A,** which is dominated by the opalescent outline of a *Ceratium* (dinoflagellate) between crossed polarizing lenses; the darkness of most of the remaining area of the photograph indicates a lack of birefringent mineral particles. Mineral grains finer than 4 μ cannot be readily distinguished from birefringent organic particles, but maximum weight estimates from particle counts indicate that they probably do not form a significant portion of the total suspended matter. In rivers and estuaries landward of the longshore

Table 2. Selected values of suspended matter, Atlantic coastal waters

Location and description	Total wt. (mg/liter)	Percent organic	Recognizable mineral grains (mg/liter)	Recognizable mineral grains (%)	Modal sizes of mineral grains (μ)
Surface waters					
Roanoke River near Plymouth, N. C.	29.1	33	0.86	3.0	8–16
Albemarle Sound (center)	5.1	24	.095	1.9	4–8
Pamlico Sound, south of Swanquarter	3.3	28	.068	2.1	4–8
Nearshore shelf off Hatteras Inlet	1.4	41	.13	9	62–125* 4–8†
Charleston Harbor	5.5	31	.19	3.5	4–8
Nearshore shelf off Helena Is., S. C.	2.4	24	.21	8.7	125–250* 4–8†
Offshore shelf southeast of Charleston	0.40	58	.0099	0.2	8–16
Blake Plateau off Charleston	.05	90	.0015	3	16–32
Subsurface waters					
Blake Plateau, 31°48'N, 79°15'W, Alvin dive 203, July 1967, 175 m	0.15	50			
Blake Plateau, 31°48'N, 79°12'W, Alvin dive 201, July 1967, 518 m current 2 to 5 cm/sec‡	1.7	76			
Blake Plateau, 31°18'N, 78°53'W, Alvin dive 200, July 1967, 543 m current approximately 50 cm/sec‡	1.8	75			
Blake Plateau, 31°18'N, 78°53'W, Alvin dive 200, July 1967, 548 m current approximately 50 cm/sec‡	2.2	83			

* Principal mode of bimodal distribution.
† Secondary mode of bimodal distribution.
‡ About 20 cm off bottom.

zone, mineral grains typically accounted for 2 to 10 percent of the total suspended matter in surface waters.

Pollutants were particularly evident in the New York Bight (the shelf
area bordered by Long Island and New Jersey) and the Straits of Florida.
Characteristic of pollutants from the New York Bight are the opaque aggregates of soot and fly ash shown in Fig. 2D.** Other artifacts, previously used
to trace the mixture of river waters into the offshore region (10) are round
iron-oxide aggregates that apparently form when iron-rich effluents are discharged into coastal waters; similar red-brown particles have been noted in
Baltimore Harbor (11) and as far seaward as the Sargasso Sea (12) (some iron
aggregates may be natural particles such as those formed in marshes and bog
waters). Another pollutant, in the form of strongly birefringent fibrous material,
is especially abundant near port areas and in the Straits of Florida. These fibers
do not resemble any of the planktonic and terrestrial plant residues that we
examined; they appear to be a form of processed cellulose. When compared
with rope shreds and various commercial cellulose products, their closest
resemblance is to toilet paper. Miami cannot be the source of the fibers, . . .
not so much because its sewage is treated to settle solids (Miami Beach discharges untreated sewage) but because material from the metropolitan Miami
area would tend to be swept northward by the Gulf Stream before it could
reach the eastern part of the Straits of Florida. Havana is a possible source,
since it discharges 50–100,000 gallons of raw sewage per day into a coastal
current that joins the Gulf Stream (13). A more likely source, however, is
refuse from ships in the densely traveled shipping lane through the Straits of
Florida to and from New Orleans and other ports on the Gulf of Mexico.

Our studies provided an opportunity to evaluate the relations between
concentrations of suspended matter and some simple measures of the trans-
parency and color of water. Previous workers have shown that the relation
between light transmissibility, as measured by the depth to which a 30-cm
white (Secchi) disk is visible, and the concentration of suspended matter is
described by a hyperbolic curve (14). Expressed in terms of weight, this relation is given by

$$D = kd\rho/w$$

where D is Secchi-disk visibility; d, mean diameter of particles; ρ, density of
particles; w, weight of suspended matter; and k, a constant. The equation
indicates an inverse log-linear relation between the weight of suspended
matter and depth of the Secchi disk, provided the mean (effective) diameter
and density of the suspended particles remain constant. The plot in Fig. 3 is
strongly linear, despite considerable variability in distribution of the sizes of
grains and in the amounts and proportion of organic and inorganic matter.
The coincidence of high organic and low organic samples on the plot suggests
that the mean sizes of the low-density combustible organic particles are
proportionately greater than those of the mineral grains or the noncombustible
biogenic particles. If the relation in Fig. 3 is applied to the contours of Secchi-

---

** Figure 2 has been omitted.

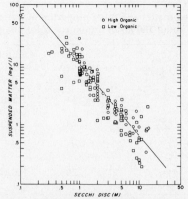

Figure 3.   Relation between suspended concentration (total) and Secchi-disk depth in inshore waters of Atlantic continental margin. Boundary between high and low organic samples taken at 50 percent combustible organic matter

disk depth reported off southern California (*15*), the 1 mg/liter contour would occur, as it does on the Atlantic shelf, within 10 km of shore.

We observed a poorer relation between Forel color (blueness of the water) and the weight concentration of particulates. On a rough basis, however, we found that water containing 1 mg/liter or more of total suspended matter appeared greenish and that it became increasingly yellowish brown or reddish brown as concentrations of suspended matter increased. Clear blue colors, which are associated with the Gulf Stream along the Florida coast and which are also found near the southeast coast of North Carolina, appear to be associated with maximum concentrations of suspended matter of a few tenths of a milligram per liter. Transitions in color of the water, which are particularly striking when seen from the air, offer a potential method for estimating the suspended matter in surface waters over large areas, provided that one calibrates intermittently with actual measurements of concentrations of suspended matter (*16*). Sharp transitions in color of the water were observed within and off the mouths of estuaries of Florida, Georgia, and the Carolinas. While salinity and temperature showed little significant difference across the boundaries, the differences in the reflective properties were invariably marked by sharp changes in total suspended matter (Table 3).

A principal aim of our study was insight into the dispersion of suspended sediment seaward from the continent. Our data showed that suspended matter moved mainly alongshore rather than directly seaward from the mouths of rivers and estuaries and that most of the mineral grains in suspension were derived from nearby sources. Some of the evidence for these conclusions is demonstrated in data collected in and near Charleston Harbor. The diverted Santee River, despite the large reservoirs that trap part of its sediment, discharges a substantial amount of suspended matter through the Cooper River and into the sea via Charleston Harbor. The concentrations shown in Fig. 1A suggest that material from Charleston Harbor moves southward. The modal size class of the mineral grains (4 to 8 μ) can be traced out of the harbor and,

Table 3.   Suspended matter and other properties of water on opposite sides (within about 100 m) of prominent color boundaries

Location	Date (May 1965)	Azimuth of boundary (deg)	Forel color (percent yellow)
Pamlico Sound	14	110	85 (north side)
(south end), N. C.			65 (south side)
St. Catherines	23	90	80 (north side)
Sound, Ga.			55 (south side)
Sapelo Sound, Ga.	23	90	90 (north side)
			80 (south side)
St. Johns River,	25	100–110	60 (north side)
Fla. (4 km off mouth)			35 (south side)

Table 3.   (cont.)

Location	Suspended matter (mg/liter) Total	Ash	Chloride (parts per thousand)	Temperature (°C)
Pamlico Sound	11.2	8.1	8.1	22.2
(south end), N. C.	3.1	1.7	7.8	22.4
St. Catherines	8.8	6.4	15.3	
Sound, Ga.	4.5	3.0	15.3	
Sapelo Sound, Ga.	13.0	9.8	14.5	
	9.8	6.6	14.5	
St. Johns River,	2.8	1.7	17.9	26.2
Fla. (4 km off mouth)	0.8	0.3	18.7	26.0

in diminishing concentrations, southwestward along the coast where it mixes with larger proportions of sands that are derived directly from local longshore areas (Fig. 1C). Seaward of Charleston Harbor the concentrations of suspended matter diminish rapidly within a short distance of shore, and distribution of the sizes of the mineral particles shows little relation to that found inshore.

Another aspect of the seaward movement of suspended matter is shown in the relations between concentration of suspended matter and chlorinity in five estuaries southwest of Cape Hatteras. Figure 4 shows that the relation between the two variables is fairly simple. Rather more complex relations prevail near the heads of the estuaries where river sediment first enters the tidal and brackish waters (17), but in the more seaward parts of the estuaries (where most of the samples in Fig. 4 come from) the gradual and linear decrease in the concentration of suspended matter with increasing chloride indicates that suspended matter decreases seaward mainly by simple dilution with seawater.

Although no subsurface samples were taken during our main period of effort in May and June 1965, we were able to sample and observe the material in suspension near the bottom during later cruises in 1966 and 1967. Samples were taken in two submarine canyons on the seaward edge of Georges Bank

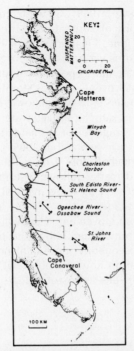

Figure 4.   Relations between suspended matter and chloride in surface waters of small river-estuary systems along the southeastern Atlantic coast

(southeast of Cape Cod; not shown in Fig. 1) with an inverted Van Dorn sampler that was triggered at a present distance (usually 0.5 to 1.5 m) above the bottom, and by means of special samplers from the deep submersible *Alvin* (18). Suspended matter in the head of Corsair Canyon and at a depth of 1500 m in Oceanographer Canyon amounted to less than 0.5 mg/liter, most of which was organic. Bottom currents at the time of sampling in Oceanographer Canyon were less than 10 cm/sec.

     Another group of samples was taken by *Alvin* on the Blake Plateau (Table 2). Two of the samples (dive 200) were taken near the axis of the Gulf Stream where the water current was about 50 cm/sec. In contrast, water farther up the column contained less than a tenth of the total suspensate noted in the bottom water. From the viewing ports of *Alvin* we observed soft gelatinous or flocculent particles, sometimes as large as 1 cm in diameter, that character-ized the upper 200 m of water, both over the Blake Plateau and in slope waters off Cape Hatteras. The sizes of these particles increased downward, reached a maximum at depths of 20 to 100 m, and then diminished rapidly to an ap-proximately constant size at deeper levels. Similar phenomena have been observed near Japan (19).

     What is the significance of our results in the context of the long-term movement of sediment on the continental margin? Because 1965 was an ex-ceptionally dry year in the North Atlantic states, our studies north of Cape Hatteras probably reflect minimum contributions of riverborne detritus. In the

South Atlantic states, however, 1965 was wetter than average, and we may have sampled concentrations of suspended matter that were a little larger than normal for May and June. On the basis of this, we conclude that the transport of suspended detritus via surface waters across the continental shelf to the regions of the continental slope is minimum during normal or near-normal conditions. Abnormal events such as storms and floods, on the other hand, have a strong but quantitatively unknown effect on the transport of detritus in coastal water. For example, surface water 20 km off Cape Canaveral (Cape Kennedy) contained 7 mg/liter of suspended matter 2 days after Hurricane Betsy traversed the area in September 1965. One month earlier, surface water in the same area contained only 0.25 mg/liter. Similar increases in the concentration of suspended matter following storms have been observed in the Bering Sea (20). Evidence on the movement of bottom sediments on the continental shelf and in estuaries of the Atlantic seaboard indicates that the dominant direction of bottom movement is landward rather than seaward (21). If sediment transport by storms is limited to the present shelf regions, from which the sediment is subsequently moved inland by bottom currents, we conclude from the information now available that the continent is presently contributing little detritus to the continental slope and deeper regions of the Atlantic Ocean.

References and notes

1. F. T. Manheim, R. H. Meade, J. V. A. Trumbull, *Int. Oceanogr. Congr., 2nd* (*Moscow*), *Abstr. Pap.* (1966), pp. 239–240; ———, G. C. Bond, *Geol. Soc. Amer. Spec. Pap. No. 101* (1968), p. 443.

2. G. C. Bond and R .H. Meade, *Chesapeake Sci.* 7, 208 (1966).

3. J. Murray and R. Irvine, *Proc. Roy. Soc. Edinburgh* 18, 229 (1891); F. A. J. Armstrong, *J. Marine Res.* 17, 23 (1958); J. Krey, D. Hantschmann, S. Wellerhaus, *Deut. Hydrogr. Z. Ergänzunsh. Reihe B No. 3* (1959), p. 73; J. Krey, *Rapp. Proces-Verbaux Reunions Cons. Perma. Int. Explor. Mer* 149, 194 (1961); M. V. Klenova, V. M. Lavrov, V. K. Nikolaeva, *Dokl. Akad. Nauk SSSR* 144, 1153 (1962); N. M. Vikhrenko and V. K. Nikolaeva, *Tr. Inst. Okeanol. Akad. Nauk SSSR* 56, 87 (1962); J. J. Groot and M. Ewing, *Science* 142, 579 (1963); E. I. Gordeev, *Dokl. Akad. Nauk SSSR* 149, 181 (1963); N. M. Vikhrenko, *Tr. Inst. Okeanol. Akad. Nauk SSSR* 68, 3 (1964); J. Krey, *Kiel. Meeresforsch.* 20, 18 (1964); E. Hagmeier, *Helgolaender Wiss. Meeresuntersuch.* 11, 270 (1964); M. V. Klenova and N. M. Vikhrenko, in *Gidrologicheskie i gidrokhimicheskie issledovaniya v tropicheskoi zone Atlanticheskogo okeana*, "*Naukova Dumka*," G. P. Ponomarenko, Ed. (Kiev, 1965), pp. 113–128; D. W. Folger and B. C. Heezen, *Geol. Soc. Amer. Program N.E. Section* (Boston, 1968), p. 27; M. Jacobs and M. Ewing, *Science* 163, 380 (1969).

4. B. Kullenberg, *Tellus* 5, 302 (1953).

5. T. Hanaoka, *Rapp. Proces-Verbaux Reunions, Cons. Perma. Int. Explor. Mer* 144, 28 (1958); A. P. Lisitsin, in *Sovremennye osadki morei i okeanov, Izdatel'stvo Akad. Nauk SSSR*, N. M. Strakhov, P. L. Bezrukov, V. S. Yablokov, Eds. (Moscow, 1961), pp. 175–231; A. P. Lisitsin, *Raspredelenie i khimicheskii sostav vzvesi iz vod Indiiskogo okeana* (Nauka, Moscow, 1964), vol. 1, p. 135; L. M. Sushchenya and Z. Z. Finenko, *Okeanologiya* 6, 682 (1966).

6. B. A. Skopintsev, S. K. Timofeeva, O. A. Vershinina, *Okeanologiya* 6, 201 (1966); D. W. Menzel and J. H. Ryther, *Limnol. Oceanogr.* 9, 179 (1964); P. T. Wangarsky and D. C. Gordon, *ibid.* 10, 544 (1965).

7. A. P. Lisitsin, *Tr. Inst. Okeanol. Akad. Nauk SSSR* 19, 204 (1956). See also J. Krey, *Kiel. Meeresforsch.* 7, 58 (1950); E. D. Goldberg, M. Baker, D. L. Fox, *J. Marine*

Res. 11, 194 (1952); J. H. Willenberger, J. H. Austin, C. A. Kiett, *J. Water Pollut. Contr. Fed.* 35, 807 (1963); K. Banse, C. A. Falls, L. A. Hobson, *Deep-Sea Res.* 10, 639 (1963).

8. Washing filters with distilled water tends to burst soft-bodied tissues and cells of marine zoo- and phytoplankton. This has the partial advantage, where plankton blooms are encountered, of helping to remove occluded salt but does not allow detailed observations of such organisms. Diatoms, coccolithophorids, and other hard-part-bearing organisms, on the other hand, remain largely undisturbed on the filters. We assume that no appreciable amount of suspensate finer than the pores of the filter passes through, in view of the fact that fine detritus that soon clogs and coats the pores tends to retain particles much finer than nominal pore diameter.

9. *Application Data Manual ADM-70* (Millipore Filter Corp., Bedford, Mass., 1964).

10. B. H. Ketchum, A. C. Redfield, J. C. Ayers, *Mass. Inst. Technol. Woods Hole Oceanogr. Inst. Pap. Phys. Oceanogr. Meteorol. 12(2)* (1951).

11. C. F. Garland, *Md. Board Natur. Resour. Chesapeake Biol. Lab. Publ. 96* (1952).

12. K. Muehlenbachs and G. C. Bond, unpublished data (1965).

13. J. G. Bengochea, personal communication (1966).

14. K. I. Ivanov, *Tr. Gos. Okeanogr. Inst., No. 15* (1950) [not seen; referred to in Lisitsin (5)]; D. Jones and M. S. Wills, *J. Biol. Ass. U.K.* 35, 431 (1956); H. Postma, *Neth. J. Sea Res.* 1, 359 (1961).

15 K. O. Emery, *Trans. Amer. Geophys. Union* 35, 217 (1954).

16. J. D. H. Strickland, *Fish. Res. Board Can. Ms. Rep. Ser. Oceanogr. Limnol. 88* (1961), p. 21 [cited by T. R. Parsons, *Progress in Oceanography*, M. Sears, Ed. (Pergamon, Oxford, 1963), vol. 1, pp. 203–239].

17. R. H. Meade, *Int. Ass. Sci. Hydrol. Publ. 78* (1968), p. 96.

18. J. D. Milliman, F. T. Manheim, R. M. Pratt, E. F. K. Zarudzki, *Woods Hole Oceanogr. Inst. Ref. 67–80* (1967).

19. N. Suzuki and K. Kato, *Bull. Fac. Fish. Hokkaido Univ.* 4, 132 (1953); S. Nishizawa, M. Fukuda, N. Inoue, *ibid. 5, 36* (1954).

20. A. P. Lisitsin, *Tr. Inst. Okeanol. Akad. Nauk SSSR* 13, 16 (1955).

21. R. H. Meade, *J. Sediment. Petrol.* 39, 222 (1969).

22. M. V. Klenova, *Dokl. Akad. Nauk SSSR* 127, 435 (1959); M. S. Barash, *Tr. Inst. Okeanol. Akad. Nauk SSSR* 56, 70 (1962).

23. N. G. Jerlov, *Optical Oceanography* (Elsevier, New York, 1968).

24. We thank J. V. A. Trumbull and A. R. Tagg of the U.S. Geological Survey, E. Uchupi, D. A. Ross, K. Bandel, and A. D. Colburn, Jr., of Woods Hole Oceanographic Institution, and T. D. Temple, Jr., and J. J. Temple of Scotland Neck, N. C., for aid in collecting samples; H. Richards and K. Muehlenbachs of WHOI for assistance in the laboratory; and D. W. Folger of WHOI, J. S. Schlee of the U. S. Geological Survey, and M. M. Nichols of Virginia Institute of Marine Science for reviewing the manuscript. Publication authorized by the director, U. S. Geological Survey. Contribution No. 2345 of the Woods Hole Oceanographic Institution.

MAX BLUMER

Scientific Aspects of the Oil Spill Problem

THE EXTENT OF MARINE OIL POLLUTION

Oil pollution is the almost inevitable consequence of our dependence on an oil-based technology. The use of a natural resource without losses is nearly impossible and environmental pollution occurs through intentional disposal or through inadvertent losses in production, transportation, refining and use. How large is the oil influx to the ocean? The washing of cargo tanks at sea, according to the director of Shell International, Marine Ltd.[1] had the potential in 1967 of introducing 2.8 million tons into the ocean, assuming that no use was made of the Load on Top (LOT) technique. With the increase in oil transport from 1967 to 1970 this potential has grown to 6 million tons. The LOT technique is not being applied to one quarter of the oil tonnage moved by tankers; consequently, these vessels introduce about 1.5 million tons of oil into the sea. The limitations of the LOT technique have been described by E. S. Dillon[2]: the technique is not always used even if the equipment exists, the equipment may be inadequate, shore receiving facilities may be lacking and principal limitations lie in the formation of emulsions in heavy seas or with heavy crude oils. Insufficient time may be available for the separation of the emulsion or the oil water interface may not be readily recognized. In addition the most toxic components of oil are also readily soluble in water and their disposal into the ocean could be avoided only if clean ballasting were substituted for the LOT technique. For these reasons it is estimated that the present practices in tanker ballasting introduce about 3 million tons of petroleum into the ocean. The pumping of bilges by vessels other than tankers contributes another 500,000 tons.[3] In addition, in-port losses from collisions and during loading and unloading contribute an estimated 1 million tons.[4]

Oil enters the ocean from many other sources whose magnitude is much less readily assessed. Among these are accidents on the high seas (Torrey Canyon) or near shore, outside of harbors (West Falmouth, Mass.), losses during exploration (oil based drilling mud) and production (Santa Barbara, Gulf of Mexico), in storage (submarine storage tanks) and in pipeline breaks, and

Max Blumer, "Scientific Aspects of the Oil Spill Problem," *Environmental Affairs*, vol. 1, no. 1 (April 1971), pp. 54–73. Reprinted by permission.
The author is Senior Scientist, Department of Chemistry, Woods Hole Oceanographic Institution, Woods Hole, Massachusetts. This paper was presented to a Conference on Ocean Oil Spills, held by the NATO Committee on Challenges of Modern Society, Brussels, November 2–6, 1970. Contribution No. 2616 of the Woods Hole Oceanographic Institution.
The author expresses his gratitude for continued support to the National Science Foundation, to the Office of Naval Research, and to the Federal Water Quality Administration.

spent marine lubricants and incompletely burned fuels. A major contribution may come from untreated domestic and industrial wastes; it is estimated that nearly 2 million tons of used lubricating oil is unaccounted for each year in the United States alone, and, a significant portion of this reaches our coastal waters.[5, 6]

Thus, the total annual oil influx to the ocean lies probably between 5 and 10 million tons. A more accurate assessment of the oil pollution of the oceans and of the relative contribution of different oils to the different marine environments is urgently needed. Such an assessment might well lie within the role of the NATO Committee on Challenges of the Modern Society.

With the anticipated increase in foreign and domestic oil production, with increased oil transport and with the shift of production to more hazardous regions (Alaska, continental shelf, deep ocean), we can expect a rapid increase of the spillage rate and of the oil influx to the ocean. Floating masses of crude oil ("tar") are now commonly encountered on the oceans and crude oil is present on most beaches. Oil occurs in the stomach of surface feeding fishes[7] and finely dispersed hydrocarbons occur in marine plants (e.g. sargassum[8]) and in the fat of fish and shellfish.[6, 9a] Hydrocarbons from a relatively small and restricted oil spill in the coastal waters of Massachusetts, U.S.A., have spread, nine months after the accident to an area occupying 5000 acres (20 km²) offshore and 500 acres (2 km²) in tidal rivers and marshes. The effect on the natural populations in this area has been catastrophic. The full extent of the coverage of the ocean bottom by petroleum hydrocarbons is unknown; chemical analyses are scarce or non-existent.

EVALUATION OF THE THREAT

Oil: immediate toxicity

All crude oils and all oil fractions except highly purified and pure materials are poisonous to all marine organisms. This is not a new finding. The wreck of the "Tampico" in Baja, California, Mexico (1957) "created a situation where a completely natural area was almost totally destroyed suddenly on a large scale. . . . Among the dead species were lobsters, abalone, sea urchins, starfish, mussels, clams and hosts of smaller forms."[10] Similarly, the spill of fuel oil in West Falmouth, Massachusetts, U.S.A., has virtually extinguished life in a productive coastal and intertidal area, with a complete kill extending over all phyla represented in that habitat (Hampson and Sanders[11] and unpublished data). Toxicity is immediate and leads to death within minutes or hours.[12]

Principally responsible for this immediate toxicity are three complex fractions. The *low boiling saturated hydrocarbons* have, until quite recently, been considered harmless to the marine environment. It has now been found that this fraction, which is rather readily soluble in sea water, produces at low concentration anaesthesia and narcosis and at greater concentration cell damage and death in a wide variety of lower animals; it may be especially damaging to the young forms of marine life.[13] The *low boiling aromatic hydrocarbons* are the most immediately toxic fraction. Benzene, toluene and xylene are acute poisons for man as well as for other organisms; naphthalene and phenanthrene are even more toxic to fishes than benzene, toluene and xylene.[14] These hydrocarbons and substituted one-, two-, and three-ring hydrocarbons of similar toxicity are abundant in all oils and most, especially the lower boiling, oil products. Low boiling aromatics are even more water soluble than the saturates and can kill marine organisms either by direct contact or through contact with dilute solutions. *Olefinic hydrocarbons,* intermediate in structure and properties, and probably in toxicity, between saturated and aromatic hydrocarbons are absent in crude oil but occur in refining products (e.g., gasoline and cracked products) and are in part responsible for their immediate toxicity.

Numerous other components of crude oils are toxic. Among those named by Speers and Whitehead,[15] cresols, xylenols, naphthols, quinoline and substituted quinolines and pyridines and hydroxybenzoquinolines are of special concern here because of their great toxicity and their solubility in water. It is unfortunate that statements which disclaim this established toxicity are still being circulated. Simpson[16] claimed that "there is no evidence that oil spilt round the British Isles has ever killed any of these (mussels, cockles, winkles, oysters, shrimps, lobsters, crabs) shellfish." It was obvious when this statement was made that such animals were indeed killed by the accident of the Torrey Canyon as well as by earlier accidents; work since then has confirmed the earlier investigation. In addition, this statement, by its emphasis only on the adult life forms, implies wrongly that juvenile forms were also unaffected.

Oil and cancer

The higher boiling crude oil fractions are rich in multiring aromatic compounds. It was at one time thought that only a few of these compounds, mainly 3,4-benzopyrene, were capable of inducing cancer. As R. A. Dean[17] of British Petroleum Company stated, "no 3,4-benzopyrene has been detected in any crude oil . . . [I]t therefore seems that the risk to the health of a member of the public by spillage of oil at sea is probably far less than that which he normally encounters by eating the foods he enjoys." However, at the time this statement was made, carcinogenic fractions containing 1,2-benzanthracene and alkylbenzanthracenes had already been isolated by Carruthers, Stewart and Watkins[18] and it was known that biological tests have shown that the extracts obtained from high-boiling fractions of the Kuwait oil . . . (method) . . . are carcinogenic." Further, "Benzanthracene derivatives, however, are evidently not the only type of carcinogen in the oil. . . ." In 1968, the year when Dean claimed the absence of the powerful carcinogen 3,4 benzopyrene in crude oil, this hydrocarbon was isolated in crude oil from Libya, Venezuela and the Persian Gulf.[19] The amounts measured were between 450 and 1800 milligrams per ton of the crude oil.

Thus, we know that chemicals responsible for cancer in animals and man occur in petroleum. The causation of cancer in man by crude oil and oil products was observed some years ago, when a high incidence of skin cancer in some refinery personnel was observed. The cause was traced to prolonged skin contact by these persons with petroleum and with refinery products.

Better plant design and education, aimed at preventing the contact, have since reduced or eliminated this hazard.[20] However, these incidents have demonstrated that oil and oil products can cause cancer in man, and have supported the conclusions based on the finding of known carcinogens in oil. These references and a general knowledge of the composition of crude oils suggest that all crude oils and all oil products containing high boiling aromatic hydrocarbons should be viewed as potential cancer inducers.

Safeguards in plant operations protect the public from this hazard. However, when oil is spilled into the environment we lose control over it and should again be concerned about the possible public health hazard from cancer-causing chemicals in the oil. We have shown that marine organisms ingest and retain hydrocarbons to which they are exposed. These are transferred to and retained by predators. In this way even animals that were not directly exposed to a spill can become polluted by eating contaminated chemicals. This has severe implications for commercial fisheries and for human health. It suggests that marketing and eating of oil contaminated fish and shellfish at the very least increases the body burden of carcinogenic chemicals and may constitute a public health hazard.

Other questions suggest themselves: Floating masses of crude oil now cover all oceans and are being washed up on shores. It has been thought that such stranded lumps are of little consequence ecologically. It has been shown that such lumps, even after considerable weathering, still contain nearly the full range of hydrocarbons of the original crude oil, extending in boiling point as low as 100°C. Thus such lumps still contain some of the immediately toxic lower boiling hydrocarbons. In addition, the oil lumps contain all of the potentially carcinogenic material in the 300–500° boiling fraction. The presence of oil lumps ("tar") or finely dispersed oil on recreational beaches may well constitute a severe public health hazard, through continued skin contact.

Low level effects of oil pollution

The short-term toxicity of crude oil and of oil products and their carcinogenic properties are fairly well understood. In contrast to this we are rather ignorant about the long term and low level effects of oil pollution. These may well be far more serious and long lasting than the more obvious short term effects. Let us look at low level interference of oil pollution with the marine ecology.

Many biological processes which are important for the survival of marine organisms and which occupy key positions in their life processes are mediated by extremely low concentration of chemical messengers in the sea water. We have demonstrated that marine predators are attracted to their prey by organic compounds at concentrations below the part per billion level.[21] Such chemical attraction — and in a similar way repulsion — plays a role in the finding of food, the escape from predators, in homing of many commercially important species of fishes, in the selection of habitats and in sex attraction. There is good reason to believe that pollution interferes with these processes in two ways, by blocking the taste receptors and by mimicking for natural stimuli. The latter leads to false response. Those crude oil fractions likely to interfere with such processes are the high boiling saturated and aromatic hydrocarbons and

the full range of the olefinic hydrocarbons. It is obvious that a very simple —
and seemingly innocuous — interference at extremely low concentration levels
may have a disastrous effect on the survival of any marine species and on many
other species to which it is tied by the marine food chain.

Research in this critical area is urgently needed. The experience with
DDT has shown that low level effects are unpredictable and may suddenly
become an ecological threat of unanticipated magnitude.

The persistence of oil in the environment

Hydrocarbons are among the most persistent organic chemicals in the marine
environment. It has been demonstrated that hydrocarbons are transferred from
prey to predator and that they may be retained in organisms for long time
periods, if not for life. Thus, a coastal spill near Cape Cod, Massachusetts,
U.S.A., has led to the pollution of shellfish by fuel oil. Transplanting of the
shellfish to clean water does not remove the hydrocarbons from the tissues.
Oil may contaminate organisms not only at the time of the spill; hydrocarbon-
loaded sediments continue to be a source of pollution for many months after
the accident.

Oil, though lighter than water, does not remain at the sea surface alone;
storms, or the uptake of organisms or minerals, sink the oil. Oil at the sea
bottom has been found after the accidents of the Torrey Canyon, at Santa
Barbara and near Cape Cod. Clay minerals with adsorbed organic matter are
an excellent adsorbent for hydrocarbons; they retain oil and may transport it
to areas distant from the primary spill. Thus, ten months after the accident at
Cape Cod, the pollution of the bottom sediments covers an area that is much
larger than that immediately after the spill. In sediments, especially if they are
anaerobic, oil is stable for long time periods. Indeed, it is a key fact of
organic geochemistry that hydrocarbons in anaerobic recent sediments survive
for millions of years until they eventually contribute to the formation of
petroleum.

COUNTERMEASURES

Compared to the number and size of accidents and disasters the present
countermeasures are inadequate. Thus, in spite of considerable improvement
in skimming efficiency since the Santa Barbara accident, only 10% of the
oil spilled from the Chevron well in the Gulf of Mexico was recovered.[22]
From an ecological point of view this gain is nearly meaningless. While we
may remain hopeful that the gross esthetic damage from oil spills may be
avoided in the future, there is no reason to be hopeful that existing or planned
countermeasures will eliminate the biological impact of oil pollution.

The most immediately toxic fractions of oil and oil products are soluble
in sea water; therefore, biological damage will occur at the very moment of
the accident. Water currents will immediately spread the toxic plume of
dissolved oil components and, if the accident occurs in inshore waters, the
whole water column will be poisoned even if the bulk of the oil floats on the
surface. The speed with which the oil dissolves is increased by agitation, and

in storms the oil will partly emulsify and will then present a much larger surface area to the water; consequently, the toxic fractions dissolve more rapidly and reach higher concentrations. From the point of view of avoiding the immediate biological effect of oil spills, countermeasures are completely effective only if *all of the oil is recovered immediately* after the spill. *The technology to achieve this goal does not exist.*

Oil spills damage many coastal and marine values: water fowl, fisheries, and recreational resources; they lead to increased erosion; they diminish the water quality and may threaten human life or property through fire hazard. A judicious choice has to be made in each case: which — if any — of the existing but imperfect countermeasures to apply to minimize the overall damage or the damage to the most valuable resources. Guidelines for the use of counter-measures, especially of chemical countermeasures, exist[23] and are being improved.[24] Some comments on the ecological effects and desirability of the existing countermeasures appear appropriate.

Detergents and dispersants

The toxic, solvent-based detergents which did so much damage in the clean-up after the Torrey Canyon accident are presently only in limited use. However, so-called "nontoxic dispersants" have been developed. The term "nontoxic" is misleading; these chemicals may be nontoxic to a limited number of often quite resistant test organisms but they are rarely tested in their effects upon a very wide spectrum of marine organisms including their juvenile forms, prefer-ably in their normal habitat. Further, in actual use all dispersant-oil mixtures are severely toxic, because of the inherent toxicity of the oil, and bacterial degradation of "nontoxic" detergents may lead to toxic breakdown products.

The effect of a dispersant is to lower the surface tension of the oil to a point where it will disperse in the form of small droplets. It is recommended that the breakup of the oil slick be aided by agitation, natural or mechanical. Thus, the purpose of the detergent is essentially a cosmetic one. However, the recommendation to apply dispersants is often made in disregard of their ecological effects. Instead of removing the oil, dispersants push the oil actively into the marine environment; because of the finer degree of dispersion, the immediately toxic fraction dissolves rapidly and reaches a higher concentration in the sea water than it would if natural dispersal were allowed. The long term poisons (e.g. the carcinogens) are made available to and are ingested by marine filter feeders, and they can eventually return to man incorporated into the food he recovers from the ocean.

For these reasons I feel that the use of dispersants is unacceptable, in-shore or offshore, except under special circumstances, e.g., extreme fire hazard from spillage of gasoline, as outlined in the Contingency Plan for Oil Spills, Federal Water Quality Administration, 1969.[23,24]

Physical sinking

Sinking has been recommended. "The long term effects on marine life will not be as disastrous as previously envisaged. Sinking of oil may result in the

mobile bottom dwellers moving to new locations for several years; however, conditions may return to normal as the oil decays."[25] Again, these conclusions disregard our present knowledge of the effect of oil spills.

Sunken oil will kill the bottom faunas rapidly, before most mobile
dwellers have time to move away. The sessile forms of commercial importance
(oysters, scallops, etc.) will be killed and other mobile organisms (lobsters)
may be attracted into the direction of the spill where the exposure will contaminate or kill them. The persistent fraction of the oil which is not readily
attacked by bacteria contains the long term poisons, e.g., the carcinogens, and
they will remain on the sea bottom for very long periods of time. Exposure
to these compounds may damage organisms or render them unfit for human
nutrition even after the area has been repopulated.

The bacterial degradation of sunken oil requires much oxygen. As a
result, sediments loaded with oil become anaerobic and bacterial degradation
and reworking of the sediments by aerobic benthic organisms is arrested. It
is one of the key principles of organic geochemistry that hydrocarbons in
anaerobic sediments persist for millions of years. Similarly, sunken oil will
remain; it will slow down the resettlement of the polluted area; and it may
constitute a source for the pollution of the water columns and of fisheries
resources for a long time after the original accident.

For these reasons I believe that sinking of oil is unacceptable in the
productive coastal and offshore regions. Before we apply this technique to the
deep ocean with its limited oxygen supply and its fragile faunas we should
gather more information about the interplay of the deep marine life with
the commercial species of shallower waters.

Combustion

Burning the oil through the addition of wicks or oxidants appears more attractive from the point of view of avoiding biological damage than dispersion
and sinking. However, it will be effective only if burning can start immediately after a spill. For complete combustion, the entire spill must be covered
by the combustion promoters, since burning will not extend to the untreated
areas; in practice, in stormy conditions, this may be impossible to achieve.

Mechanical containment and removal

Containment and removal appear ideal from the point of avoiding biological
damage. However, they can be effective only if applied immediately after the
accident. Under severe weather conditions floating booms and barriers are
ineffective. Booms were applied during the West Falmouth oil spill; however,
the biological damage in the sealed-off harbors was severe and was caused
probably by the oil which bypassed the booms in solution in sea water and in
the form of wind-dispersed droplets.

Bacterial degradation

Hydrocarbons in the sea are naturally degraded by marine microorganisms.
Many hope to make this the basis of an oil removal technology through

bacterial seeding and fertilization of oil slicks. However, great obstacles and many unknowns stand in the way of the application of this attractive idea.

No single microbial species will degrade any whole crude oil; bacteria are highly selective and complete degradation requires many different bacterial species. Bacterial oxidation of hydrocarbons produces many intermediates which may be more toxic than the hydrocarbons; therefore, organisms are also required that will further attack the hydrocarbon decomposition products.

Hydrocarbons and other compounds in crude oil may be bacteriostatic or bacteriocidal; this may reduce the rate of degradation, where it is most urgently needed. The fraction of crude oil that is most readily attacked by bacteria is the least toxic one, the normal paraffins; the toxic aromatic hydrocarbons, especially the carcinogenic polynuclear aromatics, are not rapidly attacked.

The oxygen requirement in bacterial oil degradation is severe; the complete oxidation of 1 gallon of crude oil requires all the dissolved oxygen in 320,000 gallons of air saturated sea water. Therefore, oxidation may be slow in areas where the oxygen content has been lowered by previous pollution and the bacterial degradation may cause additional ecological damage through oxygen depletion.

Cost effectiveness

The high value of fisheries resources, which exceeds that of the oil recovery from the sea, and the importance of marine proteins for human nutrition demand that cost effectiveness analysis of oil spill countermeasures consider the cost of direct and indirect ecological damage. It is disappointing that existing studies completely neglect to consider these real values.[17] A similarly one-sided approach would be, for instance, a demand by fisheries concerns that all marine oil production and shipping be terminated, since it clearly interferes with fisheries interests.

We must start to realize that we are paying for the damage to the environment, especially if the damage is as tangible as that of oil pollution to fisheries resources and to recreation. Experience has shown that cleaning up a polluted aquatic environment is much more expensive than it would have been to keep the environment clean from the beginning.[26] In terms of minimizing the environmental damage, spill prevention will produce far greater returns than cleanup — and we believe that this relationship will hold in a *realistic* analysis of the overall cost effectiveness of prevention or cleanup costs.

THE RISK OF MARINE OIL POLLUTION

The risk to marine life

Our knowledge of crude oil composition and of the effects of petroleum on marine organisms in the laboratory and in the marine environment force the conclusion that petroleum and petroleum products are toxic to most or all marine organisms. Petroleum hydrocarbons are persistent poisons. They enter the marine food chain, they are stabilized in the lipids of marine organisms and they are transferred from prey to predator. The persistence is especially severe for the most poisonous compounds of oil; most of these do not normally occur in organisms and natural pathways for their biodegradation are missing.

Pollution with crude oil and oil fractions *damages the marine ecology* through different effects:

1. Direct kill of organisms through coating and asphyxiation.[27]
2. Direct kill through contact poisoning of organisms.
3. Direct kill through exposure to the water soluble toxic components of oil at some distance in space and time from the accident.
4. Destruction of the generally more sensitive juvenile forms of organisms.
5. Destruction of the food sources of higher species.
6. Incorporation of sublethal amounts of oil and oil products into organisms resulting in reduced resistance to infection and other stresses (the principal cause of death in birds surviving the immediate exposure to oil[28]).
7. Incorporation of carcinogenic and potentially mutagenic chemicals into marine organisms.
8. Low level effects that may interrupt any of the numerous events necessary for the propagation of marine species and for the survival of those species which stand higher in the marine food web.

The degree of toxicity of oil to marine organisms and the mode of action are fairly well understood. On the other hand, we are still far from understanding the effect of the existing and increasing oil pollution on the marine ecology on a large, especially world wide, scale.

Few, if any, comprehensive studies of the effects of oil spills on the marine ecology have been undertaken. Petroleum and petroleum products are toxic *chemicals*; the long term biological effect of oil and its persistence cannot be studied without chemical analyses. Unfortunately, chemical analysis has not been used to support such studies in the past and conclusions on the persistence of oil in the environment have been arrived at solely by visual inspection. This is not sufficient; a sediment can be uninhabitable to marine bottom organisms because of the presence of finely divided oil, but the oil may not be visually evident. Marine foods may be polluted by petroleum and may be hazardous to man but neither taste nor visual observation may disclose the presence of the toxic hydrocarbons.

A coordinated biological and chemical study of the long-term effect and fate of a coastal oil spill in West Falmouth, Massachusetts, U.S.A. has shown that even a relatively low boiling, soluble and volatile oil persists and damages the ecology for many months after the spill. In this instance about 650 tons of #2 fuel oil were accidentally discharged into the coastal waters off the Massachusetts coast. I wish to summarize our present findings of the effect of this accident.

Persistence and spread of the pollution[9a, b]

Oil from the accident has been incorporated into the sediments of the tidal rivers and marshes and into the offshore sediments, down to 42 feet, the greatest water depth in the sea. The fuel oil is still present in inshore and offshore sediments, eight months after the accident. The pollution has been spreading on the sea bottom and now covers at least 5000 acres offshore and 500 acres of marshes and tidal rivers. This is a much larger area than that affected immediately after the accident. Bacterial degradation of the oil is slow; degradation is still negligible in the most heavily polluted areas and the more rapid degradation in outlying, less affected, areas has been reversed by the influx of less degraded oil from the more polluted regions. The kill of bottom plants and animals has reduced the stability of marshland and sea bottom; increased erosion results and may be responsible for the spread of the pollution along the sea bottom.

Bacterial degradation first attacks the least toxic hydrocarbons. The hydrocarbons remaining in the sediments are now more toxic on an equal weight basis than immediately after the spill. Oil has penetrated the marshes to a depth of at least 1–2 feet; bacterial degradation within the marsh sediment is still negligible eight months after the accident.

Biological effects of the pollution[11, 12]

Where oil can be detected in the sediments there has been a kill of animals; in the most polluted areas the kill has been almost total. Control stations outside the area contain normal, healthy bottom faunas. The kill associated with the presence of oil is detected down to the maximum water depth in the area. A massive, immediate kill occurred offshore during the first few days after the accident. Affected were a wide range of fish, shellfish, worms, crabs and other crustaceans and invertebrates. Bottom living fishes and lobsters were killed and washed up on the beaches. Trawls in 10 feet of water showed 95% of the animals dead and many still dying. The bottom sediments contained many dead clams, crustaceans and snails. Fish, crabs, shellfish and invertebrates were killed in the tidal Wild Harbor River; and in the most heavily polluted locations of the river almost no animals have survived.

The affected areas have not been repopulated, nine months after the accident. Mussels that survived last year's spill as juveniles have developed almost no eggs and sperm.

Effect on commercial shellfish values[9a, b]

Oil from the spill was incorporated into oysters, scallops, soft-shell clams and quahaugs. As a result, the area had to be closed to the taking of shellfish.

The 1970 crop of shellfish is as heavily contaminated as was last year's crop. Closure will have to be maintained at least through this second year and will have to be extended to areas more distant from the spill than last year. Oysters that were removed from the polluted area and that were maintained in clean water for as long as 6 months retained the oil without change in composition or quantity. Thus, once contaminated, shellfish cannot cleanse themselves of oil pollution.

The tidal Wild Harbor River, a productive shellfish area of about 22 acres, contains an estimated 4 tons of the fuel oil. This amount has destroyed the shellfish harvest for two years. The severe biological damage to the area and the slow rate of biodegradation of the oil suggest that the productivity will be ruined for a longer time.

Some have commented to us that the effects measured in the West Falmouth oil spill are not representative of those from a crude oil spill and that #2 fuel oil is more toxic than petroleum. However, the fuel oil is a typical refinery product that is involved in marine shipping and in many marine spillages; also, the fuel oil is a part of petroleum and as such it is contained within petroleum. Therefore, its effect is typical, both for unrefined oil and for refinery products. In terms of chemical composition crude oils span a wide range; many lighter crude oils have a composition very similar to those of the fuel oils and their toxicity and environmental danger corresponds respectively. However, many crude oils contain more of the persistent, long term poisons, including the carcinogens, than the fuel oils. Therefore, crude oils can be expected to have even more serious long term effects than the lower boiling fuel oils.

The pollution of fisheries resources in the West Falmouth oil spill is independent of the molecular size of the hydrocarbons; the oil taken up reflects exactly the boiling point distribution of the spilled oil. Thus, spills by other oils of different boiling point distributions can be expected to destroy fisheries resources in the same manner.

We believe that the environmental hazard of oil and oil products has been widely underestimated, because of the lack of thorough and extended investigations. The toxicity and persistence of the oil and the destruction of the fisheries resources observed in West Falmouth are typical for the effects of marine oil pollution.

The risk to human use of marine resources

The destruction of marine organisms, of their habitats and food sources directly affects man and his intent to utilize marine proteins for the nutrition of an expanding population. However, the presence in oil of toxic and carcinogenic compounds combined with the persistence of hydrocarbons in the marine food chain poses an even more direct threat to human health. The magnitude of this problem is difficult to assess at this time. Our knowledge of the occurrence of carcinogens in oil is recent and their relative concentrations have been measured in very few oils. Also, our understanding of the fate of hydrocarbons, especially of carcinogens, in the marine food chain needs to be expanded.

Methods for the analysis of fisheries products for the presence of hazardous hydrocarbons exist and are relatively simple and the analyses are inexpensive. In spite of this no public laboratory in the United States — and probably in the world — can routinely perform such analysis for public health authorities. There is increasing evidence that fish and shellfish have been and are now being marketed which are hazardous from a public health point of view. Taste tests, which are commonly used to test for the presence of oil pollutants in fish or shellfish, are inconclusive. Only a small fraction of petroleum has a pronounced odor; this may be lost while the more harmful long term poisons are retained. Boiling or frying may remove the odor but will not eliminate the toxicity.

The risk to the recreational use of marine resources

The presence of petroleum, petroleum products and petroleum residue ("tar," "beach tar") is now common on most recreational beaches. Toxic hydrocarbons contained in crude oil can pass through the barrier of the human skin and the prolonged skin contact with carcinogenic hydrocarbons constitutes a public health hazard. Intense solar radiation is known to be one of the contributing factors for skin cancer. The presence of carcinogens in beach tar may increase the risk to the public in a situation where a severe stress from solar radiation already exists.

The risk to water utilization

Many of the toxic petroleum hydrocarbons are also water soluble. Water treatment plants, especially those using distillation, may transfer or concentrate the steam-volatile toxic hydrocarbons into the refined water streams, especially if dissolved hydrocarbons are present in the feed streams or if particulate oil finds its way into the plant intake.

CONCLUSIONS

1. Oil and oil products must be recognized as poisons that damage the marine ecology and that are dangerous to man. Fisheries resources are destroyed through direct kill of commercially valuable species, through sublethal damage and through the destruction of food sources. Fisheries products that are contaminated by oil must be considered as a public health hazard.

2. Only crude estimates exist of the extent of marine oil pollution. We need surveys that can assess the influx of petroleum and petroleum products into the ocean. They should be world-wide and special attention should be paid to the productive regions of the ocean; data are needed on the oil influx from tankers and non-tanker vessels, on losses in ports, on offshore and inshore accidents from shipping, exploration and production and on the influx of oil from domestic and industrial wastes.

3. The marine ecology is changing rapidly in many areas as a result of man's activities. We need to establish baseline information on composition and densities of marine faunas and floras and on the hydrocarbon levels and concentrations encountered in marine organisms, sediments and in the water masses.

4. All precautions must be taken to prevent oil spills. Prevention measures must be aimed at eliminating human error, at the present time the principal cause of oil spills.

5. Spill prevention must be backed by effective surveillance and law enforcement. *In terms of cost effectiveness spill prevention is far superior to cleanup.*

6. Perfection and further extension of the use of the Load on Top methods is promising as a first step in reduction of the oil pollution from tankers. The effectiveness of the technique should be more closely assessed and improvements are necessary in interface detection, separation and measurement of hydrocarbon content in the effluent, both in the dispersed and dissolved state. On a longer time scale, clean ballast techniques should supersede the Load on Top technique.

7. The impact of oil pollution on marine organisms and on sources of human food from the ocean has been underestimated because of the lack of coordinated chemical and biological investigations. Studies of the effect of oil spills on organisms in different geographic and climatic regions are needed. The persistence of hydrocarbon pollution in sea water, sediments and organisms should be studied.

8. Research is urgently needed on the low-level and long term effects of oil pollution. Does oil pollution interfere with feeding and life processes at concentrations below those where effects are immediately measured? Are hydrocarbons concentrated in the marine food chain?

9. Carcinogens have been isolated from crude oil but additional efforts are needed to define further the concentrations and types of carcinogens in different crude oils and oil products.

10. The public health hazard from oil derived carcinogens must be studied. What are the levels of oil derived carcinogens ingested by man and how wide is the exposure of the population? How much does this increase the present body burden with carcinogens? Is there direct evidence for the causation of cancer in man by petroleum and petroleum products outside of oil refinery operations?

11. Public laboratories must be established for the analysis of fisheries products for toxic and carcinogenic chemicals derived from oil and oil products, and tolerance levels will have to be set.

12. The ocean has a limited tolerance for hydrocarbon pollution. The tolerance varies with the composition of the hydrocarbons and is different in different regions and in different ecological sub-systems. The tolerance of the water column may be greater than that of the sediments and of organisms. An assessment of this inherent tolerance is necessary to determine the maximum pollution load that can be imposed on the environment.

13. Countermeasures which remove the oil from the environment reduce the ecological impact and danger to fisheries resources. All efforts should be aimed at the most rapid and complete removal since the extent of the biological damage increases with extended exposure of the oil to sea water.

14. Countermeasures that introduce the entire, undegraded oil into the environment should be used only as a last resort in situations such as those outlined in the Contingency Plan of the Federal Water Quality Administration, involving extreme hazard to a major segment of a vulnerable species of waterfowl or to prevent hazard to life and limb or substantial hazard of fire to property. Even in those cases assessment of the long term ecological hazard must enter into the decision whether to use these countermeasures (detergents, dispersants, sinking agents).

15. As other countermeasures become more effective, the use of de-

tergents, dispersants and sinking agents should be further curtailed or abolished.

16. Efforts to intensify the natural bacterial degradation of oil in the environment appear promising and should be supported by basic research and development.

17. Ecological damage and damage to fisheries resources are direct consequences of oil spills. In the future, the cost of oil leases should include a fee for environmental protection.

18. Environmental protection funds derived from oil leases should be used to accomplish the necessary research and education in the oil pollution field.

References

1. Statement by J. H. Kirby, quoted by J. R. Wiggins, Washington Post, March 15, 1970.

2. Dillon, E. Scott, "Ship Construction and Operation Standards for Oil Pollution Abatement," presented to a Conference on Ocean Oil Spills, held by the NATO Committee on Challenges of Modern Society, Brussels, November 2–6, 1970.

3. Statement by C. Cortelyou, Mobil Oil Company, quoted by W. D. Smith, The New York Times, April 19, 1970.

4. Blumer, M., "Oil Pollution of the Ocean," In: *Oil on the Sea,* D. P. Hoult, ed., Plenum Press, 1969.

5. Anon., "Final Report of the Task Force on Used Oil Disposal," American Petroleum Institute, New York, N. Y., 1970.

6. Murphy, T. A., "Environmental Effects of Oil Pollution," Paper presented to the Session on Oil Pollution Control, American Society of Civil Engineers, Boston, Mass., July 13, 1970.

7. Horn, M. H., Teal, J. H. and Backus, R. H., "Petroleum Lumps on the Surface of the Sea," Science, *168,* 245, 1970.

8. Youngblood, W. W. and Blumer, M., unpublished data, 1970.

9a. Blumer, M., Souza, G., and Sass, J., "Hydrocarbon Pollution of Edible Shellfish by an Oil Spill," Marine Biology, *5,* 195–202, 1970.

9b. Blumer, M., Testimony before the Conservation and Natural Resources Subcommittee, Washington, D.C., July 22, 1970.

10. North, W. J., "Tampico, a Study of Destruction and Restoration," Sea Frontiers, *13,* 212–217, 1967.

11. Hampson, G. R., and Sanders, H. L., "Local Oil Spill," Oceanus, *15,* 8–10, 1969.

12. Sanders, H. L., Testimony before the Conservation and Natural Resources Subcommittee, Washington, D.C., July 22, 1970.

13. Goldacre, R. J., "The Effects of Detergents and Oils on the Cell Membrane," Suppl. to Vol. 2 of Field Studies, Field Studies Council, London, 131–137, 1968.

14. Wilber, C. G., *The Biological Aspects of Water Pollution,* Charles C. Thomas, Publisher, Springfield, Ill., 1969.

15. Speers, G. C. and Whithead, E. V., "Crude Petroleum," In: *Organic Geochemistry,* Eglinton, G. and Murphy, M. R. J., eds., Springer, Berlin, 638–675, 1969.

16. Simpson, A. C., "Oil, Emulsifiers and Commercial Shell Fish," Suppl. to Vol. 2 of Field Studies, Field Studies Council, London, 91–98, 1968.

17. Dean, R. A., "The Chemistry of Crude Oils in Relation to their Spillage on the Sea," Suppl. to Vol. 2 of Field Studies, Field Studies Council, London, 1–6, 1968.

18. Carruthers, W., Stewart, H. N. M. and Watkins, D. A. M., "1,2-Benzanthracene Derivatives in a Kuwait Mineral Oil," Nature, *213,* 691–692, 1967.

19. Graef, W. and Winter, C., "3,4 Benzopyrene in Erdoel," Arch. Hyg. *152/4,* 289–293, 1968.

20. Eckardt, R. E., "Cancer Prevention in the Petroleum Industry," Int. J. Cancer, 3, 656–661, 1967.

21. Whittle, K. J. and Blumer, M., "Chemotaxis in Starfish, Symposium on Organic Chemistry of Natural Waters," University of Alaska, Fairbanks, Alaska, 1968 (in press).

22. Wayland, R. G., Federal Regulations and Pollution Controls on the U.S. Offshore Oil Industry, this conference.

23. Contingency Plan for Spills of Oil and Other Hazardous Materials in New England, U.S. Dept. Interior, Federal Water Quality Administration, Draft, 1969.

24. Schedule of Dispersants and Other Chemicals to Treat Oil Spills, May 15, 1970, Interim Schedule, Federal Water Quality Administration, 1970.

25. Little, A. D., Inc., "Combating Pollution Created by Oil Spills," Report to the Dept. of Transportation, U.S. Coast Guard, Vol. 1: Methods, p. 71386 (R), June 30, 1969.

26. Ketchum, B. H., "Biological Effects of Pollution of Estuaries and Coastal Waters," Boston Univ. Press, 1970 (in press).

27. Arthur, D. R., "The Biological Problems of Littoral Pollution by Oil and Emulsifiers — a Summing up," Suppl. to Vol. 2 of Field Studies, Field Studies Council, London, 159–164, 1968.

28. Beer, J. V., "Post-Mortem Findings in Oiled Auks during Attempted Rehabilitation," Suppl. to Vol. 2 of Field Studies, Field Studies Council, London, 123–129, 1968.

LUTHER J. CARTER

Galveston Bay: Test Case of an Estuary in Crisis

For the environmentalist in search of horror stories, Galveston Bay, now beset by an astonishing variety of problems, is a good place to look. In fact, for the second time in 2½ years members of the President's Water Pollution Control Advisory Board last month toured the bay system and expressed dismay at what they found. Nowhere are the problems of pollution control and environmental management more frustrating and complex than here on this important Gulf Coast estuary, now threatened with the loss of its valuable fishery and recreational resources.

As is true of most environmental problems elsewhere, a factor contributing to the problems of Galveston Bay has been the rapid growth of population and industrial activity in the surrounding area. This growth, which has created vast new demands on water supplies and waste disposal facilities, has been rivaled in Texas only by that in the Dallas-Fort Worth region. Galveston and Texas City, at the mouth of the bay, together have some 115,000 people, and their commercial and industrial activities (such as the complex of oil refineries and chemical plants at Texas City) are significant. But the big growth, of course, has taken place in and around Houston, which sprawls over the flat coastal prairie near the head of the bay.

Luther J. Carter, "Galveston Bay: Test Case of an Estuary in Crisis," *Science*, vol. 167 (February 20, 1970), pp. 1102–1108. Copyright 1970 by the American Association for the Advancement of Science. Reprinted by permission.

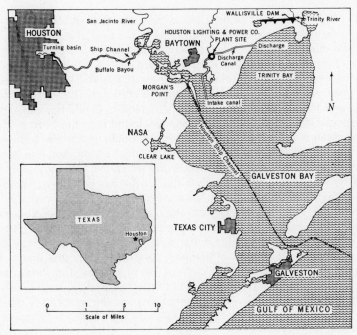

Figure 1

A major event in the history of Houston and the bay area was the construction of the Houston Ship Channel in 1914, which allowed ocean-going vessels to pass through the bay and continue up Buffalo Bayou to the turning basin in Houston, 50 miles from the Gulf of Mexico. The Ship Channel was to make Houston a major port, now surpassed in total tonnages handled by only two other U.S. ports, New York and New Orleans. Moreover, land along the Ship Channel and Buffalo Bayou was to become prime industrial property, especially attractive to oil companies seeking refinery sites near the Texas oil fields and handy to major shipping lanes. Today, the Ship Channel is lined with refineries, chemical and petrochemical plants, fertilizer factories, gypsum and cement plants, a steel mill, and other industrial facilities. This industrial growth has helped to push the population of the Houston metropolitan area to nearly 2 million, or about three times what it was 30 years ago.

Consider for a moment Galveston Bay as it is and as it used to be. Extending over 533 square miles, the bay is the largest of the estuaries on the Texas coast. The bay still supports major commercial and sports fisheries, and oysters, shrimp, crabs, and redfish, sea trout, and other finfish are plentiful. However, nearly half of the bay is now closed to oyster harvesting because of pollution, although fortunately the most productive oyster reefs are in waters still open to harvesting. Fishery biologists are worried that, given the degradation and numerous man-made changes in the bay environment, the bay's productivity for marine life will decline. And, since the bay is an important nursery for shrimp and certain fish (such as croakers, anchovies, and menhaden) which spend part of their life cycle in the Gulf of Mexico, conditions that hurt fishing in the bay will hurt fishing in the Gulf also.

Like other estuaries, Galveston Bay is a brackish body of water which, in general, becomes less salty toward the head of the bay where there is an inflow of fresh water from tributaries. For oysters brackish water is essential, as they can survive in neither fresh water nor seawater. The juvenile forms of shrimp and finfish such as menhaden also require brackish water, although these species do best in the lower salinities found near the head of the bay. The bay waters are enriched by nutrients brought in by the tributaries or flushed out of the shallows and marshes by tidal action, and this too helps to account for the abundance of marine life which this estuary supports.

Fifty years ago perhaps nearly a fifth of the bay bottom was covered by exposed oyster shell, much of it lying in extensive semifossilized shell reefs. Representative Bob Eckhardt, Democratic congressman from Houston and long a crusader for protection of the bay, has described these reefs: "[They] are like a miniature mountain range under water. Their sluices and ridges provide a nursery ground for myriads of marine organisms. This minute marine life, in turn, provides food for the next cycle of life in the bay, the shrimp and the smaller fishes. The shrimp and the small fishes then provide food for the large fish, the game species such as the channel bass and the spotted sea trout. . . ."

RADICAL CHANGES

The bay environment has experienced, and is still undergoing, radical changes. Consider the following:

Shelldredging. Shelldredgers have removed most of the shell from the bay, often taking exposed shell as well as shell underlying a heavy layer of silt. Shell is valuable in highway construction and for other uses (as in the manufacture of cement), and from it fortunes have been made. The U.S. Army Corps of Engineers has moved finally to protect major reefs that are still left and state authorities have tightened their own formerly inadequate regulations for protection of reefs. Little shelldredging is now being done, but until recently, the dredges were taking millions of cubic yards of shell from the bay each year. Not only were shell reefs destroyed but in some cases the dredging and washing of shell caused the silting up of parts of reefs bearing live oysters.

Water diversions. Livingston Reservoir, which has just been built on the Trinity River (the largest of the bay's tributaries) by the City of Houston and the Trinity River Authority, will store water largely for diversion to Houston. Its effect on the bay will be twofold: first, the flow of fresh water into the bay will be reduced, salinities will be increased, and the production of shrimp, oysters, and other marine life may be hurt; second, while most of the water diverted to Houston will later be returned by way of the Ship Channel, it will return in a used — and polluted — condition. The San Jacinto River (the bay's second largest tributary) was dammed by the City of Houston in 1954, and now, except during periods of high flow, most of its water is used by the city and discharged as waste water into the Ship Channel.

Still other diversions may be in the offing. A $752-million navigation project would open up the Trinity River to barge traffic all the way to Dallas and Fort Worth, some 360 miles by river from the bay, and further reduce flows of fresh water into the bay. This project has been authorized by Congress, and $150,000 for advanced planning has been appropriated. An even more ambitious proposal, known as the Texas Water Plan, calls for the construction (as part of a multibillion-dollar program to meet water needs throughout the state) of a 400-mile canal just inland from the Gulf of Mexico, to link together all major rivers flowing into the Gulf. The Water Plan, still being promoted by the Texas Water Development Board despite its rejection in a referendum last November, is supposed to provide for an ample flow of water into the estuaries but many people fear that the estuaries would be shortchanged during times of water scarcity.

Loss of marshlands. The Wallisville Dam, a project of the U.S. Army Corps of Engineers, is being built on the Trinity River about 4 miles upstream from where it enters Trinity Bay, which is a part of Galveston Bay. Primarily, the purpose of the dam is to open the lower river to navigation and to keep salt water from intruding upstream to the intakes of water supply and irrigation systems. Because the dam has little storage capacity, the project will never substantially reduce the flow of fresh water into the bay. But it is eliminating 20,000 acres of brackish ponds, sloughs, marshes, and bottomland, nearly all of which biologists of the U.S. Fish and Wildlife Service regard as prime shrimp and finfish nursery grounds with an annual productive capacity of not less than $300 an acre and probably more.

BENEFITS LESS THAN COSTS

The biologists' estimates, which are not based on field studies, are disputed by the Corps of Engineers. But if the estimates are correct, or even if they are not more than 80 percent wrong, the annual cost of the Wallisville project — in terms of lost fishery resources alone — will be larger than the benefits. And the cost referred to here does not take into account either the possible decline in the productivity of the bay fishery caused by the loss of nutrients from the Trinity River marshes to be impounded or the loss of the excellent waterfowl habitat which these marshes afford. The dam could have been built farther upstream in order to avoid, or at least mitigate, the loss of resources that are peculiar to the tidal marshes.

Pollution. The Houston Ship Channel, or that part of it which follows Buffalo Bayou from Houston to Galveston Bay (a distance of about 25 miles), ranks as one of the filthiest stretches of water in the United States, especially at its upper end. Roy W. Hann, Jr., a professor of environmental engineering at Texas A & M University, who has made some 180 trips on the channel gathering data on its condition, says that industrial pollutants and huge volumes of poorly treated domestic sewage from Houston and its suburbs are imposing on the channel a daily waste load that is the equivalent of the raw sewage of a city of 2 to 3 million people. Often, dissolved oxygen is totally lacking in much of the channel.

According to Hann, the major polluters include firms such as Diamond Alkali Corporation, Shell Chemical Corporation, Sinclair Refining Company, Signal Oil Company, Humble Oil and Refining Company, and U.S. Plywood-Champion Papers, Inc. The channel would remain polluted for years even if all effluents were cleaned up tomorrow, for its bottom is covered by a 2-foot-thick blanket of putrid sludge. On their recent tour of the bay system, members of the President's Advisory Board were appalled to see ships actually churning up oil from this sludge.

Bad as the pollution in the Ship Channel is, it would be more tolerable if it were not endangering Galveston Bay. Wastes from the Ship Channel are by far the bay's worst pollution problem, although it has other pollution sources such as the City of Galveston which is discharging 1.5 million gallons of raw sewage into bay waters each day.

Still other alterations of the bay environment are occurring, for example, the filling in of some marshland in the Galveston area to provide waterfront sites for housing developments. And the Houston Lighting and Power Company (HLP) is well along with a project that is far-reaching in its possible environmental implications. Next year HLP will complete construction of the first 750,000-kilowatt unit of its 1.5-million-kilowatt, gas-fired generating plant on Cedar Bayou. The site is just east of Baytown on the peninsula separating the northwest part of the bay from Trinity Bay and is several miles north of a large rolling mill being constructed along the bayou by the U.S. Steel Company. Originally, HLP had planned to draw up to nearly 1 billion gallons of cooling water a day directly from the Houston Ship Channel, running this highly polluted water through the plant and then discharging it into the relatively clean waters of Trinity Bay.

Conservation groups were outraged, and HLP, fearing that the Corps of Engineers might withhold the permit required, modified the plan by routing the cooling water intake system away from the Ship Channel. Nevertheless, the U.S. Department of the Interior, in a report prepared in 1968 by its southwest regional office, has expressed concern, that, by comparison with the waters of Trinity Bay, the cooling water discharged from the plant will be more polluted, of higher salinity, and from 7° to 12°F warmer. The effect on marine life will be bad and perhaps disastrous, the report indicates. Although HLP says these fears are groundless, the test will come when the new plant begins operating.

(HLP hopes to build additional generating units at the Cedar Bayou site and, in anticipation of possible objections from regulatory agencies, it is now seeking means to avoid thermal pollution altogether. There are but two possible solutions: a closed, recycling cooling system with evaporative cooling towers or a large cooling pond through which water from the plant would be circulated before its discharge into Trinity Bay.)

Even the changes to the bay environment which HLP will cause could be dwarfed by those that might follow construction of a hurricane levee the Corps of Engineers proposes to build at or near the entrance to Galveston Bay. This latter project, which is still in the conceptual stage, could alter the entire natural regime of the bay and concentrate pollutants in the bay's middle and upper reaches, although the Army engineers are making model studies in order to design a project that would not have such effects.

The channel dredging, shelldredging, water diversions, flooding of marshes, pollution — these all represent large-scale and often heedless or inadvertent modification of the Galveston Bay environment. While rapid population and economic growth have made environmental change inevitable, hurtful effects on the bay could have been mitigated and in some cases avoided were it not for the following: first, too little has been known about the bay, and those exploiting or changing it generally have failed to think of it as a complex natural system; second, a dominant political conservatism, highly protective of industrial interests, has kept the state government from dealing effectively with polluters; and, third, the public works, pollution control, and regulatory functions relevant to the bay environment have been dispersed among a bewildering assortment of state, local, and federal agencies, often without effective coordination.

Had Galveston Bay been thought of as a *system* of interrelated parts and functions, the state surely would not, for example, have allowed shelldredgers, in 1963, to begin dredging within 300 feet of live oyster reefs (the previous limit having been 1500 feet) when no significant study of the siltation caused by dredging had been made. And the Water Quality Board presumably would not have assumed that the upper part of the Ship Channel, near Houston, could be so heavily used for waste disposal without affecting the rest of the bay — an illuminating case (of which more will be said shortly) that has involved soft regulation as well as insensitivity to the nature of the bay system.

The state's failure to do more to protect Galveston Bay and its other water resources reveals remarkable inconsistencies in its policies. Texas is a semiarid state and water is precious; as early as the 1930's, long before most other states took similar action, it required primary and secondary treatment of municipal wastes. Yet, as recently as 1967, the Water Pollution Control Board (since renamed the Water Quality Board) had a minuscule budget and only 4 full-time employees of its own. Even today, the board has only 40 enforcement officers for the entire state, which is larger than all of Illinois, Indiana, Iowa, Wisconsin, and Michigan combined.

In the Galveston Bay area, where many people suffer from unclean air and are offended by polluted water, environmental quality is an important political issue. But statewide, this has not been true. According to Congressman Eckhardt of Houston, who has built his political career by battling polluters and shelldredgers, Texas would have done more about the problems of the bay area if state legislators from the piney woods, the cow country, and the panhandle had been more willing to appropriate money for pollution control programs. And, too often, Eckhardt says, when stronger enforcement measures have been proposed, such legislators have been won over by the counterarguments and the highball and thick steak offered by industry lobbyists.

The situation that has existed in the Houston Ship Channel and the convoluted regulatory policies governing it offer ample evidence of the clout industrialists have in Texas politics. The problems of the Ship Channel take on still broader significance from the fact that the water quality standards for all the interstate and tidal waters within Texas, including the waters of the channel, have been fully approved by the U.S. Department of the Interior. These standards, as defined by Interior's Water Pollution Control Administration (FWPCA), are supposed to include not only water quality parameters for various channel segments or zones but, also, firm schedules by which industries and municipalities are to clean up their effluents and plans for the enforcement of these schedules.

Walter A. Quebedeaux, Jr., the Harris County (Houston) air and water pollution control officer, believes that, by fixing unduly permissive water quality parameters for that part of the Ship Channel in and approaching Houston, the Water Quality Board has guaranteed the continued pollution of Galveston Bay. His opinion is one which the available evidence seems to bear out. Where the Ship Channel passes through the lower part of Buffalo Bayou, near the bay, its waters are classified for support of fish life as well as for navigation and industrial uses. But, for the waters farther up the bayou, the classification does not include support of marine life, and some of the critical water quality parameters fixed for those waters are correspondingly lower. For example, at the turning basin in Houston, where the Ship Channel ends, the requirement for dissolved oxygen is fixed at 1.5 parts per million, which is not much more than what can be found in an open sewer.

30,000 dead fish

"You can't divide up the Ship Channel that way," says Quebedeaux. A heavy rain in Houston, he explains, flushes great slugs of polluted water from the upper part of the Ship Channel into the lower part, often producing fish kills. The last large kill, of 30,000 fish, occurred at Morgan's Point in September 1968, but smaller kills occurred last year at Baytown. Fish kills have at times literally driven people from their waterfront homes, causing them to take refuge temporarily in motels until the stench of decaying fish has diminished.

But even though the water quality standards for the upper part of the Ship Channel appear grossly inadequate, the industries on this part of the channel hold permits which, by the Water Quality Board's own admission, allow waste discharges of such low quality that these standards cannot be met. Furthermore, lenient as they are, the conditions of the permits are being violated by many Ship Channel industries, although Water Quality Board spokesmen claim that nearly all discharges will be brought into compliance with the permits by some time in 1971 as the industries complete construction of costly new treatment facilities. But there are no fixed deadlines for completion of this work, and *no* permit has ever been revoked. And the policy of the board has been not to revise and upgrade effluent permits until after the completion, in 1971, of a study of the channel's waste assimilative capacity.

Wide diffusion of authority among various local, state, and federal agencies responsible for using and protecting bay resources clearly has created major problems. At the local level, city and suburban governments and water districts are running their own water supply and sewage collection and treatment systems. Some 190 municipal sewage treatment plants, most of them overloaded or inefficiently run (or both), are discharging effluents into the bay system. And these local governments are just beginning to think of regional land-use zoning, although, as pressures of population and economic growth continue to mount, there is a critical need for such zoning to protect the bay from dredging and landfill operations and other harmful activities.

At the state level, the agencies responsible for the use or protection of Galveston Bay and its tributaries include, besides the Water Quality Board, the Parks and Wildlife Department (responsible for shelldredging and pollution problems affecting wildlife), the Department of Health (responsible for determining whether shellfish are safe for harvesting), the Texas Water Development Board, and even the Texas Railroad Commission. This latter agency, which regulates the oil and gas industry, several years ago was given jurisdiction over pollution caused by that industry after the Water Pollution Control Board began showing an interest in pollution from oil field brines. Four of the seven seats on the Water Quality Board are occupied by ex officio members representing the other agencies just mentioned but little visible good has come from this attempt at coordination.

Conspicuous failures of interagency coordination have occurred in the past among federal agencies responsible for protecting the bay. For instance, if the Wallisville Dam project does in fact wipe out highly valuable marine fishery resources, this will result in part from the failure of the Corps of Engineers to obtain competent field studies from the Fish and Wildlife Service before designing the project and from the failure of this latter agency to conduct such studies. Now, however, interagency collaboration seems to be becoming more effective. For example, in placing restrictions on the shelldredgers and in studying the environmental implications of the proposed hurricane levee, the Corps of Engineers is working closely with the Fish and Wildlife Service and the FWPCA.

Although the hour is late, all of the basic problems of the bay environment are under attack and there are in fact signs of progress. The Water Quality Board has had under way since 1967 a $3.5-million Galveston Bay Study, involving an investigation of population and economic growth patterns and land-use questions as well as the gathering and analysis of physical and biological data. The study, to be completed in 1971, will provide a better basis on which to design strategies for protection of the bay. For example, the study might indicate that, regardless of the level of treatment given the wastes it receives, the Ship Channel will have to be aerated mechanically to increase its assimilative capacity.

Another encouraging sign is that politicians in Texas, like those elsewhere, are beginning to speak of the environment in the same respectful way in which they speak of mother and the flag. Last year, the legislature even passed a measure sponsored by Houston legislators making corporate polluters liable to criminal prosecution. The most startling change, however, is the tough talk beginning to come from the Water Quality Board, a body which from its inception has been highly sensitive to the state's political mood.

Board demands "second effort"

The board's new chairman, Gordon Fulcher, a newspaper publisher from Atlanta, Texas, recently told *Science* that hearings will be held soon on pollution problems in the bay area to determine whether industries are complying with their effluent permits and whether those permits should be revised. "The board wants a second effort," Fulcher said. Furthermore, the board is for the first time demanding periodic reports from industry on the quality of effluents — a policy innovation that should assist the Galveston Bay Study group which has been reduced to obtaining such information by promising the Ship Channel industries that the data will not be identified with specific plants and will never be used for enforcement purposes.

Recently, the board initiated legal action against several small municipalities and water districts which are polluting Clear Lake, an embayment off of Galveston Bay near the Manned Spacecraft Center. And Fulcher even speaks matter-of-factly about the possibility of a showdown with Houston, the state's largest and most politically potent city. Houston has spent about $75 million over the past 6 years on improving its sewage collection and treatment facilities, but this improvement effort was retarded in 1968 by the voters' rejection of two large public works bond issues.

To catch up with the need for sewage facilities the city must spend perhaps as much as another $100 million, and, should the voters not approve the new bond issue currently proposed, a crisis may ensue. Fulcher observes that, if Houston or any other city refuses to clean up its domestic wastes, the board will seek a court order requiring such action and raising sewer service charges sufficiently to pay for it. "We will do whatever it takes," he says. The legislature, he adds, should assist the cleanup by appropriating money for state treatment facility grants, without which Houston and other localities have been unable to qualify for the maximum federal grants.

The Water Quality Board will be in a stronger political position to deal with recalcitrant municipalities and industries if Texans know that the failure of the state to accomplish a clean-up will only mean that federal authorities will come in and do the job. FWPCA will be able to play this supporting role better if Congress goes along with the proposals made last week by President Nixon — and made earlier by Senator Edmund Muskie of Maine — to broaden the agency's powers.

The President asked that FWPCA be given authority to approve or reject state quality standards for effluents as well as for receiving waters; and, further, that it be authorized to initiate enforcement actions even in situations where, as in the case of the Galveston Bay system, no interstate waters are involved. Under existing law, FWPCA could bring an enforcement action against Ship Channel polluters only at the request of the governor of Texas or if pollutants contaminating shellfish in the bay could be traced back to specific outfalls on the channel.

Last year the Texas Legislature authorized the establishment of a Gulf Coast Waste Disposal Authority, hoping thereby to overcome much of the present diffusion of responsibility for protection of the bay environment. Now being organized, the Authority will face a critical political test when it appeals to voters of the bay area for permission to levy taxes and issue bonds. If, however, it survives this test, the Authority will have a chance to carry out an ambitious program of regional water quality management comparable even to the work of the *Genossenschaften,* the regional water resources associations of the Ruhr. Under its legislative mandate, the Authority could build not only waste collection and treatment facilities but facilities of any other kind needed for cleaning up the bay, such as possibly an aeration system for the Ship Channel.

Further, the Authority is expected eventually to become self-supporting by levying effluent charges on the industries and municipalities from which it receives wastes. The Authority probably will base its charges on the quality of these wastes, thus giving its clients an economic incentive to improve their effluent quality by pre-treatment or industrial process changes. Polluters do not have to join the regional system, but if effluent and water quality standards are vigorously enforced by the Water Quality Board and by the Authority itself, some polluters will have no practical alternative but to join.

Still needed is a comprehensive resource management program for the Galveston Bay system, one which could complement the activities of the Waste Disposal Authority by developing water and land-use plans to protect the bay from such things as harmful water diversions and the filling in of marshes for housing or industrial sites. The Nixon administration has asked Congress to authorize a modest program of grants-in-aid to encourage states to establish such management programs for their estuarine zones.

Even if Congress acts favorably on this possibly inadequate proposal, which is all carrot and no stick, Texas and other states will be free to decide whether to have their estuaries managed systematically or left to the kind of random and conflicting forces of use and development responsible for their present condition. However, the Texas Legislature last year ordered an inventory of the state's estuarian resources and a moratorium on the sale or leasing of submerged lands until 30 June 1973, unless the inventory is completed sooner. Also, the Galveston Bay Study and the establishment of the Waste Disposal Authority could be steps in the direction of a comprehensive program of estuarine management.

In sum, Galveston Bay is providing a classic case history of an estuary that can be rescued from its troubles only by determined and imaginative effort. Other major estuaries, such as San Francisco Bay and Chesapeake Bay, are troubled by problems of their own but none has problems more difficult and complex than those of the Galveston Bay system, especially on the Ship Channel. The problems of the Ship Channel alone are enough to put the state and federal water pollution control programs to a significant test. But while optimism is not yet in order for those who would save Galveston Bay, neither is despair. The solution to the bay's problems seems to lie in large scale research, ambitious programs of pollution control and water- and land-use management, plus tough enforcement and a close watch on the outfalls.

WILLIAM ESPEY, JR. & FRANK P. BENDER
Systems Analysis of Galveston Bay

By early 1972, a water-quality management study for Galveston Bay on the Texas Gulf Coast will be complete and will provide man for the first time with not only an exact understanding of the effects of pollution in a major estuary but also an accurate management tool for selecting compatible alternatives in the dynamic shaping of the Houston area's future water-related growth.

Some of the problems for which answers and solutions may be forthcoming in the next two years include:

. . . Describing the concentrations of raw and partially treated effluents from municipal and industrial waste treatment plants and urban and agricultural runoffs. Based on this information, biological studies will permit for the first time a determination of the total effects of such a waste mix on the marine plant and animal life occupying the estuarine zones of the bay.

. . . Calculating the effects of varying fresh water inflow from tributaries of the estuary caused by an expected increase in upstream usage. An adequate supply of fresh water is the major environmental factor in the bay nursery habitat for fish life which largely supports the $190 million-per-year Texas Gulf Coast fishing industry.

. . . Determining the effects of hurricane flood protection structures on bay circulation patterns, salinity and pollution control and on all forms of fish and wildlife.

. . . Calculating the effects of thermal pollution from the many industries which use bay water in circulating-heat-transfer systems. For example, a steel manufacturer requires 20,000 gallons of water to make one ton of steel.

. . . Determining the areas of the bay which meet quality standards for an expanding population engaging in water contact sports such as swimming and water skiing.

Galveston Bay's pollution problems are certainly not unique. Similar problems exist in every industrialized country in the world. However, because the nation's third largest seaport, one of the world's most important petrochemical centers and an urban population of $2\frac{1}{2}$ million (which is expected to double by 1990 and to triple by 2020) have placed such a strain on the bay system with conflicting demands of multiple uses, an environmental inventory, regulations enforcement and monitoring of established water quality standards become critical goals.

William H. Espey, Jr., and Frank P. Bender, "Systems Analysis of Galveston Bay," *Ocean Industry*, February 1970, pp. 60–63. Reprinted by permission.
Dr. Espey is program manager, TRACOR, Inc., concerned with applying mathematical models and computer simulation techniques to water resources problems. Colonel Bender, a member of the Texas Water Quality Board, is project director of the Galveston Bay study.

These goals were some of the specific objectives of the far-reaching Galveston Bay study which was initiated three years ago under the auspices of the Texas Water Quality Board.

The long-range goal is far more ambitious: development of a realistic, controlled water environment for man. The idea of undertaking such a vast and complex task would have seemed not only baffling but also impossible just 10 years ago.

BASIC PROBLEMS

Historically, waste disposal policies in the U.S. generally have been based on the axiom of maximum permissible levels of water pollution. Indeed, it may be questioned whether there were policies at all.

Until recently, federal and state water control laws had little impact because of public ignorance of water quality problems. As a result, authorities were frustrated by meagre budgets, and were hamstrung for lack of personnel to implement programs of water quality improvement.

In other words, water quality management policies admittedly followed vague estimates of what happened when pollutants were deposited in estuaries and coastal waters. The practice was to dispose first and to investigate later, an invitation to disaster that requires no documentation, for the proof of sinister changes in the estuarine life of many coastal areas in the U.S. is dismally at hand for anyone to examine.

In defense, regulatory agencies declared that only years of intensive study could provide exact understanding of the fate of waste elements consigned to sea-bordering burying places. Even today with the present advances in the state of the art of water quality research, no one knows for sure what water quality standards should be and whether the ones we choose at any time are realistic. It is true that we have evolved standards, expressed as water quality requirements, but these are still in an evolutionary stage.

Objectives of designing mathematical models

Early in the preliminary stages of the Galveston Bay study, it was decided that the key to water quality management was the design of mathematical models which would formulate the entire physical geography of the Galveston Bay area. Information provided by the models would then be programmed for a digital computer. Last year, TRACOR, Inc., of Austin, Tex., was given the assignment with three broad objectives:

. . . Develop techniques of reliably forecasting natural or man-made variations in water quality for the prediction of changes in the estuary based on predictable future demands and for determining the probable impact of proposed structural changes in the bay.

. . . Determine cause-and-effect relationships between pollutants from any source and identify the physical/chemical/biological interactions of waste that have led to the present deteriorated quality of water in the estuary.

. . . Through water modeling, provide the information for building a program of water quality improvement and maintenance that will serve the needs not only of municipal, industrial and agricultural users but also for fisheries, recreation and wildlife propagation.

Simply defined, a mathematical model is a theoretical or actual representation of a process and is specifically designed to changing phenomena. The value of any model lies in its ability to provide management with information for use in choosing alternatives for the solution of water quality problems. The modeling approach consists of three stages: development of a water profile, verification of the profile over a wide range of environmental conditions and prediction of how the profile will be altered when new factors are introduced.

Thus, the reliability of any modeling effort to be used in the formulation of management decisions for a controlled environment depends upon sound input data from which a digital computer develops a profile.

An idea of the immensity of the modeling task was expressed in a description of the problems plaguing Galveston Bay that were contained in a report on water quality management by Allen V. Kneese and Blair T. Bowen for Resources of the Future, Inc.

"Galveston Bay," the report said, "is the largest (520 square miles), most heavily used, the most productive bay on the Texas Gulf Coast. It is also, however, plagued by waste discharges from some of the nation's fastest growing municipal and industrial areas.

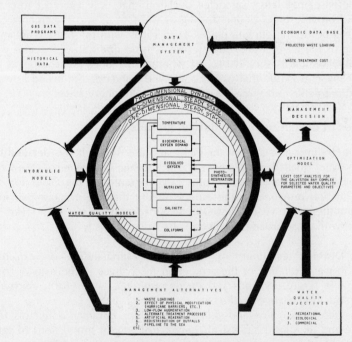

Figure 1.   Function of water quality models in management

"Galveston Bay and San Francisco Bay-Delta studies appear to be the most comprehensive water quality planning studies ever undertaken. They aim to examine the full range of alternatives including various collective measures, assign benefits and costs to alternate levels of water quality, and recommend appropriate institutional arrangements for implementation. Two facts help to account for the pioneering character of these studies: no operating agencies have major responsibilities in the planning; and the studies deal with intrastate bodies of water over which the individual state has sovereignty to the point of creating an appropriate management authority."

The magnitude of the Galveston Bay Study can be appreciated by an examination of the task objectives presented to TRACOR. The following major factors influencing the estuary were incorporated in the modeling effort: biochemical oxygen demand, dissolved oxygen, temperature, salinity, coliforms (indicator bacteria which originate in the intestinal tracts of warm-blooded animals), winds, biological nutrients, fresh water inflow, the influence of tidal velocities and the geomorphology of the bay system.

Just one parameter in the overall modeling study demonstrates the massive amounts of data needed to build a bay profile. This involves tracing advance and retreat of salinity from the Gulf of Mexico into the Galveston estuarine system. Fresh water inflow drops during the summer months, and the prediction for the future is for an even greater demand on upstream water usage and decreasing fresh water flow into the bay.

Knowledge of salinity is vital if we are to preserve the delicate balance between salt water and fresh water, the necessary brackish habitat for oysters, juvenile shrimp and crab.

Management may use a water quality model to determine salinity as part of the total bay modeling objectives. A hydraulic model is operated first to learn the behavior of currents in the bay. Any alterations in flow or physiography are included here. Output from the hydraulic model is used as input in the water quality model for the parameter of interest. Characteristics of treatment processes, waste loadings, relocation of effluent sources, and similar features are incorporated in the water quality model at this stage. When optimization (least-cost) techniques are to be employed, the operation of the optimization models are then retrieved through the data management system.

Limitations. It is most important to realize the limitations of these models. The models are capable of yielding concentration profiles for a variety of substances that may be harmful to aquatic life. However, no model can evaluate the effects of substances on aquatic life. This is a job being done by biologists as another part of the Galveston Bay study — to assess limits of concentrations of substances harmful to marine life or the ecology of an estuary.

Also, it is important to understand that water quality modeling has never been intended as a substitute for the management process. Rather, it provides a tool for management decisions that can lead to a compatible environment for man.

But while the models have limitations, they have exciting capabilities which we can expect to be brought to bear in the solution of many complex problems anticipated in the future growth of the Galveston Bay area.

In the future, the Texas City/Galveston Bay area will exert the greatest pressure for industrial land usage per 100-person unit of population in the eight-county Houston megalopolis. Modeling will provide the human equations for best-use least-cost development and optimization and waste disposal.

Demands for recreation have accelerated even faster than population growth. By 1975, 115,000 additional acres of water-related recreation land will be needed. The total estuary modeling will provide the crucial information as to how and where these vital recreation areas should be located.

The answer? Perhaps the creation elsewhere in the bay system of inviolate recreation areas. But whatever the answer, the modeling concept can provide a set of alternatives by which management can make an optimum decision.

Still another problem, for which mathematical modeling is providing key answers, is an investigation of what the effects would be if an artificial hurricane protection barrier were constructed chiefly to prevent the kind of economic disaster which occurred through flooding of coastal areas when Hurricane Carla struck Galveston in 1961.

A hydraulic model is presently being employed in the study to discover the effect on bay circulation patterns, salinity and dispersal of pollutants in Galveston Bay. One major concern is that such a barrier might prevent intrusion into the bay areas of Gulf salinity vital to the production of shellfish.

The management charged with the responsibility of creating what is certain to be man's first full-scale experiment at a controlled environment is the Gulf Coast Waste Disposal Authority which legislation made a reality last August. The Authority, embracing Chambers, Harris and Galveston counties, was given these broad powers:

1. Preparing a master plan for pollution abatement.
2. Prescribing (after public hearings and the approval of the Texas Water Quality Board) standards and criteria for waters in the Authority.
3. Conducting studies and research for control of water pollution.
4. Making water quality inspections on public and private property.
5. Adopting rules and orders to regulate pollution.
6. Regulating solid waste disposal.
7. Regulating the use of septic tanks.

The Authority is authorized to regulate water pollution by municipalities, political subdivisions, private persons and corporations and has powers of enforcement.

The Authority may acquire, construct and operate disposal systems and may contract to treat and dispose of wastes. It may develop sources of tax revenues.

Recently, at a meeting of water resource people in Houston, Klaus R. Imhoff, deputy engineer of the West German Ruhr River Association, flatly declared, "The only solution to pollution control in a dynamic industrial complex such as the Galveston Bay area is through versatile regional management of water quality."

The Texas Water Quality Board has long recognized that a water quality management program for a system as complicated as Galveston Bay does not evolve overnight. Rather, it grows and develops with the accumulation of knowledge about the system and interrelationships of water demands and uses.

An effective program must rely upon the technologies of many disciplines, including socio-economics, engineering, law, chemistry and biology — all the areas of human knowledge that can be brought to bear to solve water quality problems.

Such a program must be versatile and capable of alteration to accommodate new developments in the field of water quality analysis and to respond to new situations which present themselves in the bay. The modeling effort for the Galveston Bay study presently underway is not an end in itself but rather has the purpose of forming a foundation, a viable framework, for the management of the resources of Galveston Bay.

The job facing the new Authority is of a magnitude never before attempted. The biggest responsibility will be to develop dynamic plans that will minimize illogical and inconsistent decisions in setting water quality objectives for the Galveston Bay area.

But the Authority begins its task with the new tools of systems analysis and digital computation which provide man with the technology to recognize the good and bad points inherent in alternate decisions.

In the complex field of water resources, optimization does not necessarily mean getting the best of all possible worlds, but it does mean making the best possible use of the world as it is.

M. ALEXANDER

Possible Contamination of Earth by Lunar or Martian Life

At a conference about the possible risks of contamination of the Earth by material derived from the planets, it was stated that the existence of life on the Moon cannot rationally be precluded, the physical conditions on the lunar surface being such that life could have developed and might still be present. Although it was felt that the probability of life existing on the Moon's surface is low, the participants in the conference were unanimous in stating that "extraterrestrial life and the concomitant possibility of back contamination must be presumed to exist."[1] The fact that a quarantine programme has been established by the US National Aeronautics and Space Administration suggests that responsible individuals in that agency also believe there is a finite prob-

M. Alexander, "Possible Contamination of Earth by Lunar or Martian Life," *Nature*, vol. 222, no. 5192 (May 3, 1969), pp. 432–433. Reprinted by permission.
The author is with the Laboratory of Soil Microbiology, Cornell University.

ability that life exists on the Moon and that such life forms could conceivably affect man, species on which man relies, or organisms about which man is concerned.

It is difficult to anticipate whether representatives of some non-terrestrial biota would survive or establish themselves on Earth. Should biochemical evolution on the Moon or Mars have followed a different course from that which resulted in terrestrial life, it is likely that lunar organisms thrust into the alien environment of the Earth would not replicate and would soon die. In the absence of experience with extraterrestrial life, however, it is not possible to provide unequivocal *a priori* arguments to show that an organism developing in one biosphere might not indeed become established and use untapped environmental resources which it can utilize or which it exploits more efficiently than any terrestrial species.

Certain microorganisms inhabiting extreme environments — extreme by terrestrial standards at least — grow readily when brought into less harsh circumstances. A variety of halophiles, barophiles and acid-tolerant heterotrophs develop, occasionally quite luxuriantly, in conditions more characteristic of the habitats of animals and higher plants.[2-4] An organism originating in an environment as extreme as that of the Moon or Mars might also have a broad range of tolerances and not only proliferate in terrestrial habitats but even develop more profusely than in its original domicile.

An effective quarantine provides a useful and essential means to minimize the contamination of one region with organisms derived from another. The rigour of the programme contributes to its effectiveness, but so also does the lack of vigour, aggressiveness and evasiveness of many pathogens. The various procedures used commonly reduce the number of potentially invasive organisms to the extent that the residual population is economically, ecologically or physically manageable, but no quarantine is perfect. Decontamination of infested inanimate materials is feasible, but complete sterility is often impossible to achieve. Decontamination of an infested astronaut, on the other hand, presents problems as yet unsolved, and elimination of all microorganisms from a manned vehicle apparently cannot be achieved with current technology. The deputy surgeon general of the US Public Health Service stated, "We must make an arbitrary approach to quarantine, but must also realize that quarantine is a crude concept and a crude approach to a problem of this sort. I would not feel safe in placing a large part of my faith in it as a security method."[1]

The identities, behaviour, ecological relationships, nutrient requirements, physiological attributes and pathogenic capabilities of extraterrestrial organisms are totally unknown. Guidelines for a quarantine protocol clearly can only be based on knowledge of the current biota of this planet but with the view that there is a finite possibility that life forms arising elsewhere might have a significant influence on terrestrial species. Terrestrial saprophytes metabolize a variety of organic compounds not believed to be present in any protoplasmic combination generated during the course of evolution on the Earth,[5] and a similar enzymatic versatility may be found in the starving alien provided for the first time with a terrestrial repast.

Populations of regional groups, varieties or species of higher organisms which have not been exposed to a particular pathogen may be decimated as a result of the accidental introduction of the disease agent. Such disasters have allegedly occurred even in recent times to isolated human populations which came into contact with European explorers and settlers. Fungi and insects attacking higher plants have also been inadvertently transported from one region to another and have had significant deleterious effects on the growth of crop or non-crop species. The medical, agricultural and biological literature contains innumerable instances showing the disastrous consequences following the introduction of pathogens and other pests into previously un-exposed communities.

Previously unknown microorganisms have been observed for the first time very recently. Thus the first algal virus,[6] the first well documented instance of a virus parasitizing a filamentous fungus,[7] a virus whose host is a Basidio-mycete,[8] several new types of free-living bacteria[9-12] and bacteria which live ectoparasitically on other bacteria[13] have only been discovered in the past few years.

It is likely that several as yet uncharacterized microbial types exist in various of the Earth's ecosystems, but suitable procedures have not been devised for their cultivation. In soils, for example, the total count is invariably much greater than the viable count.[14] Parasites of aquatic algae have also yet to be grown *in vitro*.[15] Certain microorganisms living in or on higher animals and plants have not been grown apart from their hosts, and the presence of these organisms could easily go unrecognized because of the absence from the quarantine site of the specific host. Some species for which suitable cul-tural techniques have yet to be devised are clearly pathogenic; for instance, the bacterium causing leprosy, a number of disease-producing fungi and a variety of obligately parasitic protozoa.[16-19]

If extraterrestrial life exists, it is thus reasonable to assume that some of the forms will not be able to grow, will not proliferate readily or will not be recognized during the quarantine period. Biologists cannot propagate many terrestrial species *in vitro*, so it is not too fanciful to propose that they will not be able, particularly in a short period of time, to recognize the presence of life forms from space.

The quarantine designed to prevent exobiological contamination of the Earth will undoubtedly involve a number of healthy, well nourished, largely white, adult males. Yet various pathogens having no deleterious action on certain individuals affect individuals of another race, sex, age, humans suffer-ing from malnutrition and those exposed to various forms of therapy.[20, 21] The nutritional status, the environment and growth conditions likewise markedly alter the susceptibility of crop species to infection. Plants exposed to one set of circumstances may show no symptoms or be only moderately affected by a parasite, whereas disease of the same host species may be quite pronounced in other circumstances.[22, 23]

A microorganism may itself not cause disease, but it may make the animal or plant harbouring it more susceptible to potential terrestrial patho-gens. Predisposition of plants or animals to one microbial agent by a second is widely recognized.[22-25] An interaction requiring a terrestrial and a non-terrestrial species might be detected during the quarantine. On the other hand, the appropriate terrestrial organism may not be indigenous to the few test individuals, although its presence might become only too apparent in other individuals once the quarantine is lifted.

Alternatively, an environmental stress may result in the flare-up of a pathogen which resides for long periods in harmony with its host. The animal or human harbouring a latent infection may be healthy until some apparently non-specific stress makes it more vulnerable, at which time clinical symptoms first appear.[20] Similar phenomena are known in plants; for example, the rhizosphere of healthy hosts teems with potential root invaders, but only when the natural barriers are overcome does the pathogen gain entry.

Assuming that an agent harmful to man or livestock was introduced from the Moon or Mars, one might expect that a vaccine could be produced to cope with the invader. But the problems of developing a vaccine to counteract an organism the identity of which might not be recognized, the physiological attributes of which may be ill defined and the susceptibility of which to current procedures for vaccine production might be untested could easily be unresolvable in a short period of time. Moreover, an exotic form of life could not only be resistant to phagocytosis but also might not provoke antibody formation.

Limitations of space, time and money dictate that just a select few potential suscepts for lunar or Martian parasites will be included in any quarantine. Various economically important animals, crops and tree species will necessarily be ignored. Yet many parasites are notoriously host specific and, though not pathogenic to plants or animals of direct concern to American or Soviet agriculture or ecosystems, cause major losses in the populations of organisms which serve as food for Africans, Asians and Latin Americans.

Man is peculiar in desiring to maintain certain organisms for aesthetic reasons. Many of the techniques required to assess ecological disturbances, however, are so imprecise that a decline in the population density of some species would probably go undetected until the change became pronounced. Species which man neither consumes nor cherishes also have tremendous importance in nature. For example, the introduction from the Moon or Mars of a parasite of freshwater or marine algae might well have a profound impact on fish production and, because algae are important contributors to the regeneration of atmospheric oxygen, the very existence of animal life.

Fanciful speculations such as these are warranted if indeed man will return from the Moon or one of the neighbouring planets bearing alien materials. Not only may the indigenous species of the terrestrial biosphere be exposed for the first time in their evolutionary history to certain bizarre organisms, but the biosphere itself could become permanently contaminated with these forms. The outcome of such contamination clearly cannot be predicted.

The quest for life in space and the study of the physical and chemical properties of our celestial neighbours are important. These investigations satisfy man's innate and insatiable curiosity. But it is not essential that the studies be conducted, particularly in the absence of adequate biological information and techniques. The risks are far too great. The cost in dollars may be calculable, but the cost in life and in environmental modification cannot be determined.

Notes

1. Space Science Board, *Conference on Potential Hazards of Back Contamination from the Planets* (National Academy of Sciences — National Research Council, Washington, 1965).

2. Larsen, H., in *The Bacteria*, 4 (edit. by Gunsalus, I. C., and Stanier, R. Y.), 297 (Academic Press, New York, 1962).

3. Painter, H. A., *J. Gen. Microbiol.*, 10, 177 (1954).

4. ZoBell, C. E., and Morita, R. Y., *J. Bacteriol.*, 73, 563 (1957).

5. Alexander, M., *Adv. Appl. Microbiol.*, 7, 35 (1965).

6. Safferman, R. S., and Morris, M.-E., *Science*, 140, 679 (1963).

7. Banks, G. T., Buck, K. W., Chain, E. B., Himmelweit, F., Marks, J. E., Tyler, J. M., Hollings, M., Last, F. T., and Stone, O. M., *Nature*, 218, 542 (1968).

8. Hollings, M., Gandy, D. G., and Last, F. T., *Endeavour*, 22, 112 (1963).

9. Casida, L. E., *Appl. Microbiol.*, 13, 327 (1965).

10. Orenski, S. W., Bystricky, V., and Maramorosch, K., *Nature*, 210, 221 (1966).

11. Staley, J. T., *J. Bacteriol.*, 95, 1921 (1968).

12. Nikitin, D. I., and Kuznetsov, S. I., *Mikrobiologiva*, 36, 938 (1967).

13. Stolp, H., and Starr, M. P., *Antonie van Leeuwenhoek J. Microbiol. Serol.*, 29, 217 (1963).

14. Alexander, M., *Introduction to Soil Microbiology* (Wiley, New York, 1961).

15. Lund, J. W. G., in *Marine Biology*, 2 (edit. by Oppenheimer, C. H.), 193 (NY Acad. Sci., New York, 1966).

16. Koser, S. E., *Vitamin Requirements of Bacteria and Yeasts* (C. C. Thomas, Springfield, Ill., 1968).

17. Bishop, N., *Adv. Parasitol.*, 5, 93 (1967).

18. Stakman, E. C., and Harrar, J. G., *Principles of Plant Pathology* (Ronald Press, New York, 1957).

19. Yarwood, C. E., *Ann. Rev. Plant Physiol.*, 7, 115 (1956).

20. Dubos, R., in *Bacterial and Mycotic Infections of Man* (edit. by Dubos, R. J., and Hirsch, J. G.), 20 (Lippincott, Philadelphia, 1965).

21. Clark, P. F., *Ann. Rev. Microbiol.*, 4, 343 (1950).

22. Christensen, J. J., and DeVay, J. E., *Ann. Rev. Plant Physiol.*, 6, 367 (1955).

23. Yarwood, C. E., in *Plant Pathology*, 1 (edit. by Horsfall, J. G., and Dimond, A. E.), 521 (Academic Press, New York, 1959).

24. MacLeod, C. M., in *Bacterial and Mycotic Infections of Man* (edit. by Dubos, R. J., and Hirsch, J. G.), 391 (Lippincott, Philadelphia, 1965).

25. Linderman, R. G., and Tousson, T. A., *Phytopathology*, 58, 1431 (1968).

EUGENE P. ODUM

The Strategy of Ecosystem Development

The principles of ecological succession bear importantly on the relationships between man and nature. The framework of successional theory needs to be examined as a basis for resolving man's present environmental crisis. Most ideas pertaining to the development of ecological systems are based on descriptive data obtained by observing changes in biotic communities over long periods, or on highly theoretical assumptions; very few of the generally accepted hypotheses have been tested experimentally. Some of the confusion, vagueness, and lack of experimental work in this area stems from the tendency of ecologists to regard "succession" as a single straightforward idea: in actual fact, it entails an interacting complex of processes, some of which counteract one another.

As viewed here, ecological succession involves the development of ecosystems; it has many parallels in the developmental biology of organisms, and also in the development of human society. The ecosystem, or ecological system, is considered to be a unit of biological organization made up of all of the organisms in a given area (that is, "community") interacting with the physical environment so that a flow of energy leads to characteristic trophic structure and material cycles within the system. It is the purpose of this article to summarize, in the form of a tabular model, components and stages of development at the ecosystem level as a means of emphasizing those aspects of ecological succession that can be accepted on the basis of present knowledge, those that require more study, and those that have special relevance to human ecology.

DEFINITION OF SUCCESSION

Ecological succession may be defined in terms of the following three parameters (1). (i) It is an orderly process of community development that is reasonably directional and, therefore, predictable. (ii) It results from modification of the physical environment by the community; that is, succession is community-controlled even though the physical environment determines the pattern, the

Eugene P. Odum, "The Strategy of Ecosystem Development," *Science*, vol. 164 (April 18, 1969), pp. 262–270. Copyright 1969 by the American Association for the Advancement of Science. Reprinted by permission.
The author is director of the Institute of Ecology, and Alumni Foundation Professor, at the University of Georgia, Athens. This article is based on a presidential address presented before the annual meeting of the Ecological Society of America at the University of Maryland, August 1966.

rate of change, and often sets limits as to how far developments can go. (iii) It culminates in a stabilized ecosystem in which maximum biomass (or high information content) and symbiotic function between organisms are maintained per unit of available energy flow. In a word, the "strategy" of succession as a short-term process is basically the same as the "strategy" of long-term evolutionary development of the biosphere — namely, increased control of, or homeostasis with, the physical environment in the sense of achieving maximum protection from its perturbations. As I illustrate below, the strategy of "maximum protection" (that is, trying to achieve maximum support of complex biomass structure) often conflicts with man's goal of "maximum production" (trying to obtain the biggest possible yield). Recognition of the ecological basis for this conflict is, I believe, a first step in establishing rational land-use policies.

The earlier descriptive studies of succession on sand dunes, grasslands, forests, marine shores, or other sites, and more recent functional considerations, have led to the basic theory contained in the definition given above. H. T. Odum and Pinkerton (2), building on Lotka's (3) "law of maximum energy in biological systems," were the first to point out that succession involves a fundamental shift in energy flows as increasing energy is relegated to maintenance. Margalef (4) has recently documented this bioenergetic basis for succession and has extended the concept.

Changes that occur in major structural and functional characteristics of a developing ecosystem are listed in Table 1. Twenty-four attributes of ecological systems are grouped, for convenience of discussion, under six headings. Trends are emphasized by contrasting the situation in early and late development. The degree of absolute change, the rate of change, and the time required to reach a steady state may vary not only with different climatic and physiographic situations but also with different ecosystem attributes in the same physical environment. Where good data are available, rate-of-change curves are usually convex, with changes occuring most rapidly at the beginning, but bimodal or cyclic patterns may also occur.

Bioenergetics of ecosystem development

Attributes 1 through 5 in Table 1 represent the bioenergetics of the ecosystem. In the early stages of ecological succession, or in "young nature," so to speak, the rate of primary production or total (gross) photosynthesis (P) exceeds the rate of community respiration (R), so that the P/R ratio is greater than 1. In the special case of organic pollution, the P/R ratio is typically less than 1. In both cases, however, the theory is that P/R approaches 1 as succession occurs. In other words, energy fixed tends to be balanced by the energy cost of maintenance (that is, total community respiration) in the mature or "climax" ecosystem. The P/R ratio, therefore, should be an excellent functional index of the relative maturity of the system.

So long as P exceeds R, organic matter and biomass (B) will accumulate in the system (Table 1, item 6), with the result that ratio P/B will tend to decrease or, conversely, the B/P, B/R, or B/E ratios (where $E = P + R$) will in-

Table 1.   A tabular model of ecological succession: trends to be expected in the development of ecosystems

Ecosystem attributes	Developmental stages	Mature stages
Community energetics		
1. Gross production/community respiration (P/R ratio)	Greater or less than 1	Approaches 1
2. Gross production/standing crop biomass (P/B ratio)	High	Low
3. Biomass supported/unit energy flow (B/E ratio)	Low	High
4. Net community production (yield)	High	Low
5. Food chains	Linear, predominantly grazing	Weblike, predominantly detritus
Community structure		
6. Total organic matter	Small	Large
7. Inorganic nutrients	Extrabiotic	Intrabiotic
8. Species diversity — variety component	Low	High
9. Species diversity — equitability component	Low	High
10. Biochemical diversity	Low	High
11. Stratification and spatial heterogeneity (pattern diversity)	Poorly organized	Well-organized
Life history		
12. Niche specialization	Broad	Narrow
13. Size of organism	Small	Large
14. Life cycles	Short, simple	Long, complex
Nutrient cycling		
15. Mineral cycles	Open	Closed
16. Nutrient exchange rate, between organisms and environment	Rapid	Slow
17. Role of detritus in nutrient regeneration	Unimportant	Important
Selection pressure		
18. Growth form	For rapid growth ("r-selection")	For feedback control ("K-selection")
19. Production	Quantity	Quality
Overall homeostasis		
20. Internal symbiosis	Undeveloped	Developed
21. Nutrient conservation	Poor	Good
22. Stability (resistance to external perturbations)	Poor	Good
23. Entropy	High	Low
24. Information	Low	High

crease (Table 1, items 2 and 3). Theoretically, then, the amount of standing-crop biomass supported by the available energy flow (E) increases to a maximum in the mature or climax stages (Table 1, item 3). As a consequence, the net community production, or yield, in an annual cycle is large in young nature and small or zero in mature nature (Table 1, item 4).

Comparison of succession in a laboratory microcosm and a forest

One can readily observe bioenergetic changes by initiating succession in experimental laboratory microecosystems. Aquatic microecosystems, derived from various types of outdoor systems, such as ponds, have been cultured by Beyers (5), and certain of these mixed cultures are easily replicated and maintain themselves in the climax state indefinitely on defined media in a flask with only light input (6). If samples from the climax system are inoculated into fresh media, succession occurs, the mature system developing in less than 100 days. In Fig. 1 the general pattern of a 100-day autotrophic succession in a microcosm based on data of Cooke (7) is compared with a hypothetical model of a 100-year forest succession as presented by Kira and Shidei (8).

During the first 40 to 60 days in a typical microcosm experiment, daytime net production (P) exceeds nighttime respiration (R), so that biomass (B) accumulates in the system (9). After an early "bloom" at about 30 days, both rates decline, and they become approximately equal at 60 to 80 days. The B/P ratio, in terms of grams of carbon supported per gram of daily carbon production, increases from less than 20 to more than 100 as the steady state is reached. Not only are autotrophic and heterotrophic metabolism balanced in the climax, but a large organic structure is supported by small daily production and respiratory rates.

While direct projection from the small laboratory microecosystem to open nature may not be entirely valid, there is evidence that the same basic trends that are seen in the laboratory are characteristic of succession on land and in large bodies of water. Seasonal successions also often follow the same pattern, an early seasonal bloom characterized by rapid growth of a few dominant species being followed by the development later in the season of high B/P ratios, increased diversity, and a relatively steady, if temporary, state in terms of P and R (4). Open systems may not experience a decline, at maturity, in total or gross productivity, as the space-limited microcosms do, but the general pattern of bioenergetic change in the latter seems to mimic nature quite well.

These trends are not, as might at first seem to be the case, contrary to the classical limnological teaching which describes lakes as progressing in time from the less productive (oligotrophic) to the more productive (eutrophic) state. Table 1, as already emphasized, refers to changes which are brought about by biological processes *within* the ecosystem in question. Eutrophication, whether natural or cultural, results when nutrients are imported into the lake from *outside* the lake — that is, from the watershed. This is equivalent to adding nutrients to the laboratory microecosystem or fertilizing a field; the system is pushed back, in successional terms, to a younger or "bloom" state. Recent studies on lake sediments (10), as well as theoretical considerations (11), have indicated that lakes can and do progress to a more oligotrophic condition when the nutrient input from the watershed slows or ceases. Thus, there is hope that the troublesome cultural eutrophication of our waters can be reversed if the inflow of nutrients from the watershed can be greatly reduced. Most of all, however, this situation emphasizes that it is the entire drainage or catchment basin, not just the lake or stream, that must be considered the ecosystem unit if we are to deal successfully with our water pollution problems. Ecosystematic study of entire landscape catchment units is a major goal of the American plan for the proposed International Biological Program. Despite the obvious logic of such a proposal, it is proving surprisingly difficult to get tradition-bound scientists and granting agencies to look beyond their specialties toward the support of functional studies of large units of the landscape.

Food chains and food webs

As the ecosystem develops, subtle changes in the network pattern of food chains may be expected. The manner in which organisms are linked together through food tends to be relatively simple and linear in the very early stages of succession, as a consequence of low diversity. Furthermore, heterotrophic utilization of net production occurs predominantly by way of grazing food chains — that is, plant-herbivore-carnivore sequences. In contrast, food chains become complex webs in mature stages, with the bulk of biological energy flow following detritus pathways (Table 1, item 5). In a mature forest, for example, less than 10 percent of annual net production is consumed (that is, grazed) in the living state (*12*); most is utilized as dead matter (detritus) through delayed and complex pathways involving as yet little understood animal-microorganism interactions. The time involved in an uninterrupted succession allows for increasingly intimate associations and reciprocal adaptations between plants and animals, which lead to the development of many mechanisms that reduce grazing — such as the development of indigestible supporting tissues (cellulose, lignin, and so on), feedback control between plants and herbivores (*13*), and increasing predatory pressure on herbivores (*14*). Such mechanisms enable the biological community to maintain the large and complex organic structure that mitigates perturbations of the physical environment. Severe stress or rapid changes brought about by outside forces can, of course, rob the system of these protective mechanisms and allow irruptive, cancerous growths of certain species to occur, as man too often finds to his sorrow. An example of a stress-induced pest irruption occurred at Brookhaven National Laboratory, where oaks became vulnerable to aphids when translocation of sugars and amino acids was impaired by continuing gamma irradiation (*15*).

Radionuclide tracers are providing a means of charting food chains in the intact outdoor ecosystem to a degree that will permit analysis within the concepts of network or matrix algebra. For example, we have recently been able to map, by use of a radiophosphorus tracer, the open, relatively linear food linkage between plants and insects in an early old-field successional stage (*16*).

Diversity and succession

Perhaps the most controversial of the successional trends pertain to the complex and much discussed subject of diversity (*17*). It is important to distinguish between different kinds of diversity indices, since they may not follow parallel trends in the same gradient or developmental series. Four components of diversity are listed in Table 1, items 8 through 11.

The variety of species, expressed as a species-number ratio or a species-area ratio, tends to increase during the early stages of community development. A second component of species diversity is what has been called equitability, or evenness (*18*), in the apportionment of individuals among the species. For example, two systems each containing 10 species and 100 individuals have the same diversity in terms of species-number ratio but could have widely different equitabilities depending on the apportionment of the 100 individuals among the 10 species — for example, 91-1-1-1-1-1-1-1-1-1 at one extreme or 10 individuals per species at the other. The Shannon formula,

$$-\Sigma \, \frac{ni}{N} \log_2 \frac{ni}{N}$$

where *ni* is the number of individuals in each species and *N* is the total number of individuals, is widely used as a diversity index because it combines the variety and equitability components in one approximation. But, like all such lumping parameters, Shannon's formula may obscure the behavior of these two rather different aspects of diversity. For example, in our most recent field experiments, an acute stress from insecticide reduced the number of species of insects relative to the number of individuals but increased the evenness in the relative abundances of the surviving species (*19*). Thus, in this case the "variety" and "evenness" components would tend to cancel each other in Shannon's formula.

While an increase in the variety of species together with reduced dominance by any one species or small group of species (that is, increased evenness) can be accepted as a general probability during succession (*20*), there are other community changes that may work against these trends. An increase in the size of organisms, an increase in the length and complexity of life histories, and an increase in interspecific competition that may result in competitive exclusion of species (Table 1, items 12–14) are trends that may reduce the number of species that can live in a given area. In the bloom stage of succession organisms tend to be small and to have simple life histories and rapid rates of reproduction. Changes in size appear to be a consequence of, or an adaptation to, a shift in nutrients from inorganic to organic (Table 1, item 7). In a mineral nutrient-rich environment, small size is of selective advantage, especially to autotrophs, because of the greater surface-to-volume ratio. As the ecosystem develops, however, inorganic nutrients tend to become more and more tied up in the biomass (that is, to become intrabiotic), so that the selective advantage shifts to larger organisms (either larger individuals of the same species or larger species, or both) which have greater storage capacities and more complex life histories, thus are adapted to exploiting seasonal or periodic releases of nutrients or other resources. The question of whether the seemingly direct relationship between organism size and stability is the result of positive feedback or is merely fortuitous remains unanswered (*21*).

Thus, whether or not species diversity continues to increase during succession will depend on whether the increase in potential niches resulting

from increased biomass, stratification (Table 1, item 9), and other consequences of biological organization exceeds the countereffects of increasing
size and competition. No one has yet been able to catalogue all the species
in any sizable area, much less follow total species diversity in a successional
series. Data are so far available only for segments of the community (trees,
birds, and so on). Margalef (4) postulates that diversity will tend to peak
during the early or middle stages of succession and then decline in the climax.
In a study of bird populations along a successional gradient we found a
bimodal pattern (22); the number of species increased during the early stages
of old-field succession, declined during the early forest stages, and then increased again in the mature forest.

Species variety, equitability, and stratification are only three aspects of
diversity which change during succession. Perhaps an even more important
trend is an increase in the diversity of organic compounds, not only of those
within the biomass but also of those excreted and secreted into the media
(air, soil, water) as by-products of the increasing community metabolism. An
increase in such "biochemical diversity" (Table 1, item 10) is illustrated by the
increase in the variety of plant pigments along a successional gradient in
aquatic situations as described by Margalef (4, 23). Biochemical diversity within
populations, or within systems as a whole, has not yet been systematically
studied to the degree the subject of species diversity has been. Consequently,
few generalizations can be made, except that it seems safe to say that, as succession progresses, organic extrametabolites probably serve increasingly important functions as regulators which stabilize the growth and composition
of the ecosystem. Such metabolites may, in fact, be extremely important in
preventing populations from overshooting the equilibrial density, thus in
reducing oscillations as the system develops stability.

The cause-and-effect relationship between diversity and stability is not
clear and needs to be investigated from many angles. If it can be shown that biotic diversity does indeed enhance physical stability in the ecosystem, or is the
result of it, then we would have an important guide for conservation practice.
Preservation of hedgerows, woodlots, noneconomic species, noneutrophicated
waters, and other biotic variety in man's landscape could then be justified on
scientific as well as esthetic grounds, even though such preservation often
must result in some reduction in the production of food or other immediate
consumer needs. In other words, is variety only the spice of life, or is it a
necessity for the long life of the total ecosystem comprising man and nature?

Nutrient cycling

An important trend in successional development is the closing or "tightening"
of the biogeochemical cycling of major nutrients, such as nitrogen, phosphorus, and calcium (Table 1, items 15–17). Mature systems, as compared to
developing ones, have a greater capacity to entrap and hold nutrients for
cycling within the system. For example, Bormann and Likens (24) have estimated that only 8 kilograms per hectare out of a total pool of exchangeable
calcium of 365 kilograms per hectare is lost per year in stream outflow from a
North Temperate watershed covered with a mature forest. Of this, about

3 kilograms per hectare is replaced by rainfall, leaving only 5 kilograms to be obtained from weathering of the underlying rocks in order for the system to maintain mineral balance. Reducing the volume of the vegetation, or otherwise setting the succession back to a younger state, results in increased water yield by way of stream outflow (25), but this greater outflow is accompanied by greater losses of nutrients, which may also produce downstream eutrophication. Unless there is a compensating increase in the rate of weathering, the exchangeable pool of nutrients suffers gradual depletion (not to mention possible effects on soil structure resulting from erosion). High fertility in "young systems" which have open nutrient cycles cannot be maintained without compensating inputs of new nutrients; examples of such practice are the continuous-flow culture of algae, or intensive agriculture where large amounts of fertilizer are imported into the system each year.

Because rates of leaching increase in a latitudinal gradient from the poles to the equator, the role of the biotic community in nutrient retention is especially important in the high-rainfall areas of the subtropical and tropical latitudes, including not only land areas but also estuaries. Theoretically, as one goes equatorward, a larger percentage of the available nutrient pool is tied up in the biomass and a correspondingly lower percentage is in the soil or sediment. This theory, however, needs testing, since data to show such a geographical trend are incomplete. It is perhaps significant that conventional North Temperate row-type agriculture, which represents a very youthful type of ecosystem, is successful in the humid tropics only if carried out in a system of "shifting agriculture" in which the crops alternate with periods of natural vegetative redevelopment. Tree culture and the semiaquatic culture of rice provide much better nutrient retention and consequently have a longer life expectancy on a given site in these warmer latitudes.

Selection pressure: quantity versus quality

MacArthur and Wilson (26) have reviewed stages of colonization of islands which provide direct parallels with stages in ecological succession on continents. Species with high rates of reproduction and growth, they find, are more likely to survive in the early uncrowded stages of island colonization. In contrast, selection pressure favors species with lower growth potential but better capabilities for competitive survival under the equilibrium density of late stages. Using the terminology of growth equations, where r is the intrinsic rate of increase and K is the upper asymptote or equilibrium population size, we may say that "r selection" predominates in early colonization, with "K selection" prevailing as more and more species and individuals attempt to colonize (Table 1, item 18). The same sort of thing is even seen within the species in certain "cyclic" northern insects in which "active" genetic strains found at low densities are replaced at high densities by "sluggish" strains that are adapted to crowding (27).

Genetic changes involving the whole biota may be presumed to accompany the successional gradient, since, as described above, quantity production characterizes the young ecosystem while quality production and feedback control are the trademarks of the mature system (Table 1, item 19).

Selection at the ecosystem level may be primarily interspecific, since species replacement is a characteristic of successional series or seres. However, in most well-studied seres there seem to be a few early successional species that are able to persist through to late stages. Whether genetic changes contribute to adaptation in such species has not been determined, so far as I know, but studies on population genetics of *Drosophila* suggest that changes in genetic composition could be important in population regulation (*28*). Certainly, the human population, if it survives beyond its present rapid growth stage, is destined to be more and more affected by such selection pressures as adaptation to crowding becomes essential.

Overall homeostasis

This brief review of ecosystem development emphasizes the complex nature of processes that interact. While one may well question whether all the trends described are characteristic of all types of ecosystems, there can be little doubt that the net result of community actions is symbiosis, nutrient conservation, stability, a decrease in entropy, and an increase in information (Table 1, items 20–24). The overall strategy is, as I stated at the beginning of this article, directed toward achieving as large and diverse an organic structure as is possible within the limits set by the available energy input and the prevailing physical conditions of existence (soil, water, climate, and so on). As studies of biotic communities become more functional and sophisticated, one is impressed with the importance of mutualism, parasitism, predation, commensalism, and other forms of symbiosis. Partnership between unrelated species is often noteworthy (for example, that between coral coelenterates and algae, or between mycorrhizae and trees). In many cases, at least, biotic control of grazing, population density, and nutrient cycling provide the chief positive-feedback mechanisms that contribute to stability in the mature system by preventing overshoots and destructive oscillations. The intriguing question is, Do mature ecosystems age, as organisms do? In other words, after a long period of relative stability or "adulthood," do ecosystems again develop unbalanced metabolism and become more vulnerable to diseases and other perturbations?

RELEVANCE OF ECOSYSTEM DEVELOPMENT THEORY TO HUMAN ECOLOGY

Figure 1 depicts a basic conflict between the strategies of man and of nature. The "bloom-type" relationships, as exhibited by the 30-day microcosm or the 30-year forest, illustrate man's present idea of how nature should be directed. For example, the goal of agriculture or intensive forestry, as now generally practiced, is to achieve high rates of production of readily harvestable products with little standing crop left to accumulate on the landscape — in other words, a high P/B efficiency. Nature's strategy, on the other hand, as seen in the outcome of the successional process, is directed toward the reverse efficiency — a high B/P ratio, as is depicted by the relationship at the right in

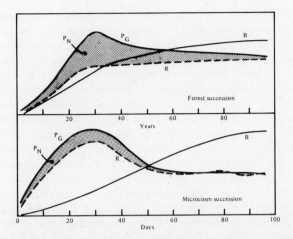

Figure 1. Comparison of the energetics of succession in a forest and a laboratory microcosm. P_G, gross production; P_N, net production; R, total community respiration; B, total biomass

Fig. 1. Man has generally been preoccupied with obtaining as much "production" from the landscape as possible, by developing and maintaining early successional types of ecosystems, usually monocultures. But, of course, man does not live by food and fiber alone; he also needs a balanced CO_2–O_2 atmosphere, the climatic buffer provided by oceans and masses of vegetation, and clean (that is, unproductive) water for cultural and industrial uses. Many essential life-cycle resources, not to mention recreational and esthetic needs, are best provided man by the less "productive" landscapes. In other words, the landscape is not just a supply depot but is also the *oikos* — the home — in which we must live. Until recently mankind has more or less taken for granted the gas-exchange, water-purification, nutrient-cycling, and other protective functions of self-maintaining ecosystems, chiefly because neither his numbers nor his environmental manipulations have been great enough to affect regional and global balances. Now, of course, it is painfully evident that such balances are being affected, often detrimentally. The "one problem, one solution approach" is no longer adequate and must be replaced by some form of ecosystem analysis that considers man as a part of, not apart from, the environment.

The most pleasant and certainly the safest landscape to live in is one containing a variety of crops, forests, lakes, streams, roadsides, marshes, seashores, and "waste places" — in other words, a mixture of communities of different ecological ages. As individuals we more or less instinctively surround our houses with protective, nonedible cover (trees, shrubs, grass) at the same time that we strive to coax extra bushels from our cornfield. We all consider the cornfield a "good thing," of course, but most of us would not want to live there, and it would certainly be suicidal to cover the whole land area of the biosphere with cornfields, since the boom and bust oscillation in such a situation would be severe.

The basic problem facing organized society today boils down to determining in some objective manner when we are getting "too much of a good thing." This is a completely new challenge to mankind because, up until now, he has had to be concerned largely with too little rather than too much. Thus, concrete is a "good thing," but not if half the world is covered with it. Insecticides are "good things," but not when used, as they now are, in an indiscriminate and wholesale manner. Likewise, water impoundments have proved to be very useful man-made additions to the landscape, but obviously we don't want the whole country inundated! Vast man-made lakes solve some problems, at least temporarily, but yield comparative little food or fiber, and, because of high evaporative losses, they may not even be the best device for storing water; it might better be stored in the watershed, or underground in aquafers. Also, the cost of building large dams is a drain on already overtaxed revenues. Although as individuals we readily recognize that we can have too many dams or other large-scale environmental changes, governments are so fragmented and lacking in systems-analysis capabilities that there is no effective mechanism whereby negative feedback signals can be received and acted on before there has been a serious overshoot. Thus, today there are governmental agencies, spurred on by popular and political enthusiasm for dams, that are putting on the drawing boards plans for damming every river and stream in North America!

Society needs, and must find as quickly as possible, a way to deal with the landscape as a whole, so that manipulative skills (that is, technology) will not run too far ahead of our understanding of the impact of change. Recently a national ecological center outside of government and a coalition of governmental agencies have been proposed as two possible steps in the establishment of a political control mechanism for dealing with major environmental questions. The soil conservation movement in America is an excellent example of a program dedicated to the consideration of the whole farm or the whole watershed as an ecological unit. Soil conservation is well understood and supported by the public. However, soil conservation organizations have remained too exclusively farm-oriented, and have not yet risen to the challenge of the urban-rural landscape, where lie today's most serious problems. We do, then, have potential mechanisms in American society that could speak for the ecosystem as a whole, but none of them are really operational (29).

The general relevance of ecosystem development theory to landscape planning can, perhaps, be emphasized by the "mini-model" of Table 2, which contrasts the characteristics of young and mature-type ecosystems in more general terms than those provided by Table 1. It is mathematically impossible to obtain a maximum for more than one thing at a time, so one cannot have

---

Table 2.   Contrasting characteristics of young and mature-type ecosystems

Young	Mature
Production	Protection
Growth	Stability
Quantity	Quality

both extremes at the same time and place. Since all six characteristics listed in Table 2 are desirable in the aggregate, two possible solutions to the dilemma immediately suggest themselves. We can compromise so as to provide moderate quality and moderate yield on all the landscape, or we can deliberately plan to compartmentalize the landscape so as to simultaneously maintain highly productive and predominantly protective types as separate units subject to different management strategies (strategies ranging, for example, from intensive cropping on the one hand to wilderness management on the other). If ecosystem development theory is valid and applicable to planning, then the so-called multiple-use strategy, about which we hear so much, will work only through one or both of these approaches, because, in most cases, the projected multiple uses conflict with one another. It is appropriate, then, to examine some examples of the compromise and the compartmental strategies.

Pulse stability

A more or less regular but acute physical perturbation imposed from without can maintain an ecosystem at some intermediate point in the developmental sequence, resulting in, so to speak, a compromise between youth and maturity. What I would term "fluctuating water level ecosystems" are good examples. Estuaries, and intertidal zones in general, are maintained in an early, relatively fertile stage by the tides which provide the energy for rapid nutrient cycling. Likewise, freshwater marshes, such as the Florida Everglades, are held at an early successional stage by the seasonal fluctuations in water levels. The dry-season drawdown speeds up aerobic decomposition of accumulated organic matter, releasing nutrients that, on reflooding, support a wet-season bloom in productivity. The life histories of many organisms are intimately coupled to this periodicity. The wood stork, for example, breeds when the water levels are falling and the small fish on which it feeds become concentrated and easy to catch in the drying pools. If the water level remains high during the usual dry season or fails to rise in the wet season, the stork will not nest (30). Stabilizing water levels in the Everglades by means of dikes, locks, and impoundments, as is now advocated by some, would, in my opinion, destroy rather than preserve the Everglades as we now know them just as surely as complete drainage would. Without periodic drawdowns and fires, the shallow basins would fill up with organic matter and succession would proceed from the present pond-and-prairie condition toward a scrub or swamp forest.

It is strange that man does not readily recognize the importance of recurrent changes in water level in a natural situation such as the Everglades when similar pulses are the basis for some of his most enduring food culture systems (31). Alternate filling and draining of ponds has been a standard procedure in fish culture for centuries in Europe and the Orient. The flooding, draining, and soil-aeration procedure in rice culture is another example. The rice paddy is thus the cultivated analogue of the natural marsh or the intertidal ecosystem.

Fire is another physical factor whose periodicity has been of vital importance to man and nature over the centuries. Whole biotas, such as those of the African grasslands and the California chaparral, have become adapted to periodic fires producing what ecologists often call "fire climaxes" (32). Man uses fire deliberately to maintain such climaxes or to set back succession to some desired point. In the southeastern coastal plain, for example, light fires of moderate frequency can maintain a pine forest against the encroachment of older successional stages which, at the present time at least, are considered economically less desirable. The fire-controlled forest yields less wood than a tree farm does (that is, young trees, all of about the same age, planted in rows and harvested on a short rotation schedule), but it provides a greater protective cover for the landscape, wood of higher quality, and a home for game birds (quail, wild turkey, and so on) which could not survive in a tree farm. The fire climax, then, is an example of a compromise between production simplicity and protection diversity.

It should be emphasized that pulse stability works only if there is a complete community (including not only plants but animals and microorganisms) adapted to the particular intensity and frequency of the perturbation. Adaptation — operation of the selection process — requires times measurable on the evolutionary scale. Most physical stresses introduced by man are too sudden, too violent, or too arrhythmic for adaptation to occur at the ecosystem level, so severe oscillation rather than stability results. In many cases, at least, modification of naturally adapted ecosystems for cultural purposes would seem preferable to complete redesign.

Prospects for a detritus agriculture

As indicated above, heterotrophic utilization of primary production in mature ecosystems involves largely a delayed consumption of detritus. There is no reason why man cannot make greater use of detritus and thus obtain food or other products from the more protective type of ecosystem. Again, this would represent a compromise, since the short-term yield could not be as great as the yield obtained by direct exploitation of the grazing food chain. A detritus agriculture, however, would have some compensating advantages. Present agricultural strategy is based on selection for rapid growth and edibility in food plants, which, of course, make them vulnerable to attack by insects and disease. Consequently, the more we select for succulence and growth, the more effort we must invest in the chemical control of pests; this effort, in turn, increases the likelihood of our poisoning useful organisms, not to mention ourselves. Why not also practice the reverse strategy — that is, select plants which are essentially unpalatable, or which produce their own systemic insecticides while they are growing, and then convert the net production into edible products by microbial and chemical enrichment in food factories? We could then devote our biochemical genius to the enrichment process instead of fouling up our living space with chemical poisons! The production of silage by fermentation of low-grade fodder is an example of such a procedure already in widespread use. The cultivation of detritus-eating fishes in the Orient is another example.

By tapping the detritus food chain man can also obtain an appreciable harvest from many natural systems without greatly modifying them or destroying their protective and esthetic value. Oyster culture in estuaries is a good example. In Japan, raft and long-line culture of oysters has proved to be a very practical way to harvest the natural microbial products of estuaries and shallow bays. Furukawa (*33*) reports that the yield of cultured oysters in the Hiroshima Prefecture has increased tenfold since 1950, and that the yield of oysters (some 240,000 tons of meat) from this one district alone in 1965 was ten times the yield of natural oysters from the entire country. Such oyster culture is feasible along the entire Atlantic and Gulf coasts of the United States. A large investment in the culture of oysters and other seafoods would also provide the best possible deterrent against pollution, since the first threat of damage to the pollution-sensitive oyster industry would be immediately translated into political action!

The compartment model

Successful though they often are, compromise systems are not suitable nor desirable for the whole landscape. More emphasis needs to be placed on compartmentalization, so that growth-type, steady-state, and intermediate-type ecosystems can be linked with urban and industrial areas for mutual benefit. Knowing the transfer coefficients that define the flow of energy and the movement of materials and organisms (including man) between compartments, it should be possible to determine, through analog-computer manipulation, rational limits for the size and capacity of each compartment. We might start, for example, with a simplified model, shown in Fig. 2, consisting of four

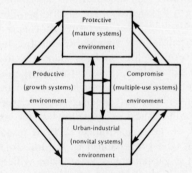

Figure 2.　Compartment model of the basic kinds of environment required by man, partitioned according to ecosystem development and life-cycle resource criteria

compartments of equal area, partitioned according to the basic biotic-function criterion — that is, according to whether the area is (i) productive, (ii) protective, (iii) a compromise between (i) and (ii) or (iv), urban-industrial. By continually refining the transfer coefficients on the basis of real world situations, and by increasing and decreasing the size and capacity of each compartment through computer simulation, it would be possible to determine objectively the limits that must eventually be imposed on each compartment in order to maintain regional and global balances in the exchange of vital energy and of materials. A systems-analysis procedure provides at least one approach to the solution of the basic dilemma posed by the question "How do we determine when we are getting too much of a good thing?" Also it provides a means of evaluating the energy drains imposed on ecosystems by pollution, radiation, harvest, and other stresses (34).

Implementing any kind of compartmentalization plan, of course, would require procedures for zoning the landscape and restricting the use of some land and water areas. While the principle of zoning in cities is universally accepted, the procedures now followed do not work very well because zoning restrictions are too easily overturned by short-term economic and population pressures. Zoning the landscape would require a whole new order of thinking. Greater use of legal measures providing for tax relief, restrictions on use, scenic easements, and public ownership will be required if appreciable land and water areas are to be held in the "protective" categories. Several states (for example, New Jersey and California), where pollution and population pressure are beginning to hurt, have made a start in this direction by enacting "open space" legislation designed to get as much unoccupied land as possible into a "protective" status so that future uses can be planned on a rational and scientific basis. The United States as a whole is fortunate in that large areas of the country are in national forests, parks, wildlife refuges, and so on. The fact that such areas, as well as the bordering oceans, are not quickly exploitable gives us time for the accelerated ecological study and programming needed to determine what proportions of different types of landscape provide a safe balance between man and nature. The open oceans, for example, should forever be allowed to remain protective rather than productive territory, if Alfred Redfield's (35) assumptions are correct. Redfield views the oceans, the major part of the hydrosphere, as the biosphere's governor, which slows down and controls the rate of decomposition and nutrient regeneration, thereby creating and maintaining the highly aerobic terrestrial environment to which the higher forms of life, such as man, are adapted. Eutrophication of the ocean in a last-ditch effort to feed the populations of the land could well have an adverse effect on the oxygen reservoir in the atmosphere.

Until we can determine more precisely how far we may safely go in expanding intensive agriculture and urban sprawl at the expense of the protective landscape, it will be good insurance to hold inviolate as much of the latter as possible. Thus, the preservation of natural areas is not a peripheral luxury for society but a capital investment from which we expect to draw interest. Also, it may well be that restrictions in the use of land and water are our only practical means of avoiding overpopulation or too great an exploitation of resources, or both. Interestingly enough, restriction of land use is the analogue of a natural behavioral control mechanism known as "territoriality" by which many species of animals avoid crowding and social stress (36).

Since the legal and economic problems pertaining to zoning and compartmentalization are likely to be thorny, I urge law schools to establish departments, or institutes, of "landscape law" and to start training "landscape lawyers" who will be capable not only of clarifying existing procedures but also of drawing up new enabling legislation for consideration by state and national governing bodies. At present, society is concerned — and rightly so

— with human rights, but environmental rights are equally vital. The "one man one vote" idea is important, but so also is a "one man one hectare" proposition.

Education, as always, must play a role in increasing man's awareness of his dependence on the natural environment. Perhaps we need to start teaching the principles of ecosystem in the third grade. A grammar school primer on man and his environment could logically consist of four chapters, one for each of the four essential kinds of environment, shown diagrammatically in Fig. 2.

Of the many books and articles that are being written these days about man's environmental crisis, I would like to cite two that go beyond "crying out in alarm" to suggestions for bringing about a reorientation of the goals of society. Garrett Hardin, in a recent article in *Science* (37), points out that, since the optimum population density is less than the maximum, there is no strictly technical solution to the problem of pollution caused by overpopulation; a solution, he suggests, can only be achieved through moral and legal means of "mutual coercion, mutually agreed upon by the majority of people." Earl F. Murphy, in a book entitled *Governing Nature* (38), emphasizes that the regulatory approach alone is not enough to protect life-cycle resources, such as air and water, that cannot be allowed to deteriorate. He discusses permit systems, effluent charges, receptor levies, assessment, and cost-internalizing procedures as economic incentives for achieving Hardin's "mutually agreed upon coercion."

It goes without saying that the tabular model for ecosystem development which I have presented here has many parallels in the development of human society itself. In the pioneer society, as in the pioneer ecosystem, high birth rates, rapid growth, high economic profits, and exploitation of accessible and unused resources are advantageous, but, as the saturation level is approached, these drives must be shifted to considerations of symbiosis (that is, "civil rights," "law and order," "education," and "culture"), birth control, and the recycling of resources. A balance between youth and maturity in the socio-environmental system is, therefore, the really basic goal that must be achieved if man as a species is to successfully pass through the present rapid-growth stage, to which he is clearly well adapted, to the ultimate equilibrium-density stage, of which he as yet shows little understanding and to which he now shows little tendency to adapt.

References and notes

1. E. P. Odum, *Ecology* (Holt, Rinehart & Winston, New York, 1963), chap. 6.
2. H. T. Odum and R. C. Pinkerton, *Amer. Scientist* 43, 331 (1955).
3. A. J. Lotka, *Elements of Physical Biology* (Williams and Wilkins, Baltimore, 1925).
4. R. Margalef, *Advan. Frontiers Plant Sci.* 2, 137 (1963); *Amer. Naturalist* 97, 357 (1963).
5. R. J. Beyers, *Ecol. Monographs* 33, 281 (1963).
6. The systems so far used to test ecological principles have been derived from sewage and farm ponds and are cultured in half-strength No. 36 Taub and Dollar medium [*Limnol. Oceanog.* 9, 61 (1964)]. They are closed to organic input or output but are open to the atmosphere through the cotton plug in the neck of the flask.

Typically, liter-sized microecosystems contain two or three species of nonflagellated algae and one to three species each of flagellated protozoans, ciliated protozoans, rotifers, nematodes, and ostracods; a system derived from a sewage pond contained at least three species of fungi and 13 bacterial isolates [R. Gorden, thesis, University of Georgia (1967)]. These cultures are thus a kind of minimum ecosystem containing those small species originally found in the ancestral pond that are able to function together as a self-contained unit under the restricted conditions of the laboratory flask and the controlled environment of a growth chamber [temperature, 65° to 75°F (18° to 24°C); photoperiod, 12 hours; illumination, 100 to 1000 footcandles].

7. G. D. Cooke, *BioScience* 17, 717 (1967).

8. T. Kira and T. Shidei, *Japan. J. Ecol.* 17, 70 (1967).

9. The metabolism of the microcosms was monitored by measuring diurnal pH changes and the biomass (in terms of total organic matter and total carbon) was determined by periodic harvesting of replicate systems.

10. F. J. H. Mackereth, *Proc. Roy. Soc. London Ser. B* 161, 295 (1965); U. M. Cowgill and G. E. Hutchinson, *Proc. Intern. Limnol. Ass.* 15, 644 (1964); A. D. Harrison, *Trans. Roy. Soc. S. Africa* 36, 213 (1962).

11. R. Margalef, *Proc. Intern. Limnol. Ass.* 15, 169 (1964).

12. J. R. Bray, *Oikos* 12, 70 (1961).

13. D. Pimentel, *Amer. Naturalist* 95, 65 (1961).

14. R. T. Paine, *ibid.* 100, 65 (1966).

15. G. M. Woodwell, *Brookhaven Nat. Lab. Pub. 924(T-381)* (1965), pp. 1–15.

16. R. G. Wiegert, E. P. Odum, J. H. Schnell, *Ecology* 48, 75 (1967).

17. For selected general discussions of patterns of species diversity, see E. H. Simpson, *Nature* 163, 688 (1949); C. B. Williams, *J. Animal Ecol.* 22, 14 (1953); G. E. Hutchinson, *Amer. Naturalist* 93, 145 (1959); R. Margalef, *Gen. Systems* 3, 36 (1958); R. MacArthur and J. MacArthur, *Ecology* 42, 594 (1961); N. G. Hairston, *ibid.* 40, 404 (1959); B. C. Patten, *J. Marine Res. (Sears Found. Marine Res.)* 20, 57 (1960); E. G. Leigh, *Proc. Nat. Acad. Sci. U.S.* 55, 777 (1965); E. R. Pianka, *Amer. Naturalist* 100, 33 (1966); E. C. Pielou, *J. Theoret. Biol.* 10, 370 (1966).

18. M. Lloyd and R. J. Ghelardi, *J. Animal Ecol.* 33, 217 (1964); E. C. Pielou, *J. Theoret. Biol.* 13, 131 (1966).

19. G. W. Barrett, *Ecology* 49, 1019 (1969).

20. In our studies of natural succession following grain culture, both the species-to-numbers and the equitability indices increased for all trophic levels but especially for predators and parasites. Only 44 percent of the species in the natural ecosystem were phytophagous, as compared to 77 percent in the grain field.

21. J. T. Bonner, *Size and Cycle* (Princeton Univ. Press, Princeton, N.J., 1963); P. Frank, *Ecology* 49, 355 (1968).

22. D. W. Johnston and E. P. Odum, *Ecology* 37, 50 (1956).

23. R. Margalef, *Oceanog. Marine Biol. Annu. Rev.* 5, 257 (1967).

24. F. H. Bormann and G. E. Likens, *Science* 155, 424 (1967).

25. Increased water yield following reduction of vegetative cover has been frequently demonstrated in experimental watersheds throughout the world [see A. R. Hibbert, in *International Symposium on Forest Hydrology* (Pergamon Press, New York, 1967), pp. 527–543]. Data on the long-term hydrologic budget (rainfall input relative to stream outflow) are available at many of these sites, but mineral budgets have yet to be systematically studied. Again, this is a prime objective in the "ecosystem analysis" phase of the International Biological Program.

26. R. H. MacArthur and E. O. Wilson, *Theory of Island Biogeography* (Princeton Univ. Press, Princeton, N.J., 1967).

27. Examples are the tent caterpillar [see W. G. Wellington, *Can. J. Zool.* 35, 293 (1957)] and the larch budworm [see W. Baltensweiler, *Can. Entomologist* 96, 792 (1964)].

28. F. J. Ayala, *Science* 162, 1453 (1968).

29. Ira Rubinoff, in discussing the proposed sea level canal joining the Atlantic and Pacific oceans [*Science* 161, 857 (1968)], calls for a "control commission for

environmental manipulation" with "broad powers of approving, disapproving, or modifying all major alterations of the marine or terrestrial environments. . . ."

30. See M. P. Kahl, *Ecol. Monographs* 34, 97 (1964).

31. The late Aldo Leopold remarked long ago [*Symposium on Hydrobiology* (Univ. of Wisconsin Press, Madison, 1941), p. 17] that man does not perceive organic behavior in systems unless he has built them himself. Let us hope it will not be necessary to rebuild the entire biosphere before we recognize the worth of natural systems!

32. See C. F. Cooper, *Sci. Amer.* 204, 150 (April 1961).

33. See "Proceedings Oyster Culture Workshop, Marine Fisheries Division, Georgia Game and Fish Commission, Brunswick" (1968), pp. 49–61.

34. See H. T. Odum, in *Symposium on Primary Productivity and Mineral Cycling in Natural Ecosystems*, H. E. Young, Ed. (Univ. of Maine Press, Orono, 1967), p. 81; ———, in *Pollution and Marine Ecology* (Wiley, New York, 1967), p. 99; K. E. F. Watt, *Ecology and Resource Management* (McGraw-Hill, New York, 1968).

35. A. C. Redfield, *Amer. Scientist* 46, 205 (1958).

36. R. Ardrey, *The Territorial Imperative* (Atheneum, New York, 1967).

37. G. Hardin, *Science* 162, 1243 (1968).

38. E. F. Murphy, *Governing Nature* (Quadrangle Books, Chicago, 1967).

Chapter 7

Environmental management: needed skills

The information we need to manage the environment will require an expansion of our manpower trained in the arts and sciences of environmental management. As this chapter indicates, we are already building such a mix of people and skills, but there is much yet to be accomplished in terms of talent recruiting and job training. In addition, our analysis and planning tools, while rapidly improving, are still in the germination stage in the disciplines which fostered them. While we have been managing the environment for years, we have not always done it on the scale we suggest is necessary, nor have we anticipated the complexities. The selections in Chapter 7 indicate some of the present capabilities and some measures still in the development stage.

Margaret Mead in "The Island Earth" expresses a need to train people who realize that we are all neighbors and what we do has ripple effects that cannot be avoided.

In far more technical terms, M. B. Dale illustrates how this systems thinking can be applied to the discipline of ecology. We once again ask our non-technical readers to make the extra effort this article requires, for the problem has to be recognized in its fullness so that we can bring our particular interests and skills to bear on some manageable portion of the work. Dale presents the major concepts and illustrates their use in a relatively short space so that we can understand where we fit into the larger whole. If each person specializes without some sense of the whole, we will have failed to grasp the message of Mead and the techniques of Dale.

The scale on which we must operate in the future, suggested in Chapter 2, puts a premium on developing skills of data acquisition, storage, and analysis. Velvyl W. Greene's article on automatic biodetecting illustrates the development that has taken place to handle the problems before us. We cannot manage unless we know the state of what we are managing, and the article is a report on some trends and complications involved in making progress in monitoring.

The next three articles illustrate environmental management techniques we might well pursue to put together the factors uncovered by our techniques of discovering dynamics and monitoring the state of systems.

Once we have information on system status and rules for change, applied tools are necessary. Morton Gorden, Marsha Gorden and John Golden describe a management model which makes the trade-offs necessary for industry to comply with standards in the most ecologically efficient way. They argue that the management of machines can benefit from the analogy of a biological ecosystem.

"USER," by Morton Gorden and Charles N. Flinkstrom, is a system of planning which constrains land use and identifies opportunities for economic growth which do minimum damage to the environment. The authors show how commerce and ecology must share the land in a way that recognizes the rules of nature. The planning system calls on the skills of persons from many disciplines, and it relies on the political process to settle value differences which must be accommodated.

M. K. Muthoo, in "The Renewable Resource Planning Problem with Special Reference to Kashmir," gives us insight into how we might at last begin to put the earth on a sustained yield basis — where we live off interest and retain our capital stock of resources. As Muthoo illustrates, such a philosophy of natural resource management will not be easy and will require considerable skill. However, the way is pointed by this article, and our motivation to acquire the skills should be high.

MARGARET MEAD
The Island Earth

In 1940 Edna St. Vincent Millay wrote a poem called "There Are No Islands, Any More," which moved those who were involved in World War II very deeply. The theme, that nowhere on this planet could man flee from man and be safe, that war and its aftermath reached to the most remote islands, tugged at the imagination of those of us who were living through the most widespread war in history, a war that culminated in the horrors of Hiroshima. People stopped talking about finding themselves an island where life could be lived out in peace with nature, and those who were fond of quoting added, from Donne, "No man is an island, entire of itself. . . ." Islands as a daydream of escape went out, and casual acquaintances stopped asking to be taken along on my field trips. When islands were mentioned, it was their vulnerabilities that were spoken of: population growth in Mauritius and Samoa; Japan's awareness of the need for population control; the devastating volcanic eruption in Bali that destroyed a third of the arable land; the unwillingness of Java's population to leave their crowded island for a less crowded one. The

Margaret Mead, "The Island Earth," *Natural History* Magazine, published by the American Museum of Natural History, January 1970, pp. 22, 102–103. Reprinted by permission.

emphasis continued to be on the theme, "no place to go, no hiding place down here." Islands pointed out the interconnectedness of men on earth and their mutual vulnerability to each other's homicidal and genocidal aims.

The emergence of Indonesia as a new nation — the fifth largest in the world — was all the more striking because this is a nation made up of 80 million people living on 3,000 islands, and people raised their eyebrows when Indonesia tried to extend the limits of sovereignty to include the inland waterways of her watery empire. Buckminster Fuller designed a map — a diomaxion map — which showed the continents of the earth as an interconnected land mass. Islands were definitely out, a handicap in some way or other to full-scale continental living.

Then came NASA and the moon program, and finally the first breathtaking photographs of the earth from the moon. Mankind joined the astronauts in their willowy, eerie, unweighted walks on the moon and saw the earth in all its isolated diversity. Earth became an island in space. The earth seen from the moon was a whole in a new sense, no longer simulated by a globe, but seen whole. Scientist fathers conversing with their small sons found themselves confused because they were still earthbound looking toward the moon, while the children were on the moon looking back toward earth.

Besides these major transforming events — the sense of political and military vulnerability that grew up after World War II, and the specific change in perspective that has grown with the space program as the earth has become planet Earth — something else has been happening. Men everywhere are becoming conscious that this planet, like any small island, is interconnected in ways other than war and rumors of war. The spread of radioactive dust; the long journey of DDT from someone's rose garden to the shell-less eggs of unborn birds and the bones of unborn children; the new, resistant strains of venereal disease and malaria, which are robbing us of our recent conquest of these dangers; the knowledge that man's activities can alter the temperature of the earth, create storms of inestimable strength, pollute the oceans as well as the small lakes and streams that are dying throughout the civilized world: all have brought home to us that the earth is an island. Interconnected the peoples of the earth are — vulnerable to each other's weapons and no longer able to defend their frontiers and their children: vulnerable also to the acts of people half a world away, as they casually dump tanks of nuclear by-products into the sea depths, which no one has yet properly explored, or send clouds of pollution through the air. As those who love and protect the wilderness and try to save a part of it for man, and as those who see their main crop destroyed by the by-products of human intervention in agriculture or animal husbandry, so now the whole world is coming to realize the interconnectedness between the way men live and whether or not their children and their children's children will have a habitable world. Not war, but a plethora of man-made things — disposable, indestructible beer cans; too much industrial waste in the lakes and streams, from antibiotics designed to protect egg-laying fowls to pesticides designed to protect the orange crop — is threatening to strangle us, suffocate us, bury us in the debris and by-products of our technologically inventive and irresponsible age.

With this new realization, which is expressing itself in a hundred differ-
ent ways, from government commissions and antipollution groups, to the
American Association for the Advancement of Science's Committtee on
Science in the Promotion of Human Welfare, to the Scientists Institute for
Public Information, to small committees in small New England towns, the
debate goes on. (A large number of these new movements were discussed
in "The New Conservation," by Richard L. Means, *Natural History,* August–
September, 1969.) With this proliferation of public interest, those who have
been fighting these battles for conservation, for protection, for soil rehabilitation, for reforestation, and those who have become more recently aware
of the dangers of pollution, overpopulation, and overload of every facility are
meeting and looking for new ways of stating their common interests. Words
like *ecosystem,* the whole interacting system in which a change in any one
variable — temperature, the number of fish or fishermen, a factory built on
the banks of a stream, or a florist's seed field five miles away — may change
the whole system, and *biosphere,* the whole natural living system of the planet
and its surrounding atmosphere, are coming into the vocabulary of the concerned all over the world. These terms come from the science of ecology, a
science that, on the whole, took as its model a pond, a lake, or a marsh and,
while allowing for interaction among every natural component, took little
cognizance of man himself, except as an interfering factor. If we wanted to
teach our children about ecosystems, the model we used was an aquarium, in
which the delicate relationships between water, plants, and aquatic creatures
had to be watched over and kept in balance.

Aquariums are indeed a fine teaching aid and will give children an idea
of the balance of the natural world, especially the great mass of urban children
who meet nature either in the form of a pet who has to be walked in the
streets or provided with "kitty litter." But it is becoming increasingly clear
that this model, over which the aquarium owner stands, like a god, presiding
over a small glass tank heated by electricity (itself vulnerable to a power failure) is only a very partial model of what is happening to us. The child's
aquarium is a model of a world almost totally dependent on man, but of
which he is a spectator and protector, not an integral part.

If, from the science of ecology, we try to develop a new profession of
those who stand guard over the environment, we stand in danger of still
leaving man outside, to become an "environmental manager," a significant
factor, but not a true part of the natural world. To the core subject of ecology,
it is suggested that we add the human sciences to train aspirant young environmental managers to deal with the problem. As new subject matters
develop in the field of urbanization — ekistics, urban planning, urban design
— there is an attempt to patch together from a number of disciplines a new
whole, a science of the total ecosystem, into which man, somewhat grudg-
ingly, is to be admitted.

I do not think this is the way to do it. We have had many decades of
various interdisciplinary projects. Either they represent a coalition of different
disciplinary interests, in which each defends his own territory, or we get new
incorporative fields, like economics or public health, which manufacture their

own psychology and educational theory to suit themselves and, in turn, become little empires defending their domains against contenders.

I believe that there is another way to develop the kind of specialists that we will need as public concern for our endangered planet and for our starving millions mounts. And this is where islands come back again. What students need to learn if they are to think about environmental protection and development is about whole inhabited ecosystems: ecosystems in which man himself, the way he plants and reaps and disposes of waste, multiplies or stabilizes his population, is a *conscious* factor. Man has molded and changed his environment since he learned to make tools and control fire. But in those days, perhaps a million years ago, he was not conscious of what he did, of how population was related to food supply, of how killing the young or eating all the eggs or gathering plants before they seeded would limit his future. It was on islands that man first began to learn these things. If there were too many people, either some would be driven out into the uncharted seas or there would be civil war. Some method of population control had to be adopted. Younger sons were forbidden to marry and infants exposed to die. Islanders knew when the birds came to nest, when the fish came to spawn, how periodic hurricanes affected their harvests. On many small islands today, the harsh realities of a rapidly changing world are forcing the men away to work, leaving only women and children at home. It was on islands that men first learned that they themselves were part of an ecosystem, so it is perhaps not surprising that the religious system of the ancient Polynesians emphasized taboo, that things were forbidden in the nature of the system itself. Under taboo, if men made no missteps they lived safely, but they had to be continuously alert to the consequences of infringement of the order of nature and the order of social life.

We need to find ways to understand, to teach children, and to prepare young men and women for careers in our interconnected and endangered world. The forces of public opinion are being marshalled nationally and internationally. A great international conference, conspicuous for its level of cooperation among usually rivalrous United Nations specialized agencies, was held in Paris in 1968. A conference on biology as the history of the future, sponsored by the International Union of Biological Sciences, was held in Chichén Itzá, Mexico, in January, 1969. At the initiative of Sweden, a great United Nations conference is being prepared for 1972. We need to have a model that will make man — always active, seldom conscious, irresponsible throughout much of history — a conscious participant in the development of planet Earth.

The smallest islands of the earth are almost all in trouble, whether it be the islands of the Hebrides, fighting the British Parliament and paying no income taxes; the burgeoning population of Mauritius; the belligerent population of Anguilla; or the small Greek islands whose men must all go away to sea. Such islands, grievously resourceless, overpopulated, and dependent upon distant and outside money, can become our models and our training grounds for the new professions that are needed. As small children were once asked to build a model of Solomon's Temple in Sunday School, or of Egyptian pyramids in day school to understand ancient civilizations centered on man alone and reflecting his natural environment, we now need materials so that each child in a class may have an island to think about: its size, its shape, its location, its weather, its resources, the habits and skills and despairs and hopes of its inhabitants, and its dependence upon world markets and diplomatic decisions in which its people have no part. And for those older students who wish to make a career of the protection and development of the whole of man's environment, a year on an island, learning the language, mastering the intricacies of the interrelationships of its living population and all its plants and creatures, would be perfect preparation for thinking about wholes. We would not need to patch disciplines together in an uneasy truce; members of various specialized disciplines could first obtain a firm grounding in their own fields and then — with a year's field work on an island — learn to articulate that speciality into a whole.

Following in Darwin's footsteps, Harold Coolidge began the trek back to islands for inspiration when he took a whole group of scientists to Galápagos in January, 1964. But the Galápagos have no human beings on them. It is the inclusion of people and their purposes that is now our problem. Nor need we ask islands — often in dire straits — to contribute, yet gain nothing from what they teach us about our planet Earth. Each student could be asked to work on some real problem, urgent to the people themselves, and thus prepare himself for the kind of world role when, in the 1970's and 1980's man's survival will hang in the balance — and the generation now growing up will have the task of saving this planet as a habitable spot for their children and their children's children.

M. B. DALE

Systems Analysis and Ecology

INTRODUCTION

Systems analysis has been presented as a desirable framework on which the investigation and comparison of ecosystems can be hung. This approach has been especially emphasized by the productivity subgroups of the International Biological Program (IBP). Claims of the importance of systems analysis are not restricted to ecology, for in other fields the results of employing these methods have been claimed to give additional insight and clarity (see e.g. Halmos and Vaughan 1950, Bush and Mosteller 1955, Glanzer and Glaser 1959, Orcutt

M. B. Dale, "Systems Analysis and Ecology," *Ecology*, vol. 51, no. 1 (Winter 1970), pp. 2–16. Reprinted by permission.
The author is with the Division of Plant Industry, CSIRO, Canberra, Australia.

1960, Harary and Lipstein 1962, Keeney, Koenig and Zemach 1967). Examples of explicit use of systems methods in ecology are few (Olson 1963, Patten 1965, Holling 1966, Watt 1968), and it is by no means clear from these examples what systems analysis is, what it does, what restrictions it imposes, nor how the variety of ecology (or more precisely ecological methodology) can be attached to this framework. This paper attempts to clarify some of the questions an ecologist must answer and the problems he must resolve before using systems methods, and to introduce some of these methods in the context of a general systems approach. It does not provide the mathematical, statistical, and other details of the use of the methods, although it is hoped that sufficient references are included to enable the interested ecologist to obtain this information. Necessary definitions are provided and the general nature of systems considered. The relationship between systems analysis and problem solving is established, and the ecosystem is examined in the framework of the problem-solving processes. An example of a systems model is presented and the problems of investigating and manipulating systems and of organizing ecosystem descriptions are considered.

SYSTEMS ANALYSIS, SYSTEMS, AND ECOSYSTEMS

Systems analysis

Systems analysis has rarely been defined when introduced into ecological studies. Watt (1968) suggests that it is the determination of those variables which are important in a system, and further adds that systems simulation, systems optimization, and systems measurement are other facets of the systems approach. Others, such as Priban (1968), view model building as the essence of the systems approach. Morton (1964) has suggested that systems analysis is no more nor less than scientific method itself, and that the distinguishing feature of the systems approach is the conscious application of scientific method to complex organizations in order that no important factor be overlooked, a view expressed by Pascal as "error comes from exclusion." These viewpoints are not necessarily mutually exclusive. Systems analysis is the application of scientific method to complex problems, and this application is further distinguished by the use of advanced mathematical and statistical techniques and by the use of computers. The computers are used as "number-crunching" calculating machines and as convenient tools for modelling systems too complex for analytic solutions to be presently possible. This modelling function is of great importance in studies of complex natural systems, for, provided the model can be treated as representing the real system for the purposes of the investigation, experiments can be performed on the model with a consequent gain in control and rapidity of response. A good model will obviously contain the important variables, so Watt's comments are pertinent. Equally, if natural systems are complex then the modelling phase of the systems analysis will be emphasized and Priban's emphasis accepted. Morton's more general view, since it includes both the others, seems the most acceptable since it does not presuppose some a priori emphasis on certain parts of the analysis.

Systems

A system is a collection of interacting entities, or alternatively it is a collection of parts, together with statements on the relationships, of some kind, between these parts. The interpretation to be given to the entities is the choice of the investigator, but the entities need not be, and in general are not, in one-to-one correspondence with "real" things. They can represent classes of things, or classes of processes if this seems necessary. The state of the system at some point in space and time is described by the values of properties of the entities, and all properties used to so describe the system are termed endogenous. Variables which affect the interrelationships between entities, but which are not included in the state description, are called exogenous and form the environment in which the system acts. If endogenous properties are interchanged with other systems outside the defined one, then the system is said to be "open" for these properties. If there is no import or export, the system is closed. Representations of systems can take a variety of forms. Perhaps the commonest is as a network (Ford and Fulkerson 1962, Harary, Norman, and Cartwright 1965) or as a matrix derived from such a network. An alternative mathematical representation is given by Rosen (1958), and an ecological example is the structural description diagrams of Dansereau, Buell, and Dagon (1966). Such general descriptions permit discussions about systems, but a computer program modelling a system is equally a representation of that particular system.

Any system is composed of subsystems defined for subsets of the entities. Each of these subsystems can be treated as a system in its own right, so that the definition of a system is recursive.* An open system, that is, one open for at least one property, can be considered as a subsystem of some "higher" order system (Cooper 1969), and since each subsystem can be decomposed into sub-subsystems, a hierarchy of systems is produced. A familiar example of such a hierarchy is . . . . . -organism-organ-tissue-cell-organelle- . . . . . Obviously some means is required to prevent infinite regress, and in practical work this termination depends on the fidelity of the model of the system to the "real" system. This fidelity requirement will be discussed later.

Finally, it is necessary to define an ecosystem. An ecosystem is a system open for at least one property, in which at least one of the entities is classed as living. This definition is very broad, but restrictions imposed by ecologists to limit this definition for particular studies have not received much consideration. It must be remembered that an ecosystem is a special case of the general system and will possess all properties of the general system. Thus there is no restriction on the number of properties which may be used to describe the system, although many ecologists have so restricted themselves, with the

---

* A simple example of recursive definition is the factorial of an integer number written $n!$. This can be calculated as follows:

$$n! = n \times (n-1) \times (n-2) \times (n-3) \times \cdots \cdots \times 3 \times 2 \times 1$$

Equally the value can be calculated from the following rule.

$$n! = \text{if } n = 1 \text{ then } 1 \text{ else } n \times (n-1)!$$

consequent introduction of difficulties with an excessively large number of exogenous variables. There is certainly no restriction to studies of productivity or energy transfer, although many applications of systems analysis in ecology have been on these problems. Population models are systems models and so is the physiognomic description of vegetation. However, since the preponderance of systems studies in ecology have been studies of productivity, it will be convenient to phrase examples in these terms.

SYSTEMS AND PROBLEM SOLVING

The recursive hierarchical nature of systems is closely paralleled in some theories of human problem solving (e.g., Simon and Newall 1962, Feigenbaum and Feldman 1963). Here an attempt is made to decompose insoluble problems into subproblems. Any subproblems remaining insoluble are further decomposed, until hopefully all subproblems and their derivatives are soluble, when an attempt is made to reintegrate the solutions into a single solution of the original problem. The parallel between problem solving and systems can be drawn more closely, however. Ross (1967) distinguishes four phases in problem solving: (1) lexical, (2) parsing, (3) modelling, and (4) analysis (see also Morton 1964). In systems analysis these same four phases can also be identified: (1) delimination of the entities or parts; (2) the choice of relationships between entities which are of interest; (3) the specification of the mechanism by which these interrelationships take place; and (4) validation of the model of the system so produced and investigation of its properties.

Ross points out that the rules under which these phases are carried out must be agreed upon a priori, which is not a simple task. An obvious example of changing rules is given by the diversity of human language, which has an additional complication due to the possible existence of several scripts for one spoken language. Some of the phytosociological arguments on vegetation description appear to be arguments regarding rules of procedure, although the situation is complicated here because it is not clear that each system is intended to contain the same information. Ecologists must therefore agree on the rules to be used, otherwise comparison of systems will not be possible. Much of the difficulty lies in the choice of entities, and this will be discussed later.

The four phases of problem solving and systems analysis are used in the following sections as a framework in which to discuss problems in systems analysis.

The lexical phase

One of the most neglected problems in systems studies is the choice of the entities or parts which compose the system. It is commonly assumed that these are self-evident; yet the arguments which have taken place in areas such as the classification of organisms or vegetation concerning sampling, description, and measures of similarity suggest that this is not true. In taxonomy a hierarchy similar to the systems hierarchy is apparent — family, genus, species, etc., and taxonomists have agreed that while studies at any level are possible, the species level is in some way more important. It is by no means clear that the species level is a consistent level: the occurrence of "difficult" genera such as *Hieracium, Rubus,* or *Quercus,* and the varied degree of subtlety in characters used to describe and distinguish species in different families such as the Umbelliferae and the Magnoliaceae, attests some inconsistency. Yet the taxonomist has a distinct advantage over the ecologist in that there exists a generating system (Williams 1967), the genetic system, which constrains the possible variation, so that the lexical phase in taxonomy rests on the interpretation of genetic event patterns; that much of the genetic information available is not at the species level but within it is a practical problem though an unfortunate one. The ecologist has no such system presently available, and in the opinion of some ecologists there is no such system.

The choice of entities for the ecosystem is in part determined by the parsing phase, that is, by the nature of the relationships with which the system is concerned. The commonest choices have been between taxonomic, structural, and functional entities. Taxonomic is a convenient adjective to describe entities based on individual organisms, populations, and the commoner taxonomic categories of species, genera, and so on. Structural entities are based on life-form criteria, trees, shrubs, herbs, and bryoids providing a simple botanical example. Life-form criteria are in general more responsive to local environmental fluctuations than taxonomic criteria, since these latter employ characters selected to be invariant within taxa, wherever possible. Functional entities have perhaps received more attention in animal ecology, e.g., herbivore, carnivore, omnivore, although a variety of similar units exists in plant ecology, though less precisely defined, e.g., xerophyte, halophyte, and saprophyte. The definition of entities is not of course concerned with the ease of identification of these parts, although it may well be essential to provide common means of identifying the entities if different systems are to be compared. Of more consequence is the possibility of conversion from one set of entities to another. If one description employs structural categories and another taxonomic categories, how can the two be compared? *Liriodendron tulipifera* is a taxon which could certainly fall into the categories of shrub or tree, and on some definitions the seedlings would be classed as herbs. Even restriction to species as entities fails to resolve the problem, for this ignores all ecotypic and ontogenetic variation and the inconsistencies in the species level noted above.

It may be true that some ecosystems can only be compared at gross levels such as autotroph and heterotroph, for example marine and terrestrial systems. Yet because the United Kingdom has some 1,700 species of vascular plants, 900 bryoids, and various numbers of lichens and fungi, whereas Oak Ridge, Tennessee, has some 2,000 species of vascular plants alone, does not imply that comparisons of the two areas are only possible at some very gross level, even though the species complements are widely different. To demand that comparisons be possible with both very similar and very different ecosystems places severe restrictions on the possible choices of entities which can be employed to describe the systems. It may also be possible to describe systems in terms of a few simple ratios, such as the efficiencies which have been proposed, but this could equally reflect the well-known half-truth that biologists, when given two numbers, divide one by the other.

Functional entities do not resolve the problems of choice any more than structural or taxonomic entities. Omnivores, for example, are both herbivorous and carnivorous, while insectiverous plants are both autotrophic and heterotrophic. Nonliving materials within the ecosystem are less well served with possibilities, while still having problems of ontogeny and chemical equilibrium, such as that between the various forms of nitrogen in the soil. Perhaps a distinction between solid, liquid, and gaseous phases is possible, but is this all?

Since the first phase of a systems analysis is the choice of entities, it is very necessary that an ecologist give considered thought to these problems. In a study of a single system, the problems may well be less acute than when comparison of systems is necessary. But the choice of entities is the ecologists' task and must not be given to the systems analysts by default.

The parsing phase

The second phase is concerned with the definition of the relationships between the selected entities. These relationships can be of any kind and need not be restricted to materials. It has been common practice in ecology to assume that the relationships are those relating to material which the system can reorder or reallocate among its parts. The relationships can, however, be spatial or temporal and need not concern materials at all. Such relationships are important in physiognomic description of vegetation. In view of the present great interest in productivity, however, attention will be concentrated on ecosystems models produced by such studies, and the properties relevant to them. These properties include energy, biomass, carbon, mineral nutrients, populations, individuals, water, and possibly information (in the form of genetic material). It does not include diversity in the sense in which this has been commonly used in ecology (Margalef 1947), which is a measure of the distribution of some property or properties over the entities, or some subset of them, in a single state description. Changes in diversity can provide useful indices of changes in the distribution caused by exogenous variables.

There is no restriction in the definition of the ecosystem given earlier on the use of several properties to describe the state of the system. The description can be multivariate. The importance of interaction between properties in such a multivariate system can be seen in work on mineral nutrient interactions and their effects on yield (Fig. 1). Such interactions are not of course limited to these particular variables. The difficulties of modelling and experimenting with multivariate systems do impose practical constraints on the investigator (Jacoby and Harrison 1962). The problem can be reduced to a univariate one by treating other properties as exogenous, although this increases the experimentation required. In comparing two systems which have been made univariate, it is essential to ensure that differences between systems do not become confounded with differences in treatment of the relocated exogenous variables.

In the context of the International Biological Program the property most

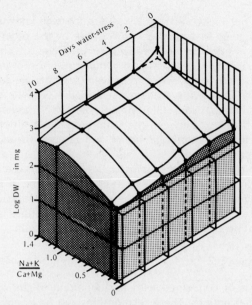

Figure 1. **Dry weight response of Atriplex inflata after 8 weeks in relation to days of withholding water and the ratio (Na + K)/(Ca + Mg)**

favored has been energy fixed as carbon, usually as total biomass. This implies a preference against edible, palatable, or otherwise desirable biomass such as protein, which preference may not always be desirable. Thus wool growth in sheep may well be related to amounts of sulfur-containing protein rather than total biomass consumed. This is not to deny the importance of energy transfer as measured by total biomass, but merely to indicate that it alone will be but a partial representation of the "real" system and may not always be the most desirable. Other choices have been made including mineral nutrients, water, radioactive contaminants, and, with growing emphasis in the United States, pollutants in general. In all these cases, however, the possibility that a multivariate system might be more useful than the univariate one must be accepted and consideration given to the requirements of such a system model.

Modelling

Fidelity. — Having fixed the entities and the properties, the next phase is the specification of the mechanisms by which changes in the system, that is in the distribution of the properties across the entities, take place. In choosing these processes, an attempt is made to make the model of the system "mimic" the real system, either to increase understanding of the system or to attain control of the system over some range of states. This difference in possible objective is characterized by differing degrees of fidelity. High fidelity implies that the model resembles the real system for a wide range of states and changes in state and as a corollary, that this similitude is obtained by designing the model to follow presumed or known processes of the real system. The range of property values, for a given range of values of exogenous variables and for some entities, are called the outputs of the system, these being the particular values of interest. Knowledge of the sensitivity of the system to changes in some processes would be used to gain greater understanding of the mechanism of action of the system, and hence higher fidelity.

However, high fidelity is not always required. Provided that the model mimics the real system over some restricted range, that is, the model outputs and the real system outputs are highly correlated, then the processes used in the model need not reflect the real system at all. As an example, in the description of spatial distributions of plants, several mathematical expressions may fit the data equally well, for example, Thomas' double poisson and the negative binomial distribution (Archibald 1948, Greig-Smith 1964). The mathematical expressions may well imply different models of the underlying real system, which may in fact agree with neither model, yet the results may be adequate. The simplest and most common ecosystem model is

Input–Ecosystem–Output

where the system itself is treated as a closed "black" box. This has been widely used in ecology (Van Dyne, Wright, and Dollar 1968), since it is the basis of univariate multiple regression. The attainment of high fidelity is expensive in time and in the effort required to obtain the precise and accurate data on which to build and validate the model. An analogy with sound reproduction is reasonably drawn. Telephone voice communication neither requires nor uses equipment necessary for the high-quality reproduction of music.* The complexity of model required to attain high fidelity must be matched by the quality of the data. To continue the sound-reproduction analogy, a scratched recording is still scratched on the best equipment. The collection of adequate and relevant data in studies of ecosystems will often be difficult if not impossible. For example, in studies of the interaction of radiant energy and a plant canopy, account must be taken of the spatial distribution of the stems and leaves. The collection of precise and detailed information on this feature is extremely difficult.

The processes to be defined must obviously depend on the choice of properties and entities. Changes in state of plant entities, for example, will require processes defining fixation of energy, carbon, nitrogen, and water, and other processes defining the reallocation of these properties among the entities. Some of the processes operate in sequence, the results of one forming an input to the next. They may also of course operate in parallel, that is, over the same time interval. This parallelism can be troublesome in some methods of investigating systems, such as simulation on digital computers which are essentially serial in operation. Special processing techniques (including special languages such as the SIMULA extension to ALGOL (Dahl and Nygaard 1966)) may be required.

---

* In statistics the problem of fidelity appears in the use of one distribution to provide an approximation to another. One example is the use of the normal distribution to approximate others such as the binomial, poisson, or Mann-Whitney U (see Siegel 1956).

The processes only change endogenous variables although they may employ both previous values of endogenous variables and exogenous variables in the calculation. It must also be realized that high fidelity in the definition of the processes does not guarantee high correlation between model and real outputs. The choice of exogenous variables also constrains the fidelity of the model. For example, consider two models of photosynthesis, one using mean day length to predict amount of carbon dioxide fixed, the other being more sophisticated and employing temperature, carbon dioxide, humidity, and radiation fluxes, together with data on spatial distribution of leaves to estimate the same value. The second might be expected to be of higher fidelity, yet by introducing appropriate stochastic variation into the first model it might be possible to make it of higher fidelity. This prediction requires less data, but the selection of the appropriate stochastic inputs would be troublesome. This emphasizes the importance of considering data-collection techniques when choosing the form of the processes (Watanabe and Abraham 1960). More than this, however, it reinforces the comment made earlier that the definition of the system is the ecologists' problem and is the result of interaction between available, or potentially available, information and the purposes for which the model is required. The modelling process may suggest areas where data-collection techniques might be improved so that a more faithful model becomes possible. One indication can be gleaned from economic models. The choice of interesting and practical models appears to be those models with 30–300 variables, with the experienced worker reducing the number (Forrester, *personal communication*).

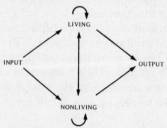

Figure 2.   The primitive model

Practical considerations. — Watt (1968) has presented a variety of approaches to the problem of defining processes; these by no means exhaust the possibilities. A very simple model of an ecosystem can be constructed consisting of four entities each of which represents a class and the properties and processes remain unspecified (Fig. 2). The same system can be presented in the form of a transition matrix, where each a_{jk} represents the probability of transfer of a property between the jth and k^{th} entity (Fig. 3). Similar matrices could be constructed for all properties, so that the entries can be interpreted as arrays of coefficients. To each of these there must be attached a corresponding process giving the next value of the a_{jk} in terms of the present and previous values of the whole matrix and any additional exogenous variables. The nature of these functions is, of course, of great interest to ecologists. The model does not include some features of human information transfer where questions of

	INPUT	LIVING	NONLIVING	OUTPUT
INPUT	o	a_{IL}	a_{IP}	o
LIVING	o	a_{LL}	a_{LP}	a_{LO}
NONLIVING	o	a_{PL}	a_{PP}	a_{PO}
OUTPUT	o	o	o	o

Figure 3. Transition matrix for the primitive model

the value, reliability, and credibility of information are involved. It would include demographic or population models which form the bulk of ecological work on systems (see Kerner 1957, 1959, Whittle 1962, Bellman, Kagiwada, and Kalaba 1966, Garfinkel 1967a, b, Watt 1968, and others). Demographic models conveniently illustrate the duality between continuous and discrete models of systems. Many population models employ systems of differential equations which provide a continuous model of the system, including fractional values for the population total. But the population in most cases is discrete, being an integer number of individuals. Of the references given above only Whittle employs a discrete model (a discrete branching Markov process), probably because of the extra effort involved in the mathematics if restriction to integer solutions is imposed.

While demographic models can certainly be included in the ecosystem concept, it is also common to restrict the definition of ecosystem to models of the movement of materials or energy (e.g., Golley 1960, Olson 1963, Witherspoon, Auerbach, and Olson 1964, Patten 1965). If this restriction is accepted, then a slightly more complex model, as shown in Fig. 4, hopefully would improve in fidelity over the primitive model of Fig. 2. Autotroph in this model includes both energy and chemical fixation. Minor variants of this model in Fig. 5 show its generality.

While the network representations of Fig. 2, 4, and 5 are convenient visual models, mathematically the transition matrices corresponding to them are more easily handled. The meaning of such matrices can be considered geometrically. Consider a system with two entities and a single property. This can be represented as a point on a graph for any state. If the system changes due to change of an exogenous variable, then the point representing the system is

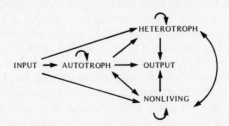

Figure 4. Developments of the model for non-demographic systems

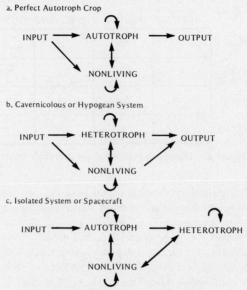

Figure 5.   Examples of restricted systems

displaced. A series of changes would trace a line, and the transition matrix contains the information describing this line. Of course in most models the graph is not in two dimensions, but the properties of the transition matrix still hold (see Keeney et al. 1967 for an extended description of this "state space" model).

The state of the system is a static description and the dynamics of changes in state are incorporated into the model by the processes. While some systems may only show changes in response to changes in exogenous variables, in many systems and certainly in ecosystems the changes in state are partly determined by the previous states of the system, that is, by its history, by means of "feedback" or "memory." This is of course also included in the processes by making these employ previous values of the endogenous variables in the calculations. If these processes themselves employ parameters which change with time, the system is evolutionary, whereas if the parameters do not change with time, the process is stationary. The difficulties introduced by considering evolutionary processes are such that the majority of models employ stationary processes, although it is fairly clear that real ecosystems are strictly evolutionary. There is little work on the mathematics of evolutionary processes, and most of this is recent and at a somewhat advanced mathematical level. It would certainly be possible to permit evolutionary processes in simulation models, but this would involve a large increase in time and effort in an already time-consuming method, since the initial state of the system must be specified very carefully for evolutionary processes. For many practical purposes over moderate time intervals the assumption of stationarity may be justified, although, as with multivariate models, the possibility of increasing fidelity by employing evolutionary models must be considered.

Analysis

The final stage of the systems approach is the analysis proper. This involves the solution of the model, in some sense, and the validation of the model outputs by comparing them to the real system outputs. In a few simple cases the model may be solved analytically using standard mathematical techniques. Models employing linear differential equations, for example, may be soluble, and in this case the sensitivity of the model to small changes in parameter values can also be calculated (Wilkins 1966). In general, however, no analytic solution will be available, and recourse must be made to the somewhat time-consuming simulation approach.

The likelihood that high fidelity will be desired suggests that stochastic models, incorporating random processes, will be preferable to deterministic models. This is due to the more realistic incorporation of variability in stochastic models and to the availability of estimates of the expected variability of the outputs. As an example of the greater realism of stochastic models, consider the spread of an infection through a population. Deterministic models suggest the existence of a critical population size at which there is a change from "no epidemic" to "epidemic" and the epidemic is of a fixed size. Stochastic models not only permit the epidemic to be variable in size, but also provide that, whatever the population size, there is an estimable chance of an epidemic occurring, and conversely of its not occurring (Bartlett 1960).

Simulation methods have been widely used both with analogue and with digital computers (Clymer and Graber 1964, International Business Machines Corporation 1966). Most of the ecological applications have used constant time increments, calculating the state of the model periodically. Less commonly event-orientated models have been attempted (Holling 1966). These essentially calculate the time interval between changes in state, so that periods when no change in state occurs require a constant computational effort independent of the length of the interval. Event orientation emphasizes the importance of recurrence intervals, which are ecologically important in determining survival times, where the event of "successful reproduction" and the event of "death" mark the intervals. Recurrence intervals are also important in migration and have been found useful in sampling vegetation (Williams, *personal communication*). Even if there are strongly periodic phenomena such as diurnal or annual cycles, an attempt to define events may force the modeller to consider his system in greater detail.

After a model of the system has been established and some means of investigating its responses has been provided, the crucial problem of the validation of the model remains. Validation may involve the functional form of the processes and the parameters supplied as constants to these processes, but primarily the interest lies in how well the model outputs mimic those of the real system, that is, in the fidelity of the model over the range of interest. If high fidelity is required there will usually be a process of successive approximation, with the model being progressively altered until the desired fidelity is obtained. This requires, of course, some measure of fidelity to assess the disparity between model and reality. Since the processes usually involve sub-systems of the model, validating the processes is essentially also a process of measuring the fidelity of a system, in that the outputs of the subsystems to the complete system should presumably also be of high fidelity.

The difficulty of validating outputs depends on the features which it is desired to mimic. If only mean values must be estimated, the disparity can be measured by a test akin to Students' t, and various techniques are available to increase the precision of the comparison, mostly developed in Monte-Carlo studies (Hammersley and Morton 1956). These include such methods as Russian roulette, antithetic variables, and regression. If, however, the variance of the outputs or features of the transient response of outputs to particular changes in exogenous variables is required, the problem is more complex. The outputs form a correlated series of observations, and the comparison and investigation of such series present considerable statistical problems (see Quenouille 1957, Robinson 1967, Jenkins and Watt 1968). Rarely do ecological models specify which features of the output are to be reproduced by the model. Watt (1961) has provided examples of functions which produce outputs of given forms, and the use of least-squares surface fitting can also aid in the selection of possible functions to provide specific output forms. Perhaps the most general techniques are those of Wiener (1949), though these require a large amount of data.

Validation of the parameters of the processes involves searching the response surface of the model to obtain "best" estimates. A variety of techniques might be of use here, including those due to Hooke and Jeeves (1961), Spang (1962), and Marquardt (1963). The general problem of estimation in simulation studies has received most attention in engineering and management studies (e.g., Burdick and Naylor 1966, Fishman 1967, Fishman and Kiviat 1967), but it must be remembered that even if the model is validated, extrapolation beyond the limits of such validation is the responsibility of the ecologist. It would be foolish to say that such extrapolation is never justified, but the justification is not mathematical or statistical.

AN AUTOTROPH SYSTEM

A diagrammatic representation of a precipitation-evapotranspiration (PET) system is used as an example of the models employed in systems analysis (Fig. 6). This is not the only model of this system since both Crawford and Linsley (1966) and Hufschmidt and Fiering (1966) incorporate simple expressions in their larger models to represent the whole of the PET system. Equally, more detailed models might be built up from the equations describing the transfer of heat and water vapor between leaf and atmosphere, and corresponding detailed study of the distribution of stem and leaves. The fidelity of the model will depend on the specifications of the processes by which the transfers of the property, here water, between entities is to be made. Such specifications have been provided and the resulting model converted to a computer program. The diagram shows only the connections between entities which were considered in the modelling.

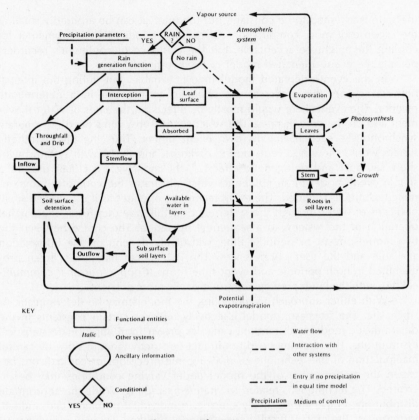

Figure 6. The PET system

Two subsystems are easily identified, one modelling the entry of water into the soil, the other modelling its return to the atmosphere. These interact at two points, since changes in the amount of leaves (and their distribution) will affect interception, and changes in the amount of roots will affect water extraction from the soil by the plant. Conversely, both leaf and root growth will be dependent on water availability.

Three other systems are explicitly included. The photosynthetic system requires inputs from the leaves and will feedback to both leaves and roots. This feedback is accomplished by the growth system which is responsible for the partition of photosynthate between the parts of the plant. The atmospheric system provides the source of water and the radiation which finally controls the loss of water. A fourth system could easily be added to introduce the effects of topography on input and output of water as runoff to or from other areas, and possibly erosion effects of such runoff. All the systems here operate in parallel in that they all operate simultaneously.

An equal time model of this system would review the description of the entities, which in this case would be the water contents and size of plant parts, at periodic intervals recalculating when necessary. During these periods the state is assumed to be constant, but the interval can be arbitrarily small at the expense of more computation. Given the periodicity of instrumental recording this might be acceptable, but the existence of continuous recorders permits the event-orientated model to be investigated.

In the event-orientated model time is variable, but during the interval between events the processes are assumed to proceed in a determinate manner. The events here would mostly be effects on the rates of water movement and on the growth rates. The systems and subsystems need not operate synchronously, each having its own event timing. Thus the photosynthetic system would show no events during darkness, and the growth system might show seasonal and ontogenetic effects. Dahl and Nygaard (1966) present a simple event model of an epidemic which illustrates the computer-programming techniques required. The event technique operates as if it followed small packages of water through the system and in this way transforms the parallel operation of the systems to a sequential operation. The choice between the two models, event or periodic time, will finally depend on the information available and the user's preferences. The PET system has in fact been programmed in both periodic and event-time forms (Cooper, *personal communication*), with the latter proving computationally more efficient.

With either approach to modelling the models may be deterministic or stochastic. The stochastic model effectively replaces certain constants in the deterministic model with random variables drawn from appropriate statistical distributions. This drawing need not in fact be strictly random since by careful manipulation of the technique of drawing, the precisions of comparisons between the performance of the model under varying conditions may be increased. The technique is related to stratified sampling. While the appropriate distributions to use are relatively specific to individual problems and, indeed, form one of the most difficult parts of model building, for very rare events it may be possible to make use of the fact that extreme values have only three possible distributions (Gumbel 1958). This might appear a marginal advantage as there remains some choice to be made. However, this particular problem is usually solved by an automatic choice of the exponential distribution probably because of its ease of computation, and without regard for the alternatives. The systems analyst may indeed accept the simple exponential distribution, but he should be aware of the alternatives.

One of the interesting possibilities of controlling the "random" numbers depends on the nonexistence of such numbers. Random numbers are, in fact, pseudorandom in that they pass some of the tests of randomness which are possible, but not all. The infinite number of such tests makes it impossible to know if any set of numbers is random. Provided that the numbers are random for the tests employed, nonrandomness can be incorporated to reduce the effects of unimportant sources of variation. Tocher (1963) considers the possibilities in some detail.

EXPERIMENTATION CONTROL AND OPTIMIZATION

The techniques and considerations of the previous sections will hopefully lead to a valid model of the ecosystem. We will now consider means of using such a model of a single system as a guide to the management of the real system. This will involve experimenting with the real and model systems, identifying the parameters of the system which will enable it to be controlled, choosing a value function by which the performance of the system is to be measured, selecting the route to some desired state, and maintaining the system at or near this desired point. The advantages of using the model system lie in the ease and rapidity with which experiments may be carried out, and the possibility of including experiments which might be totally destructive in the real system. The disadvantages lie in the restricted range of confirmed validity of the model and in its fidelity even within this range to the real system which it is desired to control.

Designing experiments for model systems will necessarily involve use of the techniques developed in statistics for efficient experimenting, though often in an unusual form. The output of the experiments forms a response surface, and special experimental designs have been developed for studying these (Box and Draper 1959, Cochran 1963, Draper and Lawrence 1965). Since the response is a correlated sequence of values, the "growth curve" techniques of Roa (1965) and Potthof and Roy (1964) may be of assistance (see also Whittle 1963, Phattaford 1965, Spent 1967). The response may of course be multivariate, and correspondingly so must the methods of analysis (see e.g. Seal 1964), and may equally involve relaxation of assumptions of normality thus necessitating the use of non-parametric methods (Box and Watson 1962, Mood and Graybill 1963, Tiku 1964). Because the experiments are carried out on the model, efficiency and precision may be improved by restrictions imposed on the model which could not be imposed on the real system. One technique would be restrictions on the choice of "random" numbers as mentioned in the previous section, such as repeating the same sequence of "random" numbers both in the control and the experimental model solutions. A computer aid design may also be used in some cases (Kennard and Stone 1969).

The experiments lead towards control of the system, enabling a manager to manipulate the system towards some point and to maintain the system in the neighborhood of this point. Almost always there will be constraints on the actions available to the manager, such as avoiding certain states, restrictions on materials, and so on. General mathematical control principles are known (e.g., Pontryagin's continuous maximization principle, for which see Fan 1966), but these have proved difficult to apply in practice. Control implies the existence of a desired state and some means of assessing the importance and hence the size of any deviation from this state. Related to this is the need to measure the effects of any control operation. These subjects have been studied in detail in operations research (Bellman 1961, Muhzam 1963, Box and Tiao 1965). Maintenance of the system near the desired point means the control of variations in the outputs of the system. For example, management of a watershed to have flow proportional to demand would be ideal for hydroelectric power generation, where overproduction is worth little and underproduction is extremely costly. The quest for high fidelity models seems to result from the detailed control necessary, coupled with an assumption that the control of endogenous variables will be more selective, more efficient, and less expensive than control of exogenous variables. The truth of this assumption is debatable since the cost of obtaining the required detail in the model must also be considered. Both endogenous and exogenous variables can be manipulated in many systems.

Efficient control will usually imply the selection of important variables for which several techniques have been developed. Sensitivity analysis (Radanovic 1966, Wilkins 1966) is widely used to study the effects of small perturbations where the effects can be assumed to be nearly linear. Other approaches for isolating important variables exist, such as stepwise multiple regression, canonical correlation analysis (Kendall 1957), multiple predictive analysis, and two-parameter numerical taxonomy (Macnaughton-Smith 1965) or factor analysis (Lawley 1940, Harman 1966). Box and Jenkins (1962) have considered some statistical aspects of control.

The development of optimal control policies is one portion of the overall control process. The goal is provided by a "supersystem," and in this case, the individual optimality of subsystems does not ensure the optimality of the system as a whole. An ecosystem might be evaluated in turn (in an appropriately organized society) by an administrative system, a political system, and a social system which employs a judicial system to enforce its control measures (Price 1965, Bulkley and McLaughlan 1966). The goals of all these evaluating systems must be defined and may often be conflicting. For the ecologist it is an evaluating function which is required rather than the goal itself, and this function may constrain the operation of the model and the operations of the managers. The existence of such an evaluating function is crucial, but two further problems are also apparent.

The first of these concerns the existence of "local" optima, which makes the search for the overall optimum more complex. Methods such as linear programming and its extensions to integer, quadratic, stochastic, and dynamic programming (Bellman 1957, Churchman, Ackoff, and Arnoff 1961, Wolfe 1962, Dantzig 1963, Watt 1963) have proved useful initial guides even if the system models do not always precisely fit the mathematical specifications (see Serck-Hanssen 1963, Watt 1963, Petrini 1964, Heady and Egbert 1964). Other workers have used statistical decision theory in efforts to determine optimal policies for action (e.g., Dillon and Heady 1960, Findler 1966).

The second problem is that of moving from the present state to the optimal one. Here the techniques of network analysis as planning aids are useful, including critical path analysis, resource allocation scheduling, program evaluation, and review techniques and transportation methods (Hein 1967, Haase 1960, Davis 1965, Martino 1965, Davis 1968). Since the majority of these methods require computer assistance with the calculation and the systems model itself will often be in the form of a computer program, it is interesting to speculate on what additional information is required to enable the computer to design its own experiments, and after analysis to report both the optimal point and the method of reaching it. Certainly cost functions, value functions, and constraints are required, but whether this is sufficient information is not known. As yet the evaluation of ecosystems is at a fairly gross level, and the ecologist is educating himself and others in the extent and degree of complexity inherent in ecosystem management, while avoiding the grosser catastrophes.

COMPARISON AND ORGANIZATION OF ECOSYSTEMS

Some of the problems of comparing ecosystems will be considered briefly. Such comparisons are desirable partly because of the spatial and temporal variation between systems, and partly because as a "pure" science ecology will include the study of patterns in ecosystems.

While it would be possible to extend the description of a system to include those with which it interacts, this will often be impracticable. The pattern of ecosystems with respect to environmental factors, and the processes of successional change are both areas where the comparison of ecosystems is desirable. Such comparisons have for the most part been made by comparing the diversity of the systems as measured by a single property. In vegetation studies this has commonly meant comparison of species lists. The emphasis placed on functional entities by Lindeman (1942) and the increasing use of indicator species has not replaced the taxonomic comparisons, and the success of floristic methods such as those of Heikurainen (1964) suggests that there is strong relationship between functional and taxonomic classes. For some purposes it may be necessary to reconsider presently unfashionable entities, such as the synusiae of Lipmaa (1939).

The process of comparison and the organization of the resulting information to exhibit the patterns of ecosystem structuring is itself a systems process. Clowes (1967), in discussing similar problems in the computer processing of pictures, again distinguishes the four phases: the definition of parts, the provision of a grammar of parts (parsing phase), the representation of this part in relationship to structure in the machine (modelling), and the final analysis of the picture representation (analysis phase). A formal process of comparing ecosystems will itself involve these four phases, although the last analytic phase will be some numerical organization method such as classification, ordination, or spectral analysis (Robinson 1967, Jenkins and Watt 1968). The ecological difficulties all lie in the selection of the entities or parts and the selection of the relationships between the parts which are of interest in the particular study. Simple examples of relationships important in some areas of ecology are the concept of "epiphyte," which involves the relationship "growing on," and the concept of stratification of vegetation involving the spatial relationships "above" and "below." Selection of the appropriate relationships from the many available is a major ecological problem.

While the processing of the ecosystem description is possible, this is not the place to discuss the means available to represent ecosystems and the techniques necessary to compare the complex structures. The majority of the problems so far encountered in this area have been solved, in the sense that something can be done, although the ecological implications of the available solutions are not always clear.

CONCLUSION

The questions to be asked of this brief account of systems analysis fall into three categories. First, what additional knowledge must the ecologist acquire before he can use systems methods? Second, what ecological questions must be answered before he can apply the methods? Third, what can he hope to gain by using such methods? These will be considered in order.

It is apparent that systems analysis includes a wide variety of mathematical and statistical techniques and borders many areas, including computation, picture processing, language processing, and problem solving. The ecologist need not be fluent in all these areas, but some means of communicating between them seems desirable. The methods used in systems analysis are rarely phrased in ecological language, and the ecologist will certainly have to phrase his questions in non-ecological terms if the developers of the methods are to assist him.

The ecological questions rest on the need for this translation, for the ecologist defines the problems in which he is interested and must interpret them to the assisting workers. For systems he must specify the parts and the relationships and be prepared to modify these definitions in the light of data-collection problems and the fidelity requirement. If he is attempting to control or modify an ecosystem in the light of his models, he must have the desired objective stated, some means of evaluating departures from this state, and some idea of the external constraints imposed on the system and its managers. As an example where the objective function has been variously interpreted, consider the problem of controlling fire in forests. Australian foresters are at present recommending frequent controlled burning as a means of reducing fire hazards. Such a solution has one disadvantage, i.e., the frequency of burning increases due to the selection of rapidly recovering and fire-tolerant species. It also ignores the problems raised by loss of nutrients due to burning and the effects of such losses on the productivity of the trees, since the environment is already nutrient poor. As a solution to the problem of reducing fire risks immediately, controlled burning is probably acceptable, but this is in fact only part of the system.

The gains to be expected from a systems approach come from the precise statement of the problems and the discipline imposed by an ordered approach to the complexities of the real system. It is unlikely that an optimal solution to any problem will be attained directly, a process of successive approximation being likely. That the discipline is helpful can be seen from experience with one technique of management, the program evaluation and review technique (PERT, see Davis 1968). This technique has been credited with saving large sums of money, yet on closer inspection the method consists of little more than an explicit statement of what goes on and in what order! It should also be clear, however, that systems analysis is not a panacea, and its use will involve the ecologist in extending his knowledge, biological and other, before gaining much reward. Hopefully the use of systems methods will prevent ecologists from joining those "who saw the effect but not the cause."*

Acknowledgments

It is a great pleasure to acknowledge the advice and aid of Professor C. F. Cooper under whose auspices I worked at the University of Michigan as a participant in a

* St. Augustine Contra Pelagium IV 60.

research project sponsored by Cooperative Research, U.S. Department of Agriculture. It is also a pleasure to record my thanks to Dr. J. Olson of Oak Ridge National Laboratory and other members of the discussion group on systems analysis. My thanks to Professor Cooper again for permission to use the PET model and to Dr. D. J. Anderson of the Australian National University for the response surface diagram.

Literature Cited

Archibald, E. E. A. 1948. Plant populations. I. A new application Neyman's contagious distribution. Ann. Bot. (London) N.S. 12: 221–235.

Bartlett, M. S. 1960. Stochastic population models in ecology and epidemiology. Methuen, London. 90 p.

Bellman, R. 1957. Dynamic programming. Princeton Univ. Press, Princeton, N.J. 342 p.
———. 1961. Adaptive control processes: a guided tour. Princeton Univ. Press, Princeton, N.J. 255 p.

Bellman, R., H. Kagiwada, and R. Kalaba. 1966. Inverse problems in biology. J. Theor. Biol. 11: 164–167.

Box, G. E. P., and N. R. Draper. 1959. A basis for the selection of a response surface design. J. Amer. Statist. Ass. 54: 622–654.

Box, G. E. P., and G. M. Jenkins. 1962. Some statistical aspects of adaptive optimisation and control. J. Roy. Statist. Soc., Ser. B, 24: 297–343.

Box, G. E. P., and G. C. Tiao. 1965. A change in level of a nonstationary time series. Biometrika 52: 181–192.

Box, G. E. P., and G. S. Watson. 1968. Robustness to non-normality of regression tests. Biometrika 49: 93–106.

Bulkley, J. W., and R. T. McLaughlin. 1966. Simulation of political interaction in multiple purpose river basin development. Mass. Inst. Technol., Dep. Civil Eng. Hydrodyn. Lab. Rep. 100. 307 p.

Burdick, D. S., and T. H. Naylor. 1966. Design of computer simulation experiments for industrial systems. Commun. Ass. Comput. Mach. 9: 329–339.

Bush, R. R., and F. Mosteller. 1955. Stochastic models for learning. John Wiley and Sons, Inc., New York. 365 p.

Churchman, C. W., R. L. Ackoff, and E. L. Arnoff. 1961. Introduction to operations research. John Wiley and Sons, Inc., New York. 645 p.

Clowes, M. B. 1967. Perception, picture processing and computers, p. 181–198. *In* N. L. Collins and D. Mitchie [ed.] Machine intelligence I. Oliver and Boyd, Edinburgh & London.

Clymer, A. B., and G. F. Graber. 1964. Trends in the development and applications of analog simulations in biomedical systems. Simulation 4: 41–58.

Cochran, W. G. 1963. Sampling techniques. John Wiley and Sons, Inc., New York. 330 p.

Cooper, C. F. 1969. Ecosystem models in watershed management, p. 309–324. *In* G. M. Van Dyne [ed.] The ecosystem concept in natural resource management. Academic Press, New York.

Crawford, N., and R. Linsley. 1966. Digital simulation in hydrology. Stanford Watershed Model IV. Stanford Univ., Dept. Civil Eng. Tech. Rep. 39. 210 p.

Dahl, O. J., and K. Nygaard. 1966. SIMULA: an ALGOL-based simulation language. Commun. Ass. Comput. Mach. 9: 671–678.

Dansereau, P., P. F. Buell, and R. Dagon. 1966. A universal system for recording vegetation. Sarracenia 10: 1–64.

Dantzig, G. S. 1963. Linear programming and extensions. Princeton Univ. Press, Princeton, N.J. 625 p.

Davis, E. W. 1965. Resource allocation in project network models: a survey. J. Ind. Eng. 14: 177–188.

Davis, J. B. 1968. Why not PERT your next resource management problem. J. Forest. 66: 405–408.

Dillon, J. L., and E. O. Heady. 1960. Theories of choice in relation to farmer decision. Iowa State Univ. Agr. Exp. Sta. Res. Bull. 485. 23 p.

Draper, N. R., and W. E. Lawrence. 1965. Designs which minimise model inaccuracies: cuboidal regions of interest. Biometrika 52: 111–118.

Fan, Liang-Tseng. 1966. The continuous maximum principle. John Wiley and Sons, Inc., New York. 411 p.

Feigenbaum, E. A., and J. Feldman. 1963. Computers and thought. McGraw-Hill Book Co., Inc., New York. 535 p.

Findler, N. V. 1966. Human decision-making under uncertainty and risk: computer based experiments and a heuristic simulation program. Proc. A. F.I. P.S. 1965 Fall Joint Computer Conf., Pt. 1: 737–752.

Fishman, G. S. 1967. Problems in the statistical analysis of simulation experiments: the comparison of means and the length of sample records. Commun. Ass. Comput. Mach. 10: 94–99.

Fishman, G. S., and P. J. Kiviat. 1967. The analysis of simulation generated time series. Manag. Sci. 13: 525–557.

Ford, L. R., Jr., and D. R. Fulkerson. 1962. Flows in networks. Princeton Univ. Press, Princeton, N.J. 194 p.

Garfinkel, D. A. 1967a. A simulation study of the effects on simple ecological systems of making rate of increase of population density dependent. J. Theor. Biol. 14: 46–58.

———. 1967b. Effect of stability on Lotka-Volterra ecological systems of imposing strict territorial limits on populations. J. Theor. Biol. 14: 325–327.

Glanzer, M., and R. Glaser. 1959. Techniques for the study of group structure and behaviour. 1. Analysis of structure. Psychol. Bull. 56: 317–332.

Golley, F. B. 1960. Energy dynamics of a food chain of an old field community. Ecol. Monogr. 30: 187–206.

Greig-Smith, P. 1964. Quantitative plant ecology. Butterworth, London. 198 p.

Gumbel, E. L. 1958. Statistics of extremes. Columbia Univ. Press, New York. 375 p.

Halmos, P. R., and H. E. Vaughan. 1950. The marriage problem. Amer. J. Math. 72: 214–215.

Hammersely, J. M., and K. W. Morton. 1956. A new Monte Carlo technique: antithetic variables. Proc. Camb. Phil. Soc. 52: 449–475.

Harary, F., and P. Lipstein. 1962. The dynamics of brand loyalty: a Markovian approach. Oper. Res. 10: 19–40.

Harary, F., R. Z. Norman, and D. Cartwright. 1965. Structural models: An introduction to the theory of directed graphs. John Wiley and Sons, Inc., New York. 415 p.

Harman, H. H. 1966. Modern factor analysis. 2nd ed. Univ. Chicago Press, Chicago. 474 p.

Hasse, M. 1960. Über die Behandlung Graphen theoretischer Probleme unter Verwendung der Matrizenrechnung. Wiss. Z. Tech. Univ. Dresden 10: 1313–1316.

Heady, E. O., and A. C. Egbert. 1964. Regional programming of efficient agricultural patterns. Econometrika 32: 374–386.

Heikurainen, L. 1964. Suptyyppien Ojituskelpoisus: metsänkasvatusta silmälläpitäen. Kirjayhytyma, Helsinki.

Hein, L. W. 1967. The quantitative approach to managerial decision. Prentice-Hall, New York. 386 p.

Holling, C. S. 1966. The functional response of invertebrate predators to prey density. Mem. Ent. Soc. Can. 48: 1–85.

Hooke, R., and T. A. Jeeves. 1961. Direct search solutions of numerical statistical problems. J. Ass. Comput. Mach. 8: 212–229.

Hufschmidt, M. M., and M. B. Fiering. 1966. Simulation techniques for design of water resource systems. Harvard Univ. Press, Cambridge, Mass. 212 p.

International Business Machines Corporation. 1966. Bibliography on simulation. Report 320-0926-0. White Plains, N.Y.

Jacoby, J. E., and S. Harrison. 1962. Multivariable experimentation and simulation models. Naval Res. Log. Quart. 9: 121–136.

Jenkins, G. M., and D. G. Watt. 1968. Spectral analysis and its applications. Holden Day, San Francisco, Calif. 525 p.

Keeney, M. G., H. E. Koenig, and R. Zemach. 1967. State space models of educational institutions. Michigan State Univ. Div. of Engineering Research. East Lansing, Mich. 48 p.

Kendall, M. G. 1957. A course in multivariate analysis. Griffin, London. 185 p.

Kennard, R. W., and L. A. Stone. 1969. Computer aided design of experiments. Technometrics 11: 137–148.

Kerner, E. H. 1957. A statistical mechanics of interacting biological species. Bull. Math. Biophys. 19: 121–146.

————. 1959. Further considerations on the statistical mechanics of biological association. Bull. Math. Biophys. 21:217–255.

Lawley, D. N. 1940. The estimation of factor loadings by the method of maximum likelihood. Proc. Roy. Soc. Edinb., a, 60: 64–82.

Lindeman, R. L. 1942. The trophic dynamic aspect of ecology. Ecology 23: 399–418.

Lippmaa, T. 1939. The unistratal concept of plant communities. Amer. Midland Natur. 21: 111–145.

Macnaughton-Smith, P. 1965. Some statistical and other techniques for classifying individuals. Home Office Res. Unit Rep. 6. H.M.S.O., London, 33 p.

Margalef, D. R. 1947. Information theory in ecology. Mems. R. Acad. Barcelona 23: 373–440. (Trans. in Gen. Systems 3:36–71. 1958).

Marquardt, D. W. 1963. An algorithm for least squares estimation of nonlinear parameters. J. Soc. Ind. Appl. Math. 11: 431–441.

Martino, R. L. 1965. Advances in network techniques: an introduction to MAP. Data Process. 8: 231–257.

Mood, A. M., and F. A. Graybill. 1963. Introduction to the theory of statistics. McGraw-Hill Book Co., Inc., New York. 443 p.

Morton, J. A. 1964. From research to industry. Int. Sci. Technol., May 1964: 82–92, 105.

Muhzam, H. 1963. On multivariate trends. Paper presented to the 5th Int. Biometric Conf., Cambridge, England.

Olson, J. S. 1963. Energy storage and the balance of producers and decomposers. Ecology 44: 322–331.

Orcutt, G. H. 1960. Simulation of economic systems. Amer. Econ. Rev. 50: 893–907.

Patten, B. C. 1965. Community organization and energy relationships in plankton. Oak Ridge Nat. Lab. Rep. ORNL-3634.

Petrini, P. 1964. Competition between agriculture and forestry under Swedish conditions. Lantbrukshögskolansannalar 30: 156 p.

Phattaford, R. M. 1965. Sequential analysis of dependent observations. Biometrika 52: 157–165.

Potthof, R. F., and S. N. Roy. 1964. A generalized multivariate analysis of variance model useful especially for growth curve problems. Biometrika 51: 313–326.

Priban, I. P. 1968. Forecasting failure of health. Sci. Cult. 34: 232–235.

Price, D. K. 1965. The scientific estate. Harvard Univ. Press, Cambridge, Mass. 321 p.

Quenouille, M. H. 1957. Analysis of multiple time series. Griffin, London. 105 p.

Radanovic, L. [ed.] 1966. Sensitivity methods in control theory. Proc. Int. Symp. Dubrovnik, Yugoslavia. Pergamon Press, New York. 456 p.

Rao, C. R. 1965. Theory of least squares when the parameters are stochastic and its application to the analysis of growth curves. Biometrika 52: 447–458.

Robinson, E. A. 1967. Multichannel time series analysis. Holden Day, San Francisco, Calif. 298 p.

Rosen, R. 1958. The representation of biological systems from the standpoint of the theory of categories. Bull. Math. Biophys. 20: 317–341.

Ross, D. T. 1967. The AED approach to generalized computer-aided design. Proc. Ass. Comput. Mach. National Meeting 1967: 367–385.

Seal, H. L. 1964. Multivariate statistical analysis for biologists. Methuen, London. 209 p.

Serck-Hanssen, J. 1963. A programming model for a fishing region in northern Norway. Regional Science Association Papers 12: 107–118. Lund Congress.

Siegel, S. 1956. Nonparametric statistics for the behavioural scientist. John Wiley and Sons, Inc., New York. 201 p.

Simon, H. A., and A. Newall. 1962. Simulation of human thinking, p. 95–131. *In* M.

Greenberger [ed.] Computers and the world of the future. Mass. Inst. Technol. Press, Cambridge, Mass.

Spang, H. A. 1962. Review of minimization techniques for non-linear functions. Soc. Ind. Appl. Math. Rev. 4: 363–365.

Spent, P. 1967. Estimation of mean growth curves. J. Theor. Biol. 17: 159–173.

Tiku, M. L. 1964. Approximating the general non-normal variance ratio sampling distribution. Biometrika 51: 83–95.

Tocher, K. D. 1963. The art of simulation. English Universities Press, London. 184 p.

Van Dyne, G. M., R. G. Wright, and J. F. Dollar. 1968. Influence of site factors on vegetation productivity. ORNL-TM 1974 Contract No. W-7405-eng-26. Oak Ridge National Laboratory. 238 p.

Watanabe, S., and C. T. Abraham. 1960. Loss and recovery of information by coarse observation of stochastic chain. Information and Control 3: 248–278.

Watt, K. E. F. 1961. Mathematical models for use in insect pest control. Can. Entomol. Suppl. 19: 1–62.

———. 1963. Dynamic programming, 'Look-Ahead' programming and the strategy of insect pest control. Can. Entomol. 95: 525–536.

———. 1968. Ecology and resource management: a quantitative approach. McGraw-Hill Book Co., Inc., New York. 450 p.

Whittle, P. 1962. Topographic correlation, power-law covariance functions and diffusion. Biometrica 49: 305–312.

———. 1963. Prediction and regulation. English Universities Press, London. 147 p.

Wiener, N. 1962. The extrapolation, interpolation and smoothing of stationary time series. Mass. Inst. Technol. Press, Cambridge, Mass. 163 p.

Wilkins, R. D. 1966. General time varying systems error sensitivity analysis. Commun. Ass. Comput. Mach. 9: 855–859.

Williams, W. T. 1967. Numbers, taxonomy and judgement. Bot. Rev. 33: 379–386.

Witherspoon, J. P., S. I. Auerbach, and J. S. Olson. 1964. Cycling of caesium-134 in white oak trees. Ecol. Monogr. 34: 403–420.

Wolfe, P. 1962. Recent developments in non-linear programming, p. 156–187. In F. L. Alt and M. Ruhinoff [ed.] Advances in computers 3.

VELVYL W. GREENE

Automatic Biodetecting and Monitoring Instruments Open New Doors for Environmental Understanding

Microbiology laboratories have witnessed, in recent years, a dramatic increase in the number and variety of instruments and devices designed to carry out technological operations automatically. The field of microbial detection and monitoring is no exception. It would be useful just to catalog the ideas and

Velvyl Greene, "Automatic Biodetecting and Monitoring Instruments Open New Doors for Environmental Understanding," *Environmental Science and Technology*, vol. 2, no. 2 (February 1968), pp. 104–112. Copyright 1968 by the American Chemical Society. Reprinted by permission of the copyright owner.

The author is associate professor of public health and of microbiology, College of Medical Sciences, University of Minnesota. This article is based on a paper presented as part of a symposium on Recent Developments in Research Methods and Instrumentation, National Institutes of Health, Bethesda, Maryland, in 1967.

instruments thus far suggested and employed, and to evaluate briefly their respective capabilities and limitations. This approach could provide an insight into the current state-of-the-art (at least with regard to non-classified research and development), and could suggest areas requiring more intensified efforts.

On the other hand, most work in automated biodetection and monitoring is part of larger programs — programs in themselves at least as interesting and challenging as the hardware they generate. A comprehensive review should consider the technological challenges as part of the larger framework of economic, philosophical, and political challenges. However, in this short discussion, I can review only briefly the background of current research. Most of the emphasis in the article will be on an analysis of the scientific problem areas involved, and an overview of the general problems. In addition, I will try to describe and discuss several detection and monitoring instruments.

However, let me add a note of caution. The field of automated instrumentation requires sophisticated electronic and mechanical engineering — areas in which my knowledge and experience are limited. Consequently, the emphasis I place in this article on microbiological aspects of the research should not be considered as an accurate and unbiased reflection of the general problem. Rather, it should be accepted only as a point of departure — and a subjective one at that.

MOVING FROM MAN TO MACHINE

Most developments in laboratory automation result from desires to save labor and money and to prevent tedium and human errors. This generalization holds for bacteriology labs, as well as others. It is certainly feasible to analyze the various steps and manipulations of a bacteriology technician and to provide electromechanical devices which can do many of the repetitive tasks automatically, and often more accurately.

Usually the transition from technician to machine is gradual: a step-wise advance from simple labor-saving devices to more sophisticated decision-making machines to ultrasophisticated, completely automatic analyzers-recorders-computers. The degree of automation and the speed of transition are usually directly related to work load and man-hour cost and inversely related to availability of hands. But even the most imaginative bacteriological planners today still visualize — at least for a few years — a place for the human technician. A human will start the equipment and care for it; choose the material for analysis and interpret data; gather samples and bring them to the machines, neatly labeled and identified; interact with the automatic devices, as it were, and thus serve as a bridge between questions, answers, operations, and meanings.

True automated biodetection and monitoring devices, however, as they are thought about today, are based on a different rationale and are being designed to meet different needs from those just described. The two national agencies which sponsor, and thereby stimulate, most of the research and development in this field are quite unequivocal in their interpretation of the word *automatic*.

NASA's exobiologists want an automated biological laboratory which does everything that machines and technicians do. They want devices to take samples and feed analyzers, analyzers which can decide by themselves which experiments to repeat and which to carry further. They want devices to read out results and interpret the data and then transmit a condensed interpretation through considerable distances. And, most remarkably, they want all this equipment to work unattended on the surface of a planet 50 million miles from the nearest technician where no one has ever been before and after an eight-month journey in the nose cone of a rocket.

Similarly, the military laboratory entrusted with our defense against a biological warfare attack is looking for devices which can be stationed, un-attended, around the periphery of strategic areas. These devices must operate continuously, sampling the environment and analyzing it for the presence of potentially lethal microorganisms. And the complete process of sampling, analysis, readout and information transmittal must be accomplished quickly at literally the speed of wind, if they are to be true warning devices.

It is entirely possible that future automated biodetection and monitoring devices might not have such strenuous requirements. One can easily visualize the use of such devices in critical hospital areas or in the food industry where they might be operated by humans as technician-machine, semiautomatic systems.

The accusation has been made, with some justification, that NASA and the military are asking us to run before we have learned to walk. In any event, it certainly is easier to proceed gradually from semiautomatic to automatic than to jump directly into a Martian laboratory. But the fact remains that those imposing the rigorous demands in automated biodetection are paying for the research and development. Any discussion of this field would be unrealistic if it did not consider the various criteria of success that NASA or the Department of Defense consider important: automation, remote operation, speed, accuracy, specificity, reliability, and sensitivity.

An operations analysis

This discussion intimates that automatic biodetection and monitoring instruments might have a variety of objectives and applications. This is true. Even though NASA and DOD share mutual interests in this field, their basic goals are different. Thus, the direction of research carried on under their respective sponsorship is different. The difficulties involved in generalizing about the subject become even more pronounced when one realizes the many other potential applications of automated biodetection systems and their inevitable diversification. Nevertheless, it should be possible to analyze the overall problem and to describe those general tasks common to all such systems.

Perhaps the most logical way to approach this analysis is to visualize the operations which a human technician would perform if instructed by a supervisor to "run some bacteriological tests on a sample of ———." It could be soil, air, milk, stools, snow from Mount Everest, or dust from Mars.

Similarly, the "tests" to be run are of no concern for the moment. (They are actually of critical concern and are discussed in detail a bit later.) All we want the technician to do is to detect the presence of viable microorganisms in a sample and to tell us something about their quantity and quality. The only condition we will impose, in order to relate this hypothetical technician to a hypothetical automated instrument, is to specify that the material tested is away from the immediate confines of the laboratory.

From these instructions, the following general events should take place in approximately the specified sequence.

1. The technician will go (or send someone) to the location in question. The technician or his substitute will be equipped with some type of sterile sampling device. Step one is getting there or being there.
2. The technician or delegate will sample the material to be analyzed. The sample will be large enough to be meaningful, small enough to be manipulatable, and representative enough to be credible. Step two is sampling.
3. The raw sample will then be transported to the laboratory (or enough of the laboratory must be transported to the sample) for processing and analysis. Subsequently, the processed sample will be transported to the analytical module. Ultimately, the analyzed sample will be discarded or, in the jargon of the system, "transported out." Sometimes the same sample will be transported to a second and third analytical module. Step three is sample transport.
4. The raw sample must be processed, making it amenable to analysis. Processing might involve pulverizing or subdividing, diluting or concentrating, eluting, mixing, purifying, and the like. It is difficult to visualize microbiological analysis without some type of processing. Step four is sample processing.
5. The sample will now be analyzed for bacteriological content. This step is probably the key one in the process and will be elaborated upon subsequently. Step five is analysis.
6. The technician will, after a given time, read out results of the analysis, answering for himself, at least, the supervisor's questions about presence of viable organisms, their quantity and quality. Step six is readout of the analytical results.
7. The technician can either convey the raw data to the original questioner for his interpretation, or can summarize and interpret the data himself, conveying the final answers to the questioner. Step seven is transmission, or interpretation and transmission.

This oversimplified operation analysis might suggest the magnitude of the task involved in a truly automated detection and monitoring system. Every step must be carried out by scrupulously integrated electromechanical machines, and the efficiency of the entire system will be no better than that of its weakest link. For example, the most ingenious analytical device will fail if it is mated with an inadequate sampler. Similarly, the best computer will have nothing to interpret if the readout device keeps mistaking noise for signal.

Research and development activities are currently under way in all phases of this program, although all are not receiving equal attention. Obviously, the different tasks are so closely interwoven and interdependent that it is unrealistic to evaluate the state-of-the-art for each task independently.

A technological advance in any step will profoundly influence the type of performance required in the other steps. Thus, the development of high volume air samplers which collect thousands of viable bacteria per minute (instead of one or two per minute) could significantly improve the reliability of those bacteriological warfare detection devices which require micrograms of protoplasm for analysis. Similarly, an analyzer which can handle either gravel or dust would preclude the need for a processor which has to reduce everything to dust.

In general, however, the mechanical and electronic aspects of automated detection and monitoring are at a more advanced level than the microbiological pieces of the problem. The fifth step, analysis, remains the most critical component of the challenge. Unfortunately, it still awaits its own breakthrough. (This statement is conditioned only in part by my amazement at the daily miracles of electronics; in part it results from years of waiting for bacteria to grow a little faster.)

Questions instruments ask

The ultimate job of any automated analytical instrument is to answer questions. When biodetection and monitoring devices are divorced from their mechanical attachments for sampling, transporting, processing, and the like, the devices become essentially biophysical answer machines.

The type of answers provided will differ, depending on the design of the instrument, and can be, for example, specific or general answers or perhaps, quantitative or qualitative answers. Answers which might satisfy NASA's exobiologists might not be sufficient for the bacteriological warfare defense monitors. Still, all approaches to automated microbiological analysis confront this axiom: The quality of the answer depends entirely on the type of question asked. Indeed, transition from science fiction black boxes to useful hardware hinges as much on our ability to rephrase a problem into a series of simple answerable questions as it does on our ability to choose electromechanical tools which might answer the question.

One might argue that the foregoing is so obvious that it hardly merits emphasis. Yet, serious frustrations in automated biodetection and monitoring research derive directly from the key words "rephrase a problem into a series of answerable questions." In colloquial terms, this is the name of the game and is worth a further explanation.

Our analytical instruments should answer five basic questions:

- Is there a viable microorganism present?
- Are you sure?
- What kind of microorganism is it?
- How many are there?
- Where did it come from?

It is not difficult to put these questions in words. However, the lack of suitable biological definitions and the primitive state of a comprehensive biological theory make it extremely difficult to restate some of these questions to machines which, after all, can answer *yes* or *no* to only one question at a time. Perhaps this is a natural result of dealing with the unique phenomenon called life. Perhaps it is only a temporary impasse which can be resolved by programming a computer with a course in sophomore biology. But it appears, at this juncture, that a real advance will be made when we learn the right questions to ask, and how to ask them.

For example, the first question implies that there is some agreement about what a viable microorganism is. (It is sometimes easier to define *love* and *justice* than to define *viable*.) To be sure, it is possible to describe many criteria and characteristics of living microorganisms. But no single criterion, or even group of criteria, is sufficiently inclusive to include bacteria, fungi, viruses, and protozoa, and, at the same time, sufficiently exclusive to exclude pollen grains, dust, wool fibers, and insect scales. Biologists mature rapidly as scientists when they start to realize that even such time honored biological watchwords as *particle size* and *reproduction* fail as objective criteria when used on unknown samples in the time frame allotted for analysis.

Nonetheless, this problem can be approached by breaking the original question into a sequence of logical and related subquestions which can each be posed independently and answered *yes* and *no*. Thus, the question about the presence of a viable microorganism might become:

- Is there a particle present?
- If yes, is it between 0.5 and 10 μ in diameter?
- If yes, does it contain carbon? Hydrogen? Nitrogen? Some other appropriate substance?
- If yes, are these elements present in certain linkages?
- Does this particle become two particles in time t under conditions c?
- Does this particle become four particles in time $2t$ under conditions c?
- Does one particle change substrate s to product p?
- Do four particles produce four times as much p?
- Does formation of product p stop when inhibitor z is introduced?

This questioning goes on as long as it takes to satisfy a predetermined set of standards.

We actually do these things and ask these questions of ourselves continually in the laboratory without recognizing the inherent logic processes. The challenge here is to recognize and define our own logic; to assign priorities to question and subquestion sequences; to select judiciously the various parameters listed as t, c, s, p, and z; and to choose enough independent questions so that the combined answers will generate as little equivocation as possible.

Of course, each subquestion might mean another analysis chamber or module, and each test adds its cost in money, weight, power, and probability of failure. But once the questions are defined, it is only a matter of engineering effort to design a test or device to answer it.

All five general questions can be attacked in this fashion. The question Are you sure? must be rephrased as a series of subquestions which, on the one hand, supply redundancy to the first question and, on the other hand, compare the unknown sample with known nonviable artifacts.

What kind of microorganism? will become a series of subquestions dealing with morphology, biochemistry, antigen-antibody specificities, nutrition, activity, pathogenicity, and the like.

How many are there? becomes deceptively easy to answer. It involves repeating the one question sequence on different quantities of sample, asking is there an organism present in 10 liters, 1 liter, 100 ml.?, and the like.

The final question Where did it come from?, should resolve the significance of our findings. NASA wants to make sure that any organism it finds on Mars came from Mars and was not an accidental stowaway. The bacteriological warfare people want to distinguish between a probable enemy offensive and an accidental sneeze. Consequently, this question will be broken down into subquestions that can be related to meteorology, to persistence, to data reproducibility among replicate samples, and to internal references about past experiences during simulated and experimental trials.

The practical automation of microbiological analysis might be considerably easier than I have previously described. No one has yet suggested that we make a device that can answer all questions equally well. Thus, the people involved in bacteriological warfare are interested primarily in pathogens, and only those present in certain concentrations. NASA exobiologists, on the other hand, are interested in any life on Mars. Yet if they can't find perfectly reproducing bacteria, they might be satisfied with a strand of DNA or a molecule of ATP.

In other words, it might be true that all approaches to automated analysis must deal with the five basic questions posed, but they do not have to deal equally with each question. Similarly, the maximum degree of accuracy, sensitivity, speed, and specificity should be ideally met by every instrument. But in practice, trade-offs and compromises, both in the quality of questions asked and the value of answers expected, have become an accepted fact of life.

Approaches to microbiological analysis

So far, I have reviewed the general features of automated biodetection and monitoring, emphasizing the basic aims of the research, the mechanical operations involved, and the underlying logic of instrumented analysis. Now it is possible to examine the actual attempts which have been and are being made to perform these tasks.

This examination could quickly generate as much confusion as enlightenment. The most direct approach would be to describe the various instruments, and to evaluate each critically. Since, however, the actual hardware is continually being altered and upgraded, and since specific instruments are usually oriented to a specific task (for example, bacteriological warfare detection of exobiology), this approach might be unfair or misleading.

Furthermore, only some of the many suggestions for automated instruments have progressed to fabricated instruments. Some suggestions are still suggestions; others are on drawing boards; still others are in that engineering-semantic limbo of breadboard models and prototypes. It is quite possible that a given analytical approach, which is not yet finally instrumented, will be mated to a suitable sampling, processing, or readout device today, and will easily become the best detector available tomorrow.

Therefore, the following discussion of automated microbiological detection will deal essentially with the approaches suggested or employed to carry out the analytical tasks. These approaches (see Table 1) are classified into three general categories:

- Approaches based on detecting and monitoring particles.
- Approaches based on detecting key biochemical components.
- Approaches based on detecting biological activity.

Table 1. Classification of automated biodetection and monitoring approaches

General category	Suggested approach	Instrument
Physical particle detection	Magnification	Vidicon microscope Mechanized microscope
	Light scattering	Particle ratio alarm Particle counters Aerosol photometers
	Volume displacement	Coulter Counter
Key biochemical components	Antigen detection	FAST AutoAnalyzer
	Dyes and staining	Partichrome analyzer J band detector
	Bioluminescence and fluorescence	Fluorimeters
	Optical activity	UV polarimeter
	Pyrolysis products detection	Pyrolizer Mass spectrometers Chromatographs
	ATP detection	Luciferin-luciferinase system
	Proteins, nucleic acids, or others	UV and IR spectrophotometers Particle electrophoresis
Biological activity	Growth (increase in cell mass or numbers)	Minivator Multivator Wolf Trap
	CO_2 evolution	Gulliver
	Phosphatase activity	Poised enzyme Multivator
	Substrate change (pH, Eh, O_2 interchange)	Wolf Trap Marbac Minivator
	Pathogenic effects	Tissue cultures

Since the different methods within each category share many of the same advantages and limitations, this classification permits a systematic evaluation of several techniques simultaneously. Furthermore, existing identifiable instruments also can be grouped in Table 1 according to their underlying methodological rationale, eliminating the need for a detailed and repetitive discussion of specific potentials and drawbacks.

Any evaluations will be subjective. No exobiology device has been tested on Mars. Performance data on bacteriological warfare devices are classified. Thus, all we can do is make educated guesses.

Particle detection approaches

Methods based on particle detection are typified by speed and the ease with which they can be automated. They are also extremely nonspecific. The demands of air pollution and industrial hygiene have made available a large number of devices which can detect and quantify particles automatically. Microorganisms are really just a special type of particle, so such instruments can be used, practically without adaptation, for many microbiological purposes. Indeed, microscopy, nephelometry, volume displacement, and photometry are standard techniques in the bacteriology laboratory where samples are known to consist of microbial particles.

Conversely, these instruments can not distinguish between a microbial particle and any other kind of particle. So they are severely restricted in an environment containing both signal and noise in unknown ratios.

The desirable qualities of particle technology can be utilized in combinations with approaches from the other categories. For example, the partichrome analyzer automatically floods particles (collected by impaction on a continuous tape) with biological stains and scans the tape with an automated microscope looking for those particles which retain the dye. Similarly, automated nephelometry and fluorimetry are used as the readout techniques for Wolf Trap, Multivator, and Minivator — all essentially bioactivity approaches.

An automatic aerosol light-scattering instrument, the particle ratio alarm, is routinely employed in bacteriological warfare monitoring, despite nonspecificity. This apparatus continually measures and records the numbers of airborne particles in various size ranges. When the ratio of $1\text{-}5\ \mu$ particles to $0.5\text{-}10\ \mu$ particles becomes significantly high, the machine sounds an alarm, because the former size range $1\text{-}5\ \mu$ is classically considered most important for pulmonary retention. Normally, the ratio should be relatively constant. In the case of a bacteriological warfare attack, however, the agent probably would be disseminated as a $1\text{-}5\ \mu$ aerosol, and the ratio would be considerably increased.

Key biochemical components

Methods based on key biochemical components may employ different analytical tools or concepts, but they are all directed toward recognizing those unique chemical structures or molecules present in biological material and absent in nonbiological material. These approaches, therefore, are more sophisticated and meaningful than the simple physical tests for particles. On the other hand, they all have certain inherent drawbacks: diminished sensitivity, increased need for sample manipulation, and inability to distinguish between biological material that is living or dead. NASA's exobiologists are interested in both, but bacteriological warfare defense must know the difference between a pathogen and powdered sawdust even though each contains DNA, protein, and ATP.

Most approaches are analytical techniques familiar to biochemists and biophysicists. The problems mainly concern miniaturization and reliability during remote operation and are not discussed in detail in this article. Certain approaches, however, may not be as familiar. These are the military's Fluorescent Antibody Staining Technique (FAST) and the pyrolizer device, as well as NASA's ATP and *J* band approaches.

The FAST system might be considered a sophisticated descendent of the partichrome analyzer. It employs a high volume sampler, incubates the sample with fluorescent tagged antibodies, deposits the reacted mixture on a transparent tape, washes away the unadsorbed antibodies and dye, scans the tape with an ultraviolet microscope, and records the numbers of fluorescent particles on the tape.

By preselecting the appropriate antiserum or mixture of antisera, it is possible to ascertain in a very short time the presence of specific types of organisms in the environment without too much interference from nonbiological and nonspecific biological noise. The sensitivity (threshold value below which there is no detection) of this device is classified, but published preliminary work suggests the system is sensitive to levels of less than one organism per liter of air.

The pyrolizer device heats a sample of collected aerosol, converting the protein into NH_4^+, which is measured in an ion detection chamber. Although this device can detect the presence of as little as 0.1 μg. of nebulized albumin per liter of air, it is of questionable use microbiologically, because of the nonmicrobiological proteinaceous noise commonly present in most environments.

The *J* bands are characteristic absorption spectra of biological chemicals (proteins, peptides, RNA, DNA, and carbohydrates, for example) after reaction with a dye, 3,3-diethyl-9-methyl 4,5,4,5, dibenzothiacarbocyanine bromide. An unknown sample can be added to a solution of this dye, and the spectral shift of absorption that occurs if the biochemicals are present will be measurable by conventional spectrometry.

ATP detection is based on the phenomenon of light emission which occurs when the firefly enzyme luciferinase reacts with its substrate luciferin. In the absence of the ATP molecule, no reaction — and thus no light emission — occurs. An ATP free enzyme-substrate mixture is prepared, and an unknown sample is added. If microorganisms are present, their ATP will trigger the reaction and the light generated can be measured photometrically. However, many nonviable biologicals contain ATP which will act as noise in this system, also.

In general, this category of approaches has great promise. Most present work involves engineering development. Most of the devices, such as polarimeters, chromatographs, spectrophotometers, and fluorimeters, lend themselves to automation and even miniaturization. However, questions about whether they can be depended on for remote operation without frequent attention, and the inherent problems of microbiochemical sensitivity and specificity, have yet to be resolved.

Biological activity approaches

Approaches using biological activity are the most sophisticated. They not only determine that something is present and that it contains biochemicals, they actually ascertain that something is doing something. If one can detect an activity characteristic of living things, the inference is fairly strong that living things are present. Furthermore, if the activity can be measured quantitatively, it might be possible to extrapolate back to the quantity of living material which is responsible for the activity.

Nevertheless, these approaches are not completely unequivocal. In almost every case, nonliving substrates can mimic a characteristic viable activity. Thus, crystals can grow, shattered glass can simulate an increase in numbers, rocks can absorb and desorb gases, substrates can deteriorate spontaneously, and the like. However, automated biodetection is never intended to do more than provide strong inferences and cannot be designed for absolute accuracies, so we will have to tolerate these potential confusions — or at least use some redundant tests to spot them.

Biological activity approaches have two significant advantages and two serious drawbacks when compared with other methods. The advantages are specificity and sensitivity. The disadvantages are relatively slow detection times and problems of specific microbial requirements.

Given enough time, one living cell can produce enough cells or chemicals or mass to be detected very easily. In contrast, the concentration of key biochemical components contained in a single cell is extremely small — usually not enough to be detected by even the most sensitive biophysical instrument.

The words "given enough time" also point out one of the disadvantages of activity detection. The generation time of the fastest organism known is not less than 15 minutes. Thus, detection time for low microbial concentrations has to be considered at least as hours, a period which does not really meet the specification of *rapid*. The second disadvantage deals with microbial diversity and environmental preference. Whereas all microbes are particles and most microorganisms share a common biochemistry, the conditions necessary to support their growth and activity differ remarkably from species to species. Thus, a given temperature, medium pH, and the like will permit certain selected organisms to grow and metabolize but will inhibit others. Unless the organism being detected is well known, it is quite possible to investigate an environment abounding with life, and miss finding it by a bioactivity approach. This is obviously the great frustration of exobiologists: What medium do Martian microorganisms prefer? How many different media should we try?

The specific methods and instruments in this category are really ingenious attempts to automate elementary bacteriology laboratory exercises.

Wolf Trap is a miniature growth chamber where turbidity changes are measured by a continuous recording nephelometer and pH changes are monitored by a recording pH electrode. Marbac measures changes in Eh of a growth medium and plots the results against time. Minivator and Multivator are multiple chambers where a given sample is simultaneously tested for growth,

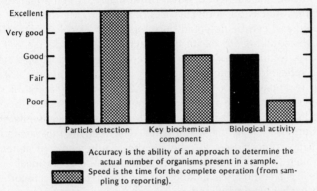

Accuracy is the ability of an approach to determine the actual number of organisms present in a sample.

Speed is the time for the complete operation (from sampling to reporting).

Table 2. Relative accuracy and speed of automated approaches

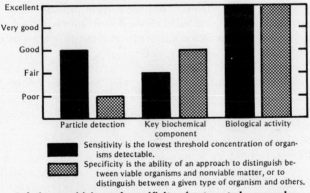

Sensitivity is the lowest threshold concentration of organisms detectable.

Specificity is the ability of an approach to distinguish between viable organisms and nonviable matter, or to distinguish between a given type of organism and others.

Relative sensitivity and specificity of automated approaches

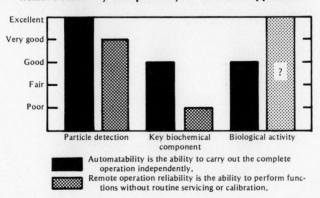

Automatability is the ability to carry out the complete operation independently.

Remote operation reliability is the ability to perform functions without routine servicing or calibration.

Relative automatability and remote operation reliability of automated approaches

fluorescence, enzyme activity, and the like. Readouts are obtained by integrated and miniaturized fluorimeters, nephelometers, colorimeters, and potentiometers.

Both Multivator and the Poised Enzyme device use substrates in which a phosphate radical is linked to some fluorescent or chromogenic moiety. The complete substrate is quenched, but if phosphatase, which apparently is a universal enzyme, attacks the molecule to liberate PO_4, the remaining fraction is also liberated and can be detected fluorimetrically or colorimetrically.

Gulliver continues to excite the imagination. This device was originally intended as a routine laboratory instrument for evaluation of water quality. It has been redeveloped into a completely automatic, remotely operable, and quite reliable apparatus. It inoculates a sample with a medium containing C^{14} labeled sugars. As the microorganisms grow, they attack the sugar and liberate radioactive CO_2 which is detected by strategically placed Geiger-Mueller counters. Of all the instruments described in this section, Gulliver and Wolf Trap come closest to meeting the requirements of general life detection, though they should by no means be considered as ideal.

Table 2 is a summary evaluation of the three general categories of automated approaches. The tabulated merits and limitations constitute a subjective critique. Also, within each category there are specific approaches which disrupt the general pattern. However, this table does provide some idea about the trade-offs involved in the field. Speed and automatability are usually gained at a sacrifice of specificity. Specificity and sensitivity are usually gained at a sacrifice of speed and reliability, and so forth.

No one approach and no one group of approaches will solve all of our problems or meet all of our needs. This is the underlying reason for NASA's concern with a planetary laboratory rather than a given single instrument. Similarly, the bacteriological warfare people are thinking of redundant monitoring systems, rather than devices.

A combination of approaches from all three categories, and perhaps several different techniques from each category working concurrently or in sequence, would augment significantly the information generated from any single experiment. But this type of development and integration is expensive and time consuming. It is fair to say that automated biodetection and monitoring still has the bulk of its history ahead of it.

MORTON GORDEN, MARSHA GORDEN
& JOHN GOLDEN, JR.

A Technique for the Systematic Identification of Pollution Reduction Measures: EMIS

THE PROBLEM

In the next decade the conflict between economic growth and pollution abatement can reach even greater intensity than at present. The brown-out, the shortage of natural resources, the rising prices for goods and the rising prices of disposal, and the social conflict engendered by the attempt to allocate public priorities will all be part of the process of trying to adjust the behavior of an industrial society which has reached the diseconomies of intensive use of nature. Adjustments are nothing new to rapidly changing societies, and there is good reason to believe that an accommodation will be reached before the predictions of the doomsday survivalists can come true. However, the adjustments are several. In this report we seek to open up the vision of alternatives available to government and private industry as they cope with the conflict between economic growth and pollution abatement.

It is the central thesis of this report that the conflict need not be inevitable and the practices which will minimize the conflict are within the realm of reason, even within the value systems we have in the nation today. Most of the report is technical and specific in terms of how to accomplish the goal, but some attention must be paid to the larger issues, for the feasibility of applying solutions lies in the will to accomplish change.

If we leave the conflict of goals unfettered, no advocate will be able to silence another, for economic growth has deep roots in American expectations, and the new concern over pollution abatement will be with us as the environment becomes saturated and even marginal increments create unexpected damage. There seems, nonetheless, to be little practical thinking on all sides that faces the fundamental issues. The visionaries are impractical, and the practical men do not see that the consequences of continuing present "practical" behavior are highly impractical indeed. Some attention to the relation between the short and long run is needed, for when dealing with nature's rejection of industrial behavior, the long term creeps on us quickly.

Under the present abatement strategy of putting restrictions on point sources of pollution, the retardation of economic growth is inevitable, for the reductions in emissions gained are wiped out by the growth in number of

Part of the work upon which this publication is based was performed pursuant to Contract No. EHS 70-121 with the National Air Pollution Control Administration, Environmental Health Service, Public Health Service, U. S. Department of Health, Education and Welfare.

emitting sources. Los Angeles reduced the number of emissions per automobile with the legislation applying to each car, and for some time the downward curve of pollution was encouraging. However, today the curve is upward again as a result of the increasing number of automobiles. The same story will repeat itself in other instances as well. Power plant restrictions gaining 99 percent efficiency of abatement will be overcome by the increase in the number of power plants and their per unit size. Unless we move to a policy of zero emissions — and the marginal costs make that a very costly price to pay for cleaning up — we are inevitably going to have to restrict economic growth.

An alternative to point source restriction is a comprehensive recycling policy which encourages complete utilization of byproducts. This approach also hits limits very early because it assumes that more materials are recyclable than in fact are — within the constraints of a marketplace responsive to consumer tastes and free enterprise production. A major change in values will have to occur before comprehensive recycling becomes a reality.

Another alternative is to ban the production of products which lead to problems of waste disposal and pollution. While this approach has merit for some limited areas of the economy, it creates an intrusive interjection of government in affairs where the state of the art of forecasting damage from new chemistries of production is only fair at best.

The most pessimistic alternative is zero growth policy, and that simply is not acceptable to large groups in society who have yet to taste the delicious despair of affluence felt by the literati writing from their summer homes in the country. Such an approach out of the mainstream of American life is an imposition on people who have not yet achieved America's promise.

All of these approaches have something to commend them for some portion of the problem. However, they all get in the way of each other. Government emphasis on subsidizing treatment plants hinders possible recycling potential. Point source restrictions force investments in abatement when money could have gone into other areas with better long- and short-term payoff. We need a way of setting disaggregated policy which applies differentially according to the dynamics of public demand, variety of industrial practice, and the decentralization of decision making inherent in our economy. Structurally, that is a tall order for a problem as complex as pollution abatement.

It is even more difficult when we include in the problem that government has a responsibility to the environment which includes some rationing or intelligent allocation of scarce nonrenewable resources. There are always pessimists who will say that in such-and-such a year we will run out of this or that precious commodity. These projections have often been confounded by the discovery of new sources in nature, new technologies which substitute materials, or a reduction of projected demand. However, at the current rate of population expansion and utilization of natural resources, the dire predictions seem saner than ever before.

Thus, when we see the conflict between growth and pollution abatement and the need for thought about natural resource allocation, the problem takes on large dimensions which require some new and complex approaches to the solutions.

Before the advent of massive data processing, the cybernetic approach to the problem would have been impossible. Information control of national industrial production by monitoring material flows to direct resources is still out of step with reality. However, we are in an era in which information can be gathered to meet the requirements of a policy needing the coordination and flexibility suggested above. In this report, we suggest a way of determining the minimum data needed by integrating data sets with abatement strategy, a way to maximize useful information by collecting data in the context of its use — and a systematic way to judge alternative approaches for particular industries in a decentralized economy. We take on a large obligation in setting out in this direction, but the obligation must be commensurate with the problem, or this proposal too will fail. We call the approach an Ecosystem of Machines Information System (EMIS).

The idea of an ecosystem of machines comes from pressing a biological analogy such that the output of some machines can become the input of others. We conceive of machines as organs in an interacting organism called an industrial economy. Without having to press the analogy any further, we can build on the basic ideas so that inputs from virgin materials might well be replaced by outputs of other machines now classified as wastes. These wastes can be converted to resources by their collection and processing to replace virgin materials. The closed loop or cycle of materials would be the ultimate application of biological reasoning to industrial production. However, as suggested earlier, recycling of materials has important limits and we must accommodate reality still further.

In addition to recycling materials, the information system must be able to indicate where substitutions of processes can avoid pollution damaging to the natural ecosystem or the wasteful use of nonrenewable resources in short supply.

Failing both of these alternatives, some form of disposal must be achieved and, hopefully, the disposal can be done in a way which returns the material to some natural use in the natural ecosystem or to be stored to enter the mechanical ecosystem at some other date.

The idea of an ecosystem of machines allows us to pursue each of these alternatives in some detailed way suited to a broad range of industries and processes. Among the major limits to applying the ecosystem idea is the lack of information in the marketplace to encourage this closed loop behavior. There are other limits which are discussed in the original report, but the availability of information is the most critical at the outset.

There was a time when we believed that the marketplace would act to incorporate pollution reduction costs in the same way it had worked to lower the costs of industrial production. We did not realize the need for systematic information until counter-examples multiplied: until experience showed that industrial plants designed in New York City were shipped to regional locations where the design simply did not take into account the presence of local markets for effluents or local sources of raw materials; until other experience showed that excessive treatment costs were borne by a large group of metal finishers who could have banded together and actually been paid for their wastes; until experience showed that separate municipal and industrial waste treatment plants were planned within one year of each other without communications that would have allowed for mutual savings.

Contrasting examples of success were also important for our reasoning. Large chemical companies, which know a great deal about themselves, realize the value of recapturing and have active programs. Fly ash producers have now banded together to make fly ash a part of the building industry materials. New industrial parks are being built with shared treatment facilities. Some paper mills now have their sites determined by ecologists. All these signs of success point the way, but they are too sporadic and localized without an institutionalization of the process to make them occur throughout the economy.

It was while recording the failures and successes over the last years that we came to design a systematic way of locating opportunities for pollution reduction. The computer allows us to make two major additions to what the marketplace already signals. First, we took the central ideas involved in pollution control and generalized them into software design. Then we started writing programs which take the basic logics of analysis and convert them into principles of interrogation for finding possible pollution controls. At the same time we began to build a large data base which can provide the information for locating industrial residues lost in the normal process of production and marketing.

This systematic identification of pollution reduction measures without reduction of economic growth leans on the pervasive biological analogy of an ecosystem of machines. We conceive of an industrial network as if it were an ecosystem composed of machines with input and output materials related to each other. Less ambitious than an input-output matrix of materials flow, but more ambitious than a simple byproduct marketing scheme, we construct a computer matching service to identify networks of materials and producers.

EMIS ROUTINES

EMIS operates by formally setting the dominant strategies toward pollution abatement into computer software as a set of systematic questions which can be asked of an expansive data base. The fundamental strategies are recovery, recycling, and reuse in different industrial processes; substitution of offending operations by less polluting processes; and waste treatment and disposal. When translated to formal reasoning, the essence of recycling is an algorithm which matches producers and consumers of the same material such that those industries which release harmful effluents or scarce resources as wastes can be matched with those industries which use the equivalent of those wastes in virgin materials. The matching process then identifies potential partners for converting "waste" into a resource by recycling within a single plant, or by recovery and recycling within the total or regional economy. The matching algorithm makes positive identification of partners.

In a generalized and simplified equation, the algorithm for the recycling computer matching is $A_i = A_j$ where i and j are two different industries and A is a material used in production as an output or input.

The strategy of substituting less polluting processes for existing ones can seek empirical content in the data base by looking for the algorithm to be satisfied as $g = f$ or h or n where g is a function or process and f, h, and n are functional equivalents.

The strategy of waste treatment and disposal seeks partners who can share the cost of treatment or treat each other's waste. The algorithm which finds these opportunities in the data base can be written in a simplified form as $b_i = b_j$ or c_s where b and c are dumped wastes and i and j and s are different industries which can share facilities.

These basic strategies are amplified in the processing by many more variations. There are also feasibility tests. However, the essence of EMIS is this matching process to identify potential partners to increase recovery, substitution, or shared costs of treatment. Each of the EMIS routines is based on each of these formal statements or some variation thereof. The routines are used in a matrix of industries in the national industrial network which we conceive of as an interacting set. The routines are defined below.

Since there are a great number of processes and industries, our first step is to list the processes and industries by the Standard Industrial Classification (SIC)[1] and to construct a matrix for interaction which will be systematically scanned for industries which can relate to each other. The rules for establishing potential relations are found in selected logical routines which interrogate the data base in the following fashion:

SYMBIO is the routine which searches for industrial processes which use, as inputs, polluting emissions from another industry's output. In essence, the search is a systematic and comprehensive byproduct identification routine. It matches potential partners for symbiotic (mutually supportive) relations.

CONCOV is the routine which searches the list of pollution abatement devices which potentially may convert a pollutant into a valuable input for another industry. It operates on the premise that there is a choice of control devices and some control techniques may convert pollutants to resources which can then be identified by SYMBIO.

SUBPRO is the routine which identifies processes which perform similar functions but are less polluting in order to see where substitutions can be made.

SHAREC is the routine which identifies processes which use the same or similar abatement procedures to explore the possibility of shared pollution control facilities.

The four routines above are based on comprehensive and systematic matching of selected industries in the Standard Industrial Classification. The matching process is augmented by three other routines which serve different purposes:

HARCOR is the routine which accepts the residual products which cannot be used by any industry and seeks the alternatives for their ultimate assimilation and natural recycling or isolation from the environment. These hard core residuals are the rejects of the scanning system.

[1] The SIC code was developed by the Bureau of the Budget, Executive Office of the President, to classify all economic establishments in the U. S. The classes to be used in EMIS include those sections of manufacturing considered to be metallurgical or chemical.

TECFOR is the routine which updates the elements of the system for projected rather than present technology and gives information concerning increasing or decreasing rates of change of the magnitude of processes in use.

FEASPO is the last logical routine. It determines the economic feasibility of taking one of the alternatives which match potential partners. This routine can also be manipulated to give the optimum strategy based on comparing the results of the various routines.

SYMBIO and CONCOV are essentially byproduct routines. In these routines, the system takes outputs of industries, which are now classified as wastes, and matches them with industries which can use the materials as inputs to their processes. This matching gives us the alternatives open for recovery, recycling, and reprocessing of materials. In these routines, all possible matches are searched and the availability of control devices to convert materials into usable material is also investigated. These routines will identify the use of a byproduct within one industrial process, within two processes of one industry, or between two or more processes of two industries. In these routines, EMIS will try to achieve the maximum amount of re-use of materials.

SUBPRO is the next step after failing to achieve a re-use of emissions. If it is impossible to re-use byproducts of a particular industrial process so that pollution can be held to a tolerable level, EMIS will use SUBPRO to search for a process which may be substituted in order to reduce this pollution or increase the re-use of byproducts. This alternative strategy has been used to reduce air pollution from power plants by changing fuels. SUBPRO would consider materials in general categories, thus identifying unthought of and unusual substitutions.

If by byproduct re-use and substitution EMIS fails to achieve the level of pollution reduction desired, it will investigate the use of common facilities to dispose of wastes (SHAREC) and attempt to ensure that those wastes do not harm the rest of the functioning ecosystem or find a way back to a natural state (HARCOR).

SHAREC functions as a collector of industries which may share either a control device or a dumping strategy. It seeks to group industries and/or processes which otherwise would not be able to utilize these pollution reduction measures. All HARCOR strategies apply to these collections made by SHAREC.

The last logical routine is FEASPO. It determines the feasibility of decisions about matching potentials and about future technical changes. Feasibility is a function of economic and social policy regarding pollution reduction, for it sets the parameters in which industry will operate. The previous policy of letting the first user have priority on the environmental resource is now changing as each new user has more damaging effects. The abatement restrictions by governments, the corporate policy as a response to public pressure, the fluctuating known supply of raw materials and the value placed on them are all matters of policy which affect feasibility.

In each case of the above routines, constraints were mentioned regarding costs of transport, location, availability of materials in a region, stability of supply, and such other considerations. In FEASPO we store the economic and social policies in terms of their economic implications for cost accounting. In this way we can be sensitive to market adjustments and make policy both as an initiator of behavior and also in response to marketplace behavior.

If rigidly done in computer analysis, the rapid updating requirement could take an enormous amount of time and suffer from overcentralization. Therefore FEASPO will require a man-machine design which allows the experience of a small staff of knowledgeable men to be current with activities and local variation. Their information can then affect the calculations in the other routines and allow the information system to operate with and ahead of the times rather than behind them.

FEASPO also can be manipulated to give the optimum strategy based on comparing the results of various routines. It can be used as an optimizing routine which recommends the costs of various alternative activities. It will compare the results of SYMBIO and CONCOV, the two byproduct routines; with SUBPRO, the substitution alternative; and with SHAREC and HARCOR, the waste disposal alternatives. For example, under a national economic and social policy encouraging recycling, the feasibility of choosing one of the byproduct alternatives would be taken over a waste and dumping strategy.

The seven routines provide the necessary information for interrogating the data base to match related industries which could use the pollutant of one as the resource of another. They can also be used to optimize abatement strategies among the alternatives generated by the system. A staff operating EMIS, either in a batch processing mode, or for more detailed and complicated interactions, in an on-line interactive mode, can search for partners to lower the costs of pollution abatement and raise the efficiency of national resource use. EMIS compares alternative strategies which could go undiscovered by traditional techniques using a lesser amount of information and habitual communications within and among industries and government agencies.

MORTON GORDEN & CHARLES N. FLINKSTROM

USER: Data Retrieval Program for Ecologically Sound Economic Development Planning

Under current land use policy, we have not adequately solved the problem of the relations between parts of an area and its whole potential. We have often destroyed resources by not considering the environmental impact of our actions, and we have incurred opportunity costs by denying future uses through incompatible placement of

The original design of this system was funded by a grant from the Southeastern Regional Planning and Economic Development District (SRPEDD) Massachusetts. We gratefully acknowledge the support, both financial and critical, which the staff provided.

demands on existing resources. A tool is needed to give us a means of satisfying the demand on our supply of resources — without the accompanying destruction. Some form of comprehensive thought must go into evaluating particular uses so they do not destroy future assets when creating benefits for the present.

It is only a matter of time before Congress asks the states to make some form of comprehensive land use plans to avoid the piecemeal destruction of our remaining assets. Formulating such a plan will be difficult without a consensus in each state to guide protection and development of the characteristics that identify each state. The political skills for achieving that consensus will be severely taxed, and the environmental manager will have to provide a tool that enhances the process of discussion while providing technical information so that valid decisions can be made. The following article suggests one such approach, which can be applied to regulate demand so that the use of land follows the constraints and opportunities nature provides.

INTRODUCTION

The Unified System for Environmental Resources (USER) is designed to provide a state or other planning region with an integrated comprehensive planning tool. The tool provides a framework which brings socioeconomic and natural resource assets into a compatible rather than an antagonistic relationship. The dominant strategy is to guide growth and the location of industry so that new development will take place within the opportunities and constraints framework defined by natural resource carrying capacities.

The system seeks to achieve ecologically sound economic development by the application of USER, an information system for land, water, and coastal zone land use decision making. The technique is discussed below, but its central thrust is to make an accounting of a state's assets and to determine the suitability of their use and potential use, from both the economic and ecological points of view. In this way, it is intended to create a new status for the state as a development area that cares about its natural history and will utilize it as a guide to its natural future. This new status seeks to take advantage of significant changes in the values of skilled labor which indicate a trend toward choosing work where play is not far away and choosing living space where the environment is a delight rather than a degrading experience.

We conceive of real public assets which have been heretofore seen as passive elements, but which are now, with the change in consumer taste and life style values, becoming active elements in a state's future potential. Most states are either unspoiled or still recuperable, and those qualities, when located near urban centers, can be a powerful attraction for new growth. A planning program for protection of the environment and an action strategy for appropriate development can make present underdevelopment a capital asset to invest in future growth.

The basic strategy for development is to guide development so it will not upset natural balances in the environment, for to upset ecological balances which nature has provided is to incur overhead costs in reclamation of degraded sites as well as to destroy unique natural attractions characteristic of a given state or region. Except for parts of immediate coastlines, highway strip developments, and other urban-suburban areas, many states have vast unused space with fine forests, open spaces, river valleys, and other natural assets which are sought by growing industries and by accompanying residential and commercial users. The tool perceives the unused land not as a failure of present development, but as a resource for future gain, especially for amenity-oriented growth industries. It perceives the decayed resources not as an infinite sink into which stopgap funds should be poured, but as potentially transferable resources to be included in a new structural face for the planning region.

The development strategy which relies on a high quality living and working environment requires two major tasks, and USER is designed to carry them out. First the tool must project, and then it must protect. Projected potential growth comes from an economic development program which puts emphasis on attracting industries and jobs which a state's department of commerce deems appropriate for the state. Highly skilled occupations which are attracted to an environment as a good place for living could be attracted by a region where the theme is ecologically sound economic development. The industries which grow around these occupations could upgrade present underemployment in the area through the compatible commercial development associated with them.

After the projecting of new opportunities by identifying growth industries and their criteria for location, the planning tool must then accomplish its second function, protection. Protection is as much a part of growth as projection.

USER will find sites in a region which can tolerate growth and clusters of compatible development within the constraints of good land use policy. Through the use of computer matching of desired criteria with available assets, USER will indicate where compatible development can proceed, while excluding those areas with precious natural assets which should be protected from harmful development. It can then offer knowledge of alternative sites to interested industry and note that the protective feature will make these sites desirable for some time to come. The twin features of USER are performed through the use of a man-machine information system which makes the matches possible.

Figure 1 indicates some of the development site criteria which a new industry would like to know before deciding upon a location. The filter in the center of the figure filters out places where locations are too fragile to meet the criteria required by the developer. Locations which can tolerate development and meet the criteria of ecologically sound growth are selected by the system.

THE CODING SYSTEM

In order to create a match between desired criteria and specific possible locations, we must create an information system to process the large amount

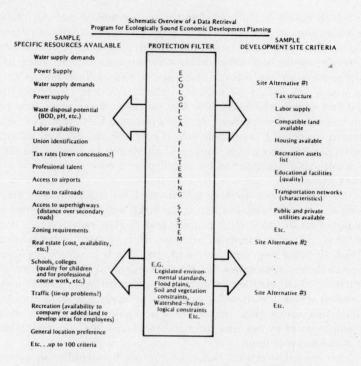

Schematic Overview of a Data Retrieval
Program for Ecologically Sound Economic Development Planning

Figure 1.   Unified system for environmental resources (USER)

of data needed. The USER agency staff planner implements the system by proceeding through three steps with the aid of a computer.

Step 1: Define locational criteria on input sheet. Locational criteria consist of the list of characteristics an industrial or commercial client seeks for his plant location. Location characteristics include those listed under development site criteria in Figure 1. The USER system has room for a detailed list of over 100 separate criteria. Site criteria can be expanded to include commercial, recreational, and residential development, and desired clusters can be formed which meet the needs of new growth industries.

Step 2: Scan state resource list for potential sites. USER will, with the use of a computer console with remote access to a larger computer, machine-scan through locational criteria from a sheet using town, municipal, and state data identified by data areas. Data areas are defined by the Universal Transverse Mercator (UTM) grid, or a state's plane coordinate system to facilitate site locations on maps. Any predetermined coordinate system would be functional.

The USER program can be initially designed to serve as a semi-automated or man-machine system. A department's economic development planner operating the office console system would have more current events at hand. Current city and town government problems, local and regional attitudes, and other judgments garnered from contacts with towns and other state agencies would enable the planner to make rank-order decisions to delete less desirable sites and thus provide a client with a usable number of alternative sites for his selection. The console operator would thus provide the human insight needed to make a comprehensive decision on output from the system. The operator will have to be given policy guidance and assistance from responsible senior people, for example, the commissioner.

The computer is programmed to do the tedious sequential search of the data bank for site locations which fit the client's site criteria as well as pass the ecological fitness check provided by a series of ecological filters. However, to keep the information system operable requires both the man and his decision making support. Site locations produced by the machine are checked by the planner. In addition to the console operator's access to a library equipped with current events, trade journals, and economic projections, he also has a map of the state overlaid with the coordinate system. As the site location computer output is identified by coordinate points, the department's economic development planner is able to utilize the map and data area overlay to indicate the approximate site location alternatives available to the client. The planner simply places an acreage-keyed land tab on the map to illustrate spatial relationships to the client.

The USER planning room would consist of a library of current information, the projections for potential clients, the computer console and its software, and a map of the state. The site location approach is to process variables (site criteria) and do the analysis on them. USER keys the criteria variables with locational tabs according to the coordinate system, so that after the processing, it can locate relevant clusters of variables in spatial terms. The analyzed clusters appearing in a section of the data area system can then be transposed to a map.

Step 3: Prepare folio for prospective new industry. An attractive and individualized folio prepared for the client should include information for each potential site, such as:

1. Town or municipal data — taxes, public utilities, access to airports, railroads, highways, power supply, schools, etc.;
2. An economic, social and historical monograph;
3. Housing availability;
4. Recreation availability;
5. Site's relation to regional framework;
6. Land and water waste assimilation capacities.

A more complete list would be developed based on a state's priorities.

These three steps, criteria input, site scanning, and site folio creation, comprise the essential information handling of USER. Of course a great deal of preparation goes into building the information system in order to reduce the location process to such a simple operation. There follows a map grid and a schematic description of a rural, coastal zone, and urban coordinate overlay system.

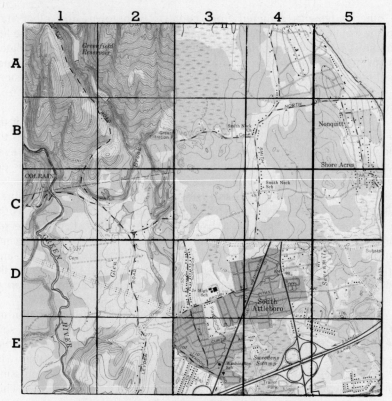

**Unified system for environmental resources (USER)
schematic rural, coastal zone, and urban coordinate overlay system**

Coordinate Codes:

Rural B2 — *Ecological Parameters:* Severe ecological constraints for development, i.e., 25–75% slopes, very stony surface soils, subsurface hardpan, and high erodibility.

Rural D2 — *Ecological Parameters:* Areas adjacent to stream have severe constraints for development, i.e., poorly drained river deposits, high water table and wet 7–9 months of the year. Other land areas are characterized by deep, well to excessively drained sandy soils — level to gently sloping with no severe ecological constraints on development evident.

Rural D2 — *Socioeconomic Parameters:* Based upon town, municipal and state data inputs, i.e., transportation network, secondary roads accessible; schools, colleges; recreation facilities; consumer goods; police and fire protection; communications media; health facilities; proximity of public and private utilities; labor availability; professional talent; financial services; real estate; zoning requirements; etc.

Coastal B5 — *Ecological Parameters:* Based upon the following data inputs and other parameters from federal, state, regional, and local sources, i.e., water quality — oxygen content, chemical analysis, turbidity, and nutrient levels; habitat quality — tidal flats, marshes, beaches, sea coast, etc.; natural resources — minerals, waterfowl, finfish, shellfish, etc. Marine resource base opportunities and constraints are identified according to fragility of the resource compared against the desired demand for use.

Coastal B5 — *Socioeconomic Parameters:* Based upon town, municipal, and state data inputs, i.e., transportation network, secondary roads accessible; ocean recreation available; population characteristics; per capita income; tax rates; water — capacity; sewerage — flow capacity, BOD loading; solid waste removal; etc.

Urban D5 — *Ecological Parameters:* A delineation of critical natural resource systems susceptible to degradation from development activities. Geological, hydrological, soils,

We have briefly mentioned the human judgments needed to operate the system so that the three steps will be well done. These judgments are given considerable attention in the implementation program which uses the political process to identify relevant values affecting operation of the system. Part of the planning process must include relations with the objects of planning: people. Too often planning considers land as its object, with the consequence that plans are ignored by people. If the ideas are to be implemented they must come from as well as be suggested to the people who are affected.

Implementation program — recognizing home rule

As part of the overall implementation program, a brief outline explaining the operation of USER and its utility to the towns and cities of a state is developed. Town and city cooperation is solicited in land, water and sea use data collection as well as governmental and service data which is used in the development of a resource list. The projected economic benefits and protection against environmental degradation is stressed in the outline.

The operating system will help towns and cities to adjust their planning to long term regional opportunities as well as indicating immediate opportunities. Areas which are constantly overlooked for development opportunities and are concerned over possible lost revenue could gain information on site criteria from USER and adjust public services or zoning to meet site criteria.

USER operations

Agencies utilizing the system will define its operations, and there are at least three major types of operations to perform comprehensive planning functions. One set of users will be private industry or its consultants hired to find locations for industrial, commercial, and residential use. This group would be encouraged to come to the state's department of commerce to make a confidential request for a list of possible locations. They would fill out the input sheet which the department's planner would use to place the computer console in operation. In a short time, perhaps while the client was waiting, a list of potential sites would be printed out. The prospective industrial representative would then be encouraged to call the town or city contacts listed to get more detailed information about the general area chosen for the site.

Another user, the most frequent user, will be the department's planner who takes a more active approach and does not wait for the clients to come. Through discussions with economists and through the projections and other library documents, he could seek sites for specific industries and then send a folio to the prospective user. In this active form, the state will have its assets publicized among people responsible for bringing new growth to the area.

---

vegetation and other ecological data would be based upon available natural resource data inputs, i.e., generally high water table evident in some locations; no severe slope limitations.

Urban D5 — *Socioeconomic Parameters:* Public and private utilities are available, i.e., water, sewerage, etc.; transportation — railroads, superhighways, primary and secondary roads, and public transportation are accessible; other parameters would be based upon town, municipal and state data inputs.

Still another user might be the cities and towns of the state. As they update their planning and zoning, they will find the system a very useful tool to indicate potential sites for municipal services, conservation areas, and other specialized use. While locating something as controversial as a town waste disposal area would require more than the judgment in the computer, at least a set of physical parameters could be met rapidly by machine scanning.

USER is thus designed to identify new bases for economic growth; to stress the natural assets of the state, including, if applicable, the coastal zone; to protect these assets from destructive growth; and specifically to identify the sites of use to potential growth industries. By the protection of the area through ecological filtering of the alternatives, new bases for economic activity will be attracted. Nationwide interest in protecting the environment to make a work and play area highly desirable coincides with a large segment of many states having large rural land areas with urban nodes. These circumstances present planning opportunities and alternatives which need comprehensive evaluation. A further development of techniques is required to make that evaluation.

TECHNIQUES FOR ECOLOGICALLY SOUND ECONOMIC DEVELOPMENT

Setting standards

A state would, of course, have the option to indicate which standards would be applied to the operation of USER. It would seem appropriate, however, to apply standards where applicable according to the laws of the state; for example, coastal and inland water quality standards adopted by the water pollution control boards of commissioners; air quality standards adopted by departments of public health; natural resource standards delineated by parameters set forth in the inland wetland acts, coastal wetland acts, acts for coastal and inland waters, and other acts administered by departments of natural resources; and other state agency standards presently adopted or expected in the future. These standards can be placed within the operating system to act as a preventive filter to warn of environmental quality deterioration from improper development activities related to water, land, and air resources.

Basic to the successful protection program implicit to the USER operation is the ecological filter. Standards are generated as a part of the filter by identifying proportions among land uses which are tolerable from the point of view of a quality environment. The technique used for this purpose recognizes that quality can be essentially described by proportions of key factors. The mixes of uses and natural conditions are key indicators of quality. The mixes can be measured.

The ratio of paved surface to permeable surface is not only of interest in aquifer recharge regions, but also as a ratio expressing the qualitative aspects of natural surroundings. The ratio of open meadows to dense forest or the ratio of one species to another as an evaluative framework for determining suitability of plant life to sustain different uses are all useful indicators of quality. As maps note urban spread, they can warn of encroachment on key qualities which are cheaply and accurately indicated with the information system.

Ratio measurements have not yet been used as indicators of quality, for most analysts have assumed the problem of quantitative indicators for quality as either conceptually impossible or empirically difficult. One problem is surely the noncommensurate units in which we measure quality. However, even an intuitive look at maps indicates the qualitative aspects of an environment. The eye scans relations which are really ratios and which have no problem with noncommensurability. The data base can be organized to improve on this intuitive judgment and note where ratios now obtain to give us quality or non-quality environments.

Recognizing that man is part of the ecosystem and chooses many of its qualities by his behavior, the system provides a method for determining proportions in the state which describe present behavior and indicate ways to identify desired behavior. Ratios of present land use in different model parts of the state are used to quantitatively describe the features of an area. These important features can then become guidelines for avoiding some patterns of development which are identified by government officials and citizen participation to be undesirable and for encouraging limits on development where local and regional values expressed indicate different proportions. The methodology of proportions is a way of quantifying the subjective values of a state's population and letting them choose, in a way easily translatable by the planner, the quality level of the environment they seek. Ratio determination provides a mechanism for developing an environmental quality index for local, regional, and state usage for developing standards. These standards in conjunction with the ecological filters generate a structure for an ecological early warning system which can have great utility in providing necessary information prior to the decision making process.

Site selection methodology

The expansion of information which USER provides increases the capacity of the planner to implement the system and for decision makers to have viable alternative solutions available to them.

TOOL 1: Projection for growth. It is assumed that a state department of commerce has extensive ongoing research and study efforts aimed at identifying growth industries which can take advantage of the human and natural resources of the state. USER will generate a broad array of land, water, and coastal zone opportunities for industrial, commercial, residential, and other development activities which can be examined by the department's economic development planners. Economists experienced in economic projections can explore resource use suggestions generated by the system and will therefore have access to information needed to identify growth industries which can take advantage of the available resources in the state. Always with an eye to competitive and comparative advantage, the economist will be familiar with the resources of the state and locations which could be attractive to potential clients. A list of potential clients for the area would be drafted and the system activated to identify specific assets of interest to particular firms. Drawing on the economic projections, the system's criteria list could be expanded to meet the needs for future growth and a matrix of potential clients and potential assets generated for the department's staff.

From pollutant to resource — The basic purpose of this approach is to identify waste management alternatives with special emphasis on ways of converting pollutants into resources. Pollutants are obnoxious for reasons of public health, esthetics, and economic costs. The opposition to reducing them would be much dampened if the pollutant could be perceived as an economic value. There is precedent to this reasoning in industries where the byproduct is presently used as an income producer. However, the number of cases where this is true is limited, and most of these cases have already been explored by industries seeking profit from their wastes. The new feature we will explore is the design of mutually interdependent industries in a network of relations especially created to take advantage of pollutant use and cost reductions through alternative waste management practices. These opportunities are not presently recognized because existing industrial facilities are not designed nor cost-accounted to take advantage of the potential for gain which the future holds. Furthermore, a sufficient and appropriate set of government incentives and disincentives has not existed which would make these potential benefits accrue to both industry and society. However, current restrictions on emissions are even now altering the economics of waste management. With USER, the new opportunities can be explored, for wastes which are feasible to recover will appear as resources in the criteria matching lists.

TOOL 2: Protection through ecological filters. The development information generated by the state's development planning agency and the USER system must be linked to protective criteria. Basic to the successful protection program are the ecological filter for land and water resources and the marine use matrix for the coastal zone.

A portion of the ecological filtering mechanism has been discussed in the previous standards section relating to land use ratio determination using the methodology of proportions to develop an environmental quality index.

However, the ecological filter also provides natural limits on the pattern of development which must be added to men's choices. The ecological filter includes a set of constraints, and then perceives the remaining resource characteristics as important assets available for development opportunities. Some examples of ecological constraints are:

1. Estuaries, marshlands, anadromous fish streams, and so forth, provide habitats for aquatic and terrestrial fish and wildlife, provide life support areas for a major portion of commercial and sport fisheries harvest; and marshlands and estuaries are ecological systems susceptible to destruction and disruption by man.
2. The carrying capacity of various soil types, forest types, and water body resistance to development must be delineated. Information such as water table depth, slope, depth to bedrock, soil permeability, flooding hazards, or erosion susceptibility are all ecological characteristics which should be placed in the framework of constraints listed in the ecological filters.

3. Identification of pollution indicators such as residential, industrial, and agricultural wastes; waterfowl reductions, fish reductions, unproductive marshes; rapid residential or industrial expansion; and other indicators which warn of saturated conditions will have to be considered.
4. Many of the natural assets of a state cannot be measured in economic benefit–cost terms and are therefore considered in terms of their amenity value to society. Natural resource information such as unique geological, hydrological, vegetative, scenic topographic features, and nonrenewable resources, as well as the location and identification of unique wildlife and aquatic habitats, need to be delineated where possible to prevent the destruction of these valuable assets from both an economic and amenity point of view.

Working with ecological limits enables the location of areas of incompatible use as well as locating areas of opportunity; the planning methodology is limit-seeking as well as opportunity-seeking.

Through the land use proportioning and through natural ecological constraints such as those suggested, USER provides protection for inland land and water resources as well as the coastal zone resources. However, additional components must be added to the tool specifically for marine use. The marine use matrix suggests these limits and opportunities.

Marine considerations — The use of the coastline and contiguous ocean waters of the coastal zone for the economic and social benefit of residents and visitors to a state is directly related to the wise use of the state's land area. Effects of physical modifications of the shoreline, while beneficial to man, can also be harmful. Dredging unsettles bottom sediments, removes bottom-dwelling marine life, reduces the water's ability to assimilate oxygen-demanding wastes, blankets fish nests, and masks out light required for photosynthesis by aquatic plants. Dredging spoils dumped as land fill increase water turbidity, smothers bottom organisms, and alters depths, changing the marine habitat. Dam construction creates barriers for anadromous fish and alters water salinity, affecting marine life such as crabs, shrimp, oysters, and lobsters. Jetty and groin construction alters the local movements of sand, changing beach ecology and upsetting attached marine organisms.

These activities all affect the ability to utilize the coastal environment for economic as well as recreational benefits. Swimming, boating, sport fishing, commercial fishing, boatyards and marinas, housing, and other coastal and marine uses cannot be maximized if a degraded environment exists.

The USER program provides the ecological framework to help the state prevent further degradation of its inland, coastal, and marine resources. A marine use compatibilities matrix is central to the protection of coastal and marine resources. The marine use matrix in USER has been modeled after the charts used in "An Ecological View of Environmental Management" by B. H. Ketchum.*

* Bostwick H. Ketchum, *Oceanus,* The Woods Hole Oceanographic Institution, Woods Hole, Massachusetts, vol. 15, no. 2 (October 1969), pp. 15–23.

With the methodology of proportions indicating balanced land use according to the level of environmental quality desired and the ecological filters and marine use matrix identifying incompatible uses and open opportunities, the components of the protective tool are put in place. Each of these components contributes a part of the information necessary to accommodate human values, natural constraints, and desirable use of a state's inland, coastal, and marine assets.

TOOL 3: Location identification. In a man-machine system design, it is possible to do selections without initially using a map for location identification. A map is a human aid to give a synthetic capability to a man who must integrate many variables. The training of many planners emphasizes visual techniques, and maps are necessary to locate information so that it can be processed.

The visual approach leads to expensive hand manipulations and preparations of data on maps. To overcome this cost in time and money, computer mapping is being developed. However, that is only letting the computer use a human synthetic aid which it does not need. The USER approach is to process variables and do analysis on them. The variables are keyed with locational tabs according to a coordinate system so that after the processing, relevant clusters of variables can be located in spatial terms. The analyzed clusters will appear within one coordinate data area, and then the information can be transposed to one map which locates information for the human viewer.

The essential difference between this approach to data processing and traditional planning is that the USER system marks variables with locational information, while the traditional planner marks map locations with variables. He puts the data on a map for understanding. USER puts data in an information handling system and locates the data only at the end of the process, thus saving a great deal of time and money in the planning process.

We can envision the operation by imagining the computer searching for data with particular characteristics, and after the search is finished, the output appears on a map. Analysis is not done by area; area is recorded as one characteristic of the many searched for, and that allows the freedom to scan an entire region for information without the slowness of the eye and of manual data preparation. The system scans for clusters of desirable characteristics, and when the system finds them by the process of elimination within the coordinate data areas, it can print them out for a precoded map.

This system is not only rapid in retrieving desired information, but it also achieves economies in data collecting and system updating. The USER data collector takes a work sheet for each variable needed by the system. Then, after the system has scanned the long list of variables and found the sought-for clusters, it can ask for spatial information. The data collecting is done by variable, which conforms to the way data is collected naturally. Furthermore, at any time new socioeconomic or ecological variables are added, the system does not have to go to the time and expense of a map overlay, but simply adds one worksheet to the system.

SUMMARY

The primary function of USER is to provide a state's department of commerce with a system to help plan for ecologically sound economic development. USER is based upon a computerized information handling system utilizing a list of development site criteria keyed with coordinate data area locational tabs for ease of spatial location on the state map. A series of filters is also keyed with locational tabs to provide an ecological fitness check to ensure development compatibility with the environment. Prior to providing site location information for potential economic development, sites are tested against environmental quality standards generated by USER. Site locations that are within the standards and compatible with desirable land, water, and marine use within the designated political units are provided to the development client for his consideration.

USER performs several functions that complement its primary purpose of ecologically sound economic development. It will identify ecologically fragile areas, serve as a guideline toward intelligent land use, and provide a framework for an essential new orderliness for future use and development of a state's land, water, and coastal zone resources.

M. K. MUTHOO

The Renewable Resource Planning Problem with Special Reference to Kashmir

Renewable resources are those natural resources which, because of their flow characteristics, can be produced and used in perpetuity. These include the attributes of soil and landscape, the biotic and water resources.

RENEWABLE RESOURCE POLICY AND PLANNING

No country has an explicit renewable resource policy, save for the formal forest policies in most developing countries and for the water resource policies

M. K. Muthoo, "The Renewable Resource Planning Problem with Special Reference to Kashmir," *Socio-Economic Planning Sciences*, vol. 4, no. 2 (June 1970), pp. 187–200. Copyright 1970 by The Pergamon Press, Great Britain. Reprinted by permission.
The author is a member of St. John's College, Oxford.
This paper is based on a lecture delivered at the Third Forest Research Course at the Commonwealth Forestry Institute, Oxford, September 1969. Thanks are due to Mr. J. J. MacGregor, Forest Economist, Oxford University, for going through the draft. However, for any omissions and the views in the paper, the author is solely responsible.

in many developed areas especially North America. This may arise because of the many disciplines involved in the management of farm, forest, range and recreation lands, livestock, wildlife and fisheries, surface and ground waters, and the difficulty in co-ordinating and dovetailing the use of these diverse resources within the socio-economic framework. But the need for co-ordinated use through the planned development of these resources is axiomatic if resource allocation is to be made in consonance with the community's objectives. This is an important requirement in poor areas, like Kashmir, where resource scarcity is a more severe bottleneck for development and where misallocation should be particularly avoided.

In this context, the aim of planning would be to prevent unco-ordinated development by providing a pattern that harmonizes competing renewable resource uses; these should complement rather than interfere with one another and the other sectors of the economy, so as to promote the objectives of economic development as closely as possible. For this purpose, renewable resources need to be appraised in the light of their contribution to the development effort. The evaluation of gains and losses ensuing from different methods and intensities of use should be the key to assigning a role to different resources. This warrants an inter-disciplinary examination of overall resource situations; it entails not only a physical and biological review of renewable resources and their renewal over time, but also social and economic analyses, i.e. total environmental assessment is called for.

The scope of this paper does not permit the spelling out of the approach to the evaluation and co-ordination of different uses. Nor should it be laid down rigidly because different resource situations deserve different treatments, especially in the absence or lack of precision of renewable resource policies. Even if such policies do exist, they should be consistent with and geared to achieve the overall development strategy; otherwise their pursuit may be inimical to society's objectives. Since the object is to evolve a management schema aimed at resolving conflicts while meeting society's goals, the planning process becomes flexible in that the use of renewable resources will vary according to social needs. In the following discussion, emphasis will be laid on the analysis of the problem of planning the use of renewable resources for realizing the objectives of a developing country.*

Regions and resources — reconnaissance

Renewable resources are the components of a system, comprising a "set of objects together with relationships between the objects and between their attributes" (Hall and Hagen, 1956). The use of one unit or kind of resource is likely to influence the use of others. It is misplaced isolation to plan their use atomistically or independently, as is the general practice. The preparation of integrated plans for all these resources would be ideal. However, the interdependence of their use exists not only among themselves but also between them and the man-made capital and the human resources of a country. Be-

---

* The nature of the problem and the broad stages of its analysis are summarized in the diagram and the table at the end of the paper.

cause of these interdependencies and the related factor of demand conditioned by economic, institutional, cultural and political features, integrated planning of all renewable resources in any large country would be a stupendous problem. This is so also because there can be no once-for-all integration and adjustments have to be made from time to time.

Two main possibilities exist to render the problem manageable as well as realistic. One is to plan the use regionally while keeping national objectives in view. This could be more useful than an excessively aggregated treatment in a country with diversity in renewable resources and socio-economic conditions. Renewable resource planning "should be based upon detailed descriptions and analyses" (Kuerger *et al.*, 1963), because national aggregates can only be broad and indicative to cover the heterogeneity of prevailing circumstances and purposes.

The inherent vagueness in the nationwide treatment of resource uses is exemplified by the all-embracing forest policies of different countries.* Gane (1969) has cited the ambiguity of Trinidad's national forest policy. In India the main aim of the policy is to have 33.3 percent of the total land area under forests (Govt. of India, 1968). The rationale behind this figure is wanting, having been established on an *ad hoc* basis. Such a policy can cause conflicts in land use because it considers neither the demands of competing uses nor the overall resource situation and their relationships with developmental aims. These defects apart, it is imprecise about the regions or kind of forest cover desired and the implementation of its objective is problematic. It cannot but be so because the demand of industries and consumers for commodities, the comparative advantage and suitability for producing different products, including protection needs, vary immensely in different regions. Questionable in itself though the aggregate objective of 33.3 percent of forest land area is, here we need only point out that it should not imply that Kashmir should reduce its existing forest area of 58 percent or that afforestation is technically and economically superior to covering the largely desert area of Rajasthan State with grass merely to extend its forest cover from the present 12 percent. These instances show that national policies for renewable resources can be a proper guide through regional planning. A national plan would be more realistic if it is an appropriate sum total of the regional plans which cater to regional considerations while keeping the country's developmental aims in view.

The second way to make the problem manageable is through stage by stage analyses, feeding back the results of one analysis on to another to incorporate the dynamic relationships between different use patterns. Planning would then become practical by dividing the renewable resources into say two broad categories of land and water-based resource. This conforms to the institutional and organisational arrangements and macro-planning strategy in Kashmir and most other countries, where land resource development is

---

* An exception seems to be the proposed revision of the forest policy for Queensland in the Australian Commonwealth. If formally accepted, it will be the first case of a specific policy for a region, no doubt simultaneous to the existence of a National Forest Council which looks at plans in a "federal" way.

dealt with under "agricultural production sector" separately from that of water resources.

Such a division is convenient and less arbitrary. Either resource has physical and economic characteristics of its own besides being somewhat independent. This division is realistic in many developing areas where one of the two resources can be treated peripherally, because either it is abundant to such an extent or the demand for it is comparatively so small that such analysis could be made more clearly. Little could be gained from dealing jointly with both the land and water resources of Kashmir giving equal emphasis to each, because water availability over the predictable future will not be a limiting factor in development. Almost three quarters of the entire flow of the many rivers of the Indus basin is contributed by the rains and snowfall in their catchments in Kashmir (Khan, 1961). The region abounds in perennial water potential and the problem in the water resource field is to use its development so that other sectors can benefit at the same time. The intensification of water-using activities within the region would be complementary because these would not involve diversion of the flow or any significant diminution of the downstream water. The conceivable land resource use adjustments in Kashmir are, therefore, unlikely to cause economically adverse effects on water resource uses or vice versa. Nevertheless, a complete evaluation would allow for the costs and benefits of the watershed protection and erosion influences of various adjustments and of the water requirements of different production and processing techniques. If that is done, an initially weak relationship between analyses of the two main resource categories is not likely to jeopardize the theoretical ideal of an integrated treatment of the entire renewable resource base.

A broad division is not inapt because the results of a few main analyses can be adequately synthesized for higher level decision-making. This may be achieved by forward and backward redesigning of the few renewable resource systems till the analytical process strikes a chord in tune with total developmental objectives and constraints of complementary resources. Caution, nevertheless, has to be exercised to ensure that the problem is not decomposed in a way that it does not meet the realism of a particular situation. In any case, decomposition should be limited only to what is necessary to make the treatment of the problem tractable in practice. An integrated solution would be nearer the optimum than one that is less so, even if subsequent synthesis is possible, because many disjointed analyses cannot be synthesized easily without some mutual inconsistency.

The division between the water and land resource sectors would be more realistic if the latter were delineated co-extensively with a watershed region so that the two analyses can be integrated for comprehensive planning of a river basin that may constitute a composite, identifiable, economic unit. Thus the division has to be considered together with the problem of identifying geo-economic regions. This is a reason why planning the use of renewable land resources for the entire Kashmir valley as a region would be theoretically suitable and practically useful.

To facilitate a proper demarcation of regions and resources, a reconnaissance of the renewable resources of an area is necessary. This may be considered parallel to the preliminary survey reports of industrial projects that precede detailed surveys of raw materials and markets, the approach to which we shall now consider. The results of the "preliminary survey" may, of course, be subject to amendment as a result of subsequent surveys and analyses.

Inventory

After delineating the scope of the problem, the starting point for its analysis is the appraisal of the nature and magnitude of the present renewable resource uses. This would include mapping the present uses on geotopographic sheets, now available for most developing countries. These may be augmented by quick aerial and other surveys, especially when proper field maps are unavailable, and enlarged to enable the relevant detail to be distinguished. Besides the data about production functions, information about infra-structure, rural socio-economy, tenure systems, seasonal and spatial variations should be simultaneously collected. Such data are essential for subsequent stages of the analysis and their lack is often a practical planning problem.

A detailed survey of the present use pattern gives clues to local resource conditions and socio-economic, cultural, institutional and historical features, in response to which it has emerged. The need for this survey is fundamental because it provides a basis from which to gauge the desirability of bringing about changes. Its importance deserves to be stressed as renewable resource planning in practice tends to assume a Utopian frame by ignoring the existing uses; either because data about them are difficult to come by and both their collection and processing need considerable skill or because they are considered as an irrational outcome of traditions. King (1963) argues for disregarding the present land use on the grounds that it "will not necessarily indicate the possible productivity of land" and may not be the "best use commensurate with the suitability of land", being influenced by "social pressures."

Here we must point out the distinction between technical and economic efficiency in order to suggest that the best use cannot be defined in an *ex-ante* manner only from the suitability of a renewable resource. This is because technical efficiency measures use of inputs and production of outputs in physical terms and economic efficiency measures these in terms of costs and benefits. The problem of how to use different renewable resources is not merely to examine their suitability in producing different products, but of choosing among different technically suitable combinations the one that represents the least sacrifice or the maximum profit to society. This would depend upon the relative prices of factors and products which reflect their scarcity in relation to demand. This distinction should reveal the conflict in arguments of King's type. These are a plea for technically "best uses", being divorced from "social pressures" and other factors. The latter would include the effect of location on the feasibility of a resource use.

The economically and socially most desirable use geared towards society's objectives need not necessarily be technically most suitable, for the costs of such a use may be prohibitive or its products may not be in demand or so scarce as those resulting from a technically less suitable use. A sloping area may be technically most suitable for use under permanent vegetation such as a forest or grassland because it is most efficient in protection against losses of soil and excessive run-off. But an appraisal of present use may show that the area is already well terraced to prevent these losses, and irrigation and other facilities stand established so that the continuance of the present cropping practice may produce more social gains than conversion to other uses. This can happen because the latter involve immediate investment and delayed returns compared with the existing use, for which capital costs are already sunk and only maintenance and operation costs are required for uninterrupted benefits.

Present-use survey portrays the rural socio-economic structure. It yields information about the assets on the ground and capital works of land and water development such as bunds and terraces, drainage and irrigation, animal and other draught power, logging facilities, plantations and propagation nurseries, commodity processing plants, harvesting equipment and warehousing. It involves a study of the existing management and supervisory machinery and its scope for handling capacity expansion and modifications in use pattern. Through it data accrue about the current solvency of various renewable resource producers, shown by the royalty and tax revenues from sale of timber and grazing rights, the incomes, indebtedness and liabilities of peasants, and about local demand, marketing, lines of export and communications network. Such an inventory is a pre-requisite for the further development of renewable resources.

The advantage of surveying current use will be to identify reference points for change towards a potentially better use; it will show where deficiencies and impediments exist. The present use pattern may not be socially the best because societies are dynamic and their objectives change, if they are not to stagnate. In developing countries, much of the rural sector activity does not undergo market exchange. Considerable distortions and imperfections in renewable resource-based production and consumption exist because of physical inaccessibility and economic disequilibria including resource immobility, share-cropping and other practices, which act as disincentives to producers for investing to the level of marginal productivity. Agents of change in the renewable resource sector are scarcer than elsewhere. Since the masses concerned with these resources are ignorant, changes to ensure socially desirable realignments cannot be expected to permeate this sector without much delay. In developed countries too, know-how is not readily applied by producers because technological progress outstrips the capacity of communications media. For these reasons, the next two steps in the analysis are firstly to explore alternative possibilities of using a renewable resource and secondly to evaluate their comparative merits.

Feasibility study

The two aforementioned steps are analogous to a feasibility study in conventional project analysis in that they show whether a particular renewable resource use is feasible or not, i.e. whether it is technically suitable and economically (and/or financially) justifiable. The difference is that they analyse not only whether an option is worthwhile but also place the various options in a ranking order. This is important as our problem is not restricted to the usual accept or reject options of a particular project. It cannot be solved by an independent or single feasibility test, because the problem is of choosing among the numerous production activities possible over a renewable resource base.

The first step involves a biotechnical assessment of renewable resources. Since these resources comprise a biome of living elements, such an assessment can be best devised ecologically by taking into consideration the interactions between the fauna and flora and their environment. This complexity is unique to renewable resources. Hence the need to combine the investigation of the biogeocoenotic relationships of an ecosystem with the technical opportunities of using it.

The above relationships are often innumerable depending upon the array of climatic, edaphic and biotic factors and their local and regional variations. To make the investigation operational, the problem may be approached by identifying the factors which are limiting, in descending order of their constraining influence on different uses. The problem then is to evolve a sieving mechanism suitable for an area, which successively concentrates on an apparently more dominant or discernible environmental factor among a number of multicollinear variables related with the suitability of some uses, and eliminates other factors and corresponding unsuitable options.* One may classify broad climatic groups which occupy certain localities or elevation zones in the region and which are individually compatible with certain kinds of uses. Each of them may include sub-zones classifiable by edaphic or vegetational features and vice versa. By further subdivision of a region according to locally limiting factors correlated with other sub-dominant factors of the environment, its suitability may be assessed for the entire area on a microlocality basis, so that total areas possible for different uses and their location become known.

Use-possibility is not to be assessed purely on the inherent features of a resource base. That would be a faithful reproduction of the natural potential. Different techniques of using a resource should be considered for each successive broad limiting group so that the lower level environmental factors do not act as constraints unless they appear so in conjunction with feasible technological options. The adoption of all available technologies especially those of advanced countries, such as of the use of heavy combine harvesters, may not be possible or useful in a developing area. This problem involves the study of current techniques in different localities of a region, in neighbouring regions and similar areas abroad, of relevant experimental evidence for possible improvements and crop and livestock responses, of the scope for providing new input mixes and materials including increased credit and ancillary requirements, and of the demand and consumer tastes vis-a-vis changes in quality and proportion of different products. The choice would be limited to technologies suitable for the stage of development, standards of present skills and capacity to acquire new ones, and the climatic and topographic condi-

---

* Multicollinearity in a renewable resource ecosystem exists because explanatory variables are highly correlated; i.e. omitted variables may affect but cannot be isolated.

tions. Nevertheless, the scope in renewable resource use remains immense through a diverse and wide choice of input substitution and kind and quality of commodity production.* This is more so in backward areas like Kashmir, where prevalent technology is primitive and adoption even of feasible intermediate technology could be a leap forward.

Considered together with techniques of renewable resource uses, there will usually be many mutually exclusive options or possibilities of using an acre of land or any other resource. This leads on to the second step of ranking the options according to their social costs and benefits. Such analysis is the relevant appraisal technique when the purpose of planning is to meet society's objectives. This is germane to renewable resource utilization because the problem of planning concerns the entire society, these resources being dispersed spatially and economically with many externalities manifest in their use. This argument no doubt rests on the assumption that society is willing to plan the use of these resources in the interests of development and has an adequate institutional infrastructure for planning and follow-up action. Nevertheless, the planning process itself should unfold the problem of follow-up in a particular region and the need for strengthening the existing or establishing new implementing agencies.

The evaluation criterion should be devised to rank the comparative efficiency of options in using the bundle of renewable resources and complementary factors of production such as labour and capital. Efficiency in resource utilisation is an appropriate criterion because in resource-poor†

---

* The choice of techniques exists not only in factor combinations for producing a unit output as usually understood, e.g. the choice between labour-intensive and capital-intensive or between extensive and intensive renewable resource use. It extends to the method of producing a commodity, e.g. artificial or natural regeneration of a forest, snow skidding or water floating, road or skyline crane haulage, fertilizing or manuring, irrigating or moisture-conserving, sequential crop rotations or inter-cropping, compact tree blocks or linear strips along farm boundaries. Both the alternative factor proportions and the methods of mixing them need to be explored.

† Resource poverty refers to the deficiency of economic resources at the command of society for meeting its developmental ends. Resources imply that a demand exists for them and that factors of production exist to exploit them. The mere abundance of a renewable resource, such as forests in Kashmir, does not contribute to resource availability unless it is economically accessible, which, among other things, involves the removal of physical inaccessibility. Similarly, a "resource" is not an economic resource if it is not in demand or is not scarce, such as water in cycle in Kashmir. The development of a renewable resource for economic use is then possible either by creating demand through the development of other sectors of the economy or by combining it with other resources such as capital, through which it becomes utilisable. In either case, investment is required. Resources for this are more deficient in developing economies giving rise to their overall resource poverty and stagnation, though other reasons may also contribute. Therefore we deduce that economy of investment resources through deployment on an efficiency basis should rank supreme in judging the merits of options. It should thus not be surprising to have a result from our analysis where no use of a renewable resource may be a better use than using it for producing something. It is an erroneous argument of most renewable resource producers (and planners in Kashmir) that it is better to make use of their resources than say leaving land fallow or a forest unexploited. But, no use may be economical than some use when the latter, even though profitable in absolute magnitude, may involve diversion of society's limited resources from a more productive opportunity within or outside the renewable resource sector.

countries the criterion should be one by which the admissibility of options remains unaffected by their magnitude. This would ensure that the limited resources are allocated to more productive options to help mitigate the overall resource scarcity. This would avoid the waste of resources likely through projects aimed to maximise the absolute sum of net benefits and which is the criterion usually favoured in developed countries. Absolute maximisation may not be irrelevant in economies where resource shortage is not acute or where opportunities for alternative investment are insufficient and the choice is between one or the other large (and often prestige) project. In addition to the fact that the floor and ceiling for scale in renewable land resource use-possibilities are wider apart than in industrial and power projects, these assumptions do not hold in poor countries where investment opportunities are many compared with total resources especially capital, as in Kashmir.

For a realistic appraisal of efficiency, prevailing prices cannot be relied upon because of greater price distortions in developing countries, particularly in the renewable resource sector where the prices hardly correspond to real factor costs or product benefits. Renewable resource activities, including forestry monopolised by the state in Kashmir, are little exposed to inter-regional and international comparisons of production efficiency. This is in contrast to some industrial projects, for they may be explicitly export or import-substitution oriented or simply because similar projects exist abroad and comparison is easy. Thus the comparative disadvantage or desirability of renewable resource activities is masked. This is more so for peasant agriculture and livestock activities, because many inputs and products may not be priced at all.

To permit the economy to derive the benefits of international trade and resource flows, the various commodities need to be compared with foreign products and substitutes. Thereby investment can be channelled in activities which are more efficient on the basis of a region's factor proportions and location in comparison to its trading partners. Factors of production like labour in a socio-economic evaluation need to be priced in a manner that reflects their social opportunity cost to the economy, so that resources are transferred only when they are less productive in the foregone alternative. Besides the social* pricing of factors and products commensurate with the degrees of unemployment and scarcity, the main problems in the efficiency appraisal of options lie in the proper measurement of their economic consequences, including non-marketable and spill-over effects, and of the discounting of costs and benefits over time to weight them by society's† time preference rate.

---

* Social refers to a measurement from the economy's point of view so that divergencies between private and social costs and benefits, because of externalities and imperfections including trade barriers and artificial exchange rates, are also taken into account.

† Society's as against private time preference would be consistent with the growth rate target set by society and, therefore, with the savings rate necessary for reaching this chief economic objective. This reflects society's normative judgement about foregoing present consumption for increased future consumption through investment and is the social rate of transformation at different points in time. Alternatively, it is the

Preparation of plan

The choice among options cannot be made directly from their ranking because of mutual exclusiveness and interdependence among them. The choice is complicated by restrictions associated with resource availabilities and renewable resource products' demand, product flow patterns and input requirements of different activities, by institutional constraints of budget, organisation, ownership, incomes and seasonal labour fluctuations, by employment, distribution and other subsidiary objectives, and by lower and upper bounds acting upon different renewable resource uses. The bounds may operate endogenously such as the minimum requirements for watershed protection or the maximum area possible for a particular renewable resource use on the basis of bio-technical suitability. Or they may be set exogenously through the economy's structure, because of, say, limitations of transport such that not only the effective demand for but also the production of certain goods and services is constrained to a maximum. Alternatively, legislation or the demand for an immobile commodity, such as outdoor recreation, amenity or national defence, may warrant at least a minimum magnitude of certain activities. Priorities among options then cannot be struck in a straightforward manner according to the descending order of their efficiency; the problem is no longer the maximisation of efficiency but of optimization of resource allocation so that those most desirable options are selected which are compatible with each other and do not violate the aforestated constraints and bounds.

In industrial project planning, a feasibility study plays the role of initial selection of the most suitable option or the overall design, so that preparation of the plan or the project report can proceed directly after that. But, because of the nature of our problem and the difficulty of choice pointed out above, the use of an appropriate operations research technique* is called for at this stage of renewable resource planning. This is because an optimal plan can be framed only after simultaneously taking account of all the interrelationships. The latter represent the objective function of efficiency, the constraints and bounds acting differently on the various component activities, and the mutual exclusiveness, the effect of which cannot be specified in advance. These relationships may be expressed as an algorithm, i.e. they are described as a

---

premium placed on enjoyment by society now rather than later. This would influence the choice of techniques, e.g., capital intensive long maturing projects vs. quick yielding less durable options.

* The technique should be a prescriptive aid for objectively studying the renewable resource system. The system would be cast as a model with explicitly defined relationships between the parameters which society is willing and capable of adjusting and the measures of merit or the objective function. The model would be aimed at determining optimal values of the decision parameters, keeping in view the input and output relationships of alternative renewable resource uses, total resource availability and demand for different products. Such an aid can thus help solve the problem of finding optimal combinations and quantities of different commodities to be produced and the production process by which the activities can and should be pursued.

succession of interconnected equations and/or inequalities juxtaposed in relation to each other.

For reaching a solution, quantification of the parameters in the algorithm is an essential prerequisite. This may be done ordinally or cardinally, depending upon the objective of the analysis. In renewable resource planning in developing countries absolute figures cannot be very reliable. Nor are they crucial, because the choice is not about independent magnitude of a particular component or project but of the comparative effectiveness in the use of society's scarce resources. Therefore, a method which can evaluate ordinally the efficiency of options is appropriate enough.

The technique should be capable of linking dependent activities such as farming and farm forestry and of transfering substitute activities such as production of commodities from a resource base or their importation from outside. It should be amenable to parametric manipulation or experimentation, to incorporate the effect of ranging resource and other constraints and to reveal the opportunity costs associated with each, so that changes that can contribute to objective maximisation are pinpointed. The analysis should commensurately reflect the flow of economic consequences of different uses during their initiation and operation and the comparative magnitudes of their influence over time during the planning period on financial, institutional and social features. It should also allow for generating a number of optimal plans† to cater for different assumptions and purposes. This would be on the lines of sensitivity analysis involving initially different as well as changing time preference rates, varying demand and price estimates, riskiness of alternatives and multiplicity of objectives. This would help ensure a choice which is more suitable from the public view-point and a better complement to the overall development plan, because high level decision-making can then be more flexibly and effectively co-ordinated with information available through macro-level planning.

For all this, the use of a computer is inescapable; otherwise it is practically inconceivable to attain an optimum solution for a set of simultaneous equations comprising a large matrix, many activities in which have feed-back effects on the rest and vice versa. Computer models are useful because once constructed, the data can be re-run for changes over time and for redesigning and subsequent analyses of the system.

We aim to integrate renewable resource planning with regional and

---

† The prefix *an* to *optimal plan* in one paragraph earlier and elsewhere signifies that we do not claim to attain *the* best of all possible economic decisions, unless by coincidence. The true optimum is difficult to achieve in the renewable resource sector where institutional and other non-economic constraints heavily militate against reaching it. Here, we suggest that it is possible to have more than one "optimal" plan in the sense of sub-optimizing, depending upon the optimality premises made in building the model and in attaching value to its various parameters. This is useful because the data about renewable resources in particular are not accurate in developing countries, especially those involving technological forecasting, and because the ultimate decisions are subject to the vagaries of policy makers. Nevertheless, given an explicit statement of the assumptions behind an optimal plan, it will be closer to the optimum if arrived at through the analysis than without it. This will also help to remove subjectivity in resource allocation and rationalise the decision-making process.

national development planning through analyses based on society's objectives, social time preference and social costs and benefits and by imposing socio-economic and institutional constraints in the process of selecting an optimal plan. But, there is an inherent distinction between the two planning processes. This arises because some renewable resources such as of forestry and horti-culture are subject to long production cycles. For a realistic appraisal of their efficiency, our planning horizon has to be longer than the short periods adopted in economic planning, such as five years in Kashmir. No doubt, this requires that the consequences corresponding to the economic planning period should be spelt out separately and in detail to match resource con-straints and rest of the economy's requirements as closely as possible; this should find expression in the optimisation model itself. But, for a commen-surate evaluation of options, efficiency ranking should be done on the assump-tion that all the renewable resource use adjustments are carried out simul-taneously in the first year. Thus the effective economic length of each option would extend over the entire resource planning period, irrespective of the number of crop rotations involved.

Therefore, though we should allow for the periodicity and timing of consequences, so that the optimisation process includes a multi-period anal-ysis of labour, capital, budget, incomes, product output levels and demand, this process does not explicitly deal with inter-temporal interdependence of options and phasing of priorities. This is the problem of investment schedul-ing. It necessitates an analysis to evaluate the effect of varying the dates of initiating different projects or options so that the overall efficiency is maxi-mised by postponing certain options in favour of diverting resources for start-ing others earlier. Such dynamic investment planning may be done either during or after the optimisation process. Its aim is to improve upon an "opti-mum" plan by pinpointing the most efficient scales in relation to timing of mutually consistent options without violating any restrictions.

The analysis to study the effect of different installation dates involves successively shorter periods of economic life of options within the planning period. Since the likely benefits in the subsequent planning period of options of which their economic lives actually extend to that period is irrelevant for the present period, one has to attribute the salvage value of the assets and disposal costs at the cut-off limit. This conforms to the principle that at the beginning of a planning period, sunk costs are not to be counted in the esti-mation of the consequences of an option. Besides the problem of valuation of assets at different points in time of their economic lives, scheduling involves the identification and evaluation of activities that would be pursued during the intervening periods.

Implications of planning

The problem that remains to be studied after producing an optimal plan, which considers both the interdependence of the options and their dynamic aspects, is of the impact of the plan and the complementary measures neces-sary for its implementation. The impact analysis should reveal the difference that would ensue in the course of the economy through the proposed renewable resource use adjustments. It would help the co-ordination of overall planning and in guiding the development of the rest of the economy in relation to the potential of resources employed for, and generated through, utilising the renewable resources. This analysis is useful for the success of the plan itself by virtue of properly directing the orientation of concomitant activities such as the development of necessary infrastructure and renewable resource product processing facilities. Importantly, it will facilitate higher level decision-making when confronted with more than one feasible plan, the desirability of which has been advocated earlier, because the one which produces the most congenial impact on other sectors and the objectives of society would become easily discernible. The chief requisite of this analysis then is to relate the consequences of optimal plans with the requirements of the rest of the economy. Though designed for some other purpose, the input-output analytical technique may be suitably used for studying this aspect of the problem.

The inter-industry analysis would not bring out the nature of the effects of social and institutional obstacles on renewable resource use adjustments. The planning process cannot be rounded off without an analysis of these impediments and accordingly for proposing suitable measures for counteracting them. While placing reliance on the involvement and agreement of the people through co-operation, extension and demonstration, because the plan cannot succeed without public consent, these measures may include legal, monetary, fiscal and organisational reforms for the implementation of the plan.

Since the causes of some of these impediments traceable to the socio-psychological, cultural and religious background of the people may be deeply rooted, these may be difficult to remove merely through a planned* development of renewable resources. Some of the impediments may be mutually causative so that they have to be considered in the total developmental context, of which economic development is one aspect among the factors constituting the human ecological framework. Therefore, the study of these factors in a detailed manner for their implications on the optimal plan is necessary not only towards the end of the problem analysis, but should also precede the use-possibility assessment for a proper feasibility study. This avoids wasteful effort in considering options which society is not conditioned to accept. One such example is the option of beef production in an economy where Hindus are the main consumers and producers as in India, where society is resistant to changes in religious mores.

THE OVERALL PROBLEM

In a nutshell, we have attributed three main dimensions to the problem of planning the use of renewable resources. These involve the sciences of sociology, renewable resource ecology and economics. Accordingly, the problem can be broken down into three successive analyses to find out (a) what is

---

* Unless planning can be centralized and its implementation enforced from above. Our schema does not consider such a situation.

adoptable or not, i.e. socio-cultural, (b) what is possible or not, i.e. bio-chemical, and (c) what is gainful or not, i.e. economic.

Though the problem analysis may be done along the above lines the stages cannot be rigidly followed because of their interplay on each other and because the total problem is a blended sum of the three dimensions, involving both the inter-temporal and the inter-resource relationships among and between themselves. The problem of renewable resource planning can, therefore, be properly classed as a systems analysis* in which changes at one end of the system are properly reflected further on in the chain of relation-ships, as well as their feedback effects. Systems designing should evaluate the effects of all relevant changes in the total framework through the stages of analysis, of different resource use coefficients and influences on constraints, bounds and maximand(s), and at different points of time.

This may be done in two main ways. One is to simulate the basic model of the system and then to carry out successive changes in the model till a design which is an improvement over the present use pattern is achieved. Simulation technique, however, may not lead to the optimal design either because it may fail to incorporate changes which would be even better and/or because all combinations of component changes may not be explored. The chosen design, though an improvement over the present one, may represent a hump in the successive simulations before reaching the peak, which may be separated by one or more depressions. Thus, one would neither know when to stop the analytic process nor be sure of having struck the best design even if one has. An alternative, which involves more labour and complexity but does not suffer from these disadvantages, would be first to evaluate all feasible changes for each resource use and then to try *all* permutations and combinations† of the options. There would be no distinction between the components of the basic model and their options such that combinations among and between the present and possible uses are explored jointly as well. Such an iteration technique would go through all the humps and depressions and it would be possible to locate a design in which the overall deficiency in using the bundle of resources is at the peak.

Our planning problem pertains to the mode of moving from the present use of renewable resources and not to producing an idealised future. Abstract objectivity is, therefore, neither the aim nor could that be useful. We should not restrict ourselves to the conventional line that "good scientists should ask only 'How?' never 'What for?' " (Schultz, 1967). Without asking both the questions, renewable resource planning may not cater to the aims of develop-ment. Systems designing should handle both the questions by marshalling facts on either account. "Planning results in blueprints for future development; it recommends courses of action for the achievement of desired goals" (Bollens and Schmandt, 1965). The systems analysis cannot find what is "best" unless

* In general, systems-analysis is the process of reviewing a complex organisation taking into account the interactions of parts of the organisation and their effect on the whole.

† Permutation means arrangement and combination means selection (Liu, 1968). The idea is to select options in such an order and magnitude that the objective is maxi-mized without violating the constraints.

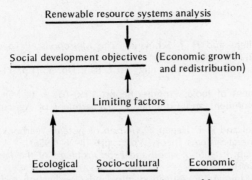

Figure 1.   Diagram showing the framework of renewable resource planning

the purpose of the analysis is known. The study of society's objectives vis-a-vis renewable resources is indispensable. In poor countries, this will generally be simpler, because the problems of environmental quality are less pressing especially in rural areas. A quantitative approach is important because the major concern is economic development and alleviation of material poverty. The problem there is the more mundane one of maximising an objective function which suitably expresses the socio-economic efficiency of alternative systems designs. Nevertheless, this expression needs to be weighted for other objectives or they have to be introduced as constraints in efficiency maximisation, because besides economic growth, developing societies often set redistributional and other goals.

To conclude, the planning process should be able to combine purpose, facts and considered estimates of an area's renewable resource potential. A rational plan will be the product of integrated analyses of the limiting roles of socio-cultural, ecological and economic factors in a total environmental context, in which national and regional developmental aims and relationships with other sectors are taken into account. The approach to such a systems analysis is schematically represented in the above diagram (Fig. 1) and the various steps of the analysis are tabulated (Table 1).

Table 1. Showing the chronological steps in the systems analysis

---

0 Object of analysis (policy and development strategy)
1 Delineation of problem (total problem analysis — regions and
      renewable resources)
2 Present use survey (basic model analysis — mapping, review
      of techno-economic data and obstacles to resource adjustments)
3 Use possibility assessment (biotechnical analysis)
4 Options appraisal (benefit-cost analysis)
5 Optimization (operations analysis)
6 Investment scheduling (dynamic analysis)
7 Inter-industry relationships (impact analysis)
8 Implementation of the plan (administrative and institutional
      infrastructure analysis)

References

1. J. C. Bollens and H. J. Schmandt, *The Metropolis: its people, politics and economic life*, p. 278. Harper, New York (1965).

2. M. Gane, Priorities in planning, C.F.I. Pap. No. 43, pp. 11–12. University of Oxford (1969).

3. Government of India, Progress Report 1960–65, p. 6. Min. of Food, Agric., Community Development and Cooperation (Department of Agriculture) New Delhi (1968).

4. A. D. Hall and R. E. Hagen, *Definition of system*. Yearbook, Soc. for the Advancement of General Systems Theory, Vol. I, pp. 18–28 (1956).

5. G. H. Khan, *Irrigation, Flood and Food Problems of the Jammu and Kashmir State*, pp. 6–11 (1961).

6. K. F. S. King, An investigation into land classification techniques and land use planning methods with particular reference to tropics and British Guyana. Unpub. D.Phil. Thesis, Oxford Univ. pp. 10–11, (1963).

7. R. R. Krueger *et al.* (Eds.) *Regional and resource planning in Canada*, p. 2. Holt, Rinehart and Winston, Toronto (1963).

8. C. L. Liu, *Introduction to combinatorial Mathematics*, p. 2. McGraw-Hill, N.Y. (1968).

9. A. M. Schultz, The ecosystem as a conceptual tool in the management of natural resources, in S. V. Ciriacy-Wantrup and J. J. Parsons (Eds.) *Natural Resources: Quality and Quantity*, pp. 139–161. Univ. of California Press, Berkeley and Los Angeles (1967).

Chapter 8

Implementation: from science to application

We have pursued a long path from statement of the problem to methods of solution. While we did not aim at comprehensive treatment, the major issues have been introduced, and at least one approach to grasping a multi-faceted problem has been offered. However, lest the student of science and politics bring his mind to rest prematurely, we introduce a new set of issues which illustrate that comprehension of the problem is not sufficient.

Environmental management, thus far, has included mostly the regulation of natural forces by men. In this chapter, the regulation of men by men for the purpose of controlling the environment receives some attention. It is neither the last nor the least problem which must occupy the attention of both scientist and politician.

Perhaps the best way to recognize the human interaction factors is to read, even better to "hear," the innuendo and issues exposed in printed congressional hearings. Listening to the dialogue between scientists and politicians will heighten our awareness of what must be done to move from the knowledge science gives us to the application of knowledge to management.

The hearing reprinted here illustrates some difficulties government scientists have in communicating with legislators, as well as the rather fundamental issues involved not only in communications but also in basic approaches. The Congressman who challenges the technologist does so because the legislator takes a wider view of the problem. So, when the realism of technocratic frameworks suggests dealing with the problem of pollution as a pollution problem, the Congressman suggests a positive and comprehensive approach, in this case a well designed water use policy. The government scientist must retreat to the limits of the legislation and authority granted which may stand in the way of a broader approach to the overall water use problem.

After standards are set, by whatever means, the issues of who benefits and who pays are inescapable. As Richard A. Tybout demonstrates in "Economic Impact of Changes in the Water Resources of the Great Lakes," measuring benefits is a challenging task, and determining who pays is a philosophical as well as a political and economic problem.

One solution to this problem is reported by Richard D. Wilson and David W. Minnotte. There has been a great deal of discussion about asking industry to pay for abatement. Economic theorists argue that external costs — that is, environmental costs outside the individual firm — should be internalized, or brought into the firm. However, existing programs of government assistance do not have this effect, or as the calculations indicate, only partially have this effect.

Under the cost-sharing program there are still difficulties, as is suggested by Wade Green in "What Happened to the Attempts To Clean Up the Majestic, the Polluted Hudson?" Even if money is available and standards are set which recognize the realities of inertia, the task is an arduous one.

Problems are not insurmountable. Sol Seid reports progress in "Regionalization — Key to Municipal and Industrial Waste Treatment." Creative attacks result in workable solutions.

Last, Richard A. Carpenter puts the problem in a framework of industry and government cooperation necessary to make abatement work. The overall task is large, and the structure to deal with it is in place. There have been important reorganizations and new legislation since this article was written. But the problem will be solved in the working out of tasks outlined in his article.

LEON W. WEINBERGER
Testimony on Environmental Quality

A number of difficult issues are raised in this testimony. Communications between congressmen and scientists and the problems resulting from different approaches are documented here. The issue of positive planning versus cleaning up is faced. Timing of enforcement comes into the discussion. The difficult choice between accepting a good but not perfect treatment system versus waiting for a better one also comes under discussion. In this single piece of testimony, many of the environmental manager's problems are expressed.

The subcommittee met, pursuant to adjournment, at 10:09 a.m., in room 2325, Rayburn House Office Building, Washington, D.C., Hon. Emilio Q. Daddario (chairman of the subcommittee) presiding.

Mr. Daddario. This meeting will come to order. I would like all of our wit-

Reprinted from *Environmental Quality: Hearings* before the Subcommittee on Science, Research, and Development of the Committee on Science and Astronautics, U. S. House of Representatives, on HR 7796, HR 13211, HR 14605, HR 14627, Ninetieth Congress, Second Session (Washington, D. C.: Government Printing Office, 1968), pp. 147–184.

nesses at this time to come forward, if you would: Dr. Weinberger, Dr. Pecora, who will be accompanied by Mr. Frank Clarke, and Mr. Everts. If you want to break in from time to time, gentlemen, you may do so.

Our hearings on environmental quality resume today with a discussion of water pollution. The concern of this subcommittee is that scientific and engineering resources be employed in a timely manner to assure a firm basis for administrative actions.

Water quality laws have preceded air pollution abatement by several years. States have now proposed standards for approval by the Federal Government. The adoption of these standards and the subsequent enforcement of abatement action will depend on the same sort of criteria which we have been studying in air pollution. The experience with the sequence of descriptive criteria leading to prescriptive standards under the water laws may be a valuable guide to research strategy for cleaner air.

The testimony we have received so far strengthens my feeling that improved waste management has been delayed because of wrangling arguments over the effects of contaminants in the environment and an inability to compare costs of abatement with benefits to air or water quality.

In water, as in air, the average citizen, industry, or local government has no trouble in reaching a decision to eliminate gross and obvious contamination. Floating matter, suspended particles, oil slicks, and foul smells in surface waters are being dealt with as quickly as facilities can be installed in most areas. Although further engineering development may increase capacity and efficiency in sewage and industrial waste treatment plants, abatement is not awaiting research results.

However, there is less certainly in dealing with subtle effects such as persistent chemicals in industrial effluents or the warm waters from a powerplant condenser. Particular problems, including mine drainage and eutrophication of lakes and estuaries add to the complexity of the overall water quality program.

With air, the primary criterion is that for breathing by human beings. Water for drinking purposes can be obtained from the most polluted source, although distillation may be necessary. But water has so many valuable uses that a spectrum of criteria has developed. A given stream may be consciously dedicated to a combination of compatible uses — but only if cause and effect relationships are known.

The Federal laws for water pollution began with the objective of simply keeping out debris which would obstruct boating and shipping. Today, the uses for which surface waters are preserved range from sport fishing and water contact sports to industrial processing, agricultural irrigation, and pumped storage for electricity generation. Criteria differ for each use. I expect these hearings to show our capability in achieving an optimum use of our water supplies.

Our first witness today is Dr. Leon W. Weinberger, Assistant Commissioner for Research and Development, Federal Water Pollution Control Administration, Department of the Interior. Dr. Weinberger was very helpful to us in our hearings in 1966.

He has been of help to us informally over the course of years, and always generous in donating his time and advice to our committee. We thank you and welcome you here again today.

Dr. Weinberger. Thank you, sir. Mr. Chairman and members of the committee, I am pleased to appear before you to discuss research, development, and demonstration, R.D. & D., in water pollution control.

I will submit the formal statement for the record, if I may, Mr. Chairman, and abstract this full statement, and respond then to any questions.

Mr. Daddario. Proceed, if you will, please.

Dr. Weinberger. In my introductory statement I made reference to the second D of R.D. & D., because demonstration, as far as we are concerned, is one of the most important facets of our program in the prevention and control of water pollution.

In my statement I cover the following items: Role of R.D. & D. in water pollution control; cost and benefits of water pollution control; research and development programed planning; research priorities; industrial participation in research and development; allocation of research resources; some major water pollution problems; the scientific and technical bases for water quality standards; advanced waste treatment and progress; industrial pollution control progress; eutrophication and water quality criteria and use of water.

An effective water pollution control program consists of a number of elements; namely, scientific and technical answers and solutions, economic resources to construct and operate pollution control facilities, a strong enforcement and program implementation effort, adequate planning and administration, and competent manpower. Research and development is needed to provide new and improved analytical tools, scientific knowledge, and engineering controls. I, of course, do not intend to minimize the importance or role of research and development; however, we should recognize that many of the water pollution problems facing our Nation today can be alleviated by the application of existing technology. In fact, in the immediate future, the most significant progress will be made in this way. Through research and development, we will find solutions where none now exist, we will better define the effects of impurities on water uses, we will improve the effectiveness of available solutions, and we will reduce the costs of waste treatment systems. Gentlemen, I have complete confidence that we will find solutions — acceptable solutions, in my opinion — to all our pollution problems.

The solutions will be satisfactory from a scientific and technical point of view, but they will cost money. Although you may believe that it is obvious that pollution control will cost money, there are apparently many polluters who are unwilling to recognize any solution as acceptable unless it is a zero-cost solution. We shall seek these zero-cost solutions — indeed, in some instances, through wastes recovery or byproduct development, a profit may be realized — but we must be willing to pay for pollution control. What is meant by an economically acceptable solution is certainly to be the subject of considerable debate. Conventional cost-benefit analyses are not totally applicable because we are not able to define in a quantitative manner all the benefits of water pollution control nor assess the total damages resulting from water pollution. Research into the socioeconomic aspects of water pollution control may provide us with some of these analytical tools — tools which will enable us to evaluate the "intangible" benefits.

Our knowledge of the costs and benefits associated with water pollution control is rapidly improving.

The Federal Water Pollution Control Administration has just completed a study entitled "The Cost of Clean Water." This is in response to section 16(a) of the Federal Water Pollution Control Act, as amended, which directs the Secretary of the Interior to conduct a comprehensive analysis of the national requirements for and the cost of treating municipal, industrial, and effluent to attain water quality standards established under the act. The first analyses have just recently been completed as they were due for submission to the Congress in January, this month. These studies are extremely important because, although there is widespread agreement that water pollution is a significant, growing problem which must be dealt with, there are no firm estimates as to what the national requirements are, or what it will cost the Federal Government and other affected units of Government to achieve a satisfactory abatement level. Various cost estimate studies of municipal and industrial needs have been conducted in the past but they have not been sufficiently comparable in geographical coverage, time phases covered, cost criteria, types of facilities included, or in cost estimate technique to provide a fully meaningful guide to the national requirements and costs involved.

The cost of clean water study represents the initiation of what will be a continuing evaluation, aimed at developing more accurately the national costs of pollution control. Although it has not been possible to arrive at a completely definitive estimate of required costs, it is believed that the present study provides a more comprehensive cost estimate than has previously been developed and a sound base of information upon which to build future analyses. This estimate is expected to improve in accuracy with each yearly updating.

Mr. Chairman, the first volume of this report has been printed and copies can be made available to the committee and, as subsequent volumes become available, they will, of course, be provided to members of this committee and all Members of Congress.

Mr. Daddario. Do you have sufficient copies so that they could be distributed here?

Dr. Weinberger. Sir, I do not have sufficient number of copies for this, but I will see that we get them to you as quickly as we can.

Mr. Daddario. Fine. As I understand it, Dr. Weinberger, the estimate for waste treatment, sanitary sewers and water cooling requirements, for fiscal years 1969 to 1973 is somewhere between $26 and $29 billion.

Dr. Weinberger. Yes, sir. I would like to start dwelling on the research and development program and planning.

I have taken figures 1, 2, and 3 out of the report, made it available to each member of the committee as a separate item.

Figure 1 illustrates the program structure and elements of the research and development program of the Federal Water Pollution Control Administration. It represents the framework within which we can plan our program, establish goals and determine needed resources to achieve goals, allocate available resources, and evaluate the effectiveness of ongoing research. Subprograms 11, 12, 13, 14, and 15 contain the elements dealing with specific sources of wastes. One note, it includes such matters as mine drainage, oil production, animal feed lots, irrigation return flow, various industrial wastes, various sources of municipal wastes. Subprogram 16 is a general category containing the elements of pollution identification, fate and persistence of pollutants in the environment, water quality control, eutrophication, water resources planning and resource data, cold climate research, and basic research; subprogram 17 contains the elements dealing with waste treatment; and subprogram 18 is the research on water quality requirements or effects of water pollutants on all water uses.

One of the purposes of introducing figure 1 is to indicate the scope of our research and development effort, ranging all the way from identification of pollution to various means for solving problems caused by pollution. The element 1608 — water quality control encompasses pollution control techniques such as recovery and reuse, product modification, process change, elimination, dispersion, dilution, detention, diversion, and even environmental treatment, that is, treatment of wastes in streams. This structure for categorizing our research and development was established last year and we believe will facilitate interagency coordination and cooperation. The categories are compatible with those established by the Committee on Water Resources Research of the Federal Council for Science and Technology.

The research program of the Federal Water Pollution Control Administration is directed primarily to the solution of water pollution problems.

In planning research, a major tack is to establish priorities of research within available resources and the directives provided by legislation. In our program, priorities are based on the needs, recommendations, and ongoing research of the following:

1. FWPCA regional directors and their staffs. They are knowledgeable of the problems as they exist or may develop in their respective regions (river basin);
2. FWPCA program directors at headquarters;
3. Other Federal agencies;
4. State and local agencies;
5. University professors and researchers;
6. Consultants and advisory groups;
7. Committee on Water Resources Research; and
8. Industrial groups.

The setting of research priorities and the allocation of research resources is still, to a considerable extent, based on a subjective analysis. The analysis, however, has considerable merit when carried out by competent, knowledgeable people who have available to them the information obtained from answers to the following series of questions.

I will not read the questions. Let me suggest that the type of question we are talking about which helps us establish our priorities is as follows:

What are the problems in water pollution or water quality control? Having identified the problems, what answers and solutions do we need? When do we need these answers? What answers and solutions are already available? Who has or should have the responsibility for seeking answers? What are the chances and incentives for obtaining better answers? When will the research, development, and demonstration be completed? On the basis of answers to these questions, gentlemen, it is possible to establish priorities which can be assigned to the various elements which I have indicated on figure 1.

The implementation of approved program plans consists of a number of aspects and I have listed these in my report.

The allocation of resources: The research and development program of the FWPCA is conducted through both in-house and extramural support. The in-house effort is conducted at our major laboratories and field sites.

It is obvious that to have a successful research and development program, in addition to the competence available in the Federal Government, the best scientific and engineering talent in the Nation, including that available in the university and private research institutions, industries, and in State and municipal organizations, must be included in the national effort to control water pollution.

Mr. Daddario. Dr. Weinberger, when you talk about the best scientific and technical manpower available, how about the manpower presently existing which has the responsibility to maintain the waste treatment plants now in existence? I have a letter from a Mr. Charles Pitkat, of Connecticut, who works at the Vernon waste treatment plant. He and a group of people who work at these plants get together on occasion and try to help each other out from the standpoint of skills and abilities to do a better job. He says, and I quote:

One place that you can improve treatment is in the operator field. We need much more training than is now available. With all the talk going on about making police professionals or technicians, why cannot an operator have this same interest? Because of the background of operators, such as basic education, age, available time and the like, it is extremely hard to have us qualify to become a professional engineer. Yet, there is nothing available that would enable us to go to, say, three or four years of night school and end up as an accepted technician in this field. Professional people are reluctant to talk to or deal with nonprofessional people. If you look around in the design end of treatment plants, I would say you will find not one engineer concern who has someone who operated a plant on his staff. And yet we are the people who have the actual contact and control of their design.

I bring that up because we talk about scientists and technicians, yet when we had the hearings some time ago it showed quite clearly that many of our waste treatment plants were not operating at their full capacity for no other reason but that the people who were working on them just did not have the capability to maintain them at the highest possible level. Therefore the plants were not doing as good a job as they ought to do.

There was a desire on the part of these people to be able to do more. It was suggested, as I recall it, that perhaps we create an itinerant group of technicians who could go from waste treatment plant to waste treatment plant. They would help make assessments and tell these people what could be done to improve the plants, and by so doing reduce the waste and pollution problem which presently exists.

You talk about scientists and technicians, and yet you leave out the people who turn the switch and who see these things deteriorate around them — people who want to do a better job and cannot.

Dr. Weinberger. Mr. Chairman, our agency has last month submitted a report on manpower and training. Again, I would be very happy to make copies of that report available. This report agrees with the chairman completely, that one of the big gaps in our pollution control effort is an effective treatment plant operation. As a matter of fact, in the projections of manpower needs, the greatest need was indicated in the treatment plant operator category. Within our program, we are initiating within the month a technical training program which will supplement our professional training program. The purpose of the technical training program is to help develop institutions or curriculums or courses very much along the line that the chairman has suggested as one of the ways of doing this. We have a number of proposals which we are currently reviewing to help establish perhaps 2-year courses, junior college courses, specialized technical courses, to supplement some of the limited work going on right now at various States and which we are doing in-house.

Mr. Daddario. Dr. Weinberger, is it possible to put together some competent teams and have them review the procedures that are going on in certain plants? They could develop a checklist and give the people who are there some information as to what can be done at the moment while such a program of training is going on. Is this something that we should do or not?

Dr. Weinberger. Yes, sir; we should do it. It has again been done to a somewhat limited extent. There are some of the manuals, a number of programs, night courses, courses available in some of the high schools, at some of the universities, for operators to receive some of the training. There have been some instruction manuals prepared. One of the areas of research that I dwell on relates to this from the point of view of research and development. One of the things that we are attempting to do is to come up with procedures so that a plant can be operated in a more effective way. It is much more than just the matter of trained manpower. I made the statement that if there is a gap between the research man and the practitioner or the designer, then there is a chasm between the designer and the operator.

Mr. Daddario. Which is the point this gentleman makes in his letter to me.

Dr. Weinberger. And there are at least two things: what the chairman has suggested is certainly a very critical matter. The second one which we would hope to accomplish through R. & D. is to make it possible to operate our treatment facilities with better control devices, better instrumentation.

Mr. Daddario. Are you talking about those plants we will be building or plants presently existing?

Dr. Weinberger. Presently existing, sir. There is no reason, with the advances being made in control technology and instrumental methods, why some of these plants cannot be updated so that we can operate these on the basis of their design, at least, which will result in a very significant step forward in pollution control.

Mr. Daddario. The updating, however, involves some assessment as to where it is now and what needs to be done. This is a gap that, if filled, could lift up the whole level of this particular effort and immediately cause some improvement, in fact, considerable improvement.

Dr. Weinberger. Yes, sir; unquestionably.

Mr. Daddario. Your hope is that we will be developing an ability to make such an assessment so that each community can, in an expeditious way, come to a determination as to where it stands or what can be done, and what it will cost, and how much more improvement will come about as a result.

Dr. Weinberger. Yes, sir; this is certainly one of the administration's goals, to accomplish this.

Mr. Daddario. Fine, Doctor.

Mr. Fulton?

Mr. Fulton. The question to me is: Maybe we are starting at the wrong end. Instead of being under the apple tree trying to catch the apples with our apron, why don't we go in from the constructive side, that is, the best use of water and air supplies, both for current use and for longtime purposes? Why don't we start like that instead of talking pollution? It should take in the whole field.

Dr. Weinberger. I certainly do not have any comment to make other than to agree with Mr. Fulton, that in looking at water pollution, water pollution is obviously part of a much larger water resource problem. The whole matter of effective utilization of all of our waters and water resource planning is one of the activities that is being undertaken by the executive branch through Water Resources Council, among other agencies. So that the need for an overview of our total water program is certainly in order.

Mr. Fulton. Instead of just putting our programs for 17 States on reclamation, why don't we in Congress have the programs for all States with an overall purview of the best use of the U.S. resources? You see, we limit, in the Federal program, reclamation to only 17 States. That takes in half of Texas and then goes on west but it does not affect the need of any State east of the Mississippi River.

Dr. Weinberger. I could not comment on reclamation.

Mr. Fulton. This is a trap. I am from Pennsylvania.

Dr. Weinberger. I was going to comment————

Mr. Daddario. Did you have to be advised that that was a trap?

Dr. Weinberger. No.

Mr. Fulton. I could see his light touch, he was feathering it a little bit.

Dr. Weinberger. I hope not. I was going to comment by saying that insofar as the water quality control aspects, the responsibility given to us by the Congress touches all of the States of the United States.

Mr. Fulton. My point is maybe we should have an overall view which includes these problems wherever they are rather than putting them just geographically by States or taking the end result of the problem, such as pollution.

Dr. Weinberger. I would say personally, I think the need for an objective assessment of our water resources and water utilization is certainly in order. I say this, having served on a committee of the National Academy which issued a report on alternatives in water management, which deals with the subject and dwells on the subject.

Mr. Fulton. I believe we have to watch that we keep the language so that the average person, such as we, Congressmen, can understand it. When you, Dr. Weinberger and your fellow scientists, and the chairman of the committee, Mr. Daddario, use words like eutrophication, wouldn't it be better just to call it clogging a lake through overenrichment? When I hear the word "eutrophication" I wonder whether it is building up or down, making hotter or colder. You see, I cannot tell just from the word what it means. I would imagine most of the people in the audience cannot.

Mr. Daddario. Doctor, the reason I put that word into my opening statement this morning was to see if I could get a reaction from Mr. Fulton. It was sort of a trap. The other day when that same word came up he went into the very root of it for some 5 or 10 minutes and I thought that he made a very good case. So I used it this morning.

Mr. Fulton. Having gone to Harvard, it gets to be difficult at times when they throw things out like that. I wrestled with them like a dog.

Dr. Weinberger, I was very intrigued by your extra "D" in R.D. & D. I must say I had hoped you would get better results from the Federal Water Pollution Control Administration because there you only have one "D." So could I make a suggestion to the Department that they correct that and give you the extra "D." You seem to want it.

I could point out to you that Abraham Lincoln had a story about Mary Todd, his fiance, later Mary Todd Lincoln. He said to her one time in an argument that actually while she had two "d's" in "Todd," God, for a long time, had been satisfied with one. So I hope you will be satisfied with one "D."

Mr. Daddario. We could carry that a step further, following Mr. Fulton's story: The "D" could be classified under "Divinity."

Seriously, however, a recent ruling of the Second Circuit Court of Appeals stated that the Federal Power Commission should not have licensed Consolidated Edison to build a Storm King Mountain plant without considering the total environmental impact, esthetic tranquility, et cetera. Do you know of any similar rulings? Are we now able to provide regulatory agencies with useful environmental information so that such determinations could be made? What implications, particularly in consideration of what Mr. Fulton said about taking a look at the whole thing, do you see in decisions of this kind which do include tranquility and esthetics?

Dr. Weinberger. Mr. Chairman, quite a bit of that information is available. We obviously need more. When the water quality standards program was established by the Congress we called together a group of experts to help us establish the criteria by which we could assess the various water uses.

The various water uses include not only municipal use, industrial, agricultural, propagation of fish and other aquatic life, but also water for esthetic purposes. These consultants, and I believe they were some 80 in number, reviewed the kinds of water that it would be desirable to have to protect all of these values. This has been issued in a report. I have a copy of it. I would be pleased to get copies to the members. It represents a rather thick document.

Mr. Daddario. This document which I now show you?

Dr. Weinberger. Yes, sir. It represents some of the best thinking, best available information dealing with the protection of our water for various uses. Some of the information is descriptive, some of it indicates we should be protecting the amenities, the senses of people, other recommendations are rather specific, scientific, quantitative, in such areas as toxicants, such areas as thermal radio-activity, and the like.

Mr. Fulton. Could I ask on that point?

Mr. Daddario. Have you finished?

Dr. Weinberger. Yes.

Mr. Fulton. The question comes up whether certain activities in various geographical areas are not socially destructive and should not be carried on. For example, the pollutants and the cost of cleaning up the pollutants might be more than the particular activity is either socially or economically worth.

In the case of rivers, how do we get around the fact that the Federal jurisdiction of rivers was originally limited to navigable rivers? That is, rivers used either for navigation by boats or logging, so that you had some small navigable rivers? How did the Government get jurisdiction? Would the Government have jurisdiction, for example, in the State of Pennsylvania where it is going to cost billions to clear up old mines, much more than was ever gotten out of them? Does the Government have jurisdiction, for example, in Pennsylvania and Ohio and other States to limit surface mining because it is going to cause so much trouble 1,500 miles down the Mississippi River? Should there be a limit? Can the Government move into such a field where we might just outlaw a whole industry as not being either economically or socially beneficial to the whole country?

I am on the Space Committee. When you see these new pictures of the earth from 200,000 miles out, we look like we are a sink. You can see the clouds twirling all over the earth, not just State by State. When we say we can come up with solutions, maybe that is a slightly inadequate statement.

So my point is basically, on jurisdiction, How do we approach this? Is this a new field or an extension of the old?

Dr. Weinberger. I do not think I am really competent to talk about all of the jurisdictional matters which you raise.

Mr. Fulton. You can put a statement in the record.

Dr. Weinberger. I will be happy to do that.

Mr. Fulton. Thank you. (The information requested is as follows:)

The Water Quality Act of 1965, which amended the Federal Water Pollution Control Act to provide for the establishment of water quality standards for interstate waters or portions thereof and to make the discharge of matter which reduces the quality of such waters below the water quality standards established under the Act subject to abatement, specifically provides that "nothing in this subsection (Section 10(c) of the basic Act as thus amended) shall . . . extend Federal jurisdiction over water not otherwise authorized by this Act." The basic act was amended by the Federal Water Pollution Control Act Amendments of 1961 to make the pollution of navigable waters, as well as interstate waters, which endangers the health or welfare of persons, subject to the Act's abatement authority.

The Act does not confer, nor would we expect to exercise, arbitrary power to outlaw an industry as socially or economically undesirable. Its provisions respecting the establishment and implementation of water quality standards, and the abatement of pollution, are set about with safeguards against unreasonable action.

Mr. Daddario. There is no question, however, in your mind, Dr. Weinberger, but that these problems do affect the environment of this country. We do find a relationship to ocean currents and to climatic streams which can cause problems in places throughout the world. One has an effect on the other. It is simply a challenge to our laws to adjust ourselves so that we can overcome those problems and not allow ourselves to deteriorate because we place artificial barriers in front of the accomplishment of this end objective.

Dr. Weinberger. I do not think there is any question. I did not mean not to be directly responsive to Mr. Fulton, but there is jurisdiction, of course, so far as the effect of the activities in one State as they affect another, and many of the States in terms of the existing water quality standards have to themselves make some of the decisions Mr. Fulton is raising.

Mr. Daddario. We are coming into an entirely new set of nationwide and world conditions. Because we recognize that they will cause trouble, we are beginning to adjust ourselves in order to handle them. I can see where we are going to have difficulty, but certainly it is not an impossible barrier.

Dr. Weinberger. No, sir. We, of course, on even the international phase, already have agreements as far as disposal of radioactive waste.

Mr. Fulton. Do you have the right in terms of Federal jurisdiction to ban coal mining in Pennsylvania because sulfuric waste causes pollution of the Lower Mississippi and colors the cotton grown by Mississippi?

Would you have the power to prevent the cotton from being colored, and therefore not salable, by the sulfur waste clear up in the Allegheny and Monongahela?

Dr. Weinberger. We will develop that for the record.

Mr. Fulton. Could you put a yes or no on that and we will go on?

Mr. Daddario. I would like to simply say again in this particular area, I do not know that it calls for a yes or no answer or that any Government agency has the power to do this. Rather, we as a society somehow must come up with a determination so that these derogatory or disastrous effects do not occur. Within the framework of our present free enterprise system we will make determinations which will overcome these problems because we must. It does not mean that the Federal Government will have the power. There is a whole wide stream of ramifications within which we can work.

Mr. Fulton. We may need a constitutional amendment to give the power to either the Federal Government, the States, or the local municipalities to proceed on this broad basis as a national policy for our U.S. resources.

Mr. Daddario. Dr. Weinberger, does not the general welfare clause, presently one of the foundations of our Constitution, give us a great deal of leeway in this particular area?

Dr. Weinberger. The Federal Water Pollution Control Administration at the present time does have and has exercised a certain amount of power in terms of protecting the welfare and well-being of our citizens.

Mr. Fulton. My point is, where does that power end or how far does it extend in jurisdiction? I must say you are well represented by the chairman here.

Mr. Daddario. I am not trying to represent Dr. Weinberger. I am trying to represent my own ideas. This is not a matter in which the Federal Government alone is involved, and the solution of these problems does not come from the power of the Federal Government. Rather, it comes from the hopes and ambitions of our society. I think it is important that we, as a subcommittee, view these proceedings with objectivity and flexibility of mind. It is one of the basic criteria by which we must act. . . .

RICHARD A. TYBOUT

Economic Impact of Changes in the Water Resources of the Great Lakes

My title refers to the Great Lakes, but my content refers to Lake Erie, in whose basin live 13 million people, 11.5 million of them in United States, and around whose shores lie leading American cities. Man has used Lake Erie more intensively by orders of magnitude than any of the other Great Lakes. Intensive commercial use has supplanted intensive recreational use in metropolitan areas and recreational use has spread along the shores until it is difficult, at least in the Ohio area with which I am familiar, to find any agricultural land that extends to the lake shore.

The commercial fishing industry has come and gone. Recreation continues to be a major use of the lake, despite deteriorating quality and if for no other reason because so many people have convenient access to it. Municipalities use the lake for water supply and return it in despoiled condition. Industrial plants do likewise. The shipping lanes of the midwest run its length and, indeed, the location and commercial growth of Lake Erie cities can be explained in terms of water transportation.

Lake Erie has been used intensively and we shall have even more need for it as population and gross national product grow. The same is true in lesser degree of the other Great Lakes, but they have had nowhere near the intensive use nor do they have the population recreation demand, except perhaps at the southern end of Lake Michigan. In one important respect, it is fortunate that Lake Erie comes first. Its high rate of turnover (once every 2.5 years) means that wise abatement policies can have perceptible effects within a foreseeable time. If there are lessons to be learned in the saving of one of the Great Lakes, they can be learned within a reasonable time period.

Our interest in clean up is a water quality focus, but it is worth noting that quantity variations have their costs. The activities of civilized man have

Dr. Richard A. Tybout, "Economic Impact of Changes in the Water Resources of the Great Lakes," from Proceedings of the Conversation in the Disciplines, the *Economic and Social Impact of Environmental Changes in the Great Lakes Region*, Public Information Report Number 1, Lake Erie Environmental Studies, State University College, Fredonia, New York, pp. 36–55. Reprinted by permission.
Financial assistance from the U. S. Office of Water Resources Research is gratefully acknowledged.

tended to amplify quantity fluctuations by causing more rapid run off. Land clearance in rural areas and paved surfaces in urban areas produce higher highs and lower lows. Erosion and silting become problems. Dredging has its costs; so does the loss of land by bank erosion, and quality effects are themselves produced by inert suspended matter in the lake. We recognize the various damages and problems created by quantity variations, but turn our attention to the quality problem, which seems more immediately pressing.

What I have to say about Lake Erie quality deals only with economic aspects, but these have been emphasized by the Federal Water Pollution Control Administration. To quote from the forward to the FWPCA's *Lake Erie Report* (1968):

The cleanup of Lake Erie is less a problem of engineering than it is a problem of . . . government policies, funding, and management. The technical engineering methods of waste control are known or close at hand with the main requirement being only their coordinated application.

Whether or not one accepts the FWPCA view, at least there is sufficient concern about problems of application. There is a feeling that attention should be directed to remedial measures with whatever the available technologies might be. Through sheer impact of necessity, if one reads between the lines, we must get on with the job. Experience will lead to better technologies, but the need is now. So let us look at the origins of the need.

Demand for improved water quality arises from a combination of aesthetics, recreation and deeper psychological consequences of a wasted environment. Most of these are classed as noneconomic, but in fact, they have economic consequences as much as the conventional psychological satisfactions of consumption have economic consequences and for some purposes, it is quite sufficient to measure the latter. People can make up for losses in the quality of life in one place by moving to another. The difference shows up in wage differentials and property value differentials between any two places whose only difference is environmental quality. Those who remain and reap a premium wage necessary to keep them there undertake various dodges to make up for polluted air and water through expenditures on air conditioners and swimming pools and by incurring the additional cost of vacationing at a distance where, for a while, they can forget what it looks like and smells like at home. Dollar values can be put on the effects of the environment by observing the expense to which the victims of pollution will go in their efforts to mitigate its effects.

Most of the job of measuring changes in property values or compensating income differentials due to the effects of pollution consists in eliminating the effects of other phenomena. The inherent natural advantage of one industrial or residential location or the tax structure of a city or state, or any of a number of other economic variables makes it very difficult as an econometric problem to separate out the imputed value of aesthetic or deeper psychological effects of pollution alone. The job can be done in principle. Whether sufficient data are available in practice is another question. And whether the necessary ingenuity can be brought to bear on it remains further to be seen.

For example, recreational uses of Lake Erie have increased by leaps and bounds over the past half century while the lake's quality has deteriorated at an even faster rate. A naive association of these trends would imply that decreased quality leads to higher levels of recreation or vice versa. There is something to the inverse causation, but no one with any understanding at all would overlook (1) the growth of population in the Lake Erie Basin or (2) economy-wide increases in productivity that have made it possible over the long run for the average American to increase his leisure as well as his income. A still more sophisticated observer would want to take account of the capacity of public recreation areas, their accessibility to population centers and, last but not least, the effect that crowding itself has on the quality of the recreation experience, whatever the natural attributes of the site might be. Only by a multivariate analysis taking account of at least this many phenomena could one begin to determine the unique effects of pollution.

Social science can observe events only when, as and if they occur and, unfortunately, usually in the context of many other events occurring at the same time. Because of the magnitude of separating out the pollution effects, this particular job has not been done in the comprehensive way above described.

But that does not mean that we have no information. Sometimes a sudden change, by virtue of taking place over a short time period, can be assumed to have been the only important change. Other economic and social variables have not had time to change. Such was the case at the Sterling State Park near Monroe, Michigan, on August 15, 1961. On that date, the beach was posted as unsafe for swimming because of pollution. Many other beaches on Lake Erie have been posted as unsafe for the same reason, but in this case, good attendance records were available before and afterward.[1]

	Annual attendance
1959	1,239,000
1960	911,000
1961	651,000
1962	255,000
1963	302,000

And the beach has continued at the rate of about 302,000. This includes visitation for picnicing and not swimming alone.

If we compare the last full year before posting, 1960, with the first full year after posting, 1962, there is about a 75% drop in attendance. But even between 1959 and 1960, there was about a 25% drop in attendance. Daily attendance figures during the week of closing show the same dramatic change. People continued to swim at Sterling Beach, but after posting, they did it with full knowledge. The downward trend before posting may have reflected partial knowledge of pollution and some sensory perception. The precipitous drop afterward reflected full knowledge. Here is a case where it wasn't such a rapid change in the physical environment so much as a rapid change in perception of the physical environment and, of course, perception is what people act on.

The results of the Sterling Park case have been applied by the Bureau of Outdoor Recreation to other Lake Erie beaches and to beaches on Lake Erie tributaries. The Bureau's estimates are based on analogies of other beaches with Sterling Park and take account of the downward trend in swimming before official closing. Many of the beaches exhibited poor water quality and should, in the Bureau's opinion, have been closed, but were not at the time. Therefore, the results of the study are based only on perception prior to closing in many cases. Moreover, the units are in terms of swimming activity only, not total visitation. Swimming is measured in activity days. Each individual on each day that he goes to the beach and swims accounts for one activity day.

See Table 1. The Bureau of Outdoor Recreation estimates that about $6^{1}/_{2}$ million activity days of swimming were lost in 1963 due to poor water quality. Something over 7.4 million should have been lost, in the Bureau's view, if swimming had been prohibited and this prohibition enforced at grossly polluted beaches. These estimates represent a 40 to 45% increase over 1963 swimming activity levels.

Table 1. Estimated influence of water quality on swimming activity at public beaches in Lake Erie Basin, 1963

Estimated swimming activity for year	
Total	16,455,000
At beaches with poor quality	780,000
Net if swimming prohibited where there is poor quality	15,675,000
Increase with improved water quality	
Reopening of closed beaches	1,325,000
Increased participation of present patrons	2,640,000
Increased attendance participation	2,625,000
Total increase	6,590,000
Estimated swimming activity with improved water quality	23,045,000

Source: U. S. Bureau of Outdoor Recreation, *Water Oriented Outdoor Recreation, Lake Erie Basin* (Ann Arbor, 1966), p. 9–9.

Since 1963, two trends have been in effect. First, there is a strong national increase in the demand for swimming activity days. Increased population, increased leisure and an increasing taste for outdoor swimming have combined to cause a 3% annual increase in the national demand for swimming, as projected by the Outdoor Recreation Resources Review Commission.[2] Compounded over the six years since 1963, this would raise the loss of $6^{1}/_{2}$ million activity days to roughly 8 million. The second trend is, of course, increased pollution. We do not have an exact measure of the difference in this variable as it has affected swimming since 1963, but we do know that there has been no decline in the rates of pollution input into the lake. For this reason, the 8 million activity days is a conservative figure, also because I have extrapolated the Bureau's loss from perception, i.e., $6^{1}/_{2}$ million activity days, as opposed to the Bureau's 7.4 million activity days that would have been lost if people had been forced not to swim in the unsafe waters. The latter would give a loss of 9 million activity days in 1969 on the basis of the projection. Probably something more like 10 million would be accurate if we knew the increased effect of pollution since 1963. A final point to note is that these estimates were made for the entire Lake Erie Basin. I have imputed them to the lake itself and its tributaries. This imputation seems justified, however, by a study of where pollution occurs in the Basin, as given in the Bureau of Outdoor Recreation Study.[3]

Now, how much is one activity day of swimming worth? This question has been given some attention by a number of competent analysts using several approaches. If there is no admission fee, as is generally the case of public beaches, then the amount that people will pay to get there, to use bath house facilities and for equipment that is strictly required for swimming tell us something about how they value swimming itself. It is the same as buying a pair of shoes. If I pay $20 for a pair of shoes, it doesn't matter whether $20 is the price of both shoes together or whether the right one is priced at $20 and the left one is free. As long as the two shoes are strictly complementary, i.e., I wouldn't use one without the other, the total expenditure for the package tells us the demand for the entire activity. So it is with swimming. Travel to the site is certainly required and so are some expenditures there, such as bath house fees.

A second approach is simply by analogy with private recreation beaches where there are admission fees. In both cases, account must be taken of quality deterioration due to crowding. For this purpose, studies have been made of the distance people will go to avoid crowds. Not only is it the cost of operating their automobile, but there is also the lost time in transit, which itself has value. For the self-employed who can regulate their own hours and even for others who can find ways to work more than the forty hour work week by moonlighting or less by part time, time in transit is worth money that can be reckoned at their wage rate. The national average for employees in 1968 was $6 to 7 per hour, depending on how the work forces are defined and various other fine points that are digressionary for present purposes.

A survey of various studies of recreation demand along the above lines was conducted by Clawson and Knetsch in the early 1960's. They found values ranging from $2 to $6 for an activity day of various kinds, including, but not limited to swimming, and for the United States as a whole, not just the Lake Erie Basin.[4] If we use these national averages with the Bureau of Outdoor Recreation estimates of swimming activity days precluded by pollution, we can at least get order of magnitude estimates of the demand for abatement. To get a lower estimate, we combine $2 with 8 million activity days to get $16 million per year. At the upper end of the scale, we combine $6 with 10 million activity days to get $60 million a year. Both figures are in 1965 prices. They tell us how much swimmers alone would be willing to pay, though they tell it over a rather wide range.

The same sort of analysis should be made for sports fishermen, boaters, sightseers, picnicers and others, to the extent that these recreation activities are affected by water pollution. Over and above these, as previously noted, there is a quality-of-life effect for those who live along the shores of the lake. This shows up in property values and in other ways, some of which overlap with recreation demand, but for which we do not have dollar estimates. When other kinds of recreation are included, when quality of life effects are taken into account, plus any aesthetic effects not otherwise included in the two foregoing categories, there is every reason to think that the total demand for abatement will be a good deal greater than what we have found for swimming alone.

The only industry that seems directly to suffer from deteriorated water quality is commercial fishing. Others, of course, may indirectly suffer if they are forced to pay a wage premium to keep workers in an unattractive environment, or if they supply recreation goods, or perhaps in other ways, but we refer here to direct effects of water quality.

Patterns of change in this industry are well known and, in fact, better described by others. Corresponding with the decrease in water quality has been a decrease in the quality of fish caught. There may be reasons outside of water quality that account for this decline, but the present condition of the lake and spawning grounds apparently prevent a return to high quality harvests. The important facts in the history of this industry can be represented by a few figures for its Ohio component, giving the value of the catch in 1957–1959 dollars for three selected years.[5] In 1890, the harvest was worth $1,688,000. In 1943, the figure was $6,151,000. In 1964, it was $866,000.

These changes reflect a shift from high quality to low quality fish. They also reflect a decline in total pounds of fish caught.[6] As the result of both causes, large scale operations on shore are inhibited. Vertically integrated firms that once dominated the industry have been replaced by small establishments engaged in primary fishing and operating with largely part-time employees.[7] In the eight years from 1956 to 1964, wage rates dropped from 90% of the Ohio average to 65%.[8] Shipments to market centers in Chicago and elsewhere have declined to the vanishing point. Instead, Ohio cities now rely largely on imported fish.

What is the magnitude of the loss? If 1943 is our reference year, it might appear to be the difference between $6,151,000 and $866,000, or approximately $5.3 million per year. This, however, is incorrect. The loss would, in fact, be $5.3 million if the manpower and capital that went into the fishing industry in that year had no other uses. But in point of fact, they do have other uses, for the most part, and over the course of time, manpower and capital has drifted out of fishing and into other pursuits. Presumably, the manpower at least is slightly less productive elsewhere (otherwise it would not have been in fishing in the first place) and so there is an incremental productivity loss.

By the same kind of reasoning, we can find that shipments of fish to Ohio cities from Canada or the East Coast result in higher prices to local markets because of transportation and storage. Judging from other perishable agricultural products, this might increase fish costs by 10% or so.[9] The total loss is then the result of these two effects: lower wages for displaced fishermen, higher prices for imported fish. The result is nothing like the $5.3 million annually we found by assuming that the 1943 could be substituted each year for the 1964 catch.

But there is a different question that we are also interested in. That is whether the demand for Lake Erie fish would justify, or help justify a clean up of the lake. Now, I have no idea whether the 1943 catch would be repeated with a clean up. I suspect not. But suppose we knew that the harvest would be the same as in 1943. Then, we could use the incremental loss as described above to get a figure for expected benefits. Also as noted above, it would be quite small compared with the expected recreation and other benefits.

To summarize, we have estimated swimming benefits by separating out other costs of the recreation experience. The incremental approach was described also as the method applicable in finding adverse effects of pollution on property values. Finally, we have used it to conclude that the gain from commercial fishing is likely to be small when account is taken of alternative uses of resources and alternative sources of fish supply. The conclusion is that the rather substantial case that can be made for clean up comes almost entirely from aesthetic-recreational type considerations.

So much for the demand from abatement. We now ask about the economic consequences of abatement. Somebody will have to pay for it. Manufacturers and municipalities tell us they can't afford it. How shall we deal with this issue?

We have at the Ohio State University an interdisciplinary research project entitled, "A Systems Analysis of the Western Basin of Lake Erie." See Figure 1. This basin is bounded on the east by a natural geographic configuration. It is bounded on the west by two major metropolitan areas: Detroit and Toledo. It includes most of the entire lake's problems. The Western Basin has been traditionally the most productive Ohio fishing ground. Even as recently as 1962–64, 76% of the Ohio Lake catch by weight came from the Western Basin and the Sandusky Bay combined.[10] According to the FWPCA, almost two-thirds of the total municipal waste load and nearly half of the total industrial waste load for the entire lake originate in southeastern Michigan.[11] These results are due in large part to the lack of even secondary sewage treatment for the enormous population of the Detroit area. If we add the Toledo area, the fractions become even more impressive. Finally, the Western

Figure 1.   Location map

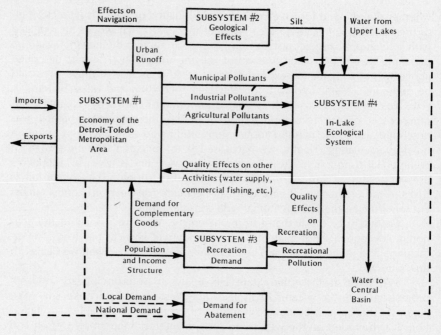

**Figure 2.   System of economic-ecological relationships
in the western basin of Lake Erie**

Basin has very attractive recreation opportunities in the islands area and on the mainland. It includes some of the best natural beaches, not all of which are closed and not all of which are even yet seriously polluted.

The model we are using is shown in Figure 2. We are applying this to the Western Basin, but it could be applied anywhere. Subsystem #1 is the on-shore economic activity, which gives rise to pollution and which will be affected by whatever efforts are made to abate pollution. It is the focus of our present attention. I have said a few things about subsystem #2 in conjunction with quantity effects and even more about subsystem #3. Subsystem #4 is entirely the province of microbiologists and others who are working on in-lake phenomena.

We are operating at the rate of about two man-years/year of professional time in both #1 and #4. This means a larger number of professional people, on the order of 3 or 4 part time in both subsystems, plus an equal amount of graduate student time in these subsystems. There is almost half a man–year/year going in subsystem #3 and nothing at present in #2. The project is now in its second year of a five-year effort.

Note the broad pattern. Economic activity on shore produces pollution which in turn affects the lake. There are feedbacks through recreation, municipal water supply and commercial fishing. But there is no market or, to the present time, no reliable mechanism by which these groups express their preference for abatement. Conceivably, since they have something to gain from abatement, one might argue that they should be expected to express their demand for abatement. They would be no worse off to pay at least the amount of their collective financial losses as a bribe to forestall some of the pollution. Why don't they do it? There are many reasons, but the most basic reason is that abatement is a collective good. That is, polluters cannot sell abatement to buyers separately like apples and oranges, or television sets. If polluters do provide abatement, all recreationists benefit, all lake-side property owners benefit and all fishermen benefit. In these circumstances, no single member of the groups to benefit could gain without all gaining. And no single member is large enough to afford the necessary size of bribe merely for his own small part in the gain. They could get together, but this requires a tremendous effort unless they do it through government.

The situation is the same as financing any public program. National defense is a public good. The technical definition of a public good is a good where consumption by one in no way presents the consumption of the same good by another. Thus, we all consume national defense, but my being protected does not stop you from being protected by the same defense establishment. Note that this is quite different from the situation with respect to apples and oranges. If I consume an apple or an orange, it is not available for anyone else to consume. Markets are well adapted to private goods like apples and oranges. But they cannot work with public goods like national defense and abatement.

Note that the problem of paying for national defense is the same as the problem of recreationists getting together to bribe a polluter to abate. I would prefer not to pay for national defense if others will pay for it. Since it is a collective good, I know I will get it anyway. So it is with abatement. At least one of the reasons we do not have a spontaneous bribery market is that no one wants to pay the bribe if he thinks others will pay.

We have spoken of bribery because it fits best the philosophical attitude that public policy has taken. This is a generalization of the rule of capture. The rule of capture is that anyone who gets to a public resource first captures it — or captures the right to use it. So polluters have been the ones to walk off with our lakes and streams.

An alternative rule is the rule of compensation, which is now gaining widespread acceptance. The rule of compensation says that anyone using a public resource must compensate anyone else damaged as a result of such use. This rule would substitute compensation of recreationists by polluters for bribery of polluters by recreationists. The present popularity of the rule of compensation derives largely from ethical considerations. The ethical position is that natural resources that are not owned by private individuals but belong to all of us. They are our heritage. If anyone damages them, he must make good to the rest of us. I accept this ethical argument. It comes late in our history, but better late than never.

Now, I want to make a separate point. This is that on purely economic ground, it can be shown that compensation is consistent with economy-wide efficiency, whereas bribery is in conflict with economic efficiency and, in fact, produces unstable markets. This is a technical argument and is digressionary to the present discussion. Moreover, it involves a stiff dose of economic theory. But I am willing to go into it later if you are interested. For the present, we note the conclusion that compensation is superior to bribery on purely technical grounds. Many people, including myself, also consider it superior on ethical grounds.

All of this explanation is relevant to the dotted line in Figure 2 which shows the throttling of pollution. The force for doing this comes through government. It cannot be expected to arise from the feedbacks that indicate the inarticulate demands of those damaged.

It is only recently that any large number of people have turned their attention to the problems of pollution clean up, and for this reason, information on costs is sparce. It deals mainly with what costs are expected to be rather than with what they have been shown to be. Experience, which can give a sound basis for cost finding, is yet to be accumulated. Consider first the case of municipal sewage treatment.

Primary sewage treatment, which is largely mechanical, is widespread, though some communities do not have even this but dump raw sewage. Secondary treatment, which consists mainly of biological processes is also widespread, though we have noted that the city of Detroit does not yet have it. Primary and secondary treatment together remove the largest part of suspended solids and oxygen demanding waste, or BOD (biological oxygen demand) from effluent waters. They remove a small part of the nutrients, phosphates, and nitrates, that cause excessive algal blooms, create an aesthetic nuisance, die and create a new kind of oxygen demand on the lake bottom. To do the job of removing most of these nutrients requires a third stage of sewage treatment, or tertiary treatment.

Another kind of problem with municipal sewage arises from the existence in older cities with combined storm and sanitary sewers. When there is heavy precipitation, the sewers are full, the treatment plant is overloaded and the bulk of the mixture of rainwater and raw sewage is by-passed around the treatment plant.

To reduce municipal pollution, the FWPCA has projected a set of remedial programs of increasing effectiveness:[12]

1st Program. Secondary treatment at all municipal sewage plants in the Lake Erie Basin, combined with the rule of separate storm and sanitary sewers in new suburban areas. This would reduce BOD and to a lesser extent phosphate outputs. Exactly how much quality improvement would be achieved in the lake is not clear. At least it is certain that some improvement would take place. FWPCA estimates a construction cost of $1 billion immediately and $1.41 billion by the year 1990. The Administration reports that with a 30 year amortization (at an undisclosed interest rate) and with operating expenses included, this program would cost $5–$6 per capita per year for the entire Lake Erie Basin. If there are 11.5 million people in the Basin, this means something like $57.5 to $69.0 million, or at the upper end of our range of swimming activity benefits expected to result from quality improvements, though we do not know whether sufficient quality improvement would result. From FWPCA descriptions of succeeding programs, it appears that more is needed for good water quality.

2nd Program. Tertiary treatment at 67 of the roughly 300 municipal plants that drain into the lake. Tertiary treatment, according to present engineering estimates, can remove in excess of 95% of the phosphates and BOD from raw sewage. Removal at this level would lead to significant improvements in the quality of the lake. FWPCA estimates an additional construction cost of $1.1 billion now, $1.7 billion in 1990 and a per capita annual expense of $7 on the same basis as the first alternative but only for precondition for tertiary, these estimates must be added to those for the first program.

3rd Program. Tertiary treatment for all municipal plants in the Lake Erie Basin. The third program was priced by FWPCA so as to include the costs of the 67 plants already discussed in the second. In other words, the second and third programs are mutually exclusive alternatives. Because the 67 plants in the second program tend to be the larger plants, and hence to have internal economies of scale, the basin-wide adoption of the 3rd program would raise the per capita cost to the higher figure of $10 instead of the $7 noted above. As before, the costs of tertiary treatment would be added to those of secondary treatment as reported for program #1.

Program #3 is the only one for which our project at Ohio State is in a position to make order-of-magnitude calculations. To do this, we used the best of eight futuristic tertiary technologies described and costed by Smith and McMichael, who are currently employed by the FWPCA.[13] Their work just appeared in mimeograph form this past June, almost a year after FWPCA publication of the above program cost estimates. For all Ohio municipalities in the Western Basin, we calculate $5.1 annual cost per capita with the least cost method of tertiary treatment using a 5% rate of discount and twenty-five year amortization period. When it is remembered that there is only one large municipality in this part of the basin, i.e., Toledo, this estimate compares exceedingly well with the FWPCA estimate of $10.

If we combine Program #1 and Program #3, the indicated cost is something on the order of $10 to $15 per capita per year, depending on whether one takes the 1968 FWPCA estimate for tertiary treatment or the 1969 Ohio State estimate. The Lake Erie Basin total with a population of 11.5 million comes to $115 to $172 million. This is considerably in excess of our swimming activity benefits, but there are more recreation activities, plus aesthetic and quality-of-life benefits. Moreover, the level of abatement is quite high — 95% removal of the two baneful ingredients BOD and phosphates, plus almost 100% removal of suspended solids. It should be noted in passing that our biology team at Ohio State does not think these are the only pollutants that need to be removed. They think nitrates and carbonates should also be removed, along with various trace minerals. As a result of these more stringent requirements, it is reasonable to expect that a complete abatement program for municipal output will turn out to higher than our annual $10 per capita, perhaps higher than FWPCA's $15.

Two other major sources of pollutants are agricultural and industrial. Industrial waste treatment involves other financial sources and for that reason is postponed for discussion below. The FWPCA includes a fourth program which it describes as "more idealistic than practical"[14] to deal with many parts of the problem, including agricultural runoff.

Program #4 is proposed as an addition to the previous list. It has several parts. First are various public works to reduce agricultural runoff, totaling a capital expenditure of $400 million, or $2 to 3 per capita per year. This part of the FWPCA's program is no more "idealistic" than the improved municipal treatment facilities. In another place, FWPCA reports that phosphorus input to the lake is composed of 72% from municipal wastes, 17% from rural run-offs, and the remainder from other sources.[15] Agricultural runoff includes other nutrients than phosphates, however, and toxic materials.

The other main part of the FWPCA's program #4 consists of the conversion of combined sewers to separate systems in older congested urban areas. This is an expensive program and is expected by FWPCA to run to $10 to $20 per capita annually, not counting the cost of time and inconvenience that would come with diverting traffic away from areas undergoing reconstruction.

Industrial wastes are of infinite variety. Neither the FWPCA nor the Ohio State group has come up with cost estimates in which I have much confidence. Only this can be said: the estimates that both groups have made are lower than the costs of treating municipal wastes. FWPCA's total industry estimate is about one quarter the total for municipalities.[16] I am not willing to say even that much about ours, except that we agree that the aggregate industrial cost is well below the aggregate municipal cost.

The foregoing estimates are based on technologies that appear to be best suited to the various industrial and municipal wastes, but no conscious effort has been made to derive a basin-wide minimum cost for a given total input of each specific pollutant into the lake. The problem of cost minimization is basically a linear programming problem. The various waste outputs each have several, not just one, pollutant in them. Similarly, the various treatment technologies each reduce in different proportions to the BOD, phosphates, suspended solids, and so on. A choice must be made among the technologies so as to allow no more than certain specified quantities of the separate pollutants to enter the entire basin. The most efficient way to do this is to minimize basin-wide costs and to allocate technologies among plants so as to achieve such cost. We have an integer programming model for doing this job, which I would be glad to describe later.

Because of the inadequacies of our knowledge of industrial treatment costs, it is not possible to pull together a comprehensive Lake Erie total, though we can take the municipal and agricultural costs together. It will be recalled that we cumulated municipal costs to $10–$15 or more per capita annually. In addition, control of agricultural runoff came to $2 to $3 per capita annually. We might say that best estimates today put the total of these two at $15 to $20 per capita annually, which corresponds to a Lake Erie total of $200 million annually, give or take 20 or 30%. Moreover, industrial costs will not double this figure. They are likely to fall a good deal shy of doubling it. Further gains in technological knowledge and perhaps a cost minimizing allotment of rights to dump throughout the basin can be expected to reduce it over a period of time.

On the benefit side, we simply don't know what the total gains might be. In absolute amounts on an annual per capita basis, the figures seem small enough and I would vote to clean up Lake Erie for a personal contribution of the indicated amount, multiplied by the number of people in my family. The majority of the voters might do likewise. But if we want to know whether the FWPCA programs get us to the neighborhood of an optimum, it will be necessary to have additional information, particularly on aesthetic benefits as these might be reflected in property values.

One final point regarding the level of abatement: I have used FWPCA figures because they give us orders of magnitude on costs. In our work at Ohio State, we are not limiting our projections to any fixed level of abatement, but will explore a wide range of costs as functions of abatement level. It is the purpose of the microbiologists to tell us the effects on water quality. What we expect to have eventually is a set of quality levels and a set of corresponding costs.

The first thing to note about the basin-wide minimization-of-cost approach is that some communities and industrial plants will be paying more than others if each separately finances an allotted level of treatment. For example, large scale municipal plants in urban areas can treat wastes more cheaply than small scale plants in relatively isolated rural areas. We expect to find that the minimum cost for the basin is achieved when raw sewage is dumped by certain very small communities and a very high intensity of treatment is conducted in urban areas. In other words, the incremental cost of a very high degree of treatment may be smaller when there is a large volume to be treated than the removal of any pollutant at all with a very small volume. In a case like this, the rural community will be paying nothing for treatment. The members of the urban community will experience certain costs per capita for treatment.

An obvious institutional answer would be to have a basin-wide public body which would have authority crossing municipal boundaries, even state and international boundaries. Taxes for the specific purpose of waste treatment would be the same throughout the basin but where the waste treatment is conducted would be determined by the cost minimizing solution. This approach seems desirable at first blush but it does have its problems. There are obvious political problems in setting up the basin-wide authority and still other problems in deciding what is meant by "uniform" taxes. Are they a given percentage of property taxes, a given flat increment or what? Moreover, there is the problem of industrial pollution.

The cost minimizing solution for industrial wastes is even more difficult to implement by making allocations among firms. Profits are at stake here and each firm will jealously guard its interests in the bargaining process that comes with the establishment of quotas and taxes. Experiences in the Delaware River Basin verify this. It was politically impossible to establish a cost minimizing allocation. The eventual result was to allocate on the basis of a fixed percentage reduction in pounds of waste allowed to come from each plant. This is clearly preferential to the older plants with greater waste producing technologies. It is a far cry from least cost removal of any given quantity of a specific pollutant going into the Delaware River. But it comes closest to being politically acceptable.

Now, there is a superior way of achieving a minimum cost solution, better than percentage allocations and, indeed, better than any realistic model of quotas from a basin-wide authority. This is to use the price mechanism that we are so familiar with in other parts of the economy. If we set a price on the right to dump each different pollutant, then the individual polluter can decide for himself whether to treat or dump, and the extent to which to treat or dump. Such prices are called effluent charges. The rule of price works just as well for either municipal or industrial plants.

Consider the previously cited case of the small rural community that might be permitted to dump everything in a cost minimizing solution. This community would pay effluent charges per unit amount of each pollutant dumped. These effluent charges would be the same as paid by the larger urban area per unit of BOD, COD, phosphates, or whatever is dumped. The difference is that the urban area would treat most of its wastes. It would treat up to the point where the cost of removing any additional pollutants was higher than the effluent charge it would have to pay upon dumping. The rural community would do the same, except in this case, the small volume of wastes would result in high unit treatment costs and a larger fraction, perhaps 100%, would be dumped.

The pricing device works in an even-handed way in that it leads to the same unit costs at the margin for treatment everywhere. This can easily be shown to be the least cost solution, for if marginal costs of treatment are increasing with higher percentage removal at any one site, as we know them to be, then any inequality of marginal costs among sites means that less efficient removal is being conducted at the higher cost site than at the lower cost site. A shift in treatment between the two sites would remove more pollutant at the low cost site than would cease to be removed at the high cost site. Uniform effluent charges at all sites would lead all of them in their own self-interest to treat up the point where marginal costs of treatment were equal to the effluent charge and to dump pollutant and pay the charge beyond that point.

The higher the effluent charge is set, the more it would pay municipalities and business firms to treat their wastes. We come to the question: How high should the effluent charge be? The answer is determined by the expected damages from pollution. If high damages are in prospect, then the effluent charge should be high. In fact, it should be as high as is necessary to compensate for any damages that will remain after the expected level of treatment has taken place. Thus, we have an interdependent system. The level of effluent charges depends on the damages and the damages depend on the amount of treatment, which in turn depends on the effluent charges. These considerations are a refinement of our previous gross comparison of costs and benefits. Here it is assumed that average damages per unit of pollutant are lower and lower with smaller and smaller pollutant outputs. Our previous cost benefit comparison assumed no decline of average damages with increased output.

One could proceed by trial and error as do conventional markets. Set a price or effluent charge and determine whether damages with the resulting level of abatement are covered, the calculations being made at the margin. If not covered, the price has not been set high enough. If more than covered, the price has been set too high. Polluters are being asked to withhold more pollution, and hence to spend more on treatment, than the value of the gain to quality-sensitive users.

The trial and error approach may be necessary in the neighborhood of the final answer, but since large investments are needed for waste treatment, it is appropriate to make a large investment in preliminary research to estimate costs and benefits as functions of the amount of waste removed. The closer we can get to the equilibrium price on the first try, the better.

It will be noted that nothing has been said about the actual conduct of treatment, i.e., whether treatment of industrial wastes, for example, takes place at each separate plant or whether it is conducted centrally. Wherever treatment takes place, scale effects must be balanced against pipeline costs of gathering waste and even the question of whether to treat balanced against such alternatives as dam construction for augmenting low flows. Even today, it is customary for business firms to pay special sewage assessments for central treatment. These assessments are not to be confused with effluent charges but should be considered as simply as payment for one among many technologies for waste removal. Similarly, if a dam is built and operated solely for the purpose of waste removal, assessments for this service could be levied against business firms to the extent that their waste treatment requirements are thereby reduced. Needless to say, the introduction of a dam into a river system would necessitate the revision of effluent charges because it is quality of water in the river, not just mass of pollutant by itself, that causes damage. Dams are probably not an alternative as far as quality of the water in the Great Lakes is concerned, but they are mentioned here to illustrate the range of alternatives that can be considered as treatment technologies.

The financial problem, it will be noted, is taken care of by the above pricing scheme. To the extent there is treatment, it is paid for internally by the firm or externally through the firm compensating the municipality or other government unit for treatment conducted on its behalf. To the extent that pollutants are dumped, compensation is paid. The same rules apply to households. With this pricing arrangement, there are only two kinds of taxes: (1) those required to pay for central treatment when it is conducted by a government unit and (2) effluent charges for dumping. The latter have two purposes, it will be recalled: to compensate those damaged and to regulate the amount of abatement.

In the practical world of affairs, things are never this simple. Instead of effluent charges, it may be convenient to have effluent standards which regulate by a percentage reduction, as in the Delaware Estuary, or by a flat reduction the amount of pollutant to be removed. If quotas so set are transferable and divisible, then a market for them will develop, they will be bought and sold, and the same optimum will be reached as with effluent charges, except the gains from sales will go to their private owners rather than those damaged or to the public.

On the other hand, if quotas for the controlled right to discharge are not transferable, then they will be taken as data. They might correspond to the allocation of pollution rights on the basis of least cost or they might not. Enough has been said to indicate that a simple quality standard is very unlikely to achieve a minimum cost allocation. And even if quotas or quality standards do come close to the least cost optimum, they are rigid in the face of technological change and do not offer the incentive to reduce waste outputs beyond meeting the standard. Effluent charges are always there and so is the incentive to adopt any improvement in the technology of waste treatment if it will permit the firm to avoid those charges. Standards may be the only politically acceptable way to proceed, but they are economically inferior to effluent charges.

A wide range of intermediate arrangements is possible by the use of existing taxes. Sewage taxes are scaled in an approximate way for the sake of administrative convenience. The most serious water polluting industries can be taxed on their products, or through property taxes, on their site by a body of water. Such property taxes have long-term effects only, unless ways can be found to adjust them to the amounts of waste removed. Taxes on products offer no incentive at all for abatement, but could cause the affected business to move elsewhere, which might be desired by some members of the community but is not likely to be the end sought by others. If tax relief in the form of credits were offered this could provide an incentive when coupled with the enforcement of standards, but is an indirect form of bribery, with the disadvantages noted previously.

Various tax approximations of the effluent charge idea will be investigated as a part of our research. In general, the object is not simply to finance abatement activity at public expense, but to bring about the adjustments among polluters and the public that will cause both groups to take account of the costs and the benefits that their actions imply. We want these to be taken into account in private decision making. This is what is implied by the problem of where and how to finance.

A final part of the research we are conducting at Ohio State is on the community impact of abatement. By this, we mean the total community effects on income and employment of whatever financing arrangements are adopted.

Any additional costs incurred, for example, by the steel industry will lead to certain adjustments within the industry. The industry would like to pass on to its customers the extra cost of abatement. If this extra cost is incurred only by Detroit steel producers, however, they might find themselves losing some of their markets to steel producers elsewhere. Or, if the steel industry is faced with abatement costs elsewhere, perhaps it will lose out to other metals that do not have as serious waste disposal problems.

Adjustments of this kind are called primary adjustments in that they accrue directly to the polluting firms. In addition, there are secondary adjustments. Thus, some of the steel produced in Detroit is consumed by the automobile industry. This means that the automobile industry faces higher costs in the form of higher steel prices. It would also, of course, face higher costs as a result of pollution charges on its own effluent. And the same is true of other industries in infinite regression.

Using a formulation akin to input-output analysis, we are working through primary, secondary and higher order effects to predict the total effect on Detroit's product markets and on income and employment in the Detroit area. The same is being done for Toledo. We then plan to carry the research out over a wide enough range of alternative abatement levels to be sure we have discovered the point at which serious impact does arise.

This involves separate market studies for each of the major products that are shipped out of Detroit and Toledo. It also involves the acquisition of input-output coefficients from the U.S. Bureau of Census for Detroit and Toledo and various other areas engaged in trade with these cities. The necessary tabulations have been on order by contract with the Census Bureau since last January. Manipulations of the data will seek to explain existing patterns of trade as given by the U.S. Census of Transportation. We then will add costs of treatment plus effluent charges to the prices of products shipped from Detroit-Toledo and will predict the new pattern of trade. The amount added for treatment and effluent will depend on the level of abatement being considered. The exact form of finance will, of course, be relevant. If treatment is conducted, for example, out of general tax revenues, the results will be different than if the more discriminating levies of sewage and effluent charges are used.

In principle, this part of the job is not unlike other studies of the effect of taxes on the location of industry, though careful studies of this subject are themselves sparse. One such study has been carried out by Professor John Matilla of Wayne State University in Detroit for a conference on our project that was held just three weeks ago. His results give employment and income effects of increased state and local taxes, but we cannot use them without having more accurate estimates of industrial abatement costs than we now have.

To give some idea of the order of magnitude of the economy-wide effect, note that the total of state and local taxes paid in the Detroit standard metropolitan area in 1967 was approximately $1.2 billion.[17] The FWPCA estimated a capital cost of $110 million for industrial abatement facilities in southeastern Michigan, but gave no estimate of operating expenses.[18] If these capital costs are spread over the entire area, they will add approximately 0.6 of one percent in state and local taxes (with 25 year amortization at 5%). They will not, of course, be spread over the entire area, but will fall on the pollution generating industries, which include food processing, paper, chemicals, petroleum, steel and automobiles. The polluting members of these industries account for 58% of the value added by manufacture in Detroit, but, of course, still a relatively small part of the tax base when nonmanufacturing businesses and households are included. The costs of abatement could fall heavily on selected industries, but are not likely to have serious effect on the Detroit area as a whole in view of their limited size in relation to total state and local taxes.

Whatever the effect on particular plants, firms and municipalities, we see it as a shift in the structure of costs. Present patterns of cost are based on institutions carried over from the past, including whether implicitly or explicitly, an attitude toward pollution that is reflected in the rule of capture. As population grows relative to natural resources, it becomes important to recognize a public right in quality of the environment. If this right had been recognized from the beginning, another approach to pollution would have been followed. We would have less products that produce by-product pollution and a less polluted environment. I doubt that material progress would have been slowed in any noticeable degree.

References

1. U.S. Bureau of Outdoor Recreation, *Water Oriented Outdoor Recreation in the Lake Erie Basin* (Lake Central Region, Ann Arbor, Michigan, 1966), Table 9–1.

2. Deduced from *Outdoor Recreation for America*, A Report of the President to the Congress by the Outdoor Recreation Resources Review Commission (Washington: U.S. Government Printing Office, 1962), Report #26, Table 6.

3. *Op. cit.,* reference 1, supra, pp. 9–16.

4. Marion Clawson and Jack L. Knetsch, *Economics of Outdoor Recreation* (Baltimore: Johns Hopkins Press, 1966), Ch. 11.

5. Figures are from Donald W. Lewis, *The Decline of the Lake Erie Commercial Fishing Industry in Ohio,* Doctoral Dissertation, The Ohio State University (1966), p. 14.

6. *Ibid.,* pp. 9, 78, 111.

7. *Ibid.,* p. 16.

8. *Ibid.,* p. 18.

9. For order of magnitude figures on value added by rail transportation, see D. Philip Locklin, *Economics of Transportation,* 6th Ed. (Homewood, Ill.: Irwin, 1966), p. 35.

10. Lewis, *op. cit.,* p. 109. Forty-six percent came from the Western Basin as defined in Figure 1, thirty percent came from the Sandusky Bay.

11. U.S. Federal Water Pollution Control Administration, *Lake Erie Report* (Washington, 1968), p. 72.

12. *Ibid.,* pp. 84–86.

13. Robert F. Smith and Walter F. McMichael, "Cost and Performance Estimates for Tertiary Wastewater Treating Processes to Reduce the Pollution Load on Streams," U.S. Federal Water Pollution Control Administration, Robert A. Taft Water Research Center (Cincinnati, June, 1969), mimeographed.

14. FWPCA, *op. cit.,* note 11, supra, p. 84.

15. *Ibid.,* p. 2.

16. *Ibid.,* p. 85.

17. Personal communication, Professor John M. Matilla.

18. *Op. cit.,* note 11, supra, p. 85.

RICHARD D. WILSON & DAVID W. MINNOTTE

Government / Industry Cost Sharing For Air Pollution Control

Several existing federal and state provisions act to reduce the cost to industry of controlling air pollution. Included are the federal corporate income tax, depreciation allowances, investment credits, Small Business Administration loans, Economic Development Administration aid, and state tax laws. These provisions give government assistance to industry amounting to as much as 59 percent of the cost of air pollution control. Numerous bills have been introduced in Congress that would give additional government aid to industry in the form of special across-the-board tax allowances for air pollution control equipment. A typical bill of this type would result in the government bearing an additional 11 percent of these costs. There are several possible objectives for this kind of additional aid; however, none of these seem valid when the amount of present assistance is recognized. From this analysis, it would seem that additional across-the-board tax subsidies for air pollution control equipment are neither required nor advisable. Future studies and/or experience may show certain firms or industries for which air pollution control will be too great a burden and for which additional government assistance is advisable. When such cases are found, legislation should be enacted only after the pros and cons of the various assistance methods are considered.

The Air Quality Act of 1967 outlines the process through which clean air is to be obtained in our country. It has already been shown that the benefits to be derived from air pollution control seem to far exceed the costs of achieving clean air, even though these costs of control are often substantial.[14, 17, 18]

Governmental bodies are, however, faced with the problem of achieving improved air quality in a manner that will not prove too great a burden on our nation's industries. This desire had led to the introduction of numerous bills, at federal and state levels, that would give tax breaks to firms installing pollution control equipment.

In order that requirements for these added tax breaks can be properly evaluated, it is important that the costs of air pollution control be clearly understood. Costs to industry are most often stated in terms of the total installed cost of the equipment. This cost, often several million dollars, ignores

Richard D. Wilson and David W. Minnotte, "Government/Industry Cost Sharing for Air Pollution Control," *Journal Air Pollution Control Administration,* vol. 19, no. 10 (October 1969), pp. 761–766. Reprinted by permission.
Mr. Wilson is Technical Advisor to the Assistant Commissioner for Standards and Compliance of the National Air Pollution Control Administration, Consumer Protection and Environmental Health Service, U. S. Department of Health, Education and Welfare. Mr. Minnotte was associated with NAPCA's Division of Abatement and is presently Vice President of Minnotte Corporations, Pittsburgh.

many important factors, and, hence can lead to false conclusions and inappropriate legislation.

The cost of pollution control equipment is not typically borne by the firm in any 1 year, but is spread over the life of the equipment. The appropriate figure for analysis is, therefore, the stream of cash flows which results from this purchase decision. Such cash flows result from the capital, operating, and maintenance costs incurred. In addition, these costs must be viewed in light of present tax laws because, as will be shown, these laws may result in government assistance amounting to over half the total cost of control.

The purpose of this paper is to discuss the impact on industry of present governmental policies that tend to reduce the cost to industry of air pollution control equipment and to discuss the need for additional cost sharing programs on industry. An appropriate method for evaluating the costs of pollution control equipment will also be illustrated.

THE EFFECT OF EXISTING GOVERNMENT PROGRAMS

Several existing federal and state provisions act to reduce the cost to industry of controlling air pollution. These programs are often overlooked although their impact is substantial. For this reason, these programs will be discussed in general before their impact is illustrated in more detail by means of an example.

The corporate income tax of 48 percent levied on corporate income above $25,000 results in the Federal Government's sharing in the revenue of our nation's corporations. It also, however, results in a sharing of expenses. The sharing in revenue is obvious and needs no further discussion. The sharing in expenses is, however, somewhat more subtle and can best be shown through an example.

A corporation whose net income (revenue less expenses) is $1,000,000 will pay taxes of $480,000. If pollution control equipment that results in an additional $100,000 in expenses and no additional revenue is added, the net revenue will become $900,000 because these added expenses are deductible. The tax paid is now $432,000, a reduction of $48,000 or 48 percent of the added expense. Viewing this another way, it can be said that the Federal Government, through reduced taxes, pays 48 percent of the bill for air pollution control. Capital, operating, and maintenance expenses are affected in this way.

Accelerated depreciation methods are allowed by the Internal Revenue Service for capital equipment expenditures such as those for air pollution control. Because most firms use accelerated rather than straight-line depreciation for tax purposes, the difference acts as an interest-free loan to the firm. This effect will be illustrated in the following section.

An investment tax credit of 7 percent of the capital cost of new equipment is given by the Federal Government on capital investments including those for air pollution control equipment. Because this credit is given in the year in which the equipment is purchased rather than in equal increments over the life of the equipment, it has the additional benefit of giving an interest-free loan similar to that of the accelerated depreciation.

The Small Business Administration can make direct loans, either by itself or in conjunction with banks, and can guarantee loans made by banks to firms defined as small businesses. Small businesses constitute over 90 percent of the firms in industries facing the greatest pollution abatement.[6] The major benefit to hardship firms would be guaranteed access to loans for purchasing pollution abatement equipment and facilities and the low interest at which these loans are available.

The Economic Development Administration can offer technical and financial assistance to any firm or plant, regardless of size, if pollution abatement actions would tend to limit modernization, expansion, or solvency of the facility. Such plants must usually be in a county designated as a depressed area; however, nearly one third of the land area in the United States is so defined.[6] The EDA can pay, in all areas, up to 100 percent of the costs of technical studies for the purpose of identifying least costly methods of abating pollution for plants in towns or sections of cities threatened by reduced economic activity.

Nearly all states levy an income tax on corporate profits. These taxes range from 2 to 9 percent, average about 5.5 percent and assist industries just as the Federal income tax does. State taxes are, however, deductible from income subject to the Federal Income Tax and thus the actual added average savings amounts to 2.75 percent.

Twenty-eight states presently have special tax laws relating to pollution control equipment.[1] These laws either exempt pollution equipment from property taxes, offer rapid write-offs for income tax purposes, or both. Their effect is to increase the government share of the cost of air pollution control equipment.

CASE STUDY

In order to provide a clearer understanding of the portion of the cost of pollution control equipment borne by the government as a result of reduced tax liabilities associated with cash expenses, depreciation allowances, and investment credits, a detailed example of the cost of control equipment to a typical plant in the steam-electric power-generating industry will be presented. The effect of depreciation allowances and investment credits on industry in general has been discussed in numerous papers. Examples of these analyses are found in Brown,[3] Chase,[4] Dousett,[8] Hall,[10] and Johnson.[12]

Although the example deals with a specific industry, the conclusions drawn from the calculations will be applicable to all industries. As will become clear later, this is the result of the universality of depreciation practices for fixed assets, the uniformity of tax rates and the insensitivity of the calculations to variables such as interest rates, assumed equipment life, and maintenance costs.

The plant chosen to be representative of the power-generating industry operates four 272 megawatt capacity coal-fired boilers. In order to satisfy the assumed particulate control requirements in its region the plant must have an over-all collection efficiency of 98 percent. This degree of control will be achieved by using an electrostatic precipitator on each boiler with a design efficiency of 99.5 percent. The high design efficiency is necessary due to the low sulfur content of the fuel. A high maintenance cost factor is assumed in order to maintain the desired high collection efficiency. The average installed cost for the entire control system was calculated to be $4,080,000 with an annual operation and maintenance cost of $232,386. Technical assistance on costs was furnished by John O'Connor of the Economic Effects Research Division, NAPCA. Background information concerning the costing method used can be found in *Control Techniques for Particulate Air Pollutants*.[5]

The analysis will consist of the calculation and comparison of the cash flow resulting from the equipment purchase decision (assuming a zero tax rate) and the cash flow of tax savings (assuming a 48 percent tax rate). A comparison of these two cash flows will indicate the amount of the total equipment cost borne by the government as a result of tax policies.

The effective tax rate is assumed to be 48 percent which was the Federal tax rate before the addition of the temporary 10 percent surtax. The 48 percent rate breaks up into a normal tax of 22 percent and a surtax of 26 percent on income over $25,000.

The method of comparing these two cash flows requires a brief explanation because the equipment purchase decision will result, not in a single, immediate cash payment, but in a whole stream of cash payments. It is not correct to compare the value of two streams of cash by simply adding the payments because this would neglect the time value of money. One way to allow for the time value of money is to imagine that all the receipts and payments in the stream are immediately deposited or withdrawn from an interest paying bank account. Given this assumption, a single point can be selected in time and the two cash streams compared by calculating their respective effects on the depositor's balance at this specified point in time, with the interest paid by the bank representing the time value of money.

The most meaningful point in time for a decision maker is the present and thus the cash flows in this analysis will be compared by calculating their present values. Many tables have been published that can be used to calculate the present value of a stream of cash flows for selected interest rates and time periods. The present value of a stream of cash flows represents the amount of cash that must be deposited or withdrawn now in the interest-paying bank account to produce the desired cash stream in later years.

The comparison of the present values of cash streams will be meaningful, of course, only if the interest rates used in the calculations are correct representations of the time value of money to the particular decision maker who is making the comparison. For any particular firm, the time value of money is represented by the after-tax return that the firm can earn on new investments. A conservative approach, which is used throughout this paper, leads to the assumption that the amount a company can earn on invested capital is equal to the after-tax cost of the debt needed to finance the investment. In other words, if no other projects were available the company could retire the loan, which would give them a return equal to the after-tax interest expense.

This is conservative in that a typical firm in its capital budgeting process will normally set its minimum earnings standard for new investments equal to the average cost of capital, which is a weighted average of the after-tax cost of debt and equity. Because equity financing is almost always more expensive than debt, the minimum acceptable projects will have a return greater than the after-tax cost of debt alone. Thus, the average return on new investments for a typical firm will be greater than the after-tax debt expense. If a higher value for the time value of money had been used in the example, the portion of the cost borne by the government would have been greater.

One other important factor in present value analysis is the time period over which cash flows are discounted. A reasonable solution in this case is to consider the cash flows over the presumed useful life of the control equipment. As shown in Column 1 of Table 1, a reasonable life for the air pollution equipment in question was assumed to be 15 years. Year 0 indicates the time immediately preceding the initial investment and years 1 through 15 indicate the end of the particular year in question.

The means of financing the $4,080,000 installed cost of the control equipment is a 10 percent interest bond with principal payable in equal annual amounts over the life of the equipment. The interest expense in each year (shown in Column 3) is 10 percent of the outstanding principal in that year. The 10 percent interest expense was assumed to be a reasonable cost for a loan considering the present prime interest rate and other market conditions.

The results of the analysis will vary with the type of financing. If the loan had been a 10 percent interest bond with principal payable in a single balloon payment at the end of year 15, the amount of the cost borne by the government would have been greater. A typical firm will have borrowing terms between the range of equal annual payments and a single payment at the maturity date of the loan. To preserve the conservative approach, the equal annual payment loan was used in the analysis because it will result in the lowest government cost sharing within the range of principal repayment schemes just mentioned.

Column 4 is the operating and maintenance expense of keeping the equipment operating at its required efficiency. This figure takes into account the cost of fly ash removal and any value received by the use or sale of the fly ash. These costs have been assumed to occur in equal amounts throughout the equipment life. It is quite possible that these costs will be lower in the early years and greater in later years.

The sum of the principal, interest, and operation and maintenance cash payments (Column 5) in each year is the total cash outflow associated with the equipment purchase decision assuming a zero tax rate. Column 6 is the present value of the cash payments in Column 5 at a 5.2 percent discount rate, which is the after-tax cost of debt. The after-tax cost of the 10 percent bond with a tax rate of 48 percent is one minus the tax rate of 48 percent multiplied by the interest expense of 10 percent which is equal to 5.2 percent.

Table 1. Power plant cash flow calculations

1 Equipment life	2 Principal payments	3 Interest	4 Operation & maintenance	5 Pre-tax cash flow	6 Present value of pre-tax cash flow	7 Deductible expenses	8 Tax savings
0					−7,660,870		
1	−272,000	−408,000	−232,486	−912,486		−640,486	+307,433
2	−272,000	−380,800	−232,486	−885,286		−613,286	+294,377
3	−272,000	−353,600	−232,486	−858,086		−586,086	+281,321
4	−272,000	−326,400	−232,486	−830,886		−558,886	+268,265
5	−272,000	−299,200	−232,486	−803,686		−531,686	+255,209
6	−272,000	−272,000	−232,486	−776,486		−504,486	+242,153
7	−272,000	−244,800	−232,486	−749,286		−477,286	+229,097
8	−272,000	−217,600	−232,486	−722,086		−450,086	+216,041
9	−272,000	−190,400	−232,486	−694,886		−422,886	+202,985
10	−272,000	−163,200	−232,486	−667,686		−395,686	+189,929
11	−272,000	−136,000	−232,486	−640,486		−368,486	+176,873
12	−272,000	−108,800	−232,486	−613,286		−341,486	+163,817
13	−272,000	−81,600	−232,486	−586,086		−314,086	+150,761
14	−272,000	−54,400	−282,486	−558,886		−286,886	+137,705
15	−272,000	−27,200	−232,486	−531,686		−259,686	+124,649

Table 1 (continued)

1 Equipment life	9 Depreciation SYD	10 Depreciation tax savings	11 Investment credit	12 Total tax savings	13 Present value of tax savings	14 After-tax cash flow	15 Present value of after tax cash flow
0			+285,600	+837,833	+4,103,111	−74,645	−3,557,759
1	−510,000	+244,800		+522,857		−362,429	
2	−476,000	+228,480		+493,481		−364,605	
3	−442,000	+212,160		+464,105		−366,781	
4	−408,000	+195,840		+434,729		−368,957	
5	−374,000	+179,520		+405,353		−371,133	
6	−340,000	+163,200		+375,977		−373,309	
7	−306,000	+146,880		+346,601		−375,485	
8	−272,000	+130,560		+317,225		−377,661	
9	−238,000	+114,240		+287,849		−379,837	
10	−204,000	+98,920		+258,473		−382,013	
11	−170,000	+81,608		+229,097		−384,189	
12	−136,000	+65,280		+199,721		−386,365	
13	−102,000	+48,960		+170,345		−388,541	
14	−168,000	+32,640		+140,969		−390,717	
15	−34,000	+16,320					

Assuming the decision maker can earn 5.2 percent interest in a hypothetical bank account, paying $7,660,870 in year zero or paying the 15 year cash stream in Column 5 would be a matter of indifference to him.

The next step is to calculate the present value of the stream of tax savings that result from the equipment purchase. Column 7 is the sum of the interest and operation and maintenance expenses that are deductible cash expenses. The tax savings as shown in Column 8 are equal to 48 percent of the sum of the expenses.

In addition to the cash expenses of interest, operation and maintenance there is the additional noncash depreciation expense which must be taken into account. Rapid depreciation methods will result in a higher depreciation charge in an asset's early years and a lower charge in its later years than straight-line depreciation. The consequent reduction in taxes during the early years, though offset by an increase in later years, represents a net gain in the present value of a firm's future cash flows. For tax purposes, then, firms with taxable income have an economic incentive to use rapid depreciation. A common form of rapid depreciation is the sum of the year's digits (SYD), which is shown in Column 9.

To calculate the sum of the years' digits depreciation expense deductible from taxable income in the t'th year of life of an asset with a legal life of T years, multiply the difference between its original capitalized value and its estimated salvage value (assumed to be zero in the example) by the factor

$$\frac{T-t+1}{T\frac{(T+1)}{2}}$$

It is important to emphasize that charges to income for depreciation do not in themselves affect the total inflow of cash from operations. The allowance of depreciation expense as a deduction from income subject to taxation does, however, have an important effect on the outflow of cash necessary to satisfy tax requirements. The consequences of any allowable expense is a reduction of the tax liability. The tax shield from depreciation is equal to the full amount of depreciation each year multiplied by the applicable tax rate; which is 48 percent. Column 10 shows the tax savings resulting from SYD depreciation expenses.

There will be a tax saving from one other factor which is the investment credit. The investment credit is equal to 7 percent of current outlays for depreciable assets subject to certain maximum limitations. The President has recently recommended that the 7 percent investment credit be rescinded. If this occurs and the credit no longer applies to pollution control equipment, the calculations in this paper would be slightly modified, although the conclusions would remain the same. The amount of tax shield allowed in any 1 year is $25,000 plus 50 percent of the tax liability over $25,000. Any excess credit may be carried back against previous tax liabilities for 3 years or carried forward against future tax liabilities for 7 years.[7]

The credit is charged against income taxes due on current income. For tax purposes all firms must take the full amount of investment credit in the year the assets are purchased which will result in the maximum tax reduction at the earliest possible time. Electric utilities, unlike most industries, receive the 7 percent investment credit on only 3/7 of their current outlays for depreciable assets. In this analyses, it is assumed, however, that the full 7 percent credit applies to the pollution control equipment. This assumption is made so that the results will be more representative of industry in general. The investment credit in this example amounts to 7 percent of the installed cost of $4,080,000 or $285,600 as shown in Column 11. The full amount, of course, is a tax saving.

The total tax saving (Column 12) is thus the sum of the tax savings from the cash expenses of interest, operation and maintenance, the noncash depreciation charge, and the investment credit. The present value of this stream of tax savings at a 5.2 percent discount rate is shown in Column 13 to be $4,103,111. Assuming the time value of money is 5.2 percent, a decision maker would not care whether he received $4,103,111 in year zero or the 15-year cash stream shown in Column 12.

It is now possible to compare the present values of the cash stream assuming a zero tax rate and the cash stream of tax savings using a 48 percent tax rate to determine the portion of the control cost shared by the government through decreased tax liabilities. The ratio of the present value of tax savings to the present value of the cash flow with zero tax rate is 53.6 percent. The government bears 53.6 percent of the cost of air pollution control as a result of reduced tax liabilities associated with cash expenses, depreciation allowances, and investment credits. The inclusion of other factors such as State income taxes and exemptions, and low interest loans could increase the government cost sharing by an average of 5 percent. Approximately 59 percent of the cost of air pollution control is, therefore, borne by government.

Columns 14 and 15 of Table I show the calculation of the present value of the after-tax cash stream of payments resulting from the equipment purchase decision. Column 14 is the sum of the pre-tax cash flows (Column 5) and the tax savings (Column 12). This after-tax cash flow and thus the present value will indicate the portion of the pretax cash flow borne by the company. The sum of the present value of the tax saving and the after-tax cash flow will, of course, equal the present value of the pre-tax cash flow.

All assumptions were made to result in the most conservative estimate of industry's share of the cost. The final ratio was found to be fairly insensitive to variables such as principal repayment terms, interest rate, equipment life, and maintenance expense. For example, if the principal were assumed to be repaid in one lump sum at the end of year 15, the cost borne by industry would decrease about 4 percent. The results drawn from the calculations will thus be applicable to other industries because of the insensitivity of these variables within the range of assumptions deemed practical for most industries. Variables that would cause substantial variations in results, such as the tax rate, are found to be uniform throughout all industry.

An underlying premise in the analysis is that a particular firm will have sufficient taxes payable to utilize investment credit and depreciation allowances. This may not be true in some industries where high operating costs or strict competition result in low margin operations. The previous analysis is not viable in these special cases. One other assumption that has been implied throughout the analysis is that the firm does not pass any of the cost of air pollution control on to customers, suppliers, or stockholders. This again reflects a conservative approach in that any of the costs that can be passed on as increased prices to customers, decreased prices to suppliers, or decreased dividends will, of course, lessen the impact of the pollution control cost to the firm. Since the passing on of costs to customers would lead to increased taxable revenue, it would result in a shifting of part of the previously discussed government assistance onto the consumer. Actually, this would mean that the people would be paying directly for a portion of the costs as consumers and paying indirectly for a portion of the costs as taxpayers. Thus, the effect of the government cost sharing is to provide a kind of insurance policy which guarantees that industry will not have to pay more than 41 percent of the cost of air pollution control.

As a final point of interest, it should be noted that the after-tax decrease in cash shown in the example will not necessarily be the cost reflected in the income statement for any particular firm. This is a result of the fact that many firms will account for depreciation and investment credit charges differently for reporting purposes than for tax purposes. The choice of whether the use of separate records (a deferred accounting procedure), or no separation of records (a flow-through procedure) is more appropriate, is presently in a state of flux.

The main point of controversy centers around the fact that there will be discrepancies in the reported incomes between the two methods in years of fluctuating asset growth. The Accounting Principles Board of the American Institute of Certified Public Accountants has recommended both methods at one time or another,[2] but present trends indicate that the "deferred" procedure will result in a truer representation of income. The choice of accounting procedures, although it will affect the portrayal of income, will not affect the value of an investment for a firm.

THE NEED FOR ADDITIONAL GOVERNMENT AID

Numerous bills have been introduced in Congress that would give special tax treatment to firms installing pollution control equipment. Many such bills have been introduced to date in the first session of the 91st Congress.[16] A typical bill of this type would raise the investment tax credit to 20 percent for pollution control equipment and would allow firms to depreciate this equipment in the first year. These benefits would apply on an across-the-board basis.

Raising the investment credit to 20 percent would give additional assistance amounting to 7.0 percent of the total cost incurred in air pollution control. (Calculated in a manner similar to the previous example.) Allowing a firm to depreciate equipment in 1 year would result in additional assistance of 4.4 percent. A typical bill, therefore, would increase the total assistance by 11.4 percent to a total of 65.0 percent. This could total as high as 70 percent if the effects of loans and state taxes are considered.

The desirability of these additional cost sharing programs can only be measured in terms of their meeting a specified objective. There seem to be three possible objectives for this type of legislation and it is seldom clear which one is being considered by the author of any particular bill. For this reason, the desirability of this type of legislation will be discussed in relation to each possible objective.

The first objective that might be considered is the use of tax credits as incentives for firms to install air pollution control equipment. Tax incentives (e.g., the 7 percent investment credit) normally make capital investments more profitable for a firm. For example, a typical firm may have an administrative policy of investing in capital equipment that will give them a 20 percent return on their investment. If an investment credit were added, it would increase the return on some investments that were previously below the 20 percent cutoff level to a point above the level and the firm would therefore increase its total investment.

Air pollution investments are not, however, revenue producing. (Equipment that results in a net revenue would be installed for process reasons and not air pollution control reasons.) In order for a tax credit to act as an incentive for air pollution control it must, therefore, cover 100 percent of the net cost of installing and operating the equipment plus an amount equal to the required return on investment. Only this amount of assistance would make an investment in air pollution equipment as attractive to the firm as other investment opportunities. This statement is backed up by the National Air Pollution Control Administration's experience during the period from October 10, 1966 to March 9, 1967, during which the investment credit was allowed only for pollution control facilities. Only 23 applications for this credit have been received, and these originated from only 10 different firms.

It has been shown that the proposed bills could increase total assistance to an amount as high as 70 percent. Even this large amount of assistance would not be enough to act as a true incentive. One could argue that pollution control has a benefit to the firm in terms of public relations. It is doubtful, however, if even this consideration could make pollution control profitable for most firms. One must conclude that the proposed tax cost sharing programs would not be likely to result in firms installing pollution control equipment voluntarily.

The second objective of government cost sharing might be the fulfillment of a perceived obligation or desire of government to share in the cost of achieving clean air. Present assistance has, however, been shown to be as great as 59 percent of the total costs, and it would not seem that additional assistance is needed to meet this objective.

The third possible objective of additional government assistance in paying for pollution control equipment might be to ease any undue burden that pollution control requirements would place on industry. It is possible that even 41 percent of the costs of air pollution control might be too much for some firms to absorb or to regain by increasing their prices or decreasing their payments to suppliers, employees, or stockholders.

In order properly to evaluate the need for this objective, a thorough understanding of the costs and burden of air pollution control to particular firms and industries is required. Information of this nature does not presently exist to the degree that would be necessary for accurate analysis, however, some data do now exist and several studies of this kind are presently being conducted by the National Air Pollution Control Administration.

Studies that have been done in this area allow some conclusions. Burden, in these studies, was measured by comparing the costs incurred for air pollution control to the value added by the industries in question. These value-added analyses have been done for the entire country by the Working Committee on Economic Incentives[6] and by the authors in the Kansas City and Ironton areas.[16, 21] In no case was the required air pollution control expenditure greater than $1/4$ of 1 percent of value added.

These facts, plus their experience in this area, lead the authors to the same conclusion reached by the Working Committee on Economic Incentives who found that:

The need and desirability of additional assistance for industry should be judged on the basis of hardship of burden on particular industries, firms or plants (or hardship on particular communities) caused by abatement actions rather than on the burden to industry as a whole.[6]

Across-the-board subsidies to industry, therefore, would not seem to be needed to overcome undue burden. Some assistance may, however, be desirable for particular firms or industries although available data does not allow one to determine which firms or industries might require such subsidies.

One final argument for across-the-board tax assistance to industry remains. Because a selective cost sharing program based on hardship would be difficult to administer, it might be more efficient to grant such assistance on an across-the-board basis. The problem with this reasoning is that such tax cost sharing programs would probably not offer help to those firms who most need it. These firms are probably those that operate rather marginally. Because of this, it is likely that the amount of taxes they are presently paying is not great enough to enable them to take advantage of tax assistance.

CONCLUSIONS

In general, then, it would appear that additional across-the-board tax based cost sharing programs for air pollution control equipment are neither required nor advisable. Future studies and/or experience may show certain firms or industries for which air pollution control will be too great a burden and for which additional government assistance is advisable. When such cases are found, legislation should be enacted only after the pros and cons of the various assistance methods are considered. There are numerous problems with various assistance methods which have not been discussed in this paper but are adequately covered in the literature. See Cost Sharing with Industry,[6] Gerhardt,[9] ABT Associates, Inc.,[11] McGinnity,[13] and Slitor.[15]

Acknowledgment

Although the analysis and conclusions presented are the responsibility of the authors, we are indebted to numerous individuals for their assistance in developing various portions of this paper. Special gratitude is extended to Richard E. Slitor, Office of Tax Analysis, U. S. Department of Treasury, whose experience and comments proved most useful.

References

1. *A Digest of State Air Pollution Laws*, U. S. Department of Health, Education and Welfare, Public Health Service No. 711; Washington, D. C.

2. American Institute of Certified Public Accountants; Accounting Principles Board, Opinion No. 2 and Opinion No. 4, N. Y. (1963, 1965).

3. Brown, Cary E., "Business Income Taxation and Investment Decision," *A.E.A. Readings on the Economics of Taxation*, p. 526–535, (1964).

4. Chase, Sam B., "Tax credits for investment spending"; *Natl Tax Jl* 32–52 (March 1962).

5. *Control Techniques for Particulate Air Pollutants*; National Air Pollution Control Administration, Pub. No. AP-51; Washington, D. C. (Jan. 1969).

6. *Cost Sharing with Industry*, Summary Report of the Working Committee on Economic Incentives, Washington, D. C. (Nov. 20, 1967).

7. *Depreciation, Investment Credit, Amortization, Depletion*. Dept. of Treas., Int. Rev. Serv., Publ. 534 (10–68).

8. Dousett, Raymond G., "Investment advantages from tax credit and accelerated depreciation," *Financial Exec*, 52–54 (June 1966).

9. Gerhardt, Paul H., "Incentives to air pollution control"; *Law and Contemporary Problems*, pp. 358–368 Spring, 1968.

10. Hall, Robert F., and Dale W. Jorgenson, "Tax policy and investment behavior," *Am Econ Rev*, 391–414 (June 1967).

11. *Incentives to Industry for Water Pollution Control: Policy Considerations;* report by ABT Associates Inc. to Federal Water Pollution Control Administration (Dec. 1967).

12. Johnson, Glen L. and Sherwood W. Newton, "Tax considerations in equipment replacement decisions"; *The Accounting Rev*, 738–746 (Oct. 1967).

13. McGinnity, John L. and Carl V. Kanter, "Taxes for air pollution control equipment; A case study," presented at the 57th APCA Annual Meeting, Houston, Texas (June 1964).

14. Minnotte, David W. and Richard D. Wilson, "Economic impact of air pollution control," presented at the Ironton-Ashland-Huntington Air Pollution Abatement Activity (July 1968).

15. Slitor, Richard E., *The Federal Income Tax in Relation to Housing*, Prepared for the Consideration of the National Commission on Urban Problems: Res Rep No. 5, Washington, D. C., (1968).

16. U. S. House of Representatives, Bills Proposed in 91st Congress, 1st Session, H.R. 808, Mr. Feighan; H.R. 299, Mr. Minshall; H.R. 754, Mr. Conte.

17. Wilson, Richard D. and David W. Minnotte; "A cost-benefit approach to air pollution control"; *JAPCA* (May 1969).

18. Wilson, Richard D. and David W. Minnotte, "Control costs vs benefits" presented at Kansas City, Kansas–Kansas City, Missouri Air Pollution Abatement Activity, (May 1968).

WADE GREENE

What Happened to the Attempts To Clean Up the Majestic, the Polluted Hudson?

Castleton-on-Hudson, N. Y. — "As a boy, I swam in the river all the time," recalls George W. Dieckelmann, the amiable, part-time mayor of Castleton-on-Hudson. "Just north of the village, we had a place they called Little Coney Island. It must have run three-quarters of a mile, and on Sundays it was just like Coney Island. But about 25 or 30 years ago, it started getting to the point that swimming was questionable. Dead fish began washing up on the beach."

Fred Favour, who owns and operates the Marineland marina on the riverbank just the other side of the New York Central tracks from Main Street, is a little too young to remember Little Coney Island, but the mention of dead fish stirs pungent recollections. "Three years ago, they washed up on the river banks six inches deep," he says, looking out at the opaque flow a few yards away from his marina office. "There was a terrible stink that permeated the entire community. I closed down the marina for four days. It got so bad we had to bury them with bulldozers."

The dead fish have become a Jobian plague of sorts to Castleton, visited on the community to some degree almost every year in recent decades. Mostly, explains George F. Prins, an old-timer who runs an insurance business on Main Street, the fish are herring which swarm up the Hudson in the spring to spawn. The herring's mortality rate goes up naturally after spawning, but no one around Castleton pretends that's all there's to it. It's the river, of course. The worst time of all was in the spring of 1965 near the end of the long drought that had afflicted the Northeast throughout the early sixties. Castletonians who could, took their vacations then and fled. Water levels were uncommonly low in the Hudson. Therefore, whatever else went into the river had that much more powerful an effect. It was simply too much for the unwary herring, which died by the millions, to hear villagers tell it.

And well the herring might have. In the wettest of times, Castleton-on-Hudson, a quiet community of 1,768 people, seven miles south and east of Albany, marks the most polluted part of one of the most polluted waterways in the nation. The majestic Hudson is a relatively modest 300 feet wide off Castleton, and runs murky brown there with the raw human and industrial waste of Albany and Troy, Watervliet and Cohoes and Rensselaer, plus the accumulated pollution of the Mohawk River, which empties into the Hudson less than 20 miles upstream from Castleton. Just north of the village, the untreated waste of the Brown Paper Company factory joins the assault. Finally,

Wade Greene, "What Happened to the Attempts To Clean Up the Majestic, the Polluted Hudson?" *The New York Times Magazine*, May 3, 1970. © 1970 by The New York Times Company. Reprinted by permission.
The author is a freelance writer specializing in social issues.

the village's own sewer mains, feeding down under gently sloping hills, disgorge into the rapidly dying waterway.

A healthy waterway, one that is hospitable to abundant marine life, depends on a certain level of oxygen dissolved in it. The amount is minute — about 10 parts of oxygen to a million parts of water will suffice for the most demanding of fish — and rivers normally absorb enough oxygen from the air to maintain this level as they flow. Unpolluted rivers do, that is. Many pollutants "pollute" most significantly by robbing the water of oxygen, thus denying sufficient amounts to marine organisms; in some cases, these pollutants combine with the available oxygen to breed positively noxious chemical compounds.

Given a long enough stretch without heavy pollution, rivers can and do cleanse themselves by bacteriological action and by picking up more oxygen as they go. The Hudson, indeed, is fishable and swimmable in places below Castleton, but at Castleton itself the effluence of an affluent society almost totally overwhelms the river. The "oxygen sag," as the pollution engineers call it, sags so low here at times, virtually to zero, that even the scavenger eels that thrive in Manhattan's famously filthy stretch of the Hudson cannot survive off Castleton. The highest forms of life inhabiting the river at Castleton during these times are rat-tailed maggots.

That is the Hudson at Castleton in spite of one of the nation's more ambitious water clean-up programs. Back in Castleton's most awful Year of the Fish, 1965, the drought was intensifying water pollution everywhere to the crisis proportions that seem so often to be the minimal spur to political action. In a spasm of awareness that pollution could seriously diminish the water resources of the state the State Legislature unanimously passed the Pure Waters Program. That November, state voters by an unprecedented 4-to-1 margin approved a $1-billion bond issue to clean up the waters. Governor Rockefeller, who had led the Pure Waters campaign, hailed the results and with characteristic high optimism promised New Yorkers unsullied rivers and lakes by 1972.

Today, two-thirds of the way toward that deadline, it is clear that the schedule has about as much chance of being met as the Long Island Rail Road had of becoming the nation's best commuter line by last October. By the dictates of one of hundreds of individual schedules assigned to polluters by the State Health Department since 1935, Castleton itself was to have completed construction of its own sewage-treatment system three months ago.

The far larger municipal treatment facilities planned for areas upstream from Castleton are years behind their original schedules. The picture is not much brighter downstream, nor in the state as a whole. Less than a third of the major polluters have built treatment plants in the four years since the Pure Waters Program got under way. As a broadside fired at the program late in January by Senator Samuel L. Greenberg of Brooklyn, ranking Democrat on the State Senate's Finance Committee, put it: "New York State will not have clean waters in 1972. It may not have clean waters in 1982."

The drought-inspired action of Governor Rockefeller and the people and legislators of New York meantime has found a broader, even more ambitious national counterpart in President Nixon's State of the Union pledge to strive to "make our water clean again, and do it now" and in his commitment of Federal billions to accomplish the job. If New York State's experience is prologue to a national water clean-up program, its lesson, if any, is that there is an immense gap between word and deed, even legislation and deed, when it comes to water purification.

In this regard, little Castleton-on-Hudson, one of 438 Hudson River polluters identified by the State Health Department, epitomizes not only the aquatic but also the human problem of pollution and its abatement. Many of the political, economic and organizational hurdles that clutter the path to ridding our waters of industrial and municipal filth can be found, highlighted, in Castleton's circuitous and far from concluded odyssey toward that estimable goal.

Castleton, 550 buildings big, nestles in the shadow of a high-arching bridge which links an eastern spur of the New York State Thruway with the main artery. Its homes are modest; they squat, ranch-high for the most part, on the hills overlooking the Hudson.

The village draws its water from inland creeks and springs, through a public water system that has just been overhauled. As long as anyone can remember, Castleton has let gravity carry its used water away, through seven collector mains, into the Hudson. For decades, health codes, Federal and state, have prohibited the draining of raw sewage into the Hudson. But until recently Castleton felt neither moral nor legal obligation to do anything about it.

Mrs. Johanna Johnson, a small gray-haired lady, has presided over the village hall for 26 years as village clerk (across the corridor from her office, which doubles as police headquarters and village board meeting chamber, is the public library; the local American Legion post is upstairs). She tells of a state official contacting the village about 15 years ago to ask what it was planning to do about its raw sewage discharges. "We told him," she says, "we're not planning to do anything until the cities up the river do something."

And Castleton *didn't* do anything, either. Then, in mid-1964, state officials again contacted the village. The late Chris Peter, then Mayor, was summoned to the State Health Department's Albany offices several times over the next year to discuss sewage treatment. He went reluctantly. Peter's feeling, recalls Don Walsh, the village's part-time judge and former village attorney, was that he wasn't "going to waste his taxpayers' money pouring into the great Hudson River a few drops of pure water compared to an inundation of sewage from the north."

Finally, in the face of a threat to take him to court, Peter signed a consent decree agreeing to a timetable by which the village would build a treatment system. But on the way out of the Health Department Building after the signing, recalls Walsh who accompanied Peter, the Mayor muttered: "We'll never ever have to do it."

That may well have been the prevailing attitude of polluters around the state in the early days of the clean-up program. Certainly there was no sense of imminent implementation about the program. The timetable Peter signed allowed a full two years before a preliminary plan had to be submitted. And soon even that distant deadline was lifted. A few months after the signing,

Castleton's timetable was, in effect, scrapped by the Health Department itself. So were hundreds of other such schedules throughout the state.

Somewhat tardily, the philosophy of regional planning caught up with the Pure Waters Program. The Health Department decreed that comprehensive regional surveys should be made before treatment plants were built to determine if and how various groups of industrial and municipal polluters could get together on joint facilities. Such facilities, it was held, would be more economical in the long run — and possibly in the short run as well. The Federal Government was beginning to get into the sewage-subsidizing business at that time itself, and it promised additional aid for sewer systems built on the basis of comprehensive surveys.

Implementing regional schemes for sewage treatment often proved to be arduous and time-consuming, however, particularly where it meant getting different units of government together. In Castleton's case, implementation proved in the end to be downright impossible. Trouble started as soon as the comprehensive survey itself was completed. Sanitary engineers in Albany contracted to do the job considered four possibilities in their report: (1) Castleton going it alone; (2) Castleton plus a small group of houses near the village plus the Brown Paper Company getting together on a joint facility; (3) a sewage system that would encompass a large portion of Schodack, the township, within whose borders Castleton, Brown and the group of houses are located; (4) a Schodack-wide system.

Castleton's officials immediately opted for (2) — as long as it was run by Castleton. Schodack officials were for (3) or (4). Brown wasn't sure whether it wanted in at all.

Castleton's interest in alternative (2) fitted a statewide pattern, according to John C. Bumstead, who was then in charge of regional planning for the Pure Waters Program. "All the nucleus communities, like a village or a city, want to annex," he says. And many of them saw a golden opportunity to do so while purifying their waters. "Once you get an outlying area locked into a sewage-treatment system," observes Bumstead, "you've got them over a barrel."

Castleton officials are hardly circumspect about what their motives were, as far as that goes. "We look with envy at the big fields around us," says Don Walsh. His main hat when not acting as village judge is as counsel for the state's Conference of Mayors, which lobbies for village and city interests in Albany. In that capacity, he allows, he is "conscious of the relationship of village and town, very conscious. . . . It's a question of who's going to provide what service." If it was going to have to treat its sewage, Castleton was determined to make as much virtue out of its necessity as possible.

On the other hand, Schodack's chief executive and the area's main veterinarian, Dr. Richard H. Drumm, was for bringing as much of Schodack and Schodackian influence into the system as possible, not only to ward off territory-hungry Castleton, but because all Schodack had at that point were septic tanks, and Drumm glimpsed a glittering future for a sewered Schodack. "It would have made the town, as far as getting developers and things like that," he said later.

What to do? A committee of Schodack, Castleton and Brown representatives was formed and held several cool, inconclusive meetings. And finally the Health Department and Federal overseers pressed their own preference: alternative (3), or Castleton, Brown and a sizable portion of Schodack in a new governmental entity called a "sewer district." Forces were at work, Walsh later contended, to turn an urban-oriented antipollution program into a rural-oriented "scheme to sewer the state."

No matter. The village unhappily went along with the state under what Bumstead calls the "general threat that they wouldn't get the money" — the state and Federal aid to build the plant — otherwise. "I never said they wouldn't get the money," Bumstead quickly adds, "I said, 'Jeez, the State of New York cannot afford to buy you a Cadillac when a Chevrolet will do.' "

But as events developed, the good people of Schodack didn't even want the Chevrolet; at least they didn't want to pay the local share for it. The state could legally oblige Castleton to clean up its sewage under health codes, but there was nothing in the law to force Schodackians outside of Castleton, with their non-polluting septic tanks, to go in on a sewage system. And when, on Nov. 5, 1968, a referendum was held in Schodack to vote on a sewer district, the Schodackians turned it down, 1,322 to 1,232. Not by much, but down.

That left the Health Department both chagrined and a little embarrassed, and Castleton back where it was three years before when it first agreed to clean up its sewage. The sequence of events that followed is outlined in the official communications between Castleton and the Health Department. In a corner of a sea of desks on the fourth floor of Building Nine in the state's sparkling new office-building "campus" on the western outskirts of Albany, Anthony Adamczyk — an earnest, 27-year-old sanitary engineer for the regional office, Pure Waters Division, Health Department, one of whose jobs was to ride herd on the Castleton clean-up — thumbed through a manila folder for a recent visitor and interpreted the contents as he thumbed:

"Twelve thirteen sixty-eight: The Health Department tells Castleton to go ahead with the treatment plant as a solo project in such a manner that outside service areas can be served eventually. Two twenty-four sixty-nine: We officially asked the village what they're doing and they replied two twenty-eight sixty-nine that they're waiting for the Brown Company to let them know if they want to come in with the village. Then there were several — well, probes by our office to see what was developing. Not much was happening, so we called a meeting at our office on six one sixty-nine. We call in the Brown Company and the village and we tell them that we're sick and tired of waiting around and we want a decision.

"In the summer and fall of '69, I was at the company and at the village. There were technical problems. The company wanted certain answers from the village as to costs. The village wanted certain guarantees from the company. The site of the sewage treatment plant was under question. This was dragging out until finally on twelve nine sixty-nine we sent a letter to the village telling them to go ahead with a solo project and if they're going to get aid they'd better hurry up and get their project in and they're only going to hurt themselves by waiting any further."

The Brown Paper Company clearly became a major thickening in the Castleton plot along the way. The company is actually a $24-million corporation, according to the value of its shares. The plant that Brown runs on the north border of Castleton is a small part of the corporation but by far the largest industry in the area. It is housed in a sprawl of low buildings, mostly brick, many over 100 years old. Its main piece of equipment is a 330-foot machine whose wire-covered cylinders dip into a gruel of white liquefied scrap paper from which it makes a low-grade cardboard, largely for product packaging — Arm and Hammer baking-soda boxes, cartons for Hartz dog-worming capsules, and so on.

The factory draws in about 1,300,000 gallons of water a day, and, like paper and pulp plants generally, its discharge (of minute cellulose fibers too small to be used in the cardboard-making process) ranks it as a rank polluter. Its effluence, in fact, is six times as polluting as Castleton's, in terms of the amount of life-supporting oxygen it absorbs. The company's discharge, Brown officials hasten to explain, is not so bad as that of some paper factories, because the plant does not process raw pulp, only waste paper. But Brown does badly enough in Health Department eyes to rate it as a Category 1 polluter — the tops. Castleton, for all its raw human waste, is in Category 2.

The Brown Company plant does not dump its waste directly into the Hudson, but a half mile away, in the Mourdener's Kill, Dutch for Murderer's Creek, which flows into the Hudson. A grisly legend attaches to the creek. Indians, the story goes, captured a young female settler there, tied her behind a horse, beat the horse into a frenzy, then released it. The horse dragged the girl until she was fatally battered.

An old book on the Hudson describes the Mourdener's Kill as a "delightful" stream. But it is not very delightful any more. "My gosh," says Castleton's Mayor Dieckelmann, "there are days you could walk across that water without sinking in." The creek runs right beside the factory and after a recent tour of the Brown plant, I was duly ushered outside to see the Mourdener's Kill. A whitish milk-of-magnesia-like liquid was flowing in the creek, steaming gently in the cold afternoon air.

Brown was originally ordered to clean up its effluence by this coming July. But state health authorities say that paper companies have been the slowest to comply with the Pure Waters Program, and the Brown factory on the Mourdener's Kill is no exception. Only last week did the factory come up with a preliminary plan for a treatment system.

But then, the Health Department has hardly pressed it to do so. The health authorities first let Brown's schedule slide while the feasibility of Brown going into a joint facility with Schodack was explored and ultimately eliminated by Schodack's voters. Then the Health Department overlooked the schedule while Brown and Castleton looked into co-purification. Going through a separate folder, regional overseer Adamczyk again reviewed official communications:

"Eleven fourteen sixty-eight. Our office contacts Brown officially and we want to know what they plan to do. They reply eleven twenty-six sixty-eight that they knew it's been defeated [the sewage district with Schodack] but then they heard that the town will probably try to run a revote and they want to see what's still going to happen in it. And then, when that fell through, the company on one fifteen sixty-nine tells our office they want to talk to the village now. Nothing happens so we contact the company on two twenty-four sixty-nine. We want to know of any status change.

"About then, I went over there and had some meetings with the company and then on six one sixty-nine we had a joint meeting with the village and company and we tell them we want an answer by August. But we couldn't get an answer by August because at that time the village engineer didn't want to put his reputation out and come up with a guesstimate as to foundation costs unless he did some borings, because he found out there was clay in the area. At least that was one excuse. There were other reasons given, too, why they couldn't come up with costs to give the company.

"Finally, we felt we couldn't go along with this any further and that prompted the letter of ten twenty sixty-nine really pinning them down as to date and this and that."

In delicate bureaucratese, the letter reminds the company that it is in violation of the original order to clean up, and that while the Health Department has been willing to wait while the company explored the possibility of a joint-treatment plant, it is not willing to wait any longer. The company can still explore the joint facility further if it wants to, the letter says. Meantime, Brown must go ahead alone. A new timetable is decreed that calls for submission of preliminary plans this month.

How much it entered into the health authorities' earlier flexibility is any outsider's guess, but at least two health officials said they understood that the Brown factory was on shaky financial grounds. This, said one of the officials, tends to be something of a predictable pose as far as industrial polluters go, but he said he thought Brown's troubles were real. In fact, as annual-report readers down the river know, the Brown Company generally has not been doing well. The factory near Castleton itself is said to have lost money in the last two years. Health authorities were also aware that the Brown Company was conglomerated into the vast bosom of the Gulf and Western Corporation last year, in the wake of which the factory on the Mourdener's Kill was experiencing personnel shifts at the top. All these factors seemed to elicit an understanding attitude from the Health Department and perhaps a reluctance to press the company too rigorously on schedule compliance.

In any case, the factory shut down one of its two machines in October, cutting production by a quarter, employment by one-tenth and pollution by about as much as production. Shortly afterward, Castleton finally sent estimates of what it would have to charge Brown to link into a municipal treatment system. And all things considered, the Brown people decided to definitely bow out of a joint Castleton-Brown operation. But Brown's president in New York, Merril L. Nash, says that the company plans to adhere faithfully to its new solo schedule, that it wants to fight pollution as much as anyone else.

That left Castleton once again back where it was in 1965, alone with its order to clean up its sewage. But this time, it faced the unfamiliar prospect of having to build a sewage system without any outside aid unless they began to move. The village fathers at last glance were definitely beginning to move. But ironically enough, the State Highway Department may loom larger in the village's acceleration than the Health Department. The Highway Department is currently building a new, broadened Route 9J south from Albany through Castleton. The strip of highway through Castleton, near the river and parallel to it, runs precisely where the village envisions laying an intercepter line to link in its seven sewer mains with its treatment plant. The highway people have told the village that if it wants to put the line under the road, fine, but it would have to let them know before it begins work on this portion of the highway this month and hand over $30,000 to cover burial costs.

"We're being forced into action because of this arrangement with the highway department," explained village attorney Don Larsen in January, "and we're either going to have to delay that and then get two agencies on our back, which is possible, but it does make for a messy situation, or we're going to have to go ahead."

On March 19, more than four years after it agreed to build a treatment system and precisely seven weeks since it was originally supposed to have completed construction of the system, Castleton formally submitted preliminary plans to the Health Department for consideration.

The average time between preliminary plan and completed construction for those treatment plants that have been built is three and a half years, so Castleton has a long way to go even if it is finally on the track. At this juncture, what generalities can be seen in both Castleton's and Brown's experience about why it takes — or is taking — such a frustratingly long time to achieve a goal which on the rhetorical level at least may even be nudging out motherhood as a politically embraceable cause?

'I don't know why anything takes so long," shrugs Mayor Dieckelmann. "Nobody takes one job and goes on with it." But Dieckelmann and others involved in the Castleton and Brown cases, and in the Pure Waters Program generally, on due reflection suggest that the pace of accomplishment is by no means an independent metaphysic, and that other factors are ultimately accountable.

One of these may be the confusion of goals that, perhaps inevitably, accompanies most public programs. In Castleton's case, the immediate abatement of existing pollution was the state's ostensible aim, but this aim came to be weighed in fact against long-run, regionwide sewage needs (which Nixon, too, has stressed) and was found wanting. In Brown's case, a swift clean-up may have been weighed subliminally at least against the welfare of a tax-paying and job-producing polluter to whom a costly treatment system may have been a crushing burden. A pre-Pure Waters, antipollution law states that pollution be dealt with consistent with "the industrial development" of the state. That requirement is no longer on the books, but the spirit behind it may well linger on.

Or perhaps a functional rather than a teleological explanation for the petty pace of the Pure Waters Program gets at the root of the matter. State Senator Greenberg offers such an explanation in his recently completed study of the program. He chalks up delays to the state's "laggard, irresolute administration and weak enforcement of antipollution laws" and the state's failure "to ride herd on" municipal polluters. Greenberg declares that only 30 percent of identified polluters are adhering to schedules, but even so "the Health Department through June, 1969, had concluded only 15 penalty proceedings against polluters," and that "violators in the concluded cases were let off with a mere slap on the wrist. The average penalty was $600. The highest penalty was $1,500."

State health officials both update and amend Greenberg's statistics. They say there have been 25 concluded cases on the administrative level, plus 15 concluded cases handled through court action. But health officials are in the somewhat ambiguous position of publicly affirming that enforcement is all that it should be, while, in private asides, suggesting that enforcement is being beefed up or should be beefed up.

Clearly, enforcement has not meant rigorously holding polluters to the letter of the law, or the day of an abatement schedule, as both the Castleton and Brown cases amply illustrate. But the state's top enforcement official, William L. Garvey, reasons thus: "It's a matter of balancing the choice. When you go into litigation, you don't go in with a sheriff — you know we're in a democratic society and we don't have Mexican justice in this country. Litigation can be time-consuming. So what you've got to do is really weigh which alternatives you should take. Should you go along with them [the polluters] a little while longer with the expectation that their objectives and their program will be reached sooner that way, or will the objectives be reached sooner by going into litigation?"

Correction, not punishment or the collection of fines, is the goal, Garvey explains. "Our philosophy is to apply the pressure and apply as much pressure as is needed to keep these people moving along. . . . We get the cases and we act on them — at least in our unit — in fairly fast order."

Another high-level official in the Pure Waters Program suggested, however, that cases were not acted on nearly fast enough at the level at which the strongest action can be taken — the Attorney General's office. The Health Department itself can only impose administrative sanctions; any case that must go to court has to be handled by the A.G.'s office. And laments this Health Department administrator, the A.G.'s office takes six months to act on a case. The same official also urges the fines for failure to meet abatement time-tables — now $500 for the first day, $100 for each succeeding day — be increased, an idea that President Nixon has endorsed in proposing $10,000-a-day fines.

On the face of it, aggressive enforcement of water-pollution laws does not exactly seem to be built into the administration of the Pure Waters Program and perhaps is not even possible under current conditions. The enforcement unit for the most part has amounted to little more than William Garvey in one tiny green-walled office in the State Health Department Building. "It's just been him really for the whole state," says one health official. "It's absolutely ridiculous."

Garvey has had only one assistant until recently, when a second was assigned to him. A law-school student has helped out in the summer. The Pure Waters Division has no attorneys of its own — it must act through the Health Department's legal office, a procedure that several Pure Waters people describe as cumbersome. And in the Attorney General's office, to handle court cases, there are only four attorneys working on both air and water pollution.

Still, you scratch the enforcement problem and you come to another, deeper one. Why so slow? "Just one word describes it," says Mayor Dieckelmann. "Money." Chief enforcer Garvey agrees, in effect, that if the money were around to build treatment facilities for industrial and municipal polluters, enforcement would be no problem. That, he laughs, is a "truism."

True, there is state and Federal aid available — either in direct subsidies to municipalities, or tax advantages to industry — but polluters cannot avoid some hefty outlays themselves. How much? In his sixth-floor walkup (until an automatic elevator is installed) office in the shadow of the State Capitol in Albany, Castleton's consulting engineer, Charlie Barrow, unrolls sketches of holding tanks, interceptor lines, centrifuges, and laconically goes over his newly calculated estimates of what Castleton's treatment system will cost. All told: $1,210,500. Subtract Federal and state aid, and the village's share is $489,000. Figure a 6 percent, 40-year bond issue, add maintenance and operations costs and subtract hoped-for payments from a nontaxpaying nursing home and school that will be using the system. The estimated cost to Castletonians comes to, at the very least, $85.82 per family per year.

Brown's treatment costs, company engineers estimate, could run as high as $300,000, or 10 percent of the capital value of the whole plant.

Critics of the Pure Waters Program now claim that the $1-billion bond issue plus $700-million as the local share (40 percent) of treatment costs was never nearly enough to do the job. The state administration recently nearly doubled its estimate of what it would take. It now figures $3.1-billion in all, toward which Rockefeller has asked, and the State Legislature approved, $750-million more in his new budget. According to the latest Pure Waters Division progress report, inflation, broader treatment objectives (regional planning, for example) and more stringent treatment standards since 1965 account for the increased costs. The critics say the administration is just getting closer to a realistic mark, which some of them put as high as $6-billion. Senator Greenberg has recommended $2.2-billion more in state money immediately.

The $4-billion in Federal money that President Nixon is planning to dole out for sewage treatment in the next four years hardly has New York Pure Waters Administrators or conservationists atwitter. Even by the most conservative estimates, the state could use fully half that amount on top of what it has spent already. Still, Assistant Health Commissioner Paul W. Eastman, in charge of the Pure Waters Program, says he is somewhat encouraged by reports that the White House is thinking of giving New York State a large slice of the national pie.

The problem in the meanwhile appears to be growing worse, as population and consumption go up faster than water-treatment facilities. Late last year, the U.S. General Accounting Office suggested that this was the situation nationally in spite of some $5.4-billion spent on sewage treatment since 1957. The New York State Health Department maintains more than 100 sampling stations around the state but claims it cannot make a significant estimate of the direction of pollution levels statewide. Conservationists in the state are less restrained, however. Stanley Spisiak, chairman of the water-resources committee of the state's Conservation Council and one of the nation's major and early crusaders against water pollution, asserts: "We have suffered more deterioration in the last four years in the waters of the State of New York . . . than in a like period of time in the history of this world."

As for Castleton-on-Hudson, Commissioner Eastman suggests that conditions there may be worse, all things considered, than when the village first began to grapple with thoughts of sewage treatment. "We have an automatic monitoring station down below the Albany-Troy area," he says, "and even with the higher flow last summer, it was recording some cases of no dissolved oxygen at all. This was a little surprising."

When, then, will Castletonians be able to swim again at Little Coney Island? State health authorities insist that treatment facilities will be sprouting up all over the place in the coming year. Deputy Health Commissioner Dwight F. Metzler recently declared that "aggressive enforcement of tight timetables can be expected," and top health officials say the state in fact began to step up the pressure on polluters last fall. Even after the great day arrives when treatment facilities at Castleton and upstream are operating, however, it may be years before Castletonians are swimming offshore. Up to seven feet of organic sludge, the heritage of decades of pollution, line the Hudson bottom in the Albany area and immediately south. This sludge will generate its own pollution as it decomposes, and nobody is at all sure how long that process will take. Then, too, there is the possibility that phosphates and other nutrients used in treating sewage will cause oxygen-robbing pollution of a different sort, no less severe in terms of making the Hudson inhospitable to aquatic life, including swimming man.

Some areas around Castleton, Commissioner Eastman cautiously, tentatively estimates, may be swimmable by the mid-seventies. Castletonians themselves aren't sure what to expect. Insurance agent George Prins thinks the day of the stinking fish, at least, may soon be past. Fred Favour says he wouldn't have built his marina three years ago if he didn't think the Hudson around Castleton was going to be a better place to boat in the foreseeable future.

Mayor Dieckelmann is optimistic, too, but patient. Looking back at the five years since Castleton first really talked to the State of New York about cleaning up its own waste, he says: "Personally, I think it's going to be pretty near that long again before this is completed."

SOL SEID

Regionalization—Key to Municipal and Industrial Waste Treatment

Regionalization — how do we define this term? Webster has no definition. Other sources do not reveal a good description. However, in the Laws of 1966 in the State of New Jersey, as approved by Governor Richard J. Hughes on August 23, 1966, which was really an amendment to the basic Water Pollution Control Statute of the State, it was stated "that the New Jersey State Department of Healh shall give due consideration to community development of comprehensive regional sewerage facilities in order to be assured insofar as is practicable that all proposed sewerage works shall conform to reasonably contemplated development of comprehensive community or regional sewerage facilities."

Perhaps many of you are wondering why there is such an emphasis on regionalization. There are a number of major considerations. These were said so beautifully by Robert S. Shaw, retired Assistant Director for Water Pollution Control — Division of Clean Air and Water, New Jersey State Department of Health in a paper given on April 25, 1968 at the New Jersey Water Pollution Control Association Conference in Atlantic City, New Jersey, that I now quote them to you.

"Every sewage treatment facility is surrounded by a blighted area; no one chooses to reside near a treatment plant no matter how well maintained and operated the plant may be; the same may be said for modern industry. This facet of the problem becomes more and more important as our population density increases."

"The larger a treatment facility the less cost per unit of volume or population. This factor is sometimes offset to a degree in the early years of operation of a large regional facility because of the large capital investment in trunk sewers."

"More efficient plant operation is attainable with large installations. The owners of large regional facilities can afford to employ capable technical manpower and they can afford properly equipped and manned laboratories. I cannot emphasize too much the importance of well equipped and maintained laboratories because, as you shall see in the not too distant future, both the State and the Federal Water Pollution Control Administrations will be requiring much more laboratory control than was anticipated even as recently as 10 years ago."

"There is much more flexibility in the operation of a large facility. Larger facilities can withstand shock loadings, whether a temporary increase in volume or a sudden slug of unusually concentrated wastes. This is very important in our industrial areas such as that served by the Middlesex County Sewerage Authority where there is such a large percentage of industrial wastes and where there is such a tremendous variety of industrial wastes."

Sol Seid, "Regionalization — Key to Municipal and Industrial Waste Treatment," from *Technical Aspects of Joint Waste Treatment,* Proceedings of an Institute held at Framingham, Massachusetts, March 5–6, 1969. A publication of the Technical Guidance Center for Industrial Environmental Control, University of Massachusetts, pp. 28–41. The author is Chief Engineer, Middlesex County Sewerage Authority.

"Another major consideration, looking into the future, is the sophistication of treatment methods to be contemplated. These are to require much more capable technical manpower not likely to be provided by small entities with limited resources. These much more sophisticated treatment methods ultimately will lead to widespread employment of wastewater reuse, groundwater recharge, etc. These developments cannot be contemplated with any degree of assurance unless entities sufficiently large to provide for employment of the most capable technical manpower can be developed."

How is such a regional body put together? Inasmuch as I am Chief Engineer of the Middlesex County Sewerage Authority, it will be used to illustrate how an Authority is started and for what purpose.

The Authority was created by the Board of Chosen Freeholders of Middlesex County in August, 1950. The reason for its creation was the intolerable pollution existing in the waters within its district. Its specific task was to find a solution to this problem. The valley's waters had been termed by the Surgeon General of the United States as "among the most polluted in the nation." A solution was planned, prosecuted vigorously, and on January 14, 1958, became a reality.

Its concept of municipal and industrial partnership in underwriting the project has been hailed as unique in solving an area problem affecting three counties and has been nationally used as a prototype for other areas.

The Middlesex County Sewerage Authority is a separate corporate entity, a body politic with perpetual succession as a governmental instrumentality for the purpose, among others, of the protection of the public safety, health and welfare, with power to sue and be sued, to adopt and use a corporate seal, to borrow money or contract debt, to issue negotiable bonds, and to provide for the rights of the holders thereof, and with the right, power, and authority to acquire, use and hold and dispose of all property, real and personal, and to make and perform all contracts and do all other acts and things and with all other powers proper or necessary to design, finance, construct, acquire and operate such a system of trunk, intercepting and outlet sewers, pumping stations, treatment plant and other plants and structures as in its judgment will provide the most effectual and advantageous plan or method for relieving any river, and its tributaries and other streams, within its sewer district, from pollution and for preventing pollution of the same.

The District and Service Area of the Middlesex County Sewerage Authority is shown in Figure 1. This district is regional in that it covers most of one county (Middlesex) and parts of two others (Somerset and Union).

Construction was started in 1956 on a system which was placed in operation on January 14, 1958. It is composed of the following:

1. 11.45 miles of Main Trunk — 60 in., 66 in., and 84 in.
2. 4.85 miles of an Interceptor 45 in. and 48 in.
3. 3.70 miles of a 72 in. Force Main extending from our large Sayreville Pumping Station to the Central Treatment Plant.
4. 3.32 miles of an 84 in. Outfall line from the Central Treatment Plant to a point almost 1.5 miles into the Bay.
5. This gives us a total of 23.32 miles of sewer.

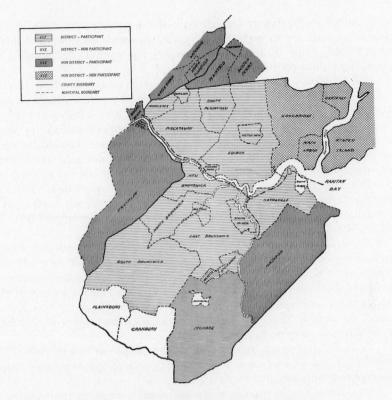

**Figure 1. Middlesex County Sewerage Authority
District and service area**

6. A Schematic Diagram of the Main (Central) Treatment Plant is shown on
   Figure 2.*
7. Also included in the system are two small and two large pumping stations.
   One large station is now being completed, and by the time this paper is
   presented, this pumping station should be in full operation. The original
   station has four 35 mgd pumps and the new one has a start-up capacity of
   67 mgd with a future expansion to 115 mgd.

The total cost of this project is approximately $39,000,000. Included in
this figure is the cost of the new large Edison Pumping Station and of land for
our proposed new microbiological treatment works with not all of the new
land purchased as yet. This figure on cost does include land acquisition, administration, counsel fees, engineering fees, laboratory tests, construction and
the reserves required by the Bond Resolution.

How and from whom does the Middlesex County Sewerage Authority get
its funds to operate? Of course, all of its original money came from its own

* Figure 2 has been omitted — Editors.

Bonds. Although the bonds are not part of the participant's debt, the participants are required to make annual payments which include bond interest and principal. Since its inception there has been additional bonding and Federal Aid for our construction program.

The Authority prepares an annual operating budget which must be introduced no later than 45 days before the end of the year which would be November 16. Final approval must be given 15 days before the end of the year which would be December 16. To the operating budget is added the interest and amortization charges. This then gives the total dollars needed for operation and paying off the debt. Based upon this total — a rate schedule is struck. This rate schedule raises only the dollars that are needed for the ensuing year.

The rate schedule is based on Flow, BOD,* Suspended Solids, and Chlorine Demand. When the rate schedule is approved each participant receives an estimated charge for the coming year based on projected flows and analytical data.

A meter and automatic proportional sampler measures and samples the flow through each participant connection. Flow readings are made daily. Composite 24-hour samples are collected daily from large participants and less frequently from small participants and are taken into the treatment plant laboratory for analyses. At the end of each quarter actual charges are calculated. By January 25 of the following year, each participant is notified of his overpayment or underpayment.

With the diversified backgrounds of the people at this Institute, it becomes important to analyze who the participants of the Middlesex County Sewerage Authority are.

First, there are 20 municipalities and local authorities from whom the Authority receives not only domestic and industrial wastewater but also some stormwater, especially where there are very old systems. The industrial plants from all of these municipal participants could conceivably amount to somewhere in the neighborhood of 500. Many are small but among the larger ones are the following:

E. R. Squibb — pharmaceuticals, penicillin, streptomycin, traces of solvents, e.g. amylacetate.

Delco Remy — neutralized inorganic acid waste.

Triangle, Conduit & Cable — possibly solvents, grease, and perhaps neutralized acid waste.

Westinghouse — mostly sewage.

Grace (Hatco Chem. Co.) — wastes from production of esters for plastic industry.

Hercules — wastes from production of alcohols, esters, polyolefins, polymers, stabilizers, and caustic waste.

Nalcon — wastes from production of plastic battery liners.

National Lead — waste from titanium pigment production.

Kimberly-Clark (Schweitzer) — wastes from the production of cigarette paper.

---

* See discussion on BOD in editor's note in "The Soil as a Resource Renovator", Chapter 4 — Editor.

Tenneco — wastes containing inorganic chemicals plus organic oils.
Union Carbide — wastes from phenolic resin production for plastics plus solvents, e.g. toluene.

Let me further illustrate what can be accomplished through a Regional Authority with the cooperation of industries and municipalities. It was in 1964 that the Middlesex County Sewerage Authority began talking about studies on Microbiological Treatment. In fact, bench studies were begun long before that. It wasn't until February 1966 that the New Jersey State Department of Health issued orders to upgrade the treatment of this agency.

The Middlesex County Sewerage Authority realizing that these new orders would be issued, began Microbiological Pilot Studies. When these orders were issued, we had only another year of study ahead of us before we would begin preliminary and then final design and construction.

The rapid expansion and development of the Authority's service area with a corresponding expansion in the Authority's system and the inevitable change in the New Jersey State Department of Health Water Criteria spurred by the aroused public demand for unpolluted water facilities and culmination of a number of years of bench studies confirmed the Authority's decision to construct and operate two microbiological wastewater treatment demonstration plants using the completely mixed and the step-aeration activated sludge systems.

The specific objectives of the project are:

1. To demonstrate the applicability and feasibility of the completely mixed and step-biosorption activated sludge wastewater treatment processes for high strength mixtures of sanitary sewage and industrial wastes.
2. To demonstrate and determine the optimum and maximum removals of chemical oxygen demand, biochemical oxygen demand, chlorine demand, and suspended solids which may be accomplished by these waste treatment processes.
3. To demonstrate and evaluate operation of these processes including rates of oxygen uptake, detention times, COD and BOD loadings, suspended solids levels, nutrient requirements, overflow rates, and sludge return rates.
4. To demonstrate the maximum effective limits of treatment of these biological processes and establish the point at which these processes must be supplemented by advanced wastewater tertiary treatment in order to attain a higher quality effluent. The higher quality effluent would have water quality characteristics satisfactory for industrial and domestic water reclamation and reuse and for discharge into water resources which require a higher quality effluent that can be produced by existing microbiological wastewater treatment processes.
5. To demonstrate the removal of nutrients such as nitrogen and phosphorus as a result of these biological processes.

Ariel A. Thomas of Metcalf & Eddy, Consulting Engineers and Sol Seid, Chief Engineer of the Middlesex County Sewerage Authority in conjunction with the staff of Infilco, Division of Fuller Company designed the two pilot plant units and projected initial programs of operation.

The pilot plants' influent at present is the primary effluent of the main plant. Both units are operating on a 20 gpm basis and have a capacity of approximately 9,000 gallons each.

An important question must be going through the minds of public officials and industrialists sitting in this audience. "How did they get everybody together?"

The gathering together of all facets of the communities was not an easy one. In 1950, the minds of the public officials were not oriented to regionalization as they are today. A public relations program was launched involving sportsmen, conservationists, the general public, civic organizations, churches, social clubs, league of women voters, interested public officials, industrialists and last but most important the full cooperation of the New Jersey State Department of Health.

The Planning Board of the county government hired Elson T. Killam of Short Hills, New Jersey, which since has become Elson T. Killam Associates, to make a survey and tell exactly what they felt was needed. They came up with the concept that there shall be a trunk sewer system and central treatment plant involving a regional system to include all municipal and industrial participants. Upon the recommendation of the Planning Board the Middlesex County Sewerage Authority was formed.

The first step taken by this board was the hiring of Metcalf & Eddy to review the Elson T. Killam report and come up with a joint final recommendation. The famous "Blue Book" was produced and then the Middlesex County Sewerage Authority began the work of getting contracts signed by participants and going into business by letting contracts for construction and final operation. It is of interest to note that the first Metcalf & Eddy report was paid for by Johnson & Johnson of New Brunswick, New Jersey. This sum was later repaid by the Authority.

It took from 1950 to 1954 to get all of the contracts signed. Construction bids were taken in 1955 and in the fall the first bit of construction was started with full steam ahead in 1956, and completion on January 14, 1958.

To get all of the contracts signed by participants was not an easy task. This required much hard work on the part of the Authority with many public relation releases, and a full length film, which was shown in the width and breadth of the country. Since then this film has traveled all over the country. Many, many night meetings with public officials, local civic bodies were held as well as meetings and conferences with industrial people.

The consummation of any regional project can be accomplished only by having the facts, educating the public, showing the importance of the project to public officials, and finally by convincing the industrialists that regionalization is the most feasible way for them to solve their problems.

In conclusion, a joint wastewater agency involving municipal and industrial participants, as proven by an agency such as the Middlesex County Sewerage Authority of Sayreville, New Jersey, is more economical and efficiently run than an individual waste treatment plant, whether it be a separate municipal or industrial system. It transcends municipal and county boundaries and

it allows the hiring of more competent personnel. It eliminates political interference because the officials are not elected, and, as in the case of the
Middlesex County Sewerage Authority non-salaried.

The information presented here today will give you a better insight into
the need for and importance of regionalization, and for the close cooperation
of industrialists, and municipal and state officials, in solving our water pollution control problems.

DISCUSSION

Kupchik: As a former public control official, I think it is certainly much easier
to maintain proper controls and checks in one large plant than to check on a
dozen different plants, particularly industrial ones difficult to get into. But it
may be time to discuss the possible disadvantages of larger plants. Would the
previous speakers address themselves to these disadvantages? Examples of
these may be: needless disinfection of industrial wastes which have no pathogenic organisms; concentration of total loading at single points in the stream
which may overtax the capacities of the stream at that stretch; the failure of
some night operators, these midnight disposers, to feed the proper effluent
into the system and to throw the entire plant out of kilter.
Seid: Perhaps I should have said more on what we mean by regionalization.
By regionalization we do not mean that there should only be one treatment
plant. In fact, within the Middlesex County Sewerage Authority area, there is
an area not serviced by us even though they are part of our district. This area
requested approval of a treatment plant. Under the state statutes, we must
approve all plans and specifications that occur in our area concurrently with
the State Department of Health. We approved this plant for one of the Ross-
more Villages which was to be enlarged to handle 5 MGD* a day. However,
this has failed to develop, and the Englehard Industries have taken this over
for a combined plant which was not what we originally approved. Originally,
not a drop of this effluent was going back to the stream. We approved reuse
from this treatment plant. They were set up to water their golf courses and to
recharge wells. However, and this might answer Mr. Klashman's question to
Mr. Byrd about bonding, we required the Forsgate Sanitation Inc., the wastewater treatment works of this development, to put up a two-million dollar
bond for an outfall which would go to the Raritan River after we approved.
What this amounts to is that if any of you are planning to get together, it
does not mean that you must develop only one treatment plant.

Let me say the following about problems in terms of industrial participants. I did not go into this in the paper, but when we started our pilot
studies, we worked very closely with the State Department of Health. We
ferreted out pollution offenders. The State Department of Health has the
power to prosecute while we only have passive power. One of the industries
was putting in fifty thousand pounds of BOD a day. When they tied into our
system, this did not affect our pilot study. We continued getting 90% removal

* Million gallons per day capacity — Editor.

of BOD without any problems. I feel strongly that the problems that are adherent to individual waste treatment, with the knowledge that the final effluent from these plants are going into a stream, are more detrimental than if you get them to a plant where there is a mixture of industrial and sanitary waste which can be properly processed. There may be some occurrence of free treatment. I do not say that this might not occur. Ariel, have you anything you want to add to this?

Thomas: I would like to comment on chlorination. It is certainly true that many industrial wastes do not have to be chlorinated for bacteriological reasons. However, the Middlesex County Sewerage Authority uses 50 mg/l of chlorine to disinfect its effluent, and it is still more economical for industries and municipalities to belong to the Authority than to do their own treatment. The Authority treatment plant is now a primary plant as Mr. Seid has already said. When the Authority constructs its secondary treatment plant, chlorination will be dropped to 15 or 20 mg/l at the most. Although the collection of industrial and domestic wastewaters in a single interceptor will require that the treated industrial wastewaters which are mixed together with the other wastewaters will have to be chlorinated, it still may be more economical to combine the two in an extensive collection system and provide chlorination for the mixture even though the industrial wastewater would not have to have been chlorinated if they had been collected or treated separately. At the present time, we are making another study in which the interceptor lines are relatively short. In this particular situation, we have recommended that the municipal wastes be collected separately from the industrial wastes and that the municipal wastes be given prechlorination with the primary settling tank being used at a contact tank before the settled chlorinated wastewater is mixed with the settled industrial wastewater for secondary treatment. The short lines and the overpowering quantity of industrial wastewater made this the most economical solution in this case. However, it was still more economical to collect the wastewaters separately, give separate primary treatment to each wastewater, and combined secondary treatment than to have the industry and municipality treat their waste completely separately.

There is no question that the collection of industrial and sanitary wastewaters from large areas and the treatment and discharge at a single point could create point loads of some significance. This could mean that thousands of pounds of effluent BOD after high degrees of treatment could be discharged to the receiving waters at a single point rather than having hundreds of pounds of BOD effluent discharged, at many points. The optimum solution, I believe, would be to discharge the effluent BOD at a uniform rate along every foot of the stream which will receive the BOD. The significance of the point load must be determined for each case for the alternates available. The dangerous point load concept applies more directly to flowing streams than to the Middlesex County Sewerage Authority where the mixture of industrial and sanitary wastewaters is collected, treated, and discharged into Raritan Bay. The alternate would have been for the individual communities or for that matter the Authority to treat the wastewater and discharge the treated waste to the Raritan River at many points.

Inasmuch as the average daily flow to the Middlesex County Sewerage Authority is now equal to the minimum supplemented flow in the river, this particular method would not have worked in this situation. The individual treatment plants would have had to provide 98 to 99 percent BOD removal in order to keep the Raritan River from being a nuisance.

We should also emphasize at this time that joint treatment doesn't necessarily mean a single treatment plant. It could mean four or ten treatment plants instead of 100. An Authority providing joint treatment in several plants has a considerable advantage over individual communities and individual industries providing treatment inasmuch as they can employ and pay high caliber specialists in wastewater treatment who can control the operations at the several plants and do a much better job on it than can individual industries and municipalities. The individual industries and municipalities don't have the financial resources to pay the high salaries required to get the high caliber men.

The other item which I would like to emphasize has been covered very well by Mr. Seid. A joint treatment plant can absorb and treat major changes in the wastewaters from contributing industries without being overloaded and put out of business by the change in wastes. The Middlesex County Sewerage Authority has nine industries who discharge directly to the system. One of these has changed its process and its product completely three times since 1959 when the Authority first went into operation. This has been done without creating any problems of treatment at the Authority plant. Another industry has added a completely new process that has caused no problems at the Authority wastewater treatment plant. These would have been difficult if not impossible problems if the industries had their own individual wastewater treatment plant. However, when 1 or 2 million gallons per day of new or different industrial waste are diluted into the 65 million gallons per day waste of the Authority they create no problem.

I probably should also have commented on four advantages for joint treatment immediately after the paper which Mr. Byrd gave. Municipal participants in joint treatment have the advantage that they can take into their system much stronger and more diverse industrial wastes when discharging to a joint treatment plant than they could if providing treatment in their own municipality. Mr. Seid covered that item.

Another advantage is that the industries are able to concentrate on production rather than on discharging and treating their waste. This means that industrial wastewaters discharged to the Middlesex County Sewerage Authority are dumped as they are produced without any consideration for the effect on the waste water treatment plant. This is possible because of the large number of industrial wastewater sources whose wastes are being mixed and combined before they reach the wastewater treatment plant. Obviously wastes which would attack the collection system or treatment structures have to be eliminated. Another advantage to industry is that when many toxic wastes, which are not dangerous to sewer maintenance people, are discharged into a joint system, the dilution reduces the concentration of the toxic material below the toxic level, therefore eliminating a major problem. The fourth advantage is the advantage to the whole area which is served by a joint system such as the Middlesex County Sewerage Authority. Inasmuch as the Authority will take practically any waste which can be produced, the environment for the new industries coming into the area is very much better than as if they had to solve their own wastewater problems.

Klashman: I want to make some observations and raise a few questions. I think Dr. Kupchik's observation that in all cases, not necessarily in Middlesex County, but in all cases a one regional plant as both Al Thomas and Sol Seid have said, is not the answer. There are some cases, obviously, where the reuse of the stream is very important, and therefore, you must have multiple discharges. As a matter of fact, in New Jersey, the state where the Middlesex County plant is located, the water resource people are very much concerned about this idea of regionalization. I think that we have to face the fact that after spending many billions of dollars, our conservationist friends, and as a matter of fact many people in government, have the idea that everything is solved. Of course, nothing could be farther from the truth. After we build these plants, we have a tremendous task in operating them. It is my observation that a majority of the plants that have been built today are not operating up to design capacity, and, in fact, are operating below capacity. If we could solve that one problem, we will have solved a large part of the whole problem. Very often the waste treatment plant which is built is the largest single investment in the community, and yet it is staffed with untrained personnel. You cannot do this and get results.

Our answer seems to be to develop some type of political institution, and we are a long way from it, that has some type of a river basin or regional authority. I want to raise this question with Sol Seid. Does Sol see the possibility in the future of the Middlesex County Sewerage Authority being expanded to take in some of the smaller plants around? I ask this because I have visited his plant and have seen a well-run laboratory and a very competent technical staff. They have, as you know, very competent consultants. In other words, they are big enough so that they can try to solve any problem that comes up. A small facility is not. My question is, is it possible for Middlesex County to expand to take in surrounding communities, and what are the political difficulties in getting something like this achieved?

Seid: To answer Lester's question quickly, we are definitely interested in involving those municipalities or industries that surround us. We have been aided in this program by the fact that the Federal Government passed its 1965 law emphasizing regionalization, and then the 1966 act which would have implemented this when they produce the money. The state of New Jersey in 1965 also passed a law which stressed regionalization. When plans are submitted to them other than regional plans and where there is a regional agency, they are turning the plans down. Right now I might say that there are three municipalities, totalling one-third of the population we now serve, who are potential customers. And to answer a question which was asked me earlier concerning our rate charges when we go into secondary treatment, Thomas and I have stuck our necks out, but we are thinking of no charge, or a maximum of 25%, since we are anticipating this type of growth. The more growth we get, the tighter we can hold our rate schedule. I might add that we started out with a rate schedule in 1958, changed it in 1959, and now for the 11th consecutive year we are still maintaining the same rate schedule because of our growth.

RICHARD A. CARPENTER
Federal Policy and Environmental Chemistry

Since Richard A. Carpenter's article was written, there has been a reorganization of responsibilities for environmental protection within the federal government. The previous diagrams in the article have been replaced with a more recent description of the agencies transferred into the new Environmental Protection Agency outlined below.

The chemical industry is viewed as a major contributor to pollution because the contaminants in the environment are, after all, chemicals, and because a great many sources of pollution are within the industry. Pollutants react with human health or property values in a chemical way, whether their source be a community sewage treatment plant, a private automobile, or an industry quite separate from conventional chemical manufacture. Thus, for a variety of reasons, chemical science and engineering have been placed on the defensive.

But as we understand more of the complex nature of pollution — waste management gone wrong — in a highly technical society, the other side of the coin is revealed. This aspect of chemistry shows the profession to be the means by which we can restore and maintain environmental quality. This article reviews federal policies, shows their dependence on science, and illustrates the constructive role for chemists and the industry — a role that is essential if federal policy for pollution abatement is to succeed.

TRADITIONAL WAYS NO LONGER WILL DO

Pollution abatement depends on many factors — economics, social institutions, public opinion, legal procedures, political judgments, and technology. The best scientific understanding of the problem will be useless without the means of implementing the knowledge. It is equally true that all the weight of public opinion will not prevail unless the technology for abatement is adequate and effective. The chemical community gets involved because the information for improved management decisions is largely chemical in nature.

A number of changes have taken place in the world recently which make it impossible for us to continue formerly or traditionally accepted practices. First, there is no longer any place to put the materials which society rejects. The population of the world is so distributed that no convenient dumping grounds, or streams, or air masses exist which are not also the natural resources of other persons. The environment probably does have a limited

Richard A. Carpenter, "Federal Policy and Environmental Chemistry," *Environmental Science and Technology*, vol. 2, no. 7 (July 1968), pp. 518–523. Copyright 1968 by the American Chemical Society. Reprinted by permission.
The author is Senior Specialist, Science and Technology, Science Policy Research Division, Library of Congress Legislative Reference Service.

assimilative capacity, but the polluter cannot use it up himself without infringing on the rights of the next user.

The second distinctive change is that man has greater powers to disrupt the environment than ever before. Radioactive materials and physiologically active chemicals are long-lived and spread throughout the biosphere. Effects which cannot be predicted may be profound and irreversible. Mistakes may be expensive and difficult to correct once they are discovered.

Third, the conservation of resources must lead to a recycle economy instead of the present "use and discard" philosophy. None of our raw materials, save sunlight, is limitless. Pollution runs contrary to good conservation science because of the second law of thermodynamics. When a material is contaminated or widely dispersed, it becomes that much more difficult to include in a recycle system. Since we must indeed use the environment heavily to support our standard of living and extend it to developing nations, a high quality environment is synonymous with efficient management.

Finally, the laws of genetics suggest that man cannot adapt to an environment drastically different from that in which he evolved. Even if we would agree to accept some of the changes in environmental values our civilization has brought on, we could not physically accommodate to them. So, preservation of a reasonably normal and stable environment is urgent and necessary. Waste management must remain under close control and be supported with adequate knowledge of human ecology.

Development of federal legislation

The Federal Government's involvement in environmental quality stems from a number of historical roots, among them being the Constitutional mandates to promote the general welfare and to regulate commerce. The Federal Government is responsible for public health; it is the only government which the citizen can turn to when lesser jurisdictions disagree, and it is the logical supporter of research and development of nationwide relevance and application.

Water pollution legislation originated in the Rivers and Harbors Act of 1899, which prohibited debris in the interests of navigation. The Public Health Service Act of 1912 concerned waterborne diseases, and the Oil Pollution Act of 1924 was designed to prevent discharges into navigable waters that would damage aquatic life, recreational facilities, and harbor installations. After a temporary act in 1948, the Federal Water Pollution Control Act of 1956 was passed; it called for states to set standards and gave enforcement authority to the Federal Government if local efforts failed. Finally, a systems approach to water pollution abatement was authorized in the Clean Waters Restoration Act of 1966.

Air pollution legislation has followed a similar path. The 1955 Air Pollution Act was a small program of research and technical assistance to local control districts. It is worth noting that the intense problem of Los Angeles had motivated almost all the scientific work done to that date. The Clean Air Act of 1963 is very similar to the Federal Water Pollution Control Act. Amendments in 1965 and 1966 have added funds and specific research tasks. The Air Quality Act of 1967 completed the federal legislation by calling for state and regional standards to be enforced locally, if possible. Federal abatement enforcement is the ultimate weapon to assure both air and water quality.

This legislative history shows that the basic policy of the government is cautious except where direct hazard to human health is involved. The first federal activity is monitoring and analysis of the environment to define pollutants, their concentration, and sources. Local governments are aided by the Federal Government in staffing and equipping offices and agencies that are charged with learning just what the problem is in the local areas. The techniques are developed under federal research grants because they are widely applicable.

Gross and obvious pollutants

As soon as knowledge about pollutants begins to accumulate, there is a tendency to leapfrog immediately into an abatement plan. In the case of gross and obvious contamination, this is justifiable and often works. Strong emotional demands for a less dirty city motivated smoke elimination in Pittsburgh and St. Louis. The technology for particulate collection and combustion control was adequate. Therefore, no refinement of the cause and effect relationships was requested. Another example is the acceptance of primary sewage treatment as the minimum which any water user must perform before the effluent goes to a receiving water.

These types of pollution are the result of contaminants which are in a different physical state (or phase) from the environment in which they are carried. That is why the average citizen sees them and recognizes them as problems. It is also why they are usually cheaply and easily removed. The remedies for particulate, floating, or suspended matter cost little in comparison to the benefits.

Subtle pollutants require research

However, the next stages of cleanup require a more convincing, scientifically established reason to spend money for abatement. A kind of leapfrogging assumption of standards in these complex, subtle cases may turn out to be very wasteful.

The control of automobile exhaust is still awaiting judgment. Emission standards are now being changed from a basis of per cent of pollutant in the exhaust gas to grams per mile, a more realistic relationship. The efficiency and operating life of the control devices are in doubt. There may be an additional expense for mandatory annual inspection and maintenance. The application of Los Angeles criteria to hardware required for the entire country has been criticized. While the situation in West Coast basins requires drastic control of reactive hydrocarbons, the rest of the nation is little troubled by photochemical smog. The improved engine designs resulting from the 1968 federal regulations are possibly all that will be necessary to control hydrocarbons and carbon monoxide outside of a few California cities.

Another area for caution is the thermal pollution of streams and estuaries by cooling water from power plants. For example, the wide adoption of a uniform temperature limit (such as 93°F.) would have enormous effects, although the limit has virtually no basis in scientific experiment. The standard would have been promulgated before the aquatic ecology research has even begun in many watersheds.

A sequential approach to standards

The recognition of the errors in cost-effectiveness judgment which can accompany a leapfrogging policy has led the Congress to a sequential approach in setting standards. The Air Quality Act of 1967 calls for the Secretary of the Department of Health, Education, and Welfare to issue criteria for each pollutant. The Federal Water Pollution Control Act calls for the Secretary of the Department of the Interior to establish a technical advisory committee on water quality criteria.

Criteria express the damage to health and welfare which can be expected from exposure to a contaminant at different concentrations and for different times. A criterion is simply a scientific presentation of cause and effect of dose-response relationship. Next, a judgment is made at the state level of how much damage society is willing to put up with, or, conversely, how much abatement the people are willing to pay for. This judgment should integrate such things as the cost of not abating, the cost of installing and operating control equipment, health effects, nuisances, and esthetic offenses.

The criterion then is used to translate the damage level into a concentration × time value for the ambient air mass. This quantitative figure (usually expressed as parts per million averaged over a short time not to be exceeded by more than a few days per year) is an ambient air standard or a receiving water standard. Integrating many local factors will produce different standards for different parts of the country, but some minimum acceptable quality can be insisted upon by review at the federal level.

The ambient environmental quality standard is then related to the individual sources of that pollutant. Emission restrictions can be calculated for all sources, taking into account, for example, stack height or stream flow, weather, climate, and terrain, so that the ambient quality is achieved. The economics of abatement technology may prevent reaching, for the time being, an ambient environmental quality goal. Enforcement is accomplished by identifying all sources and monitoring their emissions.

This sequence is highly dependent on the sciences which construct the criteria. Environmental epidemiology is basic to the entire process. Unfortunately, most of the evidence is empirical, and well designed research is just beginning.

Thus, legislation for environmental quality has placed an obligation on science to provide a sound, legally useful basis for the subtle pollutants which our senses cannot evaluate. It is perhaps fortunate that there is more than enough to be done in abating gross and obvious pollution for the next few years. The big expenditures for pollution control and the massive manipulations of the environment lie ahead — in a sense it is earlier, not later, than we think. If we give careful attention to emergency situations (such as spills or persistent inversions) we have the time to do the research and construct the organizations which will guide future control of a variety of environmental contaminants.

CURRENT LEGISLATIVE TRENDS

Congress today can be said to be leading the nation toward a better environment. It originated the recent air and water legislation. Where local political boundaries and industrial vested interests have prevented progress, Congress passed federal laws.

Most importantly, the government has supported research to identify pollutants, quantify their effects on health and property, and develop lower-cost, efficient means of control (ES&T, February, 1968, page 90). In fiscal 1968, it spent $250 million in this way:

* Pesticides: $65 million.
* Transportation, distribution, and fate of pollutants: $20 million.
* Measurement and instrumentation: $12 million.
* Social, economic, and legal aspects: $5 million.
* Prevention and control technology: $100 million.
* Effects of pollution on man, plants, animals, materials: $45 million.

The major agencies involved include the Departments of Agriculture, Commerce, Defense, Health, Education, and Welfare, Housing and Urban Development, and Interior; the Atomic Energy Commission, National Aeronautics and Space Administration, National Science Foundation, Tennessee Valley Authority, and Veterans' Administration. It is a monumental task simply to coordinate the science and technology of pollution control.

Another trend affecting legislation is that we are gaining a more sophisticated understanding of the term "quality." Cost-effectiveness is a common term in the Capitol, but it is important to pollution policy. The accepted goal today is to restore and maintain a quality of the environment without disrupting our economy and culture.

There is a great deal of uncertainty about the price people are willing to pay — in terms of money, changed habits, and restrictions on freedom of choice — for environmental quality. Of course, any proved health effects will be eliminated. And really obnoxious sights, odors, and dirtiness will be taken care of. But the quality necessary for other species and for esthetic values may seem too costly to a society which finds it difficult to understand an ecological web of life. It is not easy to quantify these benefits, but it will be all too easy to quantify the costs of achieving ever higher standards. Goals which refer to an environment with no deleterious effects on health, welfare, or the pursuit of happiness do not have much meaning in a real political context.

Laws must be legally enforceable in a practical manner. For example, odors are a nuisance, but a connoisseur of Limburger cheese might be willing

Table 1. Environmental Protection Agency

Program	Transferred from	Functions
Federal Water Quality Administration	Interior	Charged with the control of pollutants which impair water quality, it is broadly concerned with the impact of degraded water quality. It performs a wide variety of functions, including research, standard-setting and enforcement, and provides construction grants and technical assistance.
National Air Pollution Control Administration	Health, Education and Welfare	As the principal Federal agency concerned with air pollution, it conducts research on the effects of air pollution, operates a monitoring network, and promulgates criteria which serve as the basis for setting air quality standards. Its regulatory functions are similar to those of the Federal Water Quality Administration. NAPCA is responsible for administering the Clean Air Act, which involves designating air quality regions, approving State standards, and providing financial and technical assistance to State Control agencies to enable them to comply with the Act's provisions. Also sets and enforces Federal automotive emission standards.
Bureau of Water Hygiene	Health, Education and Welfare (Environmental Control Administration)	The Environmental Control Administration is the focal point within *HEW* for evaluation and control of a broad range of environmental health problems, including water quality, solid wastes, and radiation. Programs in the ECA involve research, development of criteria and standards, and the administration of planning and demonstration grants. From the ECA, the activities of the *Bureaus of Water Hygiene, Solid Waste Management,* and portions of the activities of the *Bureau of Radiological Health* are transferred. Other functions of the ECA, including those related to the regulation of radiation from consumer products and occupational safety and health remain in HEW. The *Food and Drug Administration's* pesticides program consists of setting and enforcing standards which limit pesticide residues in food. EPA will have authority to set pesticide standards and to monitor compliance with them, and to conduct related research. FDA
Bureau of Solid Waste Management	Health, Education and Welfare (Environmental Control Administration)	
Bureau of Radiological Health	Health, Education and Welfare (Environmental Control Administration)	
Pesticide Standards and Research	Health, Education and Welfare & Interior	

		retains authority to remove from the market food with excess pesticide residue.
Pesticides Registration	Agriculture (Agricultural Research Service)	Authority for research on effects of pesticides on fish and wildlife is transferred from *Interior*. This is specialized research authority under the 1958 pesticides act. Interior retains research on all factors affecting fish and wildlife. The transfer involves only one laboratory — Gulf Breeze of the Bureau of Commercial Fisheries. EPA will work closely with Bureau of Sport Fisheries and Wildlife laboratories.
		Agriculture's pesticides registration and monitoring function is transferred to EPA, to be merged with pesticides programs from HEW and Interior. Agriculture will continue research on effectiveness of pesticides, furnishing this information to EPA. EPA will handle pesticides' licensing after consideration of environmental and health effects. EPA will use Agriculture's expertise, as in evaluating efficacy of various pesticides as related to other pest control methods and effects of pesticides on non-target plants, livestock, and poultry. Agriculture's educational program on pesticide use will continue to be carried out through its extension service.
Federal Radiation Council Environmental Radiation Standards	Executive Office of the President Atomic Energy Commission & Federal Radiation Council	The *Atomic Energy Commission* is responsible for establishing environmental radiation and emission limits. These standards have been based largely on broad guidelines recommended by the *Federal Radiation Council*. AEC's standard-setting authority and FRC's functions are transferred to EPA. AEC retains responsibility for implementation and enforcement of radiation standards through its licensing authority.
Studies of Ecological Systems	Council on Environmental Quality, Executive Office of the President	Authority of the *Council on Environmental Quality* to perform studies and research relating to ecological systems is transferred to EPA. It will help EPA to measure the impact of pollutants. The CEQ retains authority to conduct studies and research relating to environmental quality.

Elizabeth M. Boswell, Analyst, Environmental Policy Division, November 24, 1970.

to put up with an affront to the senses which others would not. More basi-cally, an industrial valley, because of the payrolls involved, may accept a higher level of pollution than would a distant bureaucracy.

OPPORTUNITIES AND RESPONSIBILITIES

Chemical technology has six identifiable areas for action and response to federal policies in the environment.

First, wastes must be physically controlled. That is, the byproducts and nonusable residues from manufacturing, processing, combustion, and munic-ipal waste disposal must be contained at all times. They must be kept apart from the living environment until they can be either recycled, permanently and safely stored, or dispersed to a satisfactory low level.

Chemical engineering processing is the key to this requirement. New plants pose less of a problem than do older ones. Waste management will be much more important to process design and to the choice among competing methods. Plant location will be less important when virtually all surface waters — streams, estuaries, and coastal areas — are brought under standards. Loca-tion will continue to be important in meeting air pollution standards because weather and terrain will affect the limitations on emissions.

Second, materials must be recycled with greater ingenuity. This is the most direct way of lowering the costs of pollution abatement. Metal dusts, fly ash, sulfur oxides, solids in sewage plant effluent, and refinery vapors are examples of potential pollutants which can pay part or all of the cost of their containment and management if they are used in a recycle system.

Third, markets created by the pressure of pollution abatement legisla-tion must be satisfied. For example, the annual capital investment in pollution control equipment is estimated at several billions of dollars. To monitor the environment, automatic continuous analysis of thousands of streams and hundreds of airsheds will be necessary. Chemical treating agents, coagulants, and similar materials will continue to be in demand in abatement processes. More federal R&D funds may find their way to industry if a patent policy can be negotiated that truly serves the public interest. At present, the funding agency often simply holds the rights. Licensees of federally held patents may need some exclusivity to justify spending additional money for commercial development.

Another type of market is the replacement of products which are caus-ing trouble in the environment. Phosphate-free detergents, biodegradable plastic packaging, immobile nitrogen fertilizers, additive-free gasoline — these items may become competitive by virtue of the pollution created by present products. Uniform nationwide minimum standards are under study for air quality. Such standards would provide a large market base to attract private sector R&D effort.

Other markets may be disrupted. Sulfur recovered from stack gas would equal the present consumption; dislocations of conventional sulfur sources would occur, but very slowly. Another example is the nonreturnable bottle, an innovation of glass technology but the bane of solid waste control. It could be regulated out of the market if its private convenience value is exceeded by the public cost of disposal.

Fourth, the chemical industry must make a greater effort to assess the environmental effects of its products before they are introduced. A recent advisory report to the HEW Secretary recommended prohibiting after 1970 "general use of any new synthetic material, trace metal, or chemical until approved by the Department of Health, Education, and Welfare." Assuming that the criteria for such approval could be established at some future date, the cost to industry of the testing involved would be enormous. Despite the utopian aspects of environmental quality via regulation, the trend toward consumer protection is plain.

Synthetic organic chemicals are foreign to the natural environment and are therefore suspect from the start. The discovery of DDT throughout the biosphere is testimony to the powerful pervasiveness of chemicals — whether or not the chemical is actually a hazard. Highly technical consumer goods give little opportunity for the buyer to beware. What product-liability laws cannot accomplish, increasing regulation will attempt.

Fifth, the chemical industry must explain its problems more frankly and

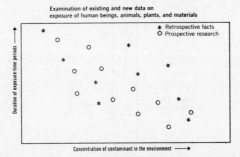

Environmental quality criteria—1.   Criteria. Establishing criteria begins with arranging the available data for a given environmental contaminant in terms of concentration and duration of exposure. Examinations of past events are supplemented by additional research

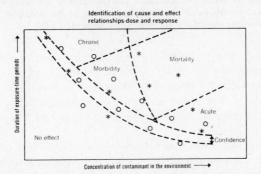

Environmental quality criteria—2.   Effects. The exposure data are then correlated with the type of response or damage to environmental quality. A region of no effect is identified, and the confidence limits of prediction of effects are derived from the total amount of evidence. A description of the dose-response relationship is obtained

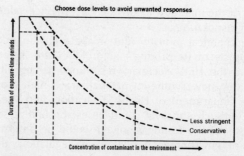

Choose dose levels to avoid unwanted responses

Environmental quality criteria—3.   Standards. Standards are chosen to avoid an unwanted degree of damage by limiting the exposure dose. Usually, a long term chronic dose is prescribed as well as a shorter term episodic exposure. Other factors such as economics, local requirements for the environment, and available technology may influence the choice of standards

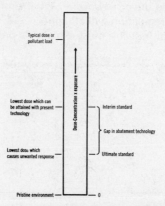

Environmental quality criteria—4.   Research and development. Treating the exposure as the product of concentration and duration, the standard may be compared with existing contamination and the pristine environment. The pristine environment will usually not be a necessary goal, and reduction of the present pollution load will usually be limited by technical-economic considerations. An interim and an ultimate standard thus become the most practical expressions of the situation. The gap between these values is an opportunity for abatement technology R&D

in greater detail. The technical literacy of the general public is increasing rapidly. Understanding the complexities of chemical manufacture, the public may temper demands for immediate abatement or overnight replacement of offending products. The vague and elusive public relations program will not withstand the scrutiny of today's citizen action groups, the press, and local enforcement officials.

Finally, the industry must provide more information to Congress. It is important that as many channels of science advice as possible be provided to the legislative process. Congress is far more receptive than industry believes. Rather than merely supply defensive statements, the chemical industry can participate in determining pollution policy from the outset. Cost sharing in research, R&D patent policy, abatement timetables, technical economics, alternatives in resource management — these issues can only be resolved in an optimum way for the nation if the industry brings its viewpoints to the discussion.

Waste management is largely a task for local governments and the private sector, but getting the job done right is everyone's business. In practical terms of profit, service, and public relations, waste management brings real opportunities to the chemical industry.

Chapter 9

Conclusions: can we manage the environment?

Breaking down a systems problem into chapters is somewhat arbitrary, for we have shown, through the collective efforts of authors, commentators, and editors, that the issues of environmental management are truly interwoven in a complex web of relationships. There have been and there will be alternative ways to view the relationships. Now, at the outset of a new decade, perspectives are affected by the newness of the issues. Relatively speaking, we have been actors on the environment first and scholars second. As the decade wears on, we will have to find a better balance between knowing and doing. In the next years, major concerns are likely to be debated in the context of a demand for action and a demand to foresee consequences. While establishing that balance, regulations will have to be written and enforced which make the first decade of public awareness of the environment a step forward and a redirection of our efforts.

There is no underestimating this task. Since the conclusion of World War II, nations have turned their attentions to more efficient exploitation of the environment in a drive to incease per capita income. In a race to meet the needs of more and more people, we have upset many local ecosystems, and there is fair warning that we have even set in motion trends that will be difficult to arrest. As we try to extract more food from the soil, pesticides add more species to the endangered list. As we give the fruits of industrialization to mass consumers, we take away other satisfactions produced by nature. This difficult problem is magnified because we do not all agree on the additions and subtractions. The arithmetic of human wants may add and subtract according to the laws of logic, but whether the sign is negative or positive is a matter for judgment. For many of the world's people, the quality of life has improved substantially. Early death and disease have been attenuated and rising standards of living have given material and spiritual rewards to more and more humans. Cataclysmic waves of natural destruction have given way to more orderly processes of dealing with potential tragedies.

Of course, we have paid a price for all this progress, but until now few people questioned that it wasn't the biggest bargain mankind had yet achieved. Man as a species showed the benefit of all this progress by increasing in historically unprecedented rates of growth. However, the time has come to question, and doubts have been raised in this book. Our conclusion must deal with our capacity to manage the environment, when the effects of our previous mismanagement are now impressed on our consciousnesses.

"ENVIRONMENT" DEFINED

The phrase *environmental management* has been used over and over again. "Environmental" has as its reference a very large set of concerns. It is almost impossible to compartmentalize and define the boundaries of the word. Can we leave out very much? The easiest boundary is the existing natural ecosystems which exist apart from man. The world of nature can be the environment. However, if this were true, we could leave the problems to naturalists or conservationists; it has been clear that the dimensions are much broader. If we broaden the definition to include man's relation to nature, we have added a complex set of interactions to our concerns, and the planners with their amenity values and the literati with their joys of nature appreciation participate in the task of managing it.

However, man's relation to man also grows out of man's relation to nature, so the environment involves the social sciences, too. The sociologist who studies overcrowding and crime also participates in the information pool needed for environmental management.

Very quickly, hope of defining the boundaries of environmental concerns fades into blurred outlines. However, if we abuse the term, we will lose sight of the target. For our purposes, the word "environment" refers to those aspects of nature's balances among the major forces of energy and matter in the biosphere which are essential for maintaining stability and life. Thus, beer cans by the side of the road are not an environmental problem, just a dirt problem, unless the number of cans we produce is responsible for altering thermal balances by energy production for manufacturing. By the same token, "wasting" our ore resources by producing beer cans is not an environmental problem. Even if we expect to run out of certain resources, that is only a problem of selfishness, not an environmental problem according to our definition. Unless the use of resources results in the depletion of some vital elements or catalysts for balancing natural equations, such use is not, by this definition, an environmental problem.

The target for environmental managers, then, is maintenance of life-support systems of the biosphere — the reactions of the carbon dioxide-oxygen cycle, the balance of the nitrogen and sulfur cycles, and the interactions of the hydrological and meteorological cycles. These are the objects of attention of the environmental manager. Other issues are essentially for the moralist, the esthetician, or the economist. Thus limiting our focus has not narrowed our perspective very far, for the balance of nature is pervasive and its maintenance will need the cooperation of others besides environmental managers.

To focus is to try to professionalize the task rather than to let it become everybody's concern, but nobody's job. If we do not profession-alize environmental management, ecology will become an ideology. Our job is too serious to leave it to universalizers. As has so often been under-scored in this book, it is the job of scientists and politicians who operate on the best available information, with professional skills and tools de-signed for the job.

"MANAGEMENT" DEFINED

While "environment" can thus be limited as an object of attention, to define "management" once again strains our ability to focus attention. Man-agement is the skill of allocating resources to achieve desired ends. As we have noted in Chapter 5, management includes considerations of values, and we are quickly called on to harmonize value conflicts. However, if the manager is responsible for environmental concerns, he recognizes conflicts of value which involve class differences, such as middle-class preferences for particular homesites, but he only pronounces on such preferences when they pollute the water supply and result in increasing erosion of hillsides. In one case of esthetic preferences, the manager is only a land use plan-ner, but if land use impinges on the environment, as we have defined it, then the role of environmental manager is called upon. If the two issues of esthetics and environment are mixed up in the environmental manager's mind, he may aid the rich over the poor or deny resources to poor countries in the name of ecology.

While environmental considerations in resource management may favor one or another group, it is important to label these value aspects as outcomes, not purposes, of the environmental manager's concerns. His attention is on life-support, not on favoring particular classes or countries. If a particular country is depleting an important element of a natural cycle, he should, as manager, seek the power and authority to stop it. However, he cannot take on the professional cloak to advance special interests.

It is clear that special interests will form around environmental issues, and to expect all interests to find harmony in the goal of maintaining nature's cycles is to hope for too much in this pluralistic world. Yet adjudi-cation of disputes either will go on with a professional orientation, or en-vironmental concerns will simply degenerate into who can get the most first before the ship goes down. For this reason, the manager is unlikely to avoid conflict, no matter how defined and compartmentalized his job. We must bureaucratize and make scientific the environmental function, but it will be difficult to resist the temptation to make environmental deci-sions without irrelevant biases, especially in light of the uncertainties and complexities outlined in Chapters 3 and 4. Our capacity to manage the environment is related to how well we can professionalize the decision makers.

The manager, then, has the task of allocating resources to maintain the health of the biosphere. He avoids unrelated issues or damages below the threshold of danger. While he must watch trends and incremental changes which could lead to systemic destruction, he stands aside from pronouncing decisions that other conflict-resolution processes in society can handle. His is the domain of science.

The training of the Solomon called to be a scientific judge has not yet been written into curricula. However, we must keep sights on targets of importance for mankind rather than for special interests. Environmental issues, broadly conceived, cannot all be handled by the environmental manager as scientist. That skill for managing the environment is a special art which will have to find its place in our political institutions, and it cannot include everything. If it did, the needed science and politics would never develop; we would mix biology and cultural preferences to the disaster of both. There is danger in the present call to humanize science by rejecting scientific canons of proof. This is not to suggest that a biologist refrain from comment on cultural preferences; but he should comment as a biologist.

LIMITATIONS

Such a definition of environmental manager has a number of limitations. For one thing, it may mean that he comments very little if there is much latitude before life-systems are destroyed. Unless the evidence is good or the doubt is reasonable, our manager may have to say nothing about the decline of environmental quality as measured by the beauty of the world.

At the interface between science and value, the consequences of value are the province of the scientist, and how to achieve and define desired values — within scientific limits — is the province of the politician.

The domain of the politician in environmental management is in assessing risk and adjudicating conflicts of values. As articles in Chapter 2 indicate, it will be a long time before questions of chronic effects on human health from low dose exposure to pollutants can be scientifically determined. The politician will be called on to assess the risks and determine whether new products should be tried or new technology financed.

Conflicts of values which arise in determining best use of the land leave much room for political choice. When to use which pesticides, when to allow how much unemployment during reorientation to an ecosane economy, how much of the limited coastal zone to use for power generation, how much marshland to save for food for fish in the sea — all are questions for which the scientist can project costs, but politicians must assess the benefits.

In sum, there is a domain for science and a domain for politics in the field of environmental management. The problem of making the distinction is not unlike the nineteenth century struggle between science and religion. As science improved its explanations of natural phenomena, the need for religious explanation dwindled, and over the course of the struggle, each set of explanations found their proper place. Such a struggle between scientists and politicians will be repeated over this new issue, but we will eventually find the proper domain of each.

The struggle between science and politics will not be easy to resolve, and keeping the separate functions in sight will be difficult. This is especially so because discourse about values in politics usually takes place in the language of "who" benefits. Political activity in a democracy is organized around competing interests, and the democratic process works toward a balance among interests. This form of dialogue is not very useful for solving the largest problems of man's survival as a species in the biosphere. It is possible that the balance politicians will strike will not be in the interest of man as a species. The warnings of scientists will go unheeded if the politics of compromise result in a slow erosion of the life-support systems on the planet. A new politics is needed to incorporate scientific messages of the degradation of the environment. The issue is not who will benefit from the struggle, for the narrow interests of a given group at a particular time may be in everyone's worst interest, including the "victor" of a particular battle.

THE IDENTITY OF MAN

The identity of any group is irrelevant in the blindness of nature's processes. We have come upon an era when the real issue is an identity crisis of man as a species.

The challenge posed as an identity crisis of man is a formidable one, but without it there will not be sufficient guidelines for the environmental manager to operate effectively, either in the domain of science or of politics. We must learn to optimize over large units. Nature does. The nation-state, the upper-class suburb, the humble fisherman are all too narrow as references for orientation toward environmental management. If man has an identity as a species, this identity will provide a sufficient base for management. The "who" in determining allocation decisions must refer to the inhabitants of the biosphere. That is all of us.

Unfortunately, previous threats to man as a species have not given us a sufficient sense of our own identity. Atomic disasters have been predicted, yet men have accepted the risks of having the weapons and have used and threatened to use them. Protecting the nation has taken precedence over risking mankind, for the nation has been the stronger identity. The territorial imperative has previously referred to too small a territory.

Some thrusts in the direction of giving us a global identity have come from current debates about man's place in the biosphere. Man-centered roles, which have allowed us to guiltlessly destroy species for the sake of some men's gains, have led to a reassessment of our place in the universe. But none of this castigating our selfishness vis à vis the other inhabitants of the biosphere has yet generated a positive statement of man as a species. Nor can we find an identity through negative statements which say we are not at the top of the pecking order of life. While humility may be a virtue, it is not the basis of building a sense of identity.

We need nothing less than a capacity to define ourselves in proper perspective. Man may be able to succeed as a species without certain other species; America may have to drop the bald eagle as a national symbol, because applying DDT to kill insects was determined more important than preserving the eagle. However, somewhere is a point of no return, and the link between man's survival and the survival of other species is essential in determining where that point is.

Some biologists warn that interrelations between man and other species are so complicated we cannot tamper with the existing balance. G. M. Woodwell's article in Chapter 3 argues that as more and more species are lost, regardless of their seeming triviality, the ecosystem on which man ultimately depends is endangered. These general statements are not sufficient to solve the environmental manager's problem in a specific case. Men and the processes of evolution have destroyed many species, and the rate of destruction is now on the increase. How many more losses can men afford?

These issues are central to the basic question of this book: Can we manage the environment? We cannot manage the environment until we have defined man in the larger context of nature. Without an identity to relate us to the world of nature, we are hard pressed to find guidelines for environmental managers. Until we have found some perspective on ourselves, until we are willing to listen to the advice of environmental scientists, and until we have given politicians the capacity to regulate relations among men so as to respect the relations of man to nature, we cannot manage the environment.

We cannot manage it, but we must. We are managing the environment today, albeit in ignorance of consequences and without the skills we concede are necessary to manage a business or household. The implication that we must manage, ready or not, is that we will need to make some interim ethical judgments to be a baseline for decisions.

We explored some of these baselines in Chapter 5. René Dubos suggests that one component of our ethical baseline is to respect the genius of place. Respect for unique characteristics is one component. We were also warned that sympathy for immediate consequences on human groups, as suggested in Jay Forrester's model, is misplaced in a new ethical system. We also were advised that economic goals will force us into difficult decisions within our present culture and social payments will have to replace individual exploitation.

Indeed, the outcome of the chapter on values is that our present culture does not provide us with anything near an adequate ethical base to deal with problems of environmental management. We are sub-optimizing managers. We do not optimize global resource use. We still are winning Pyrrhic victories over biological man. Such success may be our doom if we allocate the resources to the detriment of the earth itself.

IT DOESN'T HAVE TO BE THAT WAY

The case for man is not closed. Chapters 6, 7, and 8 show that we are making an effort, and with time and knowledge and skills the outcome can be in favor of man as a species. We will have to develop guidelines.

The key lies in some of the ideas in Chapter 4, recognition of the cyclical nature of global dynamics. The moral imperative of the environmental manager is found in respecting the cycles of nature.

To put the goal more simply, the environmental manager's job is to put man's exploitation of nature on an overall sustained yield basis modified by technology. Sustained yield in this context means using the earth's renewable resources so that the capital goods are maintained while only the interest is consumed. Under such a guideline, we do not overfish stocks so that their rate of reproduction is less than our rate of consumption. We do not cut trees faster than we can replace them. In nonrenewable resources, we do not commit all our stored energy to one generation or one set of countries until there are alternative lifestyles and technologies which minimize drain on capital stock reserves.

The enormous productive power of nature gives us a great deal of interest to live on. Energy from the sun, for example, will last as long as any manager cares to assume responsibility. Yet today it is unlikely that sustained yield management practices can satisfy the demands we have come to expect as our rights. We do not know the limit on consumption under a sustained yield philosophy. Technology and nature together, as long as they are not organized in an antagonistic mode, can increase that yield. The sustained yield is thus a variable amount in terms of what we can produce as well as what is necessary to close cycles.

Technology can be our friend, if the managers-as-scientists and politicians remain its master. Lord Bacon gave us the proper dictum — nature is our slave as long as we obey her. Technology, fit into nature's cycles, can increase the sustained yield. We can then choose whether we want more people or a better life for those already on earth. We can choose for how many generations we would like to sustain life on this planet. On a sustained yield basis, man as a species can exist for as long as we care to be stewards of the biosphere.

Where such a philosophy will lead us is too difficult to say at present. We will have to adjust as we go along. It may require that we create a static economy, or it may not. It may require that we invest more heavily in technologies, such as controlled fusion, which give energy and a capacity to return wastes to their elemental state. We may have to make this investment in spite of more pressing short-run needs. It may even be better for the world if the United States invests in fusion technology than if it increases its foreign aid budget tenfold. The highest and best use of America and Americans could be in designing the technology that goes with a sustained yield philosophy. This may have to be done at the expense of letting the rest of the world provide consumer goods. Some American factories may close, but the compromise of staying in rapidly obsolescing consumer goods production may be sub-optimal and to our detriment as a whole. We may have to recognize an international specialization of labor and pour immense amounts of money into education so that people will not regret lost jobs but gain jobs in the skilled technologies of long-lasting, low energy-consuming goods.

Perhaps the American identity is not the appropriate one to play this role. Other countries may turn to such a role. Perhaps the best thing America can do is to alter its own consumption as a message to the world. Right now, the rest of the world is aiming for high consumption, which may finish man as a species.

Nationalistic speculations are really not central to the issue: the globe must be put on a sustained yield basis, and who does it and how will have to be worked out. Someone will have to set the goal and show how nature's sustained yield and man's technology applied to increasing it can contribute to solving the fundamental problem facing us.

There is much to be done. The last time human institutions had to make an equivalent change was in the transition from feudalism to capitalism. That took several hundred years. Our rate of destruction does not give us as much time as that; but our capacity to deal with the problem has never been as great.

Epilogue

Epilogue

Experience in the last year since this book was started has indicated too many failures on the part of the scientific and political communities to relate to each other. Whether the discussions have been about power plant siting, setting emission standards, managing a bay area, or more general issues, decision makers and the scientific community need more data and analysis before positions can be confidently taken. The result has been much unconvincing argumentation. As is often the case when people do not convince each other, the voices grow louder, but not clearer. Many of the dialogues have thus fallen to the level of defensive posturing and tactical maneuvering for political allies. It is unproductive to choose sides if there can be no winners. It is time to set the dialogue in a frame of reference which incorporates the meaning of ecological reasoning for the resource allocation patterns of society.

As participants in these debates, the editors have noted the difficulties of both the scientist and the politician in dealing with each other, even when both are men of good will. Perhaps the existing state of the art makes this inevitable, but in the future, scientists and politicians will have to restructure their efforts. In the debate of the past years, some of the successful dialogues have been structured in the context of resources' limits for producing the demands environmental managers seek. Few managers will be foolish enough to destroy the source of their wealth — if the evidence is convincing that their practices will be counterproductive. Therein lies the ground for future dialogue.

In this dialogue between politicians and scientists, the most pressing demands appear to have taken the form of discovering (1) the carrying capacity of a resource being exploited, (2) the thresholds of various trends in succession patterns, (3) the contribution of incremental change to these trends, and (4) the cost and possibility of reversing processes already set in motion. We will discuss why each of these is critical to environmental management. Then we will define the challenge of how to move the politician from the area of resolving unhappy dilemmas to the more desirable position where man and nature yield positive benefits together.

1. The first format useful for structuring environmental priorities is carrying capacity. A simple example is grazing land management, where a grassland of fixed size is determined able to support a certain number of cattle. The addition of more cattle forces grazing so close to the roots that the grass cannot regenerate itself and soil erosion begins. The land's ability to carry even a lower number of cattle is thereby destroyed. Every resource has its limits for particular uses and levels of acceptable risk. Defining those limits defines the carrying capacity of the resource.

Not all resource limits can be reduced to such a simple example. The articles in this book indicate the complexity of interactions among resources and the difficulty of defining system boundaries. Defining the carrying capacity of a lake or river before it becomes useless is a more difficult task, because the carrying capacity varies according to natural events, such as rainfall. Defining limits of land use patterns before the land becomes unable to support recreation or desirable human residence must include human psychological limits and cultural preferences. However, the capacity of land and water resources to assimilate wastes is measurable under varying assumptions of use and risk. Knowing limits can determine rural areas' toleration of housing or industrial areas' capacity to sustain specific types of chemical waste. There are limits, and the politician needs scientific knowledge to be able usefully to define the consequences of one or another policy of resource management.

Defining carrying capacity is critical because this suggests to politicians that a finite resource exists which men can exploit before that resource ceases to be productive. If a politician with a four-year term of office is to convince his constituents that his policy of foregoing certain benefits from a resource is operating in their best interest, he must demonstrate clearly that the vulnerable resource will not survive many four-year terms without his policy of restraint. Defining carrying capacity is the key to linking natural succession with political succession.

2. Often, in the science of providing to managers early warning that a resource is going to exceed its carrying capacity, there are thresholds along the way which indicate steps that can be taken in time. These thresholds are discrete decision points where a change can have effects out of proportion to the expected response. When natural systems approach limits, they suffer large or catastrophic responses, not adaptive natural controls. The rapid eutrophication of a lake through excess sewage nutrients is one example. Another is the application of broad-spectrum pesticides which at some levels eliminate the natural enemies of a pest so that the pest population grows faster than the pesticides can curb it. Increasing the amount of pesticides reaches diminishing returns when it exceeds the threshold of natural balance. The resource manager needs to know at what point he exceeds the favorable rate of return of pesticide application.

3. Related to carrying capacity and threshold indicators is the third needed capability: measuring incremental change. Many political battles setting standards or enforcing regulations will be lost because of the attitude that one more little input is not going to hurt anything — that the jobs created by a new industry outweigh the little costs incurred by